PDR®
Atlas of Anatomy™

PDR®
Atlas of Anatomy™

Todd R. Olson, Ph.D.
Associate Professor
Department of Anatomy & Structural Biology
Albert Einstein College of Medicine
Bronx, New York

Illustrative Art
A.D.A.M.® Software, Inc.
Atlanta, Georgia

Cadaver Photographs
The Bassett Collection
Stanford University
School of Medicine
Stanford, California

with the assistance of
Wojciech Pawlina, M.D.
Assistant Professor
Department of
Anatomy & Cell Biology
University of Florida
College of Medicine
Gainesville, Florida

Medical Economics Company
MONTVALE, NEW JERSEY

Editor: Timothy S. Satterfield
Managing Editor: Crystal Taylor
Production Manager: Paula Huber
Project Editor: Janet M. Krejci
Illustration Planners: Mario Fernández, Wayne Hubbel, Raymond Lowman, Donna Smith, Lorraine Wrzoseck
Typesetter: The Image Foundry, Ltd., Baltimore, MD
Printer: Metropole Litho, Montreal, Canada

351 West Camden Street
Baltimore, Maryland 21201-2436 USA

Rose Tree Corporate Center
1400 North Providence Road
Building II, Suite 5025
Media, Pennsylvania 19063-2043 USA

Printed in Canada

ISBN: 1-56363-279-9

Dedication

To my family, especially my parents and my wife, Sarah, for the support and encouragement that have constantly been a part of their love; to my friends for the many pleasures and insights that I have experienced in our camaraderie; and to my teachers, colleagues, and students for having made education an exciting and rewarding lifelong endeavor.

Foreword

During the course of my training in medical illustration, I relied heavily upon the most important tool one can have in the study of gross anatomy: the anatomy atlas. The extent of my atlas collection reflected this importance; no one atlas provided the ultimate reference, so I felt I had to have them all. However, my extensive collection could not provide an adequate picture of the three-dimensional relationships within the body. In particular, superficial-to-deep relationships were a struggle to comprehend within the two-dimensional world of an anatomy atlas. Although I could discover the three-dimensional anatomical relationships in the dissection lab, standing over a cadaver all day was not a viable option. So, like most of us, I relied upon the atlas as my primary tool for learning and turned to dissection for reinforcement and the three-dimensional visualization I ultimately required. The gap between the representations of the atlas and the reality of the human body eventually led me to envision and help create a computerized, multimedia version of a dissectable human body: *A.D.A.M.,* or *Animated Dissection of Anatomy for Medicine.* The first version of *A.D.A.M.* has now evolved into a family of related products: the *A.D.A.M. Scholar Series.*

In developing that first *A.D.A.M.* product, my team of medical illustrators and anatomists assembled the most comprehensive set of medical images ever created. Presenting these images through a computer allowed a user to peel away each structure of the anatomy, one layer at a time, from the skin to the bones, and from four views. This major achievement overcame many of the limitations of the anatomy atlas, allowing students to navigate through a virtual body to any depth they chose.

At about the same time A.D.A.M. Software completed the first *A.D.A.M.* product, I met Dr. Todd Olson. From the first time he saw *A.D.A.M.,* Todd appreciated its value to our understanding of anatomy. He quickly became an advocate for the product and began to experiment with ways he could use it in his courses at Albert Einstein College of Medicine. Todd recognized early on, however, that widespread student access to the rich image database would be limited by the slow pace of computerization in medical education. In response to this recognition, A.D.A.M. Software began discussions with Williams & Wilkins about the creation of a printed atlas modeled on the strategy of the multimedia *A.D.A.M.* product: to give users the ability to explore superficial-to-deep relationships while maintaining a clear sense of orientation within the body. Further discussions led to the idea to include cadaver photographs from the world-renowned collection of David L. Bassett, M.D. As the manuscript evolved, I sensed a product with a real competitive advantage over other atlases. Some provided good illustrations but no photos; others had photos but few illustrations. I remembered my days in gross anatomy flipping from one type of atlas to the other. This product would have it all!

Todd's clear vision of what he wanted to achieve as a teacher of anatomy and the passion, talent, and commitment of A.D.A.M. medical illustrators Eric Grafman and Ed Stewart resulted in a work which, in my opinion, is one of the most impressive anatomy atlases on the market today. This atlas embodies many of the same qualities that have made the electronic *A.D.A.M.* products so valuable. From page to page, the images are arranged to give the viewer a sense of moving ever deeper into the body. Within many illustrations, a technique called "ghosting" reveals the anatomic relationships between semitransparent superficial structures and underlying structures. Additionally, *PDR® Atlas of Anatomy* allows side-by-side comparison of the A.D.A.M. images and the Bassett cadaver photographs. The resulting work represents a milestone in the presentation of anatomic information.

I like to think that this atlas represents human accomplishment at its best. The talent, dedication, and professionalism of those who created it can be seen on every page. It is my hope that as this atlas helps us more fully visualize the complexity of the human body, it can also contribute to a better understanding of ourselves as human beings, enabling us to open doors to a better educated and healthier society.

Gregory M. Swayne
President
A.D.A.M. Software, Inc.

Preface

Our knowledge of human gross anatomy has changed relatively little in the past 100 years; however, our ability to prepare realistic, readily grasped visualizations of complex, three-dimensional structures has made extraordinary strides. Computerized simulations such as the remarkable A.D.A.M. program now permit us to explore the internal geography of the human body in a vivid, comprehensible manner never before possible.

Although these striking images have been available in an electronic environment for several years, for some time I have thought it remarkable that no one had attempted to replicate these new perspectives in the traditional form of a printed anatomy atlas.

The resulting volume, now available as the *PDR® Atlas of Anatomy,* is foremost a visual guide and interactive resource to be used in conjunction with a clinical anatomy reference. In the structure and content of the atlas, I have emphasized those structures that are fundamental to the everyday concerns of all clinicians, It has not been my intention to create a comprehensive atlas nor an atlas to accompany laboratory dissection. I have included more images of fewer structures; particularly, more images of those parts of the body that present the viewer with the greatest difficulty to comprehend and appreciate three-dimensionally. It is important that those who use this atlas understand both its distinctive emphasis and limited scope, and appreciate the necessity of a more comprehensive atlas when more esoteric questions arise.

Nowhere in the *PDR® Atlas of Anatomy* is the emphasis on essential and difficult material more evident than in Chapter 4, which covers the pelvic contents and perineum. These topics are treated in a substantially expanded format than is normally found in traditional atlases for two reasons. First, the major clerkship of obstetrics and gynecology, and to a lesser extent the field of urology, dictate the necessity of knowing the basic anatomy of the pelvis and perineum. Second, experience indicates that this region is possibly the most difficult to understand. The pelvis and perineum present unique problems of spatial and surface relationships, compounded by the fact that dissection of the pelvis only partially reveals its contents in situ and is difficult and time-consuming, even for an experienced prosector working on an ideal specimen.

It is ultimately the objective in presenting patient-oriented anatomy to provide the clinician with an understanding of the composite anatomy of all or selected regions of the body; however, experience has convinced me that many find it easier to have information organized by systems. The extensive systemic sections in the *PDR® Atlas of Anatomy* meet this demand. I have included lengthy systemic sections at the beginning of the chapters on the trunk (Chapter 1), pelvis and perineum (Chapter 4), limbs (Chapters 5 and 6), and head and neck (Chapter 7). Systemic descriptions were not included in the chapters on the thoracic and abdominal contents (Chapters 2 and 3) because the systemic anatomy of the body walls of these regions is covered extensively in Chapter 1 and because the distribution and pattern of deeper neurovascular structures can be clearly appreciated in the sequence of dissection images in each of these two chapters.

In organizing the atlas, I have arranged cadaveric photographs to provide users with an overview of some of the more important dissections that are seen in the laboratory. In most cases, photographs are numerically labeled to facilitate their use in practical examination review. Their placement adjacent to corresponding A.D.A.M. images, which serve as the keys to the numbered structures in the photographs, offers the viewer a detailed artistic image (instead of a highly simplified schematic drawing) that enhances what is most important in the view.

An appreciation of both cross-sectional and radiographic anatomy is important in many areas of basic clinical work. However, given the circumscribed scope of this atlas, it was impossible to incorporate more than a limited number of cross-sectional and radiographic images into each chapter. Those that are included either best display the distribution of a prominent structure (e.g., the peritoneum) or provide another means of visualizing the relationships within a region.

Physicians' Desk Reference is proud to add this unique atlas of anatomy to its ever-growing library of practical medical reference works. This collection now includes the following volumes:

- *Physicians' Desk Reference*®
- *PDR For Nonprescription Drugs*®
- *PDR For Ophthalmology*®
- *PDR Companion Guide*™
- *PDR® Generics*™
- *PDR® Medical Dictionary*™
- *PDR® Nurse's Handbook*™
- *PDR® Nurse's Dictionary*™
- *PDR® Atlas of Anatomy*™
- *PDR® Supplements*

The pharmaceutical information in *PDR* and its major companion volumes is also available in the *PDR® Electronic Library*™ on CD-ROM, now used in over 40,000 medical practices. It is also available to any registered member of the health care community via the Internet at **www.medecinteractive.com.**

PDR welcomes you to this outstanding new aid to the understanding of human anatomy. We are confident that it will contribute to a deeper comprehension of the complex anatomical structures and relationships that underlie every medical encounter.

Acknowledgments

PDR® Atlas of Anatomy is the result of a major collective effort, and I extend my appreciation to all of the individuals who contributed to this project, in particular, Paula Huber and Tim Satterfield of Williams & Wilkins, Gregory Swayne of A.D.A.M. Software, Dr. Robert Chase of Stanford University School of Medicine, and Dr. Arthur F. Dalley II of Creighton University School of Medicine.

Dr. Wojciech Pawlina, of University of Florida College of Medicine, worked tirelessly on this project from almost its inception, and his critical advice contributed significantly to the quality of this book and, indeed, made its completion possible.

I acknowledge the talent, dedication, and professionalism of all those at A.D.A.M. Software who are responsible for the artwork in this atlas and in the original *A.D.A.M. Comprehensive.* Their efforts and commitment are clearly visible on every page of this book. I thank Ed Stewart, Eric Grafman, Lynda Leigh Levy, Lelayne Weiss, Virginia Sue Mabry, Dee Mustafa-Bowne, Bill Blakesley, Barry Golivesky, Cordero Jenkins, Cindy Quamme, Suzanne Swayne, Audra Brand, Stephanie Calabrese, Ron Collins, Mary Beth Clough, Dan Johnson, Kyle McNeir, Meredith Nienkamp, Lisa Quattrini, and Laura Petrides. In addition, I would like to extend my appreciation to Tim Brammer and Roger Jackson for their technical assistance and support.

The following individuals at Williams & Wilkins brought their expertise, enthusiasm, and commitment to quality to this project: Crystal Taylor, Mary Finch, Anne Stewart Seitz, and Janet Krejci.

I wish to thank Dottie Mims of the Image Foundry, Ltd.

My gratitude is extended to Dr. Keith Moore for use of tables from his book *Clinically Oriented Anatomy*, Third Edition, published in 1992 by Williams & Wilkins. I am grateful to Dr. Lothar Wicke for use of several radiographic images from his *Atlas of Radiographic Anatomy*, Fifth Edition, published in 1994 by Lea & Febiger.

Gregory Smith of St. Mary's College of California, Dr. Sharon Sawitzke, and Dr. Burton Dornfest provided invaluable insight and suggestions while reviewing the atlas during its production. The input of Dr. Thomas Gest into an earlier version of the project was also very helpful. Dr. Olga Malakhova of University of Florida College of Medicine deserves a special acknowledgment for the help and consultation she provided Dr. Pawlina to further his labors on the *Atlas*.

Many individuals contributed to my education as an anatomist and, thus, to this endeavor, and I extend my sincere appreciation and indebtedness to Dr. Ralph Ger, Dr. Peter Satir, Dr. Ilya Glezer, Dr. Herbert Srebnik, Professor Michael Day, and my dear friend the late Dr. Warren Kinzey.

Colleagues in the American Association of Clinical Anatomists are too numerous to name here, although I wish to acknowledge them as well as my fellow course directors here in New York: Drs. Ernest April, N. Barry Berg, Bruce Bogart, Ray Dannenhoffer, Daria Dykyj, Fakhry Girgis, Mahmood Khan, Jeffrey Laitman, Martin Levine, Leon Martino, Anthony Mercurio, Nikos Solounias, and Eugene Wenk, for the conversations that we have had about the teaching of clinical anatomy and its role in medical education.

Although all of my former and current anatomy students have contributed to my experience and insights that I developed into the concept and organization of this book, six students at Albert Einstein College of Medicine deserve recognition for their work on and support of this project: Debbie Chirnomas, Benjamin Cilento, Sharon Goldstein, Soleyman Rokhsar, Kimberly Valenti, and Christine Yuen.

Finally, I would like to thank the many students in Albert Einstein College of Medicine's Class of 1999 for their helpful comments on many of the chapters in this book.

Atlas of Anatomy Team

Anatomic Illustration

Eric D. Grafman, *Project Director and Medical Illustrator*

Ed M. Stewart, *Production Manager and Medical Illustrator*

Lynda Leigh Levy, *Medical Illustrator*

Lelayne Weiss, *Illustrator*

Virginia Sue Mabry, *Illustrator*

Dee Mustafa-Bowne, *Illustrator*

Photo Retouch

Bill Blakesley, *Medical Illustrator*

Barry Golivesky, *Graphic Designer*

Cordero D. Jenkins, *Illustrator*

Cindy Quamme, *Graphic Designer*

Post Production

Suzanne Swayne

Lelayne Weiss

Audra Brand

Product Manager

Stephanie Calabrese

A.D.A.M. Software Comprehensive Team

Gregory M. Swayne, *Executive Producer and Medical Illustrator*

Ron Collins, *Project Director and Medical Illustrator*

Mary Beth Clough, *Medical Illustrator*

Dan Johnson, *Medical Illustrator*

Kyle McNeir, *Medical Illustrator*

Meredith Nienkamp, *Medical Illustrator*

Lisa Quattrini, *Medical Illustrator*

Lelayne Weiss, *Illustrator*

Virginia Sue Mabry, *Illustrator*

Dee Mustafa-Bowne, *Illustrator*

Cindy Quamme, *Graphic Designer*

Contents

Credits

Many of the tables and all of the radiographs appearing in this atlas are used with permission from the following:

Moore, KL, Clinically Oriented Anatomy, 3rd ed. Baltimore: Williams & Wilkins, 1992.
Tables 1.1, 1.2, 1.3, 1.4, 4.1, 4.2, 5.1, 5.2, 5.3, 5.6, 6.1, 6.2, 6.3, 6.4, 6.5, 6.6, 7.1, 7.2, 7.3, 7.4, 7.5, 7.6, 7.7, 7.8, 7.9, 8.1, and 8.2.

Wicke L, Röntgen-Anatomie Normalbefund, 4th German ed. München-Wein-Baltimore: Urban & Schwarzenberg, 1992.
Radiographs in Plates 2.20, 2.36, 3.12, 3.22, 3.26, 3.28, 3.36, 5.42, 5.52, 5.58, 6.36, 6.46, 6.62, 7.1, 7.6, and 7.8.

The Publishers have made every effort to trace the copyright holders for borrowed material. If they have inadvertently overlooked any, they will be pleased to make the necessary arrangements at the first opportunity.

User's Guide

PDR® Atlas of Anatomy was designed to be an interactive pictorial guide to basic human anatomic structures and terminology as well as the three-dimensional relationships of the body's constituent parts. The next few pages explain how to use the illustrations and special features of the atlas to their fullest advantage.

Three-Dimensional Anatomy

Among the problems faced by everyone in health care, none is more universally perplexing than acquiring an appreciation of the three-dimensional relationships within the human body. Recent anatomy books have addressed this problem largely through the inclusion of cross sections and computed tomographic (CT) and magnetic resonance imaging (MRI) scans. Typically, anatomy atlases and textbooks illustrate a region from only one of the four traditional vertical perspectives (i.e., anterior, posterior, medial, lateral), and users are left to extrapolate the anatomy of the third dimension from a two-dimensional picture.

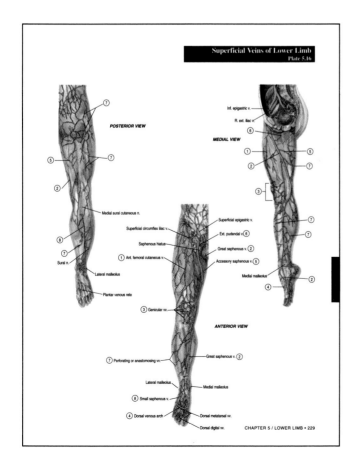

One of the most effective ways to overcome this problem is to illustrate the region in question from an orientation that is at right angles to the original perspective. Using the distinctive ability of *A.D.A.M.* illustrations to view the body from any one of the four vertical perspectives, included are at least two, sometimes more, orientations in many of the plates. For example, the medial, anterior, and posterior views of the leg in Plate 5.16 make visualizing the location, distribution, and relationships of the superficial veins, especially the clinically important saphenous vein, and cutaneous nerves of the lower limb much easier. The extensive use of these multiple views is one of the most striking and valuable characteristics of the *PDR® Atlas of Anatomy.*

Labels and Key and Test Images
The two figures here from Plate 1.48 demonstrate the **three ways that structures are labeled in the atlas** and the rationale for the labeling.

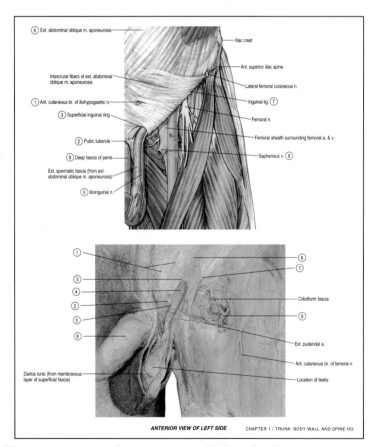

First, the ***iliac crest*** in the *top* figure and the ***cribriform fascia*** in the *lower* are **identified simply by** name because both of these structures are not present in both figures.

Second, the ***superficial inguinal ring*** and ***deep fascia of penis*** are identified by name in the *top* figure and are associated with a *circled number.* The presence of **circled numbers next to structure names** indicates that the figure is a **key image.** A key image should be used in identifying structures **labeled only by a circled number on a test image,** which is the third type of labeling used in the atlas.

Third, a **test image** is typically located on the plate to the *right* of a key image; however, sometimes a test image is placed on the *same* plate as a key image, as occurs in Plate 1.48, the example used here.

Circled numbers are placed randomly on test images to emphasize the importance of associating structural landmarks on corresponding key images and test images. The correlation of a particular number with a particular structure is valid only within a plate or within adjacent plates. For example, the **_ilioinguinal n._** is labeled ⑬ in the key image on Plate 1.48, but it is labeled ④ on Plate 1.50. The only exception to this pattern is the series of plates on the perineum (Plates 4.39–4.50) where a number is consistently assigned to a structure throughout the series.

Anatomical Nomenclature

The anglicized and classical terminology used in the *PDR® Atlas of Anatomy* follows the sixth edition of *Nomina Anatomica.* In some cases, the use of brackets [ ] and parentheses ( ) has formal meaning in the internationally recognized code of anatomical nomenclature.

        Brackets signify:
        1.   An officially recognized alternative name or synonym.
              Fibularis [Peroneus] longus m.
              L. vagus n. [CN X], where CN refers to a cranial nerve
              L. gastro-omental [gastroepiploic] v.
        2.   An equivalent anatomical name.
              Subcostal n. [T12], where T12 = 12th thoracic spinal n.
              C1 [Atlas]

        Parentheses identify:
        1.   An official name of inconsistent structures.
              (Accessory parotid gland)
              (Frontal suture)

        2.   Eponyms and alternative names that are not officially recognized as appropriate in contemporary usage.
              L. colic (splenic) flexure
              Costoaxillary (ext. mammary) v.
              Hepatopancreatic ampulla (of Vater)

        3.   Additional components of a name that are usually omitted but have been added for clarification or that are supplemental to the name.
              Greater tuberosity (of humerus)
              Acromion (process of scapula)
              Posterior basal bronchopulmonary segment (S10)

4. Motor and sensory segmental and spinal nerve levels of a peripheral nerve.

    Femoral n. (L2–L4)
    Lat. femoral cutaneous n. (L2, L3)
    Middle cluneal nn. (dorsal rami of S1–S3)

    Two adjacent spinal nn., are separated by a comma; however, when more than two spinal nn. are involved, only the cranial and caudal-most are listed, separated by a dash.

5. Conditions specific or unique to the image or dissection.

    L. rectus abdominis m. (reflected medially)
    R. primary bronchus (pulled to L.)

6. In some names, long dashes replace or are used in conjunction with parentheses.

    Biceps femoris m.—long head tendon
    Vestibular bulb of vagina—corpus spongiosum
    Superficial perineal fascia—membranous layer (Colles')
    Urinary bladder—empty

Abbreviations

The following abbreviations are used in this atlas. **Bold** entries are abbreviated everywhere they appear, other entries are sometimes abbreviated in order to save space.

&	**= and**	inf.	= inferior	nn.	= nerves
a.	**= artery**	int.	= internal	pt.	= part
aa.	**= arteries**	**L.**	**= Left**	port.	= portion
ant.	= anterior	lat.	= lateral	post.	= posterior
asc.	= ascending	**lig.**	**= ligament**	proc.	= process
br.	**= branch**	**ligg.**	**= ligaments**	**R.**	**= Right**
brr.	**= branches**	**m.**	**= muscle**	sup.	= superior
comm.	**= communicating**	**mm.**	**= muscles**	trib.	= tributary
desc.	= descending	med.	= medial	**v.**	**= vein**
ext.	= external	**n.**	**= nerve**	**vv.**	**= veins**

Another system of abbreviation is used when labels for segmental structures (i.e., vertebrae, spinal or intercostal nerves, ribs) are superimposed on or immediately adjacent to the structure. Thus, **C6** on or next to a vertebra identifies the sixth cervical vertebra; the "C" distinguishes the vertebral type and the number its segmental location. Abbreviations used this way are:

    C = Cervical
    Cc = Coccygeal
    L = Lumbar
    R = Rib
    S = Sacral
    T = Thoracic

Trunk:
Body Wall and Spine

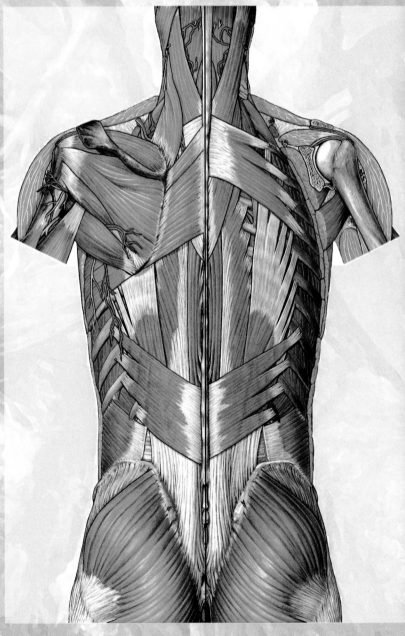

Chapter **1**

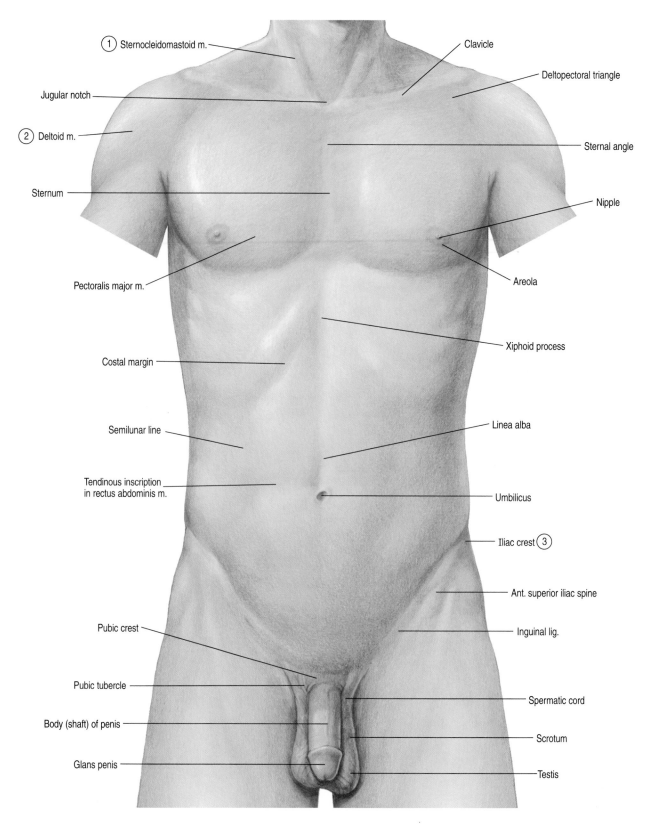

① Sternocleidomastoid m.

Clavicle

Deltopectoral triangle

Jugular notch

② Deltoid m.

Sternal angle

Sternum

Nipple

Pectoralis major m.

Areola

Xiphoid process

Costal margin

Linea alba

Semilunar line

Tendinous inscription in rectus abdominis m.

Umbilicus

Iliac crest ③

Ant. superior iliac spine

Pubic crest

Inguinal lig.

Pubic tubercle

Spermatic cord

Body (shaft) of penis

Scrotum

Glans penis

Testis

ANTERIOR VIEW

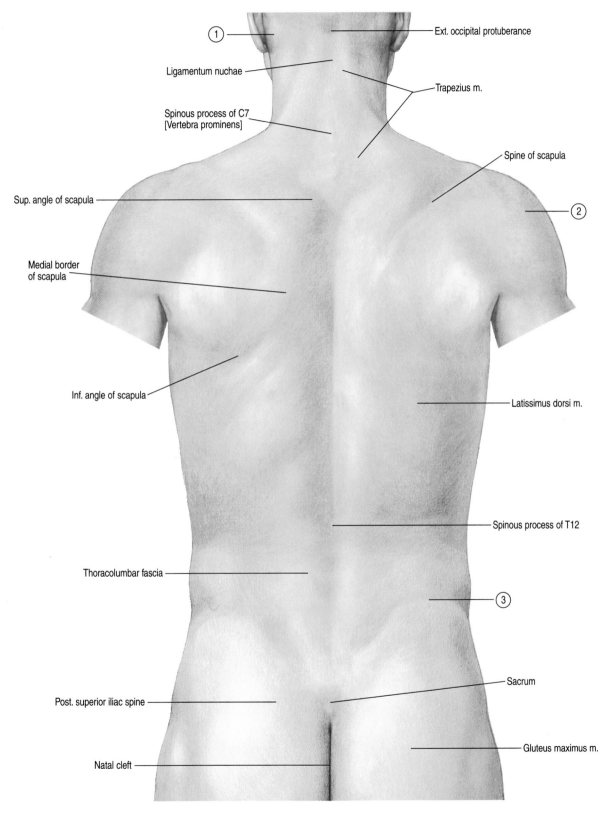

Ext. occipital protuberance

Ligamentum nuchae

Trapezius m.

Spinous process of C7
[Vertebra prominens]

Spine of scapula

Sup. angle of scapula

Medial border
of scapula

Inf. angle of scapula

Latissimus dorsi m.

Spinous process of T12

Thoracolumbar fascia

Sacrum

Post. superior iliac spine

Gluteus maximus m.

Natal cleft

POSTERIOR VIEW

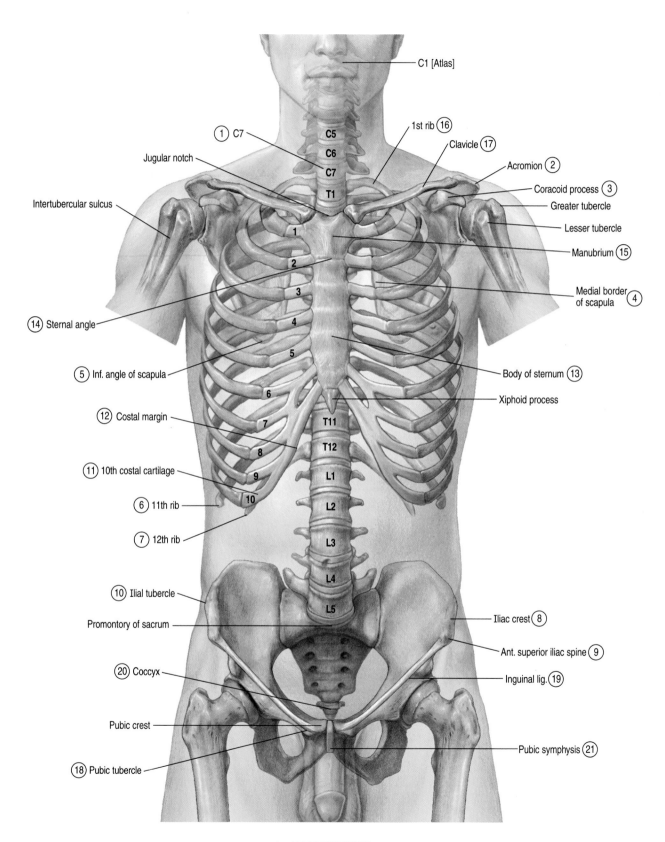

C1 [Atlas]

1st rib (16)

Clavicle (17)

(1) C7

Acromion (2)

Jugular notch

Coracoid process (3)

Greater tubercle

Intertubercular sulcus

Lesser tubercle

Manubrium (15)

Medial border of scapula (4)

(14) Sternal angle

(5) Inf. angle of scapula

Body of sternum (13)

Xiphoid process

(12) Costal margin

(11) 10th costal cartilage

(6) 11th rib

(7) 12th rib

(10) Ilial tubercle

Iliac crest (8)

Promontory of sacrum

Ant. superior iliac spine (9)

(20) Coccyx

Inguinal lig. (19)

Pubic crest

Pubic symphysis (21)

(18) Pubic tubercle

C5
C6
C7
T1

T11
T12
L1
L2
L3
L4
L5

ANTERIOR VIEW

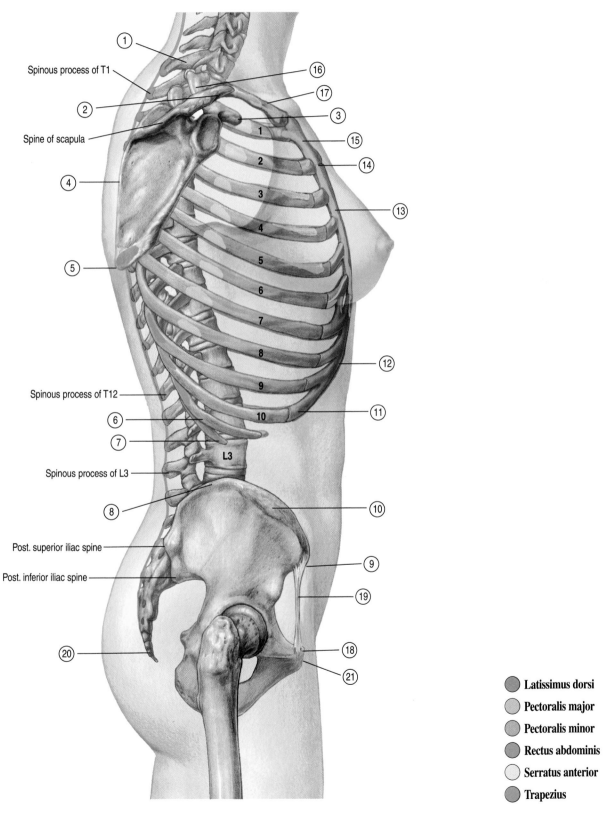

Spinous process of T1

Spine of scapula

Spinous process of T12

Spinous process of L3

Post. superior iliac spine

Post. inferior iliac spine

LATERAL VIEW

Latissimus dorsi
Pectoralis major
Pectoralis minor
Rectus abdominis
Serratus anterior
Trapezius

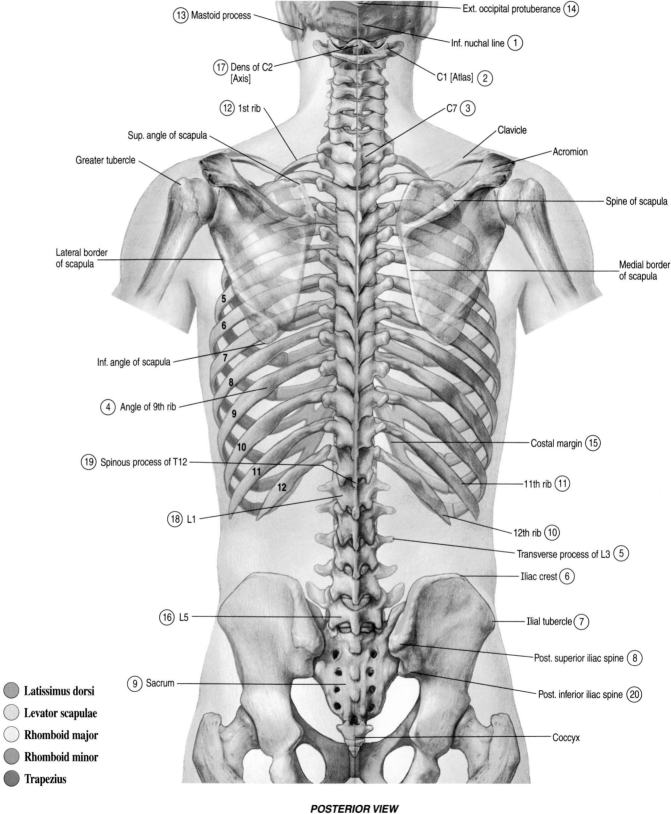

13 Mastoid process

Ext. occipital protuberance 14

Inf. nuchal line 1

17 Dens of C2 [Axis]

C1 [Atlas] 2

12 1st rib

C7 3

Sup. angle of scapula

Clavicle

Greater tubercle

Acromion

Spine of scapula

Lateral border of scapula

Medial border of scapula

5

6

7

Inf. angle of scapula

8

4 Angle of 9th rib

9

Costal margin 15

10

19 Spinous process of T12

11

11th rib 11

12

18 L1

12th rib 10

Transverse process of L3 5

Iliac crest 6

16 L5

Ilial tubercle 7

Post. superior iliac spine 8

9 Sacrum

Post. inferior iliac spine 20

Coccyx

● **Latissimus dorsi**
○ **Levator scapulae**
○ **Rhomboid major**
● **Rhomboid minor**
● **Trapezius**

POSTERIOR VIEW

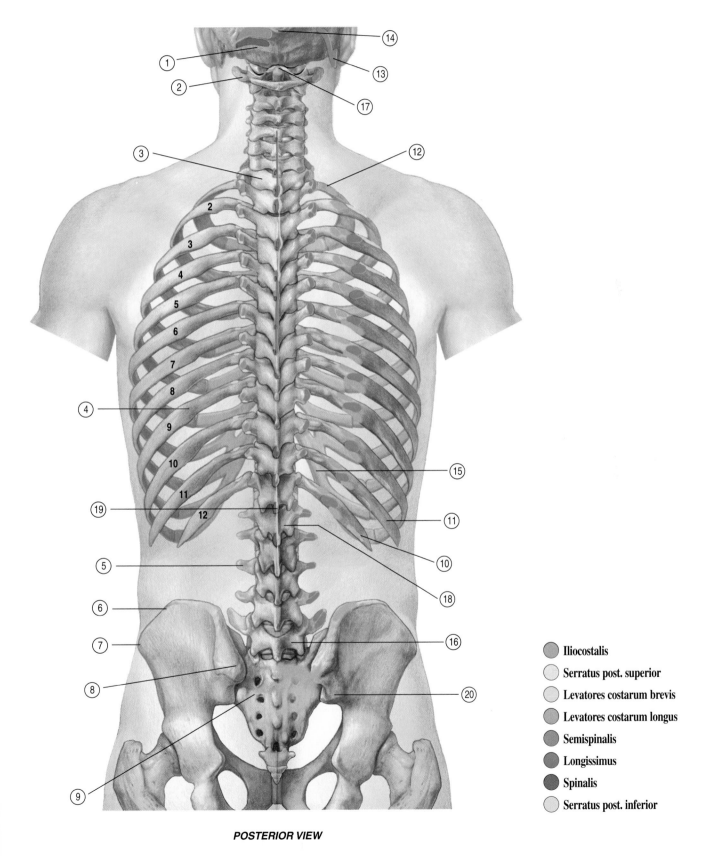

Iliocostalis
Serratus post. superior
Levatores costarum brevis
Levatores costarum longus
Semispinalis
Longissimus
Spinalis
Serratus post. inferior

POSTERIOR VIEW

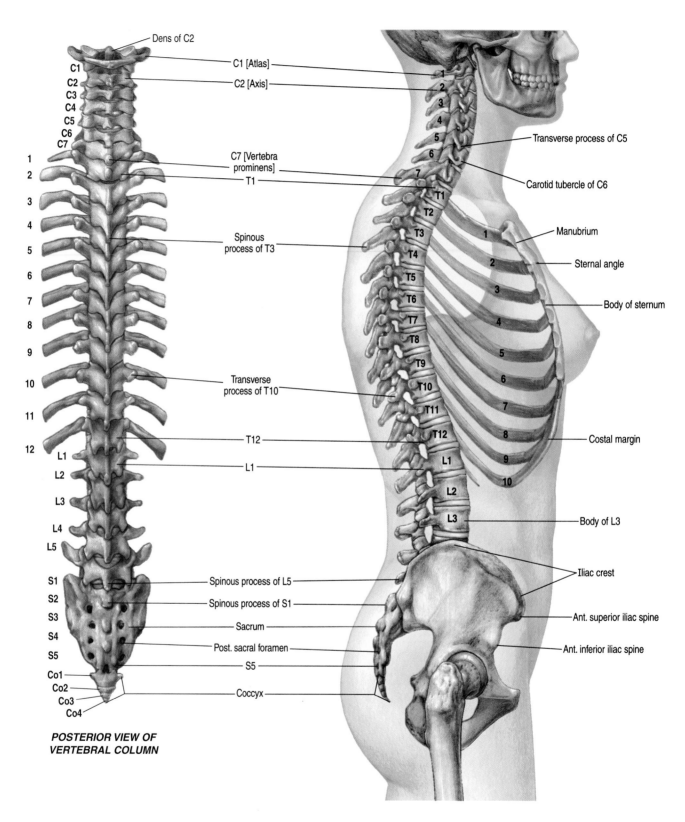

Dens of C2

C1 [Atlas]

C2 [Axis]

C1
C2
C3
C4
C5
C6
C7

1
2
3
4
5
6
7
8
9
10
11
12
L1
L2
L3
L4
L5
S1
S2
S3
S4
S5
Co1
Co2
Co3
Co4

Transverse process of C5

Carotid tubercle of C6

C7 [Vertebra prominens]

T1

Spinous process of T3

Transverse process of T10

T12

L1

Spinous process of L5

Spinous process of S1

Sacrum

Post. sacral foramen

S5

Coccyx

Manubrium

Sternal angle

Body of sternum

Costal margin

Body of L3

Iliac crest

Ant. superior iliac spine

Ant. inferior iliac spine

**POSTERIOR VIEW OF
VERTEBRAL COLUMN**

**LATERAL VIEW OF RIGHT
HALF OF SKELETON**

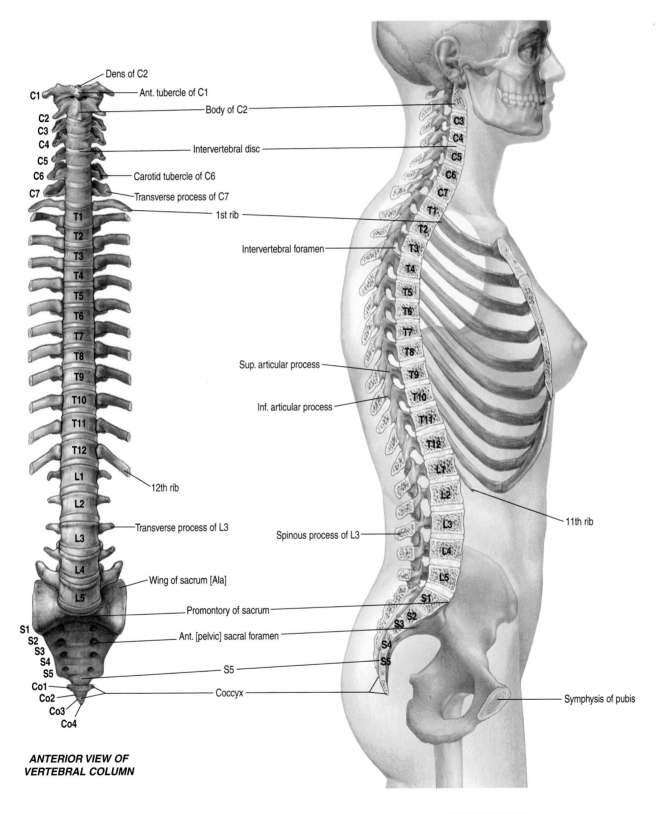

Dens of C2
C1
Ant. tubercle of C1
C2
Body of C2
C3
C4
Intervertebral disc
C5
C6
Carotid tubercle of C6
C7
Transverse process of C7
T1
1st rib
T2
T3
Intervertebral foramen
T4
T5
T6
T7
T8
Sup. articular process
T9
T10
Inf. articular process
T11
T12
L1
12th rib
L2
Transverse process of L3
L3
Spinous process of L3
L4
Wing of sacrum [Ala]
L5
Promontory of sacrum
S1
S2
Ant. [pelvic] sacral foramen
S3
S4
S5
S5
Co1
Co2
Coccyx
Co3
Co4

11th rib
Symphysis of pubis

**ANTERIOR VIEW OF
VERTEBRAL COLUMN**

**RIGHT LATERAL VIEW OF
MEDIAN SECTIONED SKELETON**

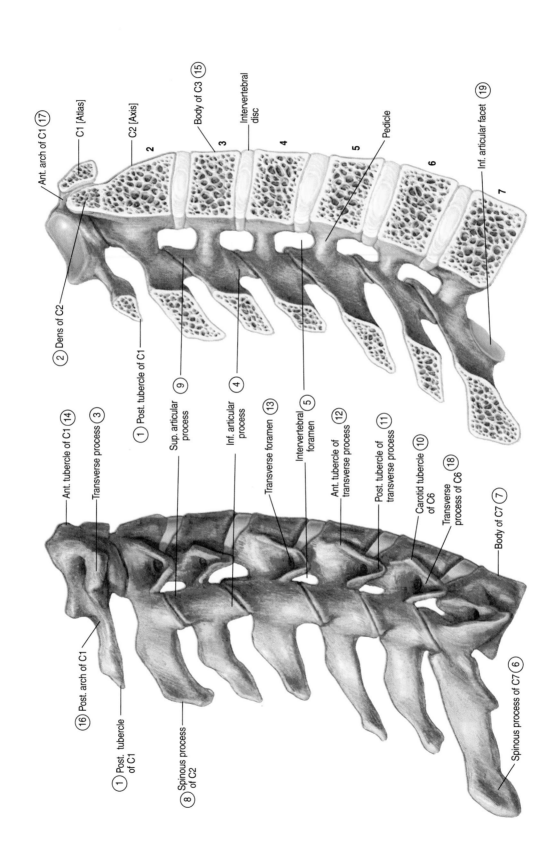

Ant. arch of C1 (17)
C1 [Atlas]
C2 [Axis]
Body of C3 (15)
Intervertebral disc
Pedicle
Inf. articular facet (19)

2
3
4
5
6
7

Dens of C2 (2)
Post. tubercle of C1 (1)
Sup. articular process (9)
Inf. articular process (4)
Transverse foramen (13)
Intervertebral foramen (5)
Ant. tubercle of transverse process (12)
Post. tubercle of transverse process (11)
Carotid tubercle of C6 (10)
Transverse process of C6 (18)
Body of C7 (7)

MEDIAN SECTION OF CERVICAL VERTEBRAE

Ant. tubercle of C1 (14)
Transverse process (3)
Post. tubercle of C1 (1)
Post. arch of C1 (16)
Post. tubercle of C1 (1)
Spinous process of C2 (8)
Spinous process of C7 (6)

LATERAL VIEW OF CERVICAL VERTEBRAE

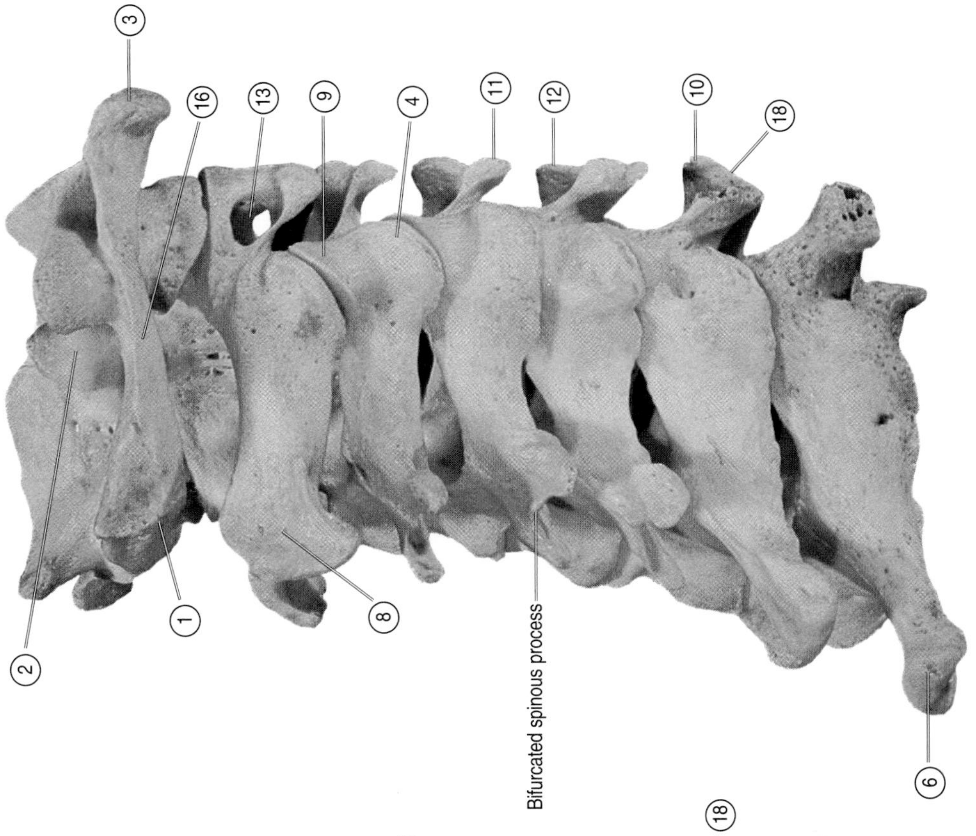

3
16
13
9
4
11
12
10
18
2
1
8
Bifurcated spinous process
6

POSTEROLATERAL VIEW OF CERVICAL VERTEBRAE

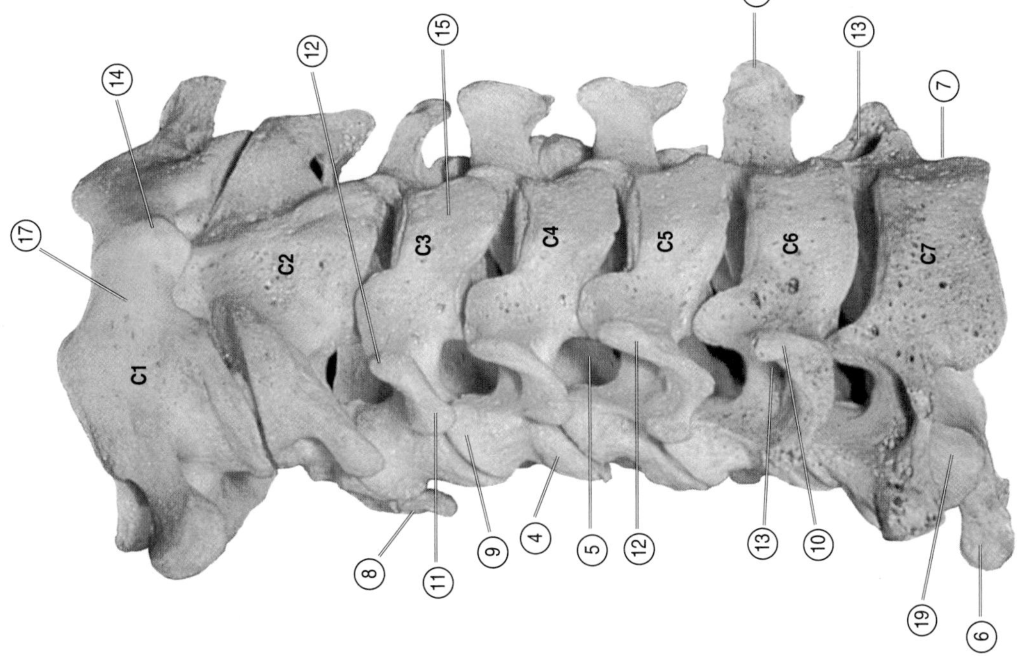

17
14
12
15
18
13
7
C1
C2
C3
C4
C5
C6
C7
8
11
9
4
5
12
13
10
19
6

ANTEROLATERAL VIEW OF CERVICAL VERTEBRAE

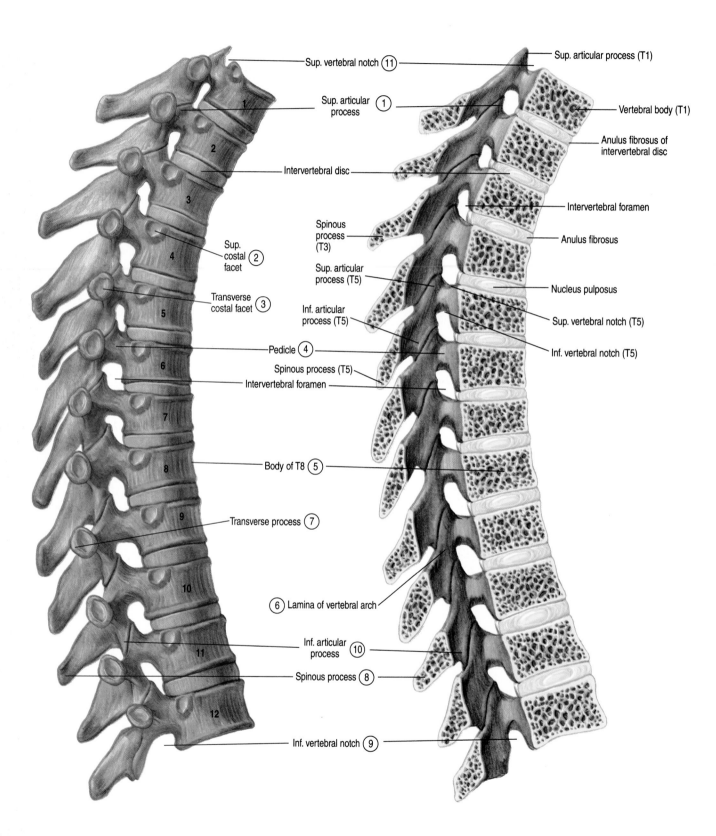

Sup. vertebral notch ⑪

Sup. articular ① process

Intervertebral disc

Sup. costal ② facet

Transverse costal facet ③

Pedicle ④

Spinous process (T5)

Intervertebral foramen

Body of T8 ⑤

Transverse process ⑦

⑥ Lamina of vertebral arch

Inf. articular ⑩ process

Spinous process ⑧

Inf. vertebral notch ⑨

Sup. articular process (T1)

Vertebral body (T1)

Anulus fibrosus of intervertebral disc

Intervertebral foramen

Anulus fibrosus

Nucleus pulposus

Sup. vertebral notch (T5)

Inf. vertebral notch (T5)

Spinous process (T3)

Sup. articular process (T5)

Inf. articular process (T5)

LATERAL VIEW OF THORACIC VERTEBRAE

MIDSAGITTAL SECTION OF THORACIC VERTEBRAE

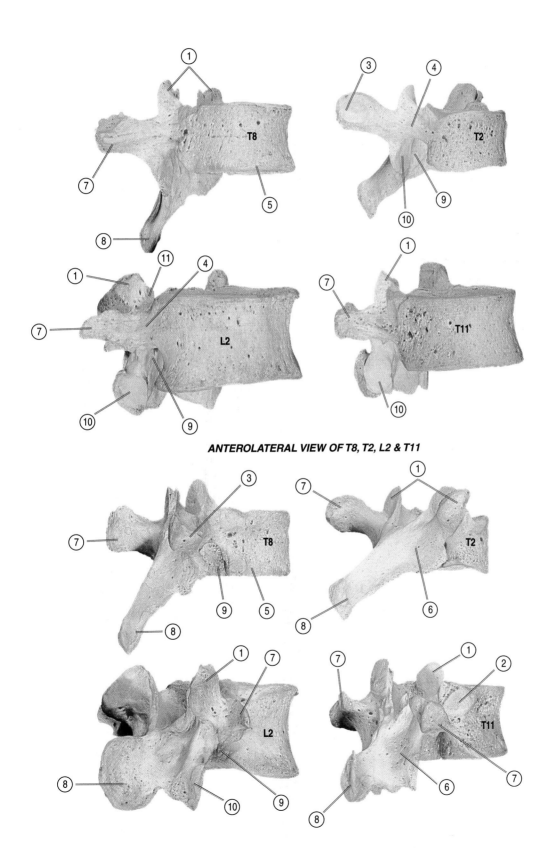

ANTEROLATERAL VIEW OF T8, T2, L2 & T11

POSTEROLATERAL VIEW OF T8, T2, L2 & T11

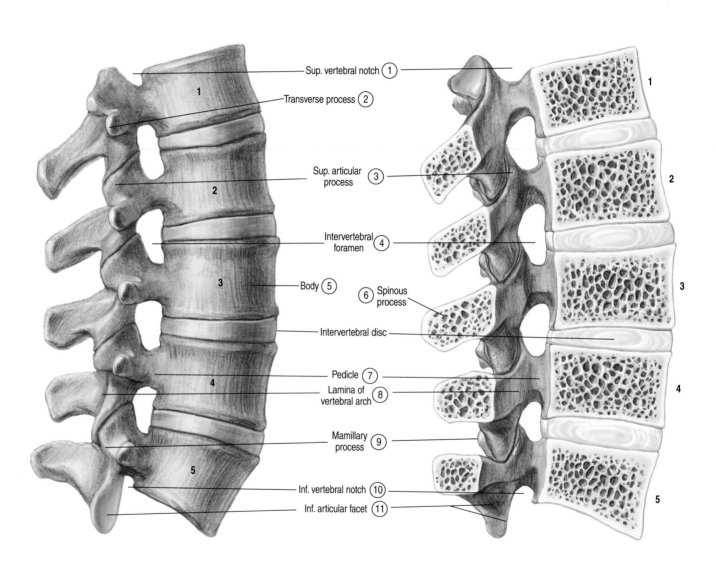

Sup. vertebral notch ①

Transverse process ②

Sup. articular process ③

Intervertebral foramen ④

Body ⑤

⑥ Spinous process

Intervertebral disc

Pedicle ⑦

Lamina of vertebral arch ⑧

Mamillary process ⑨

Inf. vertebral notch ⑩

Inf. articular facet ⑪

**LATERAL VIEW OF
LUMBAR VERTEBRAE**

**MEDIAN SECTION
OF LUMBAR VERTEBRAE**

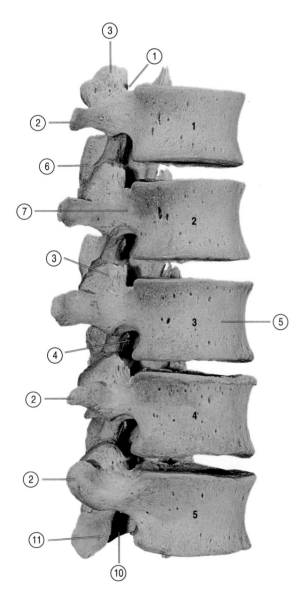

**ANTEROLATERAL VIEW
OF LUMBAR VERTEBRAE**

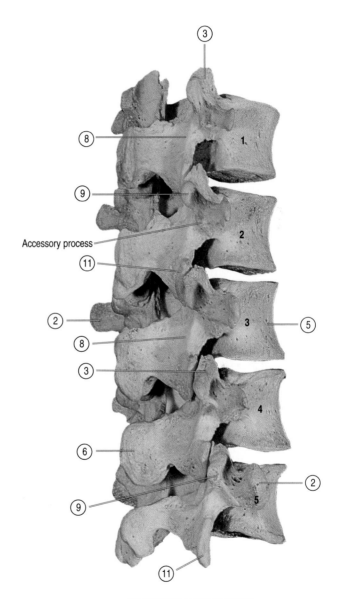

Accessory process

**POSTEROLATERAL VIEW
OF LUMBAR VERTEBRAE**

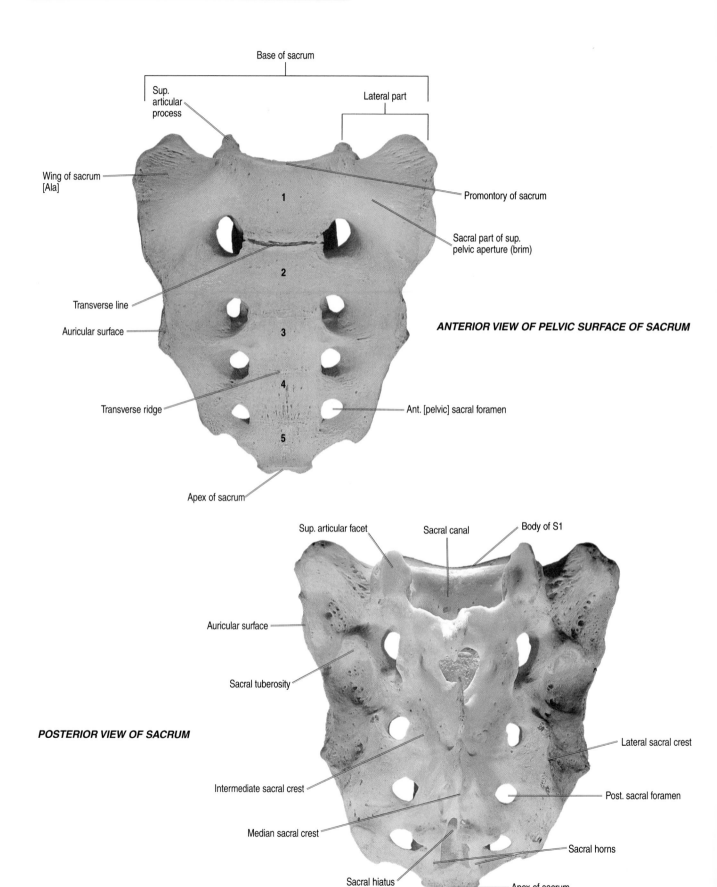

Base of sacrum

Sup. articular process

Lateral part

Wing of sacrum [Ala]

1

Promontory of sacrum

Sacral part of sup. pelvic aperture (brim)

2

Transverse line

Auricular surface

3

ANTERIOR VIEW OF PELVIC SURFACE OF SACRUM

4

Transverse ridge

Ant. [pelvic] sacral foramen

5

Apex of sacrum

Sup. articular facet

Sacral canal

Body of S1

Auricular surface

Sacral tuberosity

POSTERIOR VIEW OF SACRUM

Lateral sacral crest

Intermediate sacral crest

Post. sacral foramen

Median sacral crest

Sacral horns

Sacral hiatus

Apex of sacrum

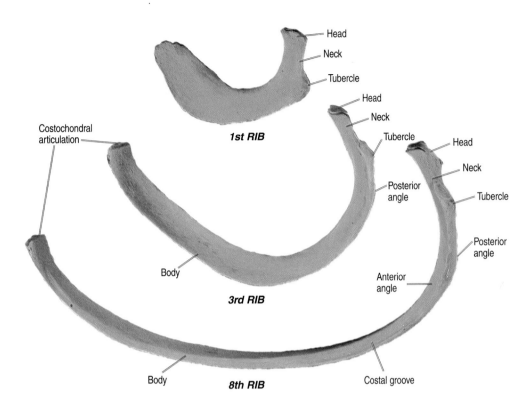

Head

Neck

Tubercle

1st RIB

Head

Neck

Tubercle

Head

Costochondral
articulation

Neck

Posterior
angle

Tubercle

Body

Posterior
angle

Anterior
angle

3rd RIB

Body

8th RIB

Costal groove

INFERIOR VIEW OF RIBS 1, 3 & 8 (RIGHT SIDE)

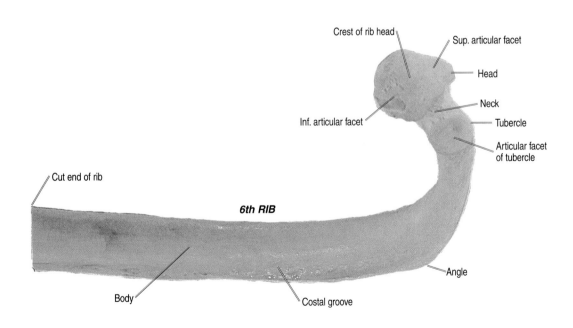

Crest of rib head

Sup. articular facet

Head

Neck

Inf. articular facet

Tubercle

Articular facet
of tubercle

Cut end of rib

6th RIB

Angle

Body

Costal groove

MEDIAL VIEW OF PROXIMAL END OF RIGHT 6TH RIB

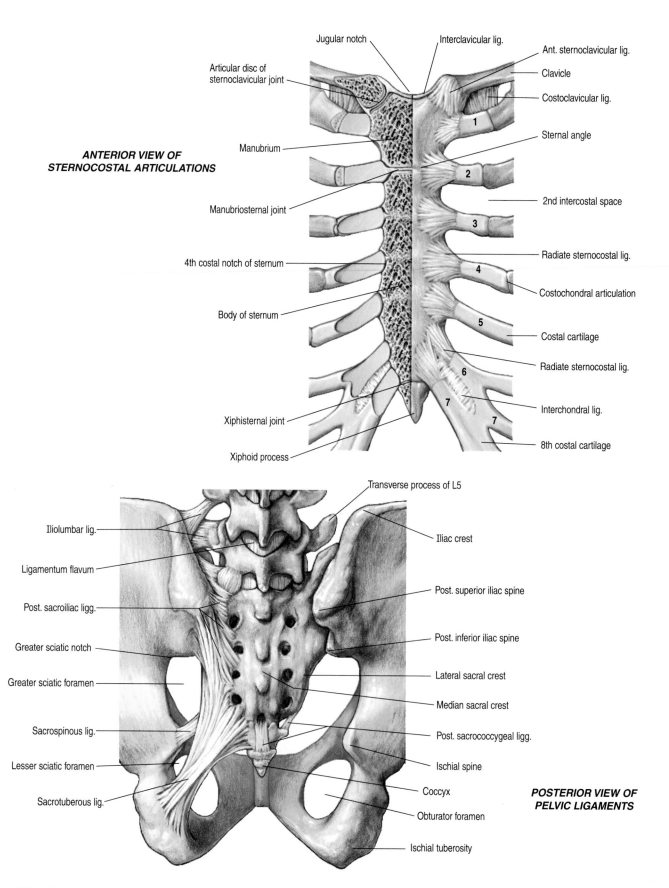

ANTERIOR VIEW OF STERNOCOSTAL ARTICULATIONS

Jugular notch

Interclavicular lig.

Ant. sternoclavicular lig.

Clavicle

Costoclavicular lig.

Articular disc of sternoclavicular joint

Manubrium

Sternal angle

2nd intercostal space

Manubriosternal joint

Radiate sternocostal lig.

4th costal notch of sternum

Costochondral articulation

Body of sternum

Costal cartilage

Radiate sternocostal lig.

Interchondral lig.

Xiphisternal joint

8th costal cartilage

Xiphoid process

Transverse process of L5

Iliolumbar lig.

Iliac crest

Ligamentum flavum

Post. superior iliac spine

Post. sacroiliac ligg.

Post. inferior iliac spine

Greater sciatic notch

Lateral sacral crest

Greater sciatic foramen

Median sacral crest

Sacrospinous lig.

Post. sacrococcygeal ligg.

Lesser sciatic foramen

Ischial spine

Sacrotuberous lig.

Coccyx

Obturator foramen

POSTERIOR VIEW OF PELVIC LIGAMENTS

Ischial tuberosity

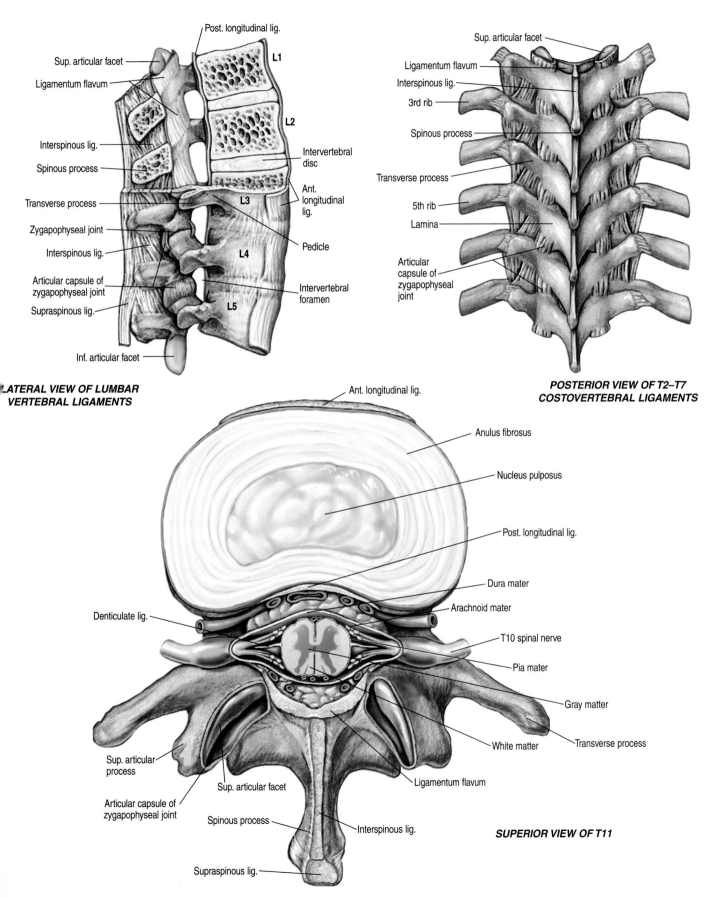

Post. longitudinal lig.

Sup. articular facet

Ligamentum flavum

L1

L2

Interspinous lig.

Spinous process

Intervertebral disc

Transverse process

Ant. longitudinal lig.

L3

Zygapophyseal joint

Interspinous lig.

Pedicle

L4

Articular capsule of zygapophyseal joint

Supraspinous lig.

Intervertebral foramen

L5

Inf. articular facet

LATERAL VIEW OF LUMBAR VERTEBRAL LIGAMENTS

Sup. articular facet

Ligamentum flavum

Interspinous lig.

3rd rib

Spinous process

Transverse process

5th rib

Lamina

Articular capsule of zygapophyseal joint

POSTERIOR VIEW OF T2–T7 COSTOVERTEBRAL LIGAMENTS

Ant. longitudinal lig.

Anulus fibrosus

Nucleus pulposus

Post. longitudinal lig.

Dura mater

Arachnoid mater

Denticulate lig.

T10 spinal nerve

Pia mater

Gray matter

White matter

Transverse process

Sup. articular process

Articular capsule of zygapophyseal joint

Sup. articular facet

Spinous process

Interspinous lig.

Ligamentum flavum

SUPERIOR VIEW OF T11

Supraspinous lig.

Muscles—Thoracic Wall
Table 1.1

Muscle	Superior or Medial Attachment	Inferior or Lateral Attachment	Innervation	Action(s)
External intercostal	Inf. border of rib that bounds intercostal space cranially	Sup. border of rib bounding intercostal space caudally, muscular from costal tubercle to end of rib with membranous connection to sternum	1st to 11th intercostal nn. & subcostal n.	Elevate ribs in inspiration
Internal intercostal		Sup. border of rib bounding intercostal space caudally, muscular from angle to sternum		
Innermost intercostal		Separated from int. intercostal mm. only by neurovascular bundle		
Subcostal	Inf. border lateral to angle of rib that bounds intercostal space cranially	Int. surface near angle of rib that bounds intercostal space caudally, best developed between ribs 6 & 12, may cross 2 intercostal spaces		Depress ribs in expiration
Transversus thoracis	Int. surface of body & xiphoid of sternum	Inf. border of 2nd to 6th costal cartilages	1st to 11th intercostal nn.	Depress costal cartilages in expiration
Levatores costarum *L. c. brevis m.* *L. c. longus m.*	Transverse processes of C7 to T11	Between tubercle & angle on ext. surface of rib caudal to vertebral attachment	Dorsal primary rami of C8 & T1 to T11 spinal nn.	Elevate ribs in inspiration; laterally flex spine
Serratus posterior superior	Inf. part of ligamentum nuchae & spinous process from C7 to T2/T3	Sup. border of 2nd to 5th ribs just lateral to angles	2nd to 5th intercostal nn.	Elevate ribs in inspiration
Serratus posterior inferior	Spinous processes & thoracolumbar fascia from T11/T12 to L3	Inf. border of 9th/10th to 12th ribs just lateral to angles	9th to 11th intercostal nn. & subcostal n.	Depress ribs in expiration

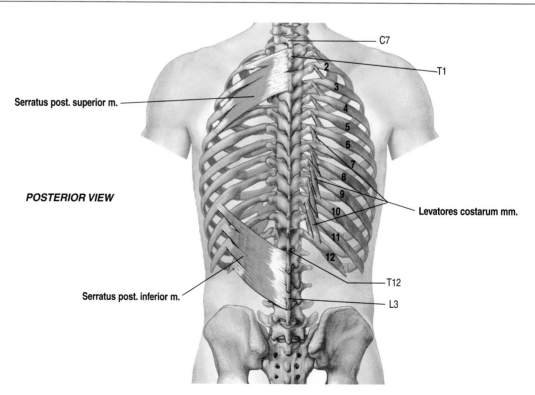

POSTERIOR VIEW

Serratus post. superior m.

Serratus post. inferior m.

Levatores costarum mm.

C7
T1
T12
L3

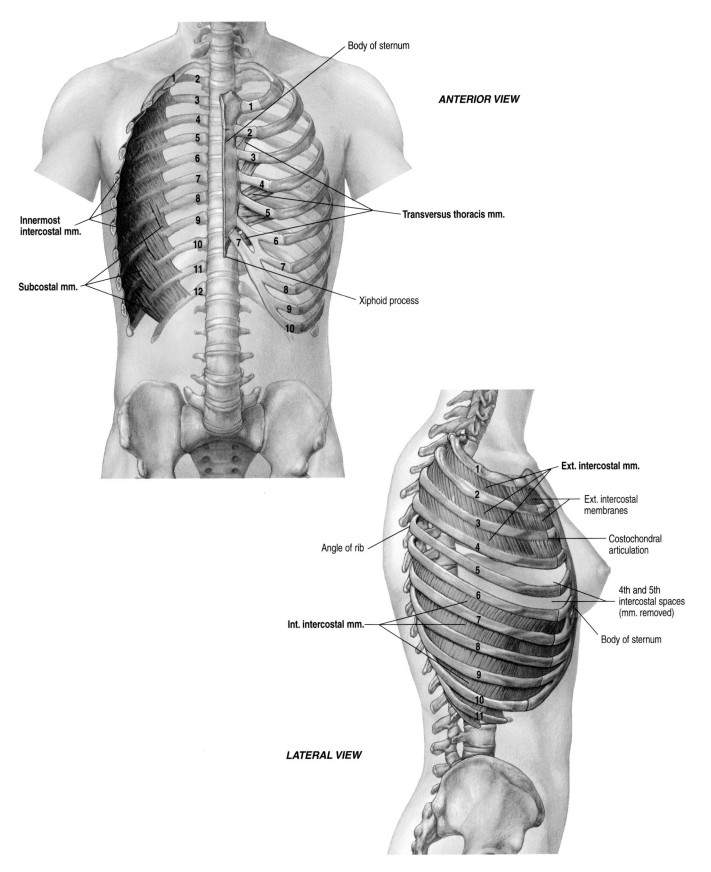

Body of sternum

ANTERIOR VIEW

1
2
3
4
5
6
7
8
9
10
11
12

1
2
3
4
5
6
7

Innermost
intercostal mm.

Subcostal mm.

Transversus thoracis mm.

Xiphoid process

7
8
9
10

Ext. intercostal mm.

Ext. intercostal
membranes

Costochondral
articulation

4th and 5th
intercostal spaces
(mm. removed)

Body of sternum

Angle of rib

Int. intercostal mm.

1
2
3
4
5
6
7
8
9
10
11

LATERAL VIEW

Muscle	Lateral or Superior Attachment	Medial or Inferior Attachment	Innervation	Action(s)
External oblique	Ext. surfaces of 5th to 12th ribs	Linea alba, pubic tubercle & ant. half of iliac crest	Inf. six thoracic nn. & subcostal n.	Compress & support abdominal viscera; flex & rotate trunk
Internal oblique	Thoracolumbar fascia, ant. two-thirds of iliac crest & lateral half of inguinal lig.	Inf. borders of 10th to 12th ribs, linea alba & pubis via the conjoint tendon	Ventral rami of inf. six thoracic & first lumbar nn.	
Transversus abdominis	Int. surfaces of 7th to 12th costal cartilages, thoracolumbar fascia, iliac crest & lateral third of inguinal lig.	Linea alba with aponeurosis of int. oblique, pubic crest & pecten pubis via conjoint tendon		Compress & support abdominal viscera
Rectus abdominis	Xiphoid process & 5th to 7th costal cartilages	Pubic symphysis & pubic crest	Ventral rami of inf. six thoracic nn.	Flex trunk & compress abdominal viscera
Quadratus lumborum	Medial half of inf. border of 12th rib & tips of lumbar transverse processes	Iliolumbar lig. & int. lip of iliac crest	Ventral rami of T12 & L1 to L4	Extend & laterally fixes the vertebral column; flex 12th rib during inspiration
Cremaster	Inf. edge of int. abdominal oblique, inguinal lig., pubic tubercle & pubic crest	Invest spermatic cord and testis	Genital br. of genitofemoral n. (L1 & L2)	Retract testis

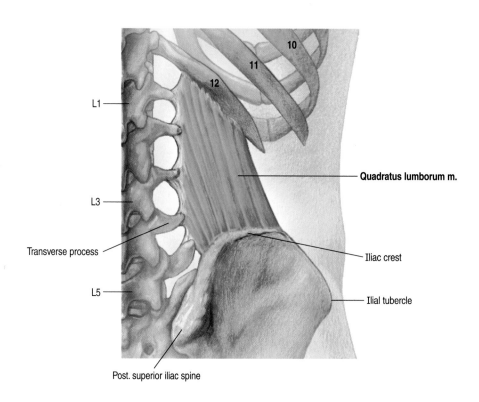

POSTERIOR VIEW

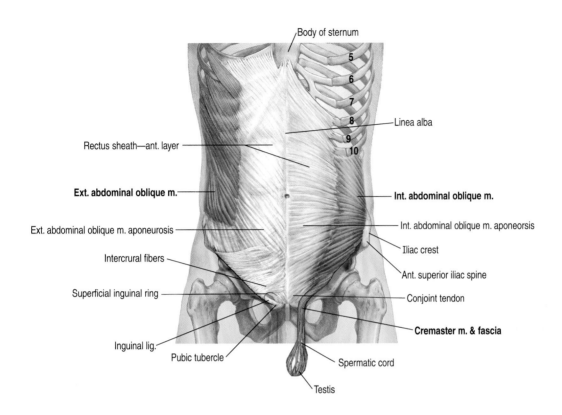

Body of sternum

5
6
7
8
9
10

Linea alba

Rectus sheath—ant. layer

Ext. abdominal oblique m.

Int. abdominal oblique m.

Ext. abdominal oblique m. aponeurosis

Int. abdominal oblique m. aponeorsis

Iliac crest

Intercrural fibers

Ant. superior iliac spine

Superficial inguinal ring

Conjoint tendon

Cremaster m. & fascia

Inguinal lig.

Pubic tubercle

Spermatic cord

Testis

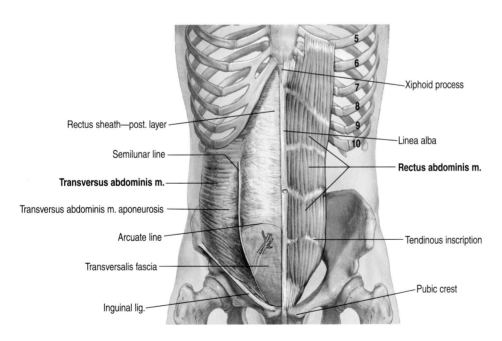

5
6
7
8
9
10

Xiphoid process

Rectus sheath—post. layer

Linea alba

Semilunar line

Rectus abdominis m.

Transversus abdominis m.

Transversus abdominis m. aponeurosis

Arcuate line

Tendinous inscription

Transversalis fascia

Pubic crest

Inguinal lig.

ANTERIOR VIEWS

Intrinsic Muscles of the Back
Table 1.3

Intrinsic Muscles of the Back[a]

Muscle	Inferior or Medial Attachment	Superior or Lateral Attachment	Innervation	Action(s)
SUPERFICIAL—SPINOTRANSVERSE GROUP				
Splenius capitis	Inf. half of ligamentum nuchae, spinous processes of C7 to T3/T4	Mastoid process, lateral third of the sup. nuchal line	Dorsal primary rami of middle cervical spinal nn.	Unilaterally, rotate & laterally flex neck to same side; bilaterally, extend the neck & head
Splenius cervicis	Spinous processes of T3/T4 to T6	Post. tubercles of transverse processes of C1 to C3	Dorsal primary rami of lower cervical spinal nn.	
INTERMEDIATE LAYER—ERECTOR SPINAE GROUP				
Iliocostalis m. *I. cervicis* *I. thoracis* *I. lumborum*	Sacrum, medial part of iliac crest, 12th to 3rd ribs	Angles of all ribs, transverse processes of C7 to C4	Dorsal primary rami of all cervical, thoracic & lumbar spinal nn.	Unilaterally, flex vertebral column to same side; bilaterally, extend vertebral column; important in maintaining erect posture while standing or walking
Longissimus m. *L. capitis* *L. cervicis* *L. thoracis*	Sacrum, transverse processes of all vertebrae from L5 to C7, transverse & articular processes of C6 to C4	Transverse processes of all vertebrae from T12 to C2; angles of all ribs, mastoid process		
Spinalis m. *S. capitis* *S. cervicis* *S. thoracis*	Spinous processes of L2/L3 to T11, ligamentum nuchae & spinous processes of T2 to C7, transverse processes of C7/C6 to C2, articular processes of C6 to C4	Spinous processes from T9/T8 to C7/C6, spinous processes of C3/C4 & C2, occipital bone between sup. & inf. nuchal lines with semispinalis m.		
DEEP LAYER—TRANSVERSOSPINAL GROUP				
Semispinalis m. *S. capitis* *S. cervicis* *S. thoracis*	Transverse processes of all vertebrae from T10 to C3, articular processes of C6 to C4	Spinous processes from T4 to C2, occipital bone between sup. & inf. nuchal lines; usually includes spinalis capitis m.	Dorsal primary rami of T6 to T1, all cervical spinal nn.	Unilaterally, lateral flex and/or rotate vertebral column & head to opposite side; bilaterally, extend vertebral column & head
Multifidus	All lamina from S4 to C2, transverse processes L5 to T1, articular processes C7 to C3	Spinous process of all vertebrae; spans 1 to 3 vertebrae	Dorsal primary rami of T6 to C1 spinal nn.	Unilaterally, lateral flex and/or rotate vertebral column to opposite side; bilaterally, extend or stabilize vertebral column
Rotatores	Transverse processes of all vertebrae L5 to T2	Lamina & roots of spinous process of next vertebra superiorly; best developed in thoracic region	Dorsal primary rami of L4 to T1 spinal nn.	

[a]The most superficial layer also includes the trapezius, latissimus dorsi, levator scapulae & rhomboid muscles which move the upper limb. The intermediate layer is formed by the serratus posterior muscles. The muscles of both of these layers are considered extrinsic to the back. The intrinsic muscles of the back form the deepest three back muscle layers.

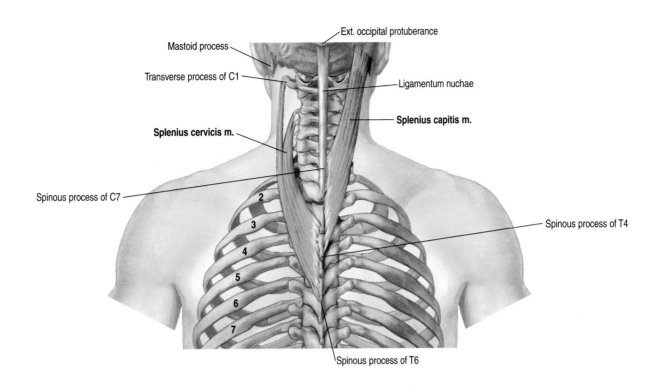

Ext. occipital protuberance

Mastoid process

Transverse process of C1

Ligamentum nuchae

Splenius cervicis m.

Splenius capitis m.

Spinous process of C7

2

3

Spinous process of T4

4

5

6

7

Spinous process of T6

POSTERIOR VIEWS

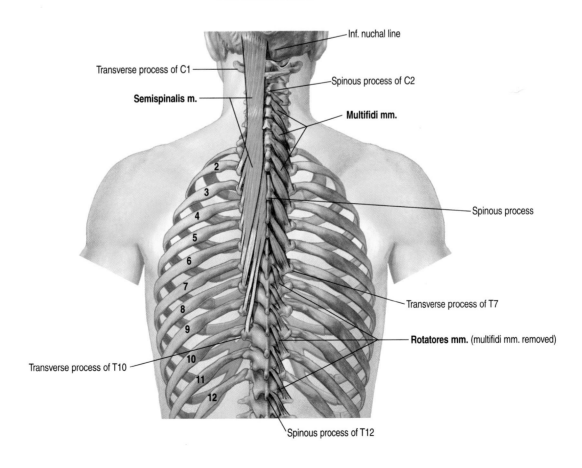

Inf. nuchal line

Transverse process of C1

Spinous process of C2

Semispinalis m.

Multifidi mm.

2

3

Spinous process

4

5

6

7

8

Transverse process of T7

9

Rotatores mm. (multifidi mm. removed)

10

Transverse process of T10

11

12

Spinous process of T12

Muscles—Erector Spinae

Plate 1.22

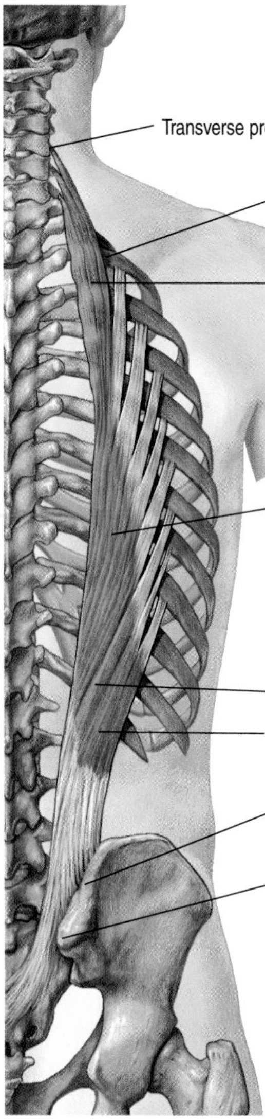
Transverse process of C4
Angle of 2nd rib
Iliocostalis cervicis m.
Iliocostalis thoracis m.
Iliocostalis lumborum m.
Iliocostalis m.
Iliac crest
Post. superior iliac spine

POSTERIOR VIEWS

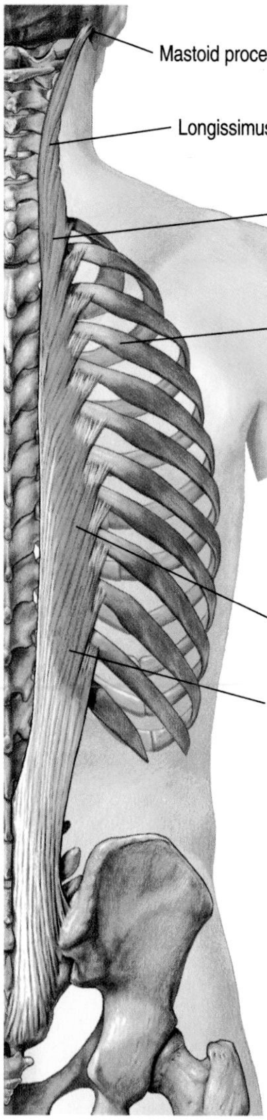
Mastoid process
Longissimus capitis m.
Longissimus cervicis m.
Angle of rib
Longissimus thoracis m.
Longissimus m.

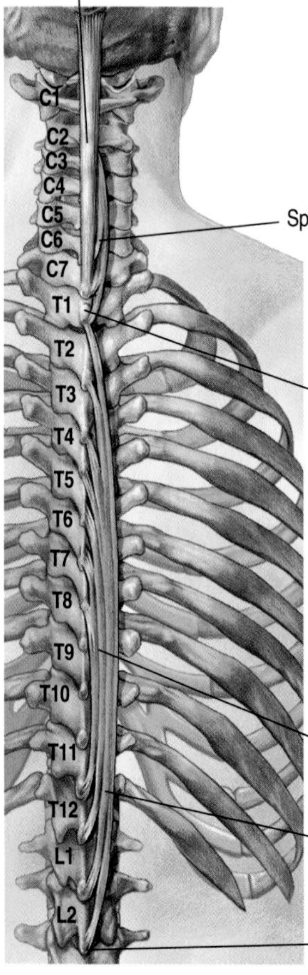
Ligamentum nuchae
C1
C2
C3
C4
C5
C6
C7
T1
T2
T3
T4
T5
T6
T7
T8
T9
T10
T11
T12
L1
L2
Spinous cervicis m.
Spinous process of T1
Spinalis thoracis m.
Spinalis m.
Spinous process of L2

Muscle	Inferior or Medial Attachment	Superior or Lateral Attachment	Innervation	Action(s)
DEEP LAYER—SUBOCCIPITAL GROUP				
Rectus capitis posterior major	Spinous process of C2	Lateral part of inf. nuchal line	Dorsal primary ramus of C1 [suboccipital] n.	Unilaterally, rotate head to same side; bilaterally, extend head at atlanto-occipital joint
Rectus capitis posterior minor	Post. tubercle of C1	Medial part of inf. nuchal line		
Obliquus capitis superior	Transverse process of C1	Sup. to inf. nuchal line		Unilaterally, rotate C1 & head to same side around odontoid process; bilaterally, extend head at atlanto-axial joint
Obliquus capitis inferior	Spinous process of C2	Transverse process of C1		

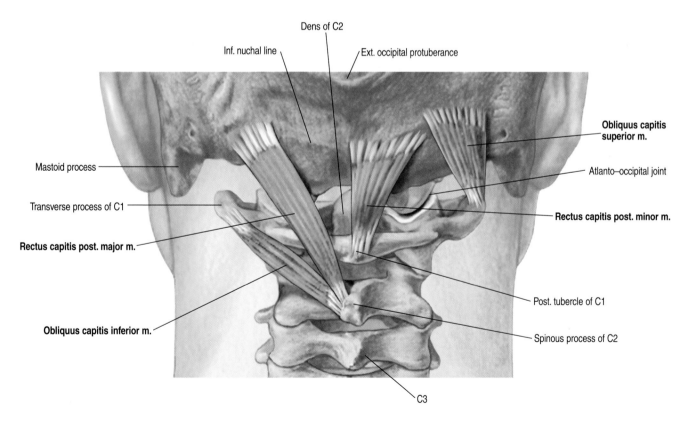

POSTERIOR VIEW

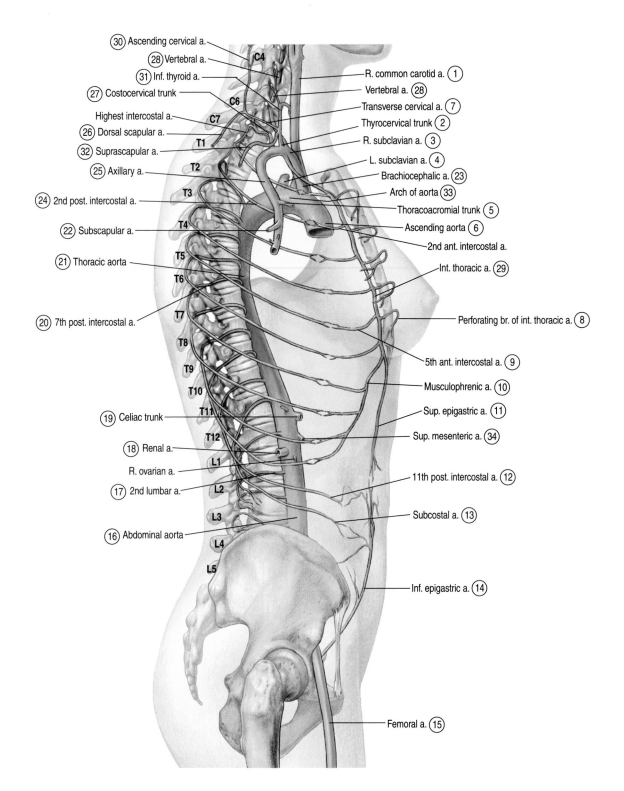

30 Ascending cervical a.

28 Vertebral a.

31 Inf. thyroid a.

27 Costocervical trunk

Highest intercostal a.

26 Dorsal scapular a.

32 Suprascapular a.

25 Axillary a.

24 2nd post. intercostal a.

22 Subscapular a.

21 Thoracic aorta

20 7th post. intercostal a.

19 Celiac trunk

18 Renal a.

R. ovarian a.

17 2nd lumbar a.

16 Abdominal aorta

C4

C6

C7

T1

T2

T3

T4

T5

T6

T7

T8

T9

T10

T11

T12

L1

L2

L3

L4

L5

R. common carotid a. 1

Vertebral a. 28

Transverse cervical a. 7

Thyrocervical trunk 2

R. subclavian a. 3

L. subclavian a. 4

Brachiocephalic a. 23

Arch of aorta 33

Thoracoacromial trunk 5

Ascending aorta 6

2nd ant. intercostal a.

Int. thoracic a. 29

Perforating br. of int. thoracic a. 8

5th ant. intercostal a. 9

Musculophrenic a. 10

Sup. epigastric a. 11

Sup. mesenteric a. 34

11th post. intercostal a. 12

Subcostal a. 13

Inf. epigastric a. 14

Femoral a. 15

RIGHT LATERAL VIEW

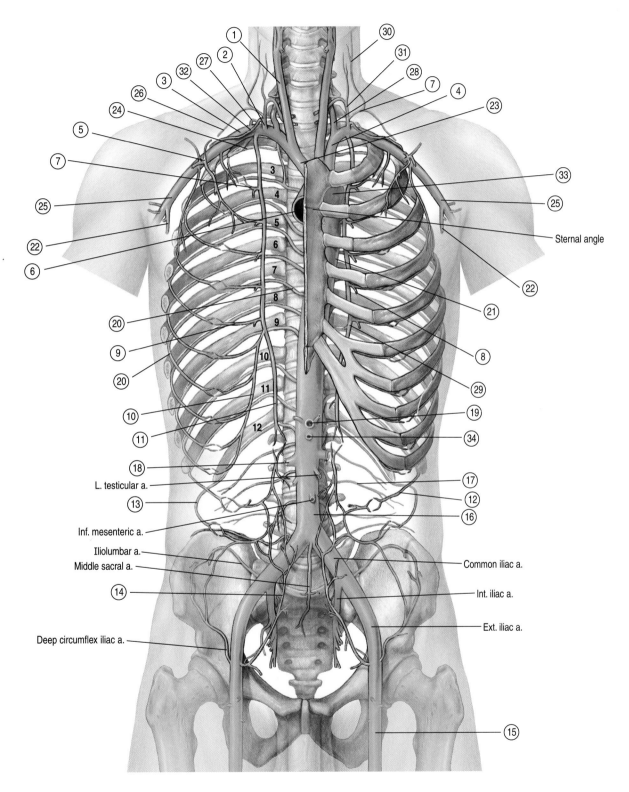

L. testicular a.

Inf. mesenteric a.

Iliolumbar a.

Middle sacral a.

Deep circumflex iliac a.

Sternal angle

Common iliac a.

Int. iliac a.

Ext. iliac a.

ANTERIOR VIEW

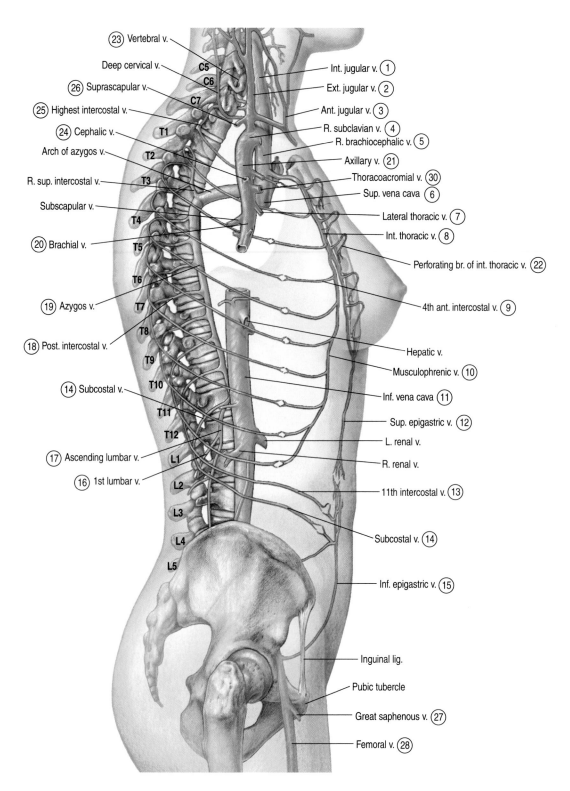

RIGHT LATERAL VIEW

- (23) Vertebral v.
- Deep cervical v.
- (26) Suprascapular v.
- (25) Highest intercostal v.
- (24) Cephalic v.
- Arch of azygos v.
- R. sup. intercostal v.
- Subscapular v.
- (20) Brachial v.
- (19) Azygos v.
- (18) Post. intercostal v.
- (14) Subcostal v.
- (17) Ascending lumbar v.
- (16) 1st lumbar v.

- C5
- C6
- C7
- T1
- T2
- T3
- T4
- T5
- T6
- T7
- T8
- T9
- T10
- T11
- T12
- L1
- L2
- L3
- L4
- L5

- Int. jugular v. (1)
- Ext. jugular v. (2)
- Ant. jugular v. (3)
- R. subclavian v. (4)
- R. brachiocephalic v. (5)
- Axillary v. (21)
- Thoracoacromial v. (30)
- Sup. vena cava (6)
- Lateral thoracic v. (7)
- Int. thoracic v. (8)
- Perforating br. of int. thoracic v. (22)
- 4th ant. intercostal v. (9)
- Hepatic v.
- Musculophrenic v. (10)
- Inf. vena cava (11)
- Sup. epigastric v. (12)
- L. renal v.
- R. renal v.
- 11th intercostal v. (13)
- Subcostal v. (14)
- Inf. epigastric v. (15)
- Inguinal lig.
- Pubic tubercle
- Great saphenous v. (27)
- Femoral v. (28)

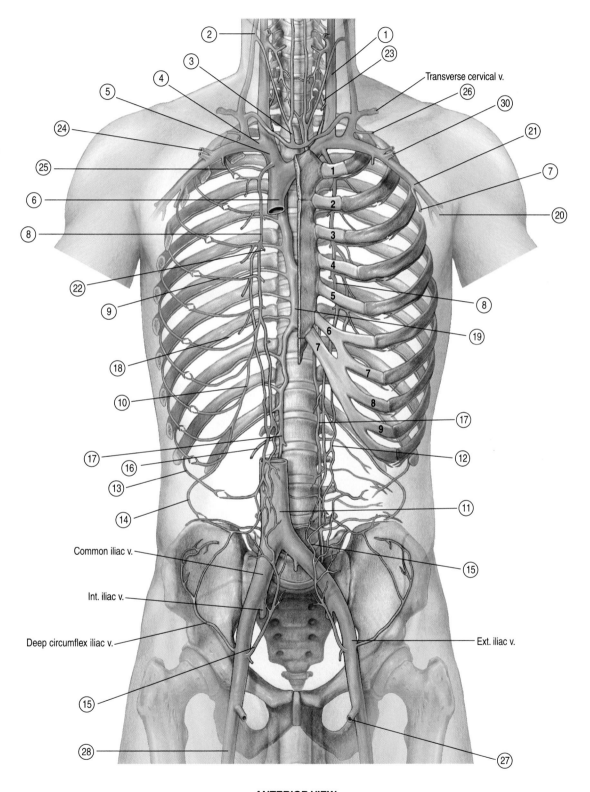

Transverse cervical v.

Common iliac v.

Int. iliac v.

Deep circumflex iliac v.

Ext. iliac v.

ANTERIOR VIEW

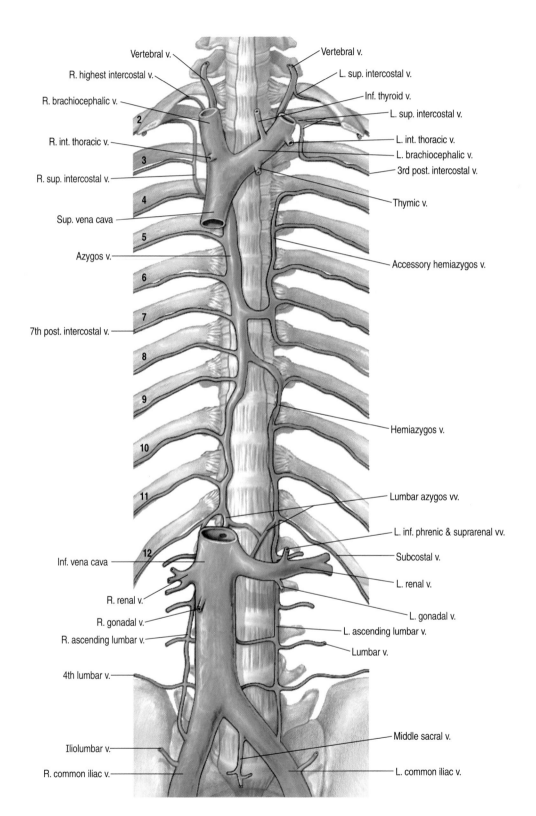

Vertebral v.
R. highest intercostal v.
R. brachiocephalic v.
R. int. thoracic v.
R. sup. intercostal v.
Sup. vena cava
Azygos v.
7th post. intercostal v.

Vertebral v.
L. sup. intercostal v.
Inf. thyroid v.
L. sup. intercostal v.
L. int. thoracic v.
L. brachiocephalic v.
3rd post. intercostal v.
Thymic v.
Accessory hemiazygos v.
Hemiazygos v.
Lumbar azygos vv.
L. inf. phrenic & suprarenal vv.
Subcostal v.
L. renal v.
L. gonadal v.
L. ascending lumbar v.
Lumbar v.

Inf. vena cava
R. renal v.
R. gonadal v.
R. ascending lumbar v.
4th lumbar v.
Iliolumbar v.
R. common iliac v.

Middle sacral v.
L. common iliac v.

ANTERIOR VIEW

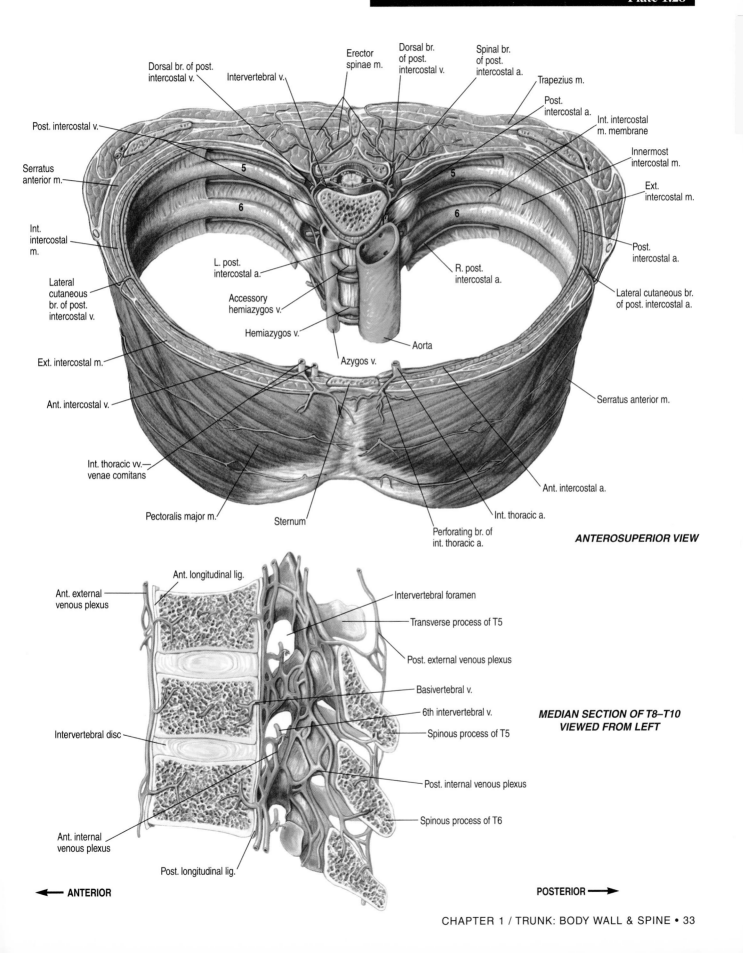

Dorsal br. of post. intercostal v.

Intervertebral v.

Erector spinae m.

Dorsal br. of post. intercostal v.

Spinal br. of post. intercostal a.

Trapezius m.

Post. intercostal a.

Int. intercostal m. membrane

Innermost intercostal m.

Ext. intercostal m.

Post. intercostal v.

Serratus anterior m.

Int. intercostal m.

Lateral cutaneous br. of post. intercostal v.

Ext. intercostal m.

Ant. intercostal v.

Int. thoracic vv.—venae comitans

Pectoralis major m.

Sternum

L. post. intercostal a.

Accessory hemiazygos v.

Hemiazygos v.

Azygos v.

Aorta

R. post. intercostal a.

Post. intercostal a.

Lateral cutaneous br. of post. intercostal a.

Serratus anterior m.

Ant. intercostal a.

Int. thoracic a.

Perforating br. of int. thoracic a.

ANTEROSUPERIOR VIEW

Ant. longitudinal lig.

Ant. external venous plexus

Intervertebral disc

Ant. internal venous plexus

Post. longitudinal lig.

Intervertebral foramen

Transverse process of T5

Post. external venous plexus

Basivertebral v.

6th intervertebral v.

Spinous process of T5

Post. internal venous plexus

Spinous process of T6

*MEDIAN SECTION OF T8–T10
VIEWED FROM LEFT*

◄— **ANTERIOR**

POSTERIOR —►

ANTERIOR VIEW

POSTERIOR VIEW

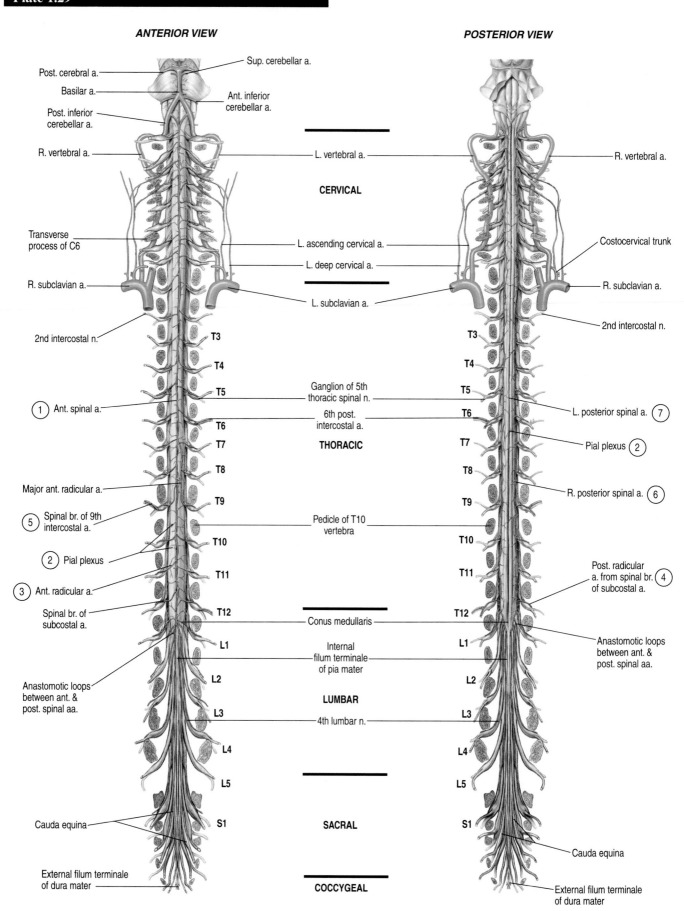

Post. cerebral a.

Sup. cerebellar a.

Basilar a.

Ant. inferior cerebellar a.

Post. inferior cerebellar a.

R. vertebral a.

L. vertebral a.

R. vertebral a.

CERVICAL

Transverse process of C6

L. ascending cervical a.

Costocervical trunk

L. deep cervical a.

R. subclavian a.

R. subclavian a.

L. subclavian a.

2nd intercostal n.

2nd intercostal n.

T3

T3

T4

T4

T5

Ganglion of 5th thoracic spinal n.

T5

(1) Ant. spinal a.

L. posterior spinal a. (7)

T6

6th post. intercostal a.

T6

T7

THORACIC

T7

Pial plexus (2)

T8

T8

Major ant. radicular a.

T9

T9

R. posterior spinal a. (6)

(5) Spinal br. of 9th intercostal a.

Pedicle of T10 vertebra

T10

T10

(2) Pial plexus

T11

T11

Post. radicular a. from spinal br. of subcostal a. (4)

(3) Ant. radicular a.

T12

Conus medullaris

T12

Spinal br. of subcostal a.

L1

Internal filum terminale of pia mater

L1

Anastomotic loops between ant. & post. spinal aa.

Anastomotic loops between ant. & post. spinal aa.

L2

L2

LUMBAR

L3

4th lumbar n.

L3

L4

L4

L5

L5

Cauda equina

S1

SACRAL

S1

Cauda equina

External filum terminale of dura mater

COCCYGEAL

External filum terminale of dura mater

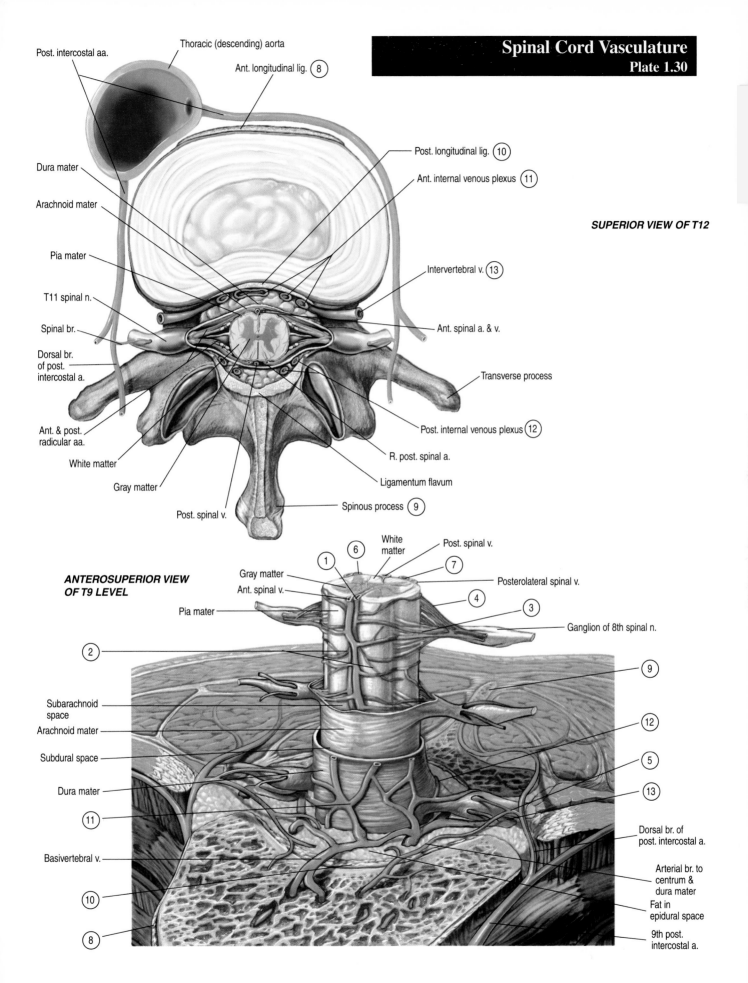

SUPERIOR VIEW OF T12

Post. intercostal aa.

Thoracic (descending) aorta

Ant. longitudinal lig. (8)

Post. longitudinal lig. (10)

Ant. internal venous plexus (11)

Dura mater

Arachnoid mater

Intervertebral v. (13)

Pia mater

T11 spinal n.

Ant. spinal a. & v.

Spinal br.

Dorsal br.
of post.
intercostal a.

Transverse process

Ant. & post.
radicular aa.

Post. internal venous plexus (12)

White matter

R. post. spinal a.

Gray matter

Ligamentum flavum

Post. spinal v.

Spinous process (9)

*ANTEROSUPERIOR VIEW
OF T9 LEVEL*

White
matter

Post. spinal v.

(6)

(1)

(7)

Gray matter

Posterolateral spinal v.

Ant. spinal v.

(4)

Pia mater

(3)

Ganglion of 8th spinal n.

(2)

(9)

Subarachnoid
space

(12)

Arachnoid mater

Subdural space

(5)

Dura mater

(13)

(11)

Dorsal br. of
post. intercostal a.

Basivertebral v.

Arterial br. to
centrum &
dura mater

(10)

Fat in
epidural space

(8)

9th post.
intercostal a.

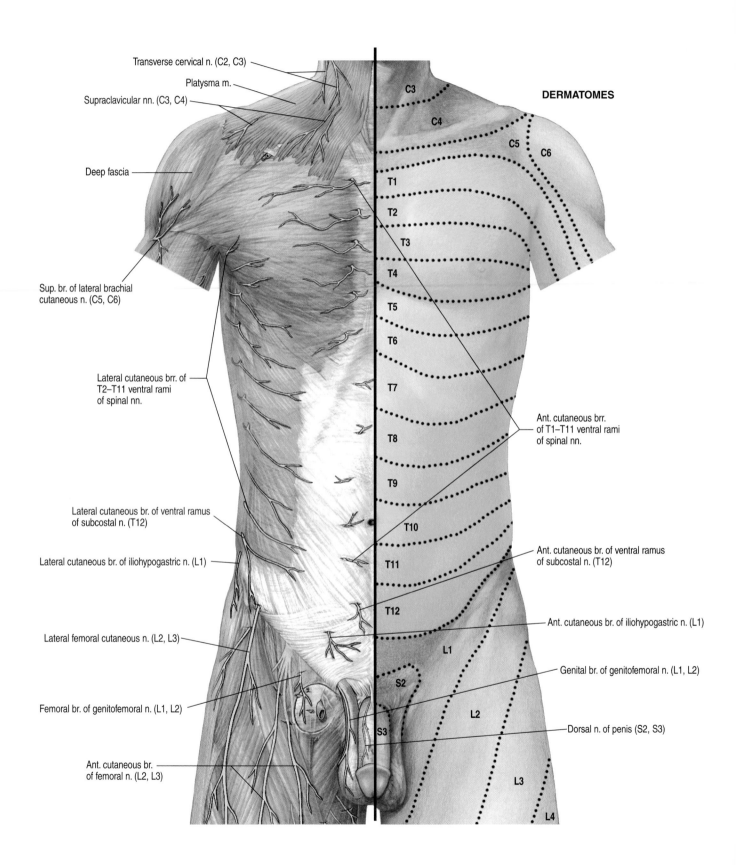

Transverse cervical n. (C2, C3)

Platysma m.

Supraclavicular nn. (C3, C4)

Deep fascia

Sup. br. of lateral brachial
cutaneous n. (C5, C6)

Lateral cutaneous brr. of
T2–T11 ventral rami
of spinal nn.

Lateral cutaneous br. of ventral ramus
of subcostal n. (T12)

Lateral cutaneous br. of iliohypogastric n. (L1)

Lateral femoral cutaneous n. (L2, L3)

Femoral br. of genitofemoral n. (L1, L2)

Ant. cutaneous br.
of femoral n. (L2, L3)

DERMATOMES

C3
C4
C5
C6
T1
T2
T3
T4
T5
T6
T7
T8
T9
T10
T11
T12
L1
S2
L2
S3
L3
L4

Ant. cutaneous brr.
of T1–T11 ventral rami
of spinal nn.

Ant. cutaneous br. of ventral ramus
of subcostal n. (T12)

Ant. cutaneous br. of iliohypogastric n. (L1)

Genital br. of genitofemoral n. (L1, L2)

Dorsal n. of penis (S2, S3)

ANTERIOR VIEW

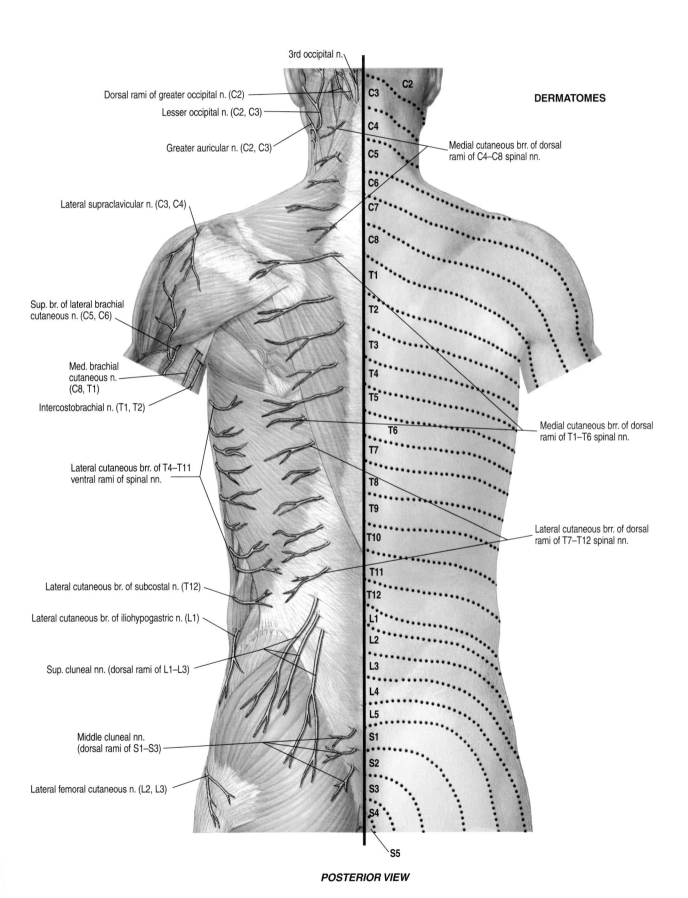

3rd occipital n.

Dorsal rami of greater occipital n. (C2)

Lesser occipital n. (C2, C3)

Greater auricular n. (C2, C3)

Lateral supraclavicular n. (C3, C4)

Sup. br. of lateral brachial cutaneous n. (C5, C6)

Med. brachial cutaneous n. (C8, T1)

Intercostobrachial n. (T1, T2)

Lateral cutaneous brr. of T4–T11 ventral rami of spinal nn.

Lateral cutaneous br. of subcostal n. (T12)

Lateral cutaneous br. of iliohypogastric n. (L1)

Sup. cluneal nn. (dorsal rami of L1–L3)

Middle cluneal nn. (dorsal rami of S1–S3)

Lateral femoral cutaneous n. (L2, L3)

DERMATOMES

Medial cutaneous brr. of dorsal rami of C4–C8 spinal nn.

Medial cutaneous brr. of dorsal rami of T1–T6 spinal nn.

Lateral cutaneous brr. of dorsal rami of T7–T12 spinal nn.

POSTERIOR VIEW

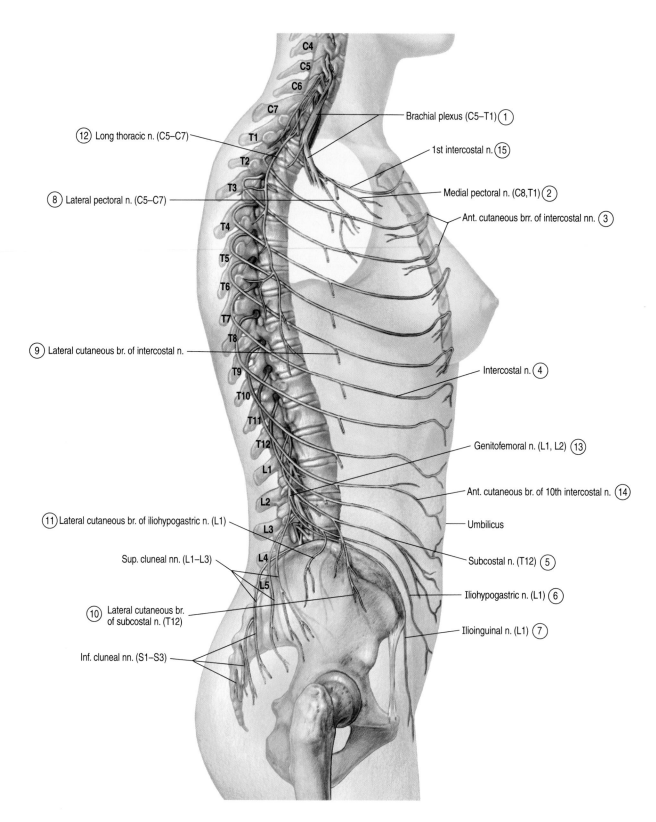

Brachial plexus (C5–T1) ①

1st intercostal n. ⑮

Medial pectoral n. (C8,T1) ②

Ant. cutaneous brr. of intercostal nn. ③

Intercostal n. ④

Genitofemoral n. (L1, L2) ⑬

Ant. cutaneous br. of 10th intercostal n. ⑭

Umbilicus

Subcostal n. (T12) ⑤

Iliohypogastric n. (L1) ⑥

Ilioinguinal n. (L1) ⑦

⑫ Long thoracic n. (C5–C7)

⑧ Lateral pectoral n. (C5–C7)

⑨ Lateral cutaneous br. of intercostal n.

⑪ Lateral cutaneous br. of iliohypogastric n. (L1)

Sup. cluneal nn. (L1–L3)

⑩ Lateral cutaneous br. of subcostal n. (T12)

Inf. cluneal nn. (S1–S3)

RIGHT LATERAL VIEW

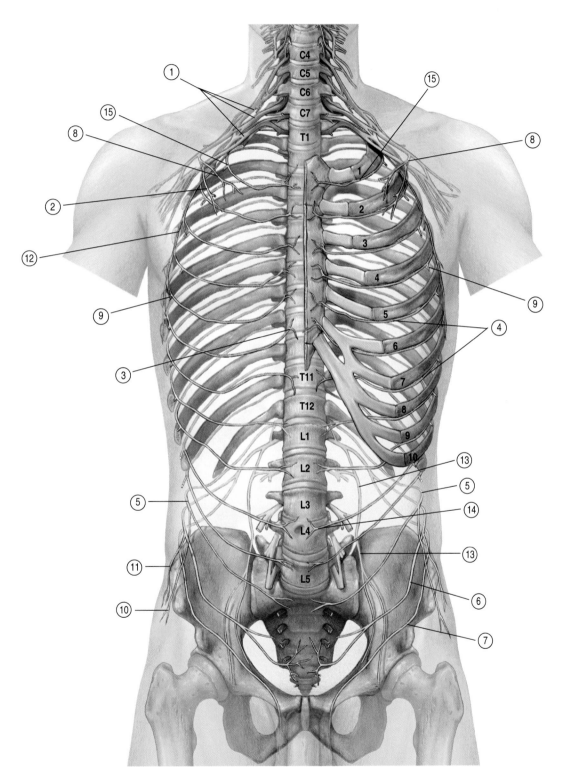

ANTERIOR VIEW

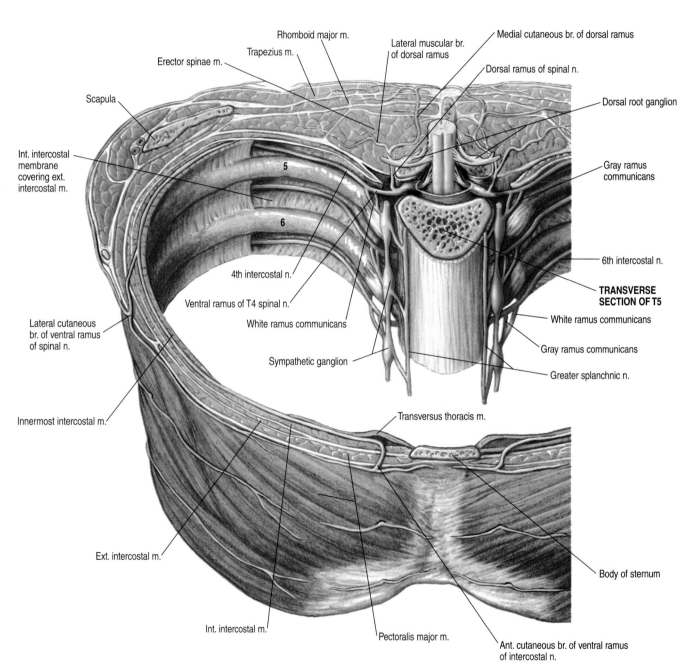

Rhomboid major m.

Lateral muscular br. of dorsal ramus

Medial cutaneous br. of dorsal ramus

Trapezius m.

Dorsal ramus of spinal n.

Erector spinae m.

Dorsal root ganglion

Scapula

Gray ramus communicans

Int. intercostal membrane covering ext. intercostal m.

5

6

6th intercostal n.

4th intercostal n.

TRANSVERSE SECTION OF T5

Ventral ramus of T4 spinal n.

White ramus communicans

Lateral cutaneous br. of ventral ramus of spinal n.

White ramus communicans

Gray ramus communicans

Sympathetic ganglion

Greater splanchnic n.

Innermost intercostal m.

Transversus thoracis m.

Ext. intercostal m.

Body of sternum

Int. intercostal m.

Pectoralis major m.

Ant. cutaneous br. of ventral ramus of intercostal n.

ANTEROSUPERIOR

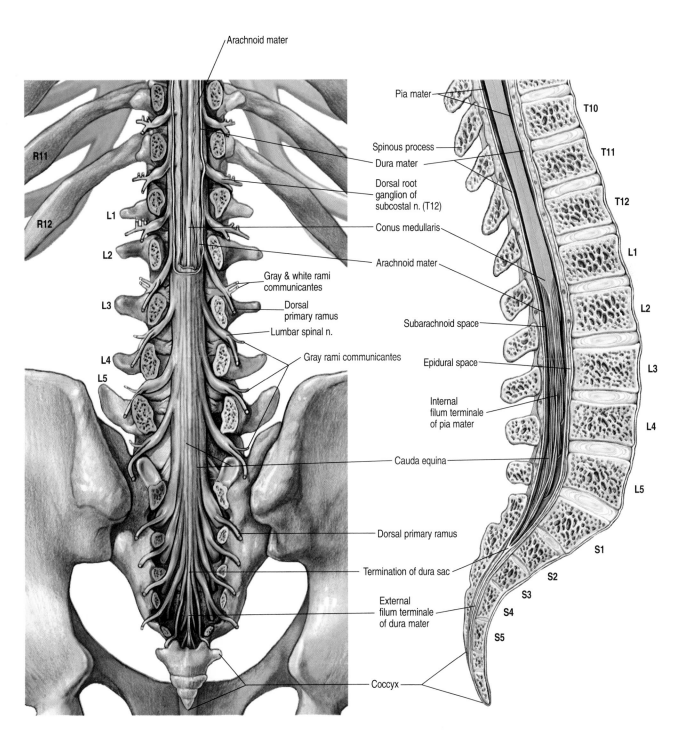

Arachnoid mater

Pia mater

Spinous process

Dura mater

Dorsal root ganglion of subcostal n. (T12)

Conus medullaris

Arachnoid mater

Gray & white rami communicantes

Dorsal primary ramus

Lumbar spinal n.

Gray rami communicantes

Subarachnoid space

Epidural space

Internal filum terminale of pia mater

Cauda equina

Dorsal primary ramus

Termination of dura sac

External filum terminale of dura mater

Coccyx

R11

R12

L1

L2

L3

L4

L5

T10

T11

T12

L1

L2

L3

L4

L5

S1

S2

S3

S4

S5

POSTERIOR VIEW

MEDIAN SECTION VIEWED FROM RIGHT

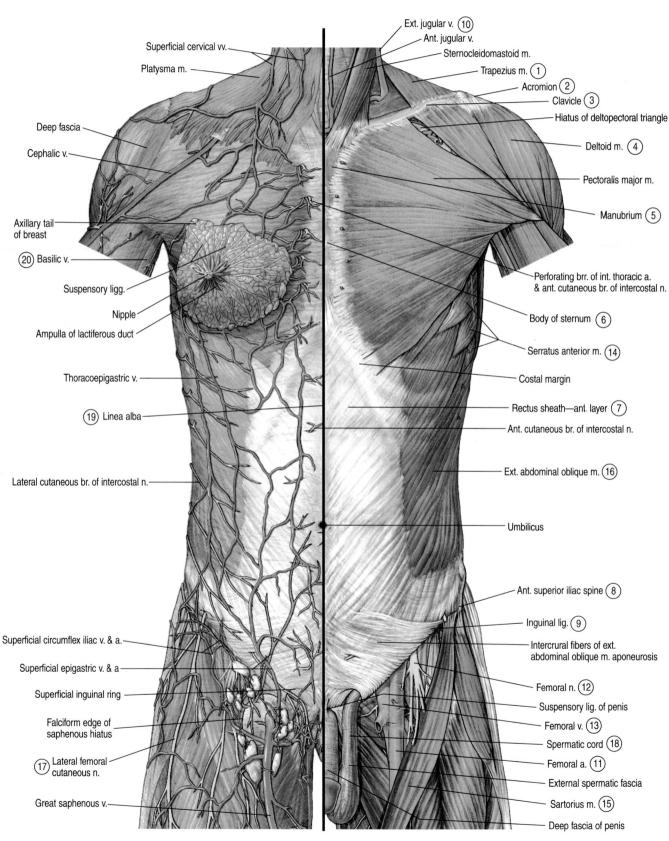

Ext. jugular v. (10)
Ant. jugular v.
Sternocleidomastoid m.
Trapezius m. (1)
Acromion (2)
Clavicle (3)
Hiatus of deltopectoral triangle
Deltoid m. (4)
Pectoralis major m.
Manubrium (5)
Perforating brr. of int. thoracic a. & ant. cutaneous br. of intercostal n.
Body of sternum (6)
Serratus anterior m. (14)
Costal margin
Rectus sheath—ant. layer (7)
Ant. cutaneous br. of intercostal n.
Ext. abdominal oblique m. (16)
Umbilicus
Ant. superior iliac spine (8)
Inguinal lig. (9)
Intercrural fibers of ext. abdominal oblique m. aponeurosis
Femoral n. (12)
Suspensory lig. of penis
Femoral v. (13)
Spermatic cord (18)
Femoral a. (11)
External spermatic fascia
Sartorius m. (15)
Deep fascia of penis

Superficial cervical vv.
Platysma m.
Deep fascia
Cephalic v.
Axillary tail of breast
(20) Basilic v.
Suspensory ligg.
Nipple
Ampulla of lactiferous duct
Thoracoepigastric v.
(19) Linea alba
Lateral cutaneous br. of intercostal n.
Superficial circumflex iliac v. & a.
Superficial epigastric v. & a
Superficial inguinal ring
Falciform edge of saphenous hiatus
(17) Lateral femoral cutaneous n.
Great saphenous v.

ANTERIOR VIEW

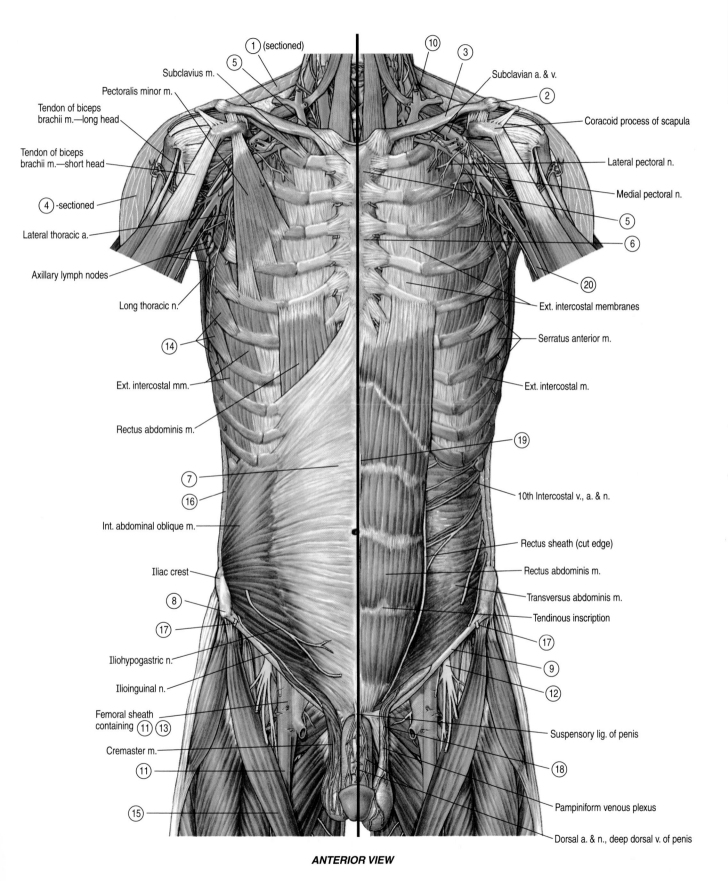

1 (sectioned)

5

Subclavius m.

Pectoralis minor m.

Tendon of biceps
brachii m.—long head

Tendon of biceps
brachii m.—short head

4 -sectioned

Lateral thoracic a.

Axillary lymph nodes

Long thoracic n.

14

Ext. intercostal mm.

Rectus abdominis m.

7

16

Int. abdominal oblique m.

Iliac crest

8

17

Iliohypogastric n.

Ilioinguinal n.

Femoral sheath
containing 11 13

Cremaster m.

11

15

10

3

Subclavian a. & v.

2

Coracoid process of scapula

Lateral pectoral n.

Medial pectoral n.

5

6

20

Ext. intercostal membranes

Serratus anterior m.

Ext. intercostal m.

19

10th Intercostal v., a. & n.

Rectus sheath (cut edge)

Rectus abdominis m.

Transversus abdominis m.

Tendinous inscription

17

9

12

Suspensory lig. of penis

18

Pampiniform venous plexus

Dorsal a. & n., deep dorsal v. of penis

ANTERIOR VIEW

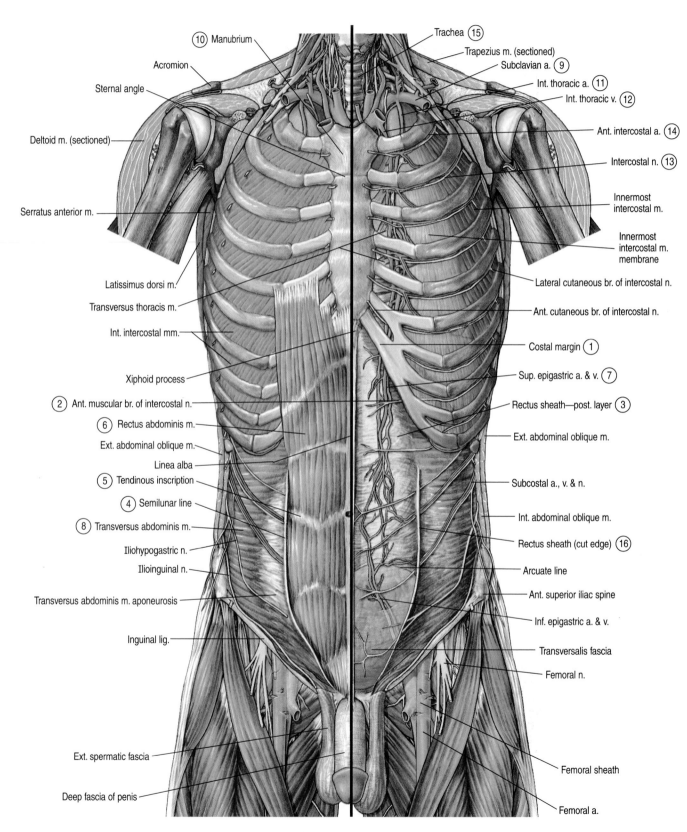

⑩ Manubrium

Acromion

Sternal angle

Deltoid m. (sectioned)

Serratus anterior m.

Latissimus dorsi m.

Transversus thoracis m.

Int. intercostal mm.

Xiphoid process

② Ant. muscular br. of intercostal n.

⑥ Rectus abdominis m.

Ext. abdominal oblique m.

Linea alba

⑤ Tendinous inscription

④ Semilunar line

⑧ Transversus abdominis m.

Iliohypogastric n.

Ilioinguinal n.

Transversus abdominis m. aponeurosis

Inguinal lig.

Ext. spermatic fascia

Deep fascia of penis

Trachea ⑮

Trapezius m. (sectioned)

Subclavian a. ⑨

Int. thoracic a. ⑪

Int. thoracic v. ⑫

Ant. intercostal a. ⑭

Intercostal n. ⑬

Innermost intercostal m.

Innermost intercostal m. membrane

Lateral cutaneous br. of intercostal n.

Ant. cutaneous br. of intercostal n.

Costal margin ①

Sup. epigastric a. & v. ⑦

Rectus sheath—post. layer ③

Ext. abdominal oblique m.

Subcostal a., v. & n.

Int. abdominal oblique m.

Rectus sheath (cut edge) ⑯

Arcuate line

Ant. superior iliac spine

Inf. epigastric a. & v.

Transversalis fascia

Femoral n.

Femoral sheath

Femoral a.

ANTERIOR VIEW

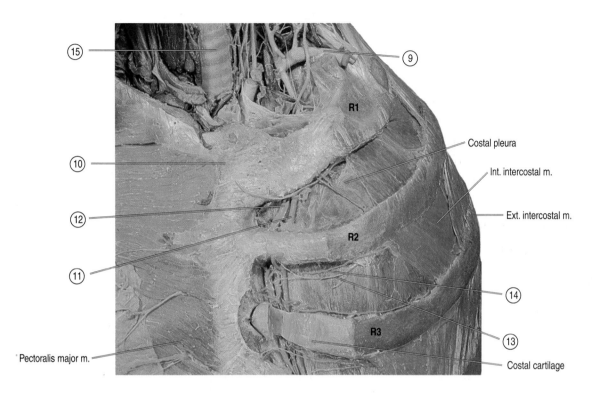

Costal pleura

Int. intercostal m.

Ext. intercostal m.

R1

R2

R3

Pectoralis major m.

Costal cartilage

ANTERIOR VIEW OF LEFT SUPERIOR PORTION OF THORACIC WALL

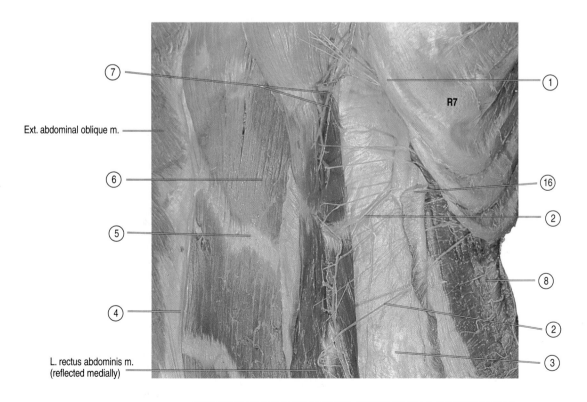

Ext. abdominal oblique m.

R7

L. rectus abdominis m.
(reflected medially)

ANTERIOR VIEW OF SUBCOSTAL PORTION OF ABDOMINAL WALL

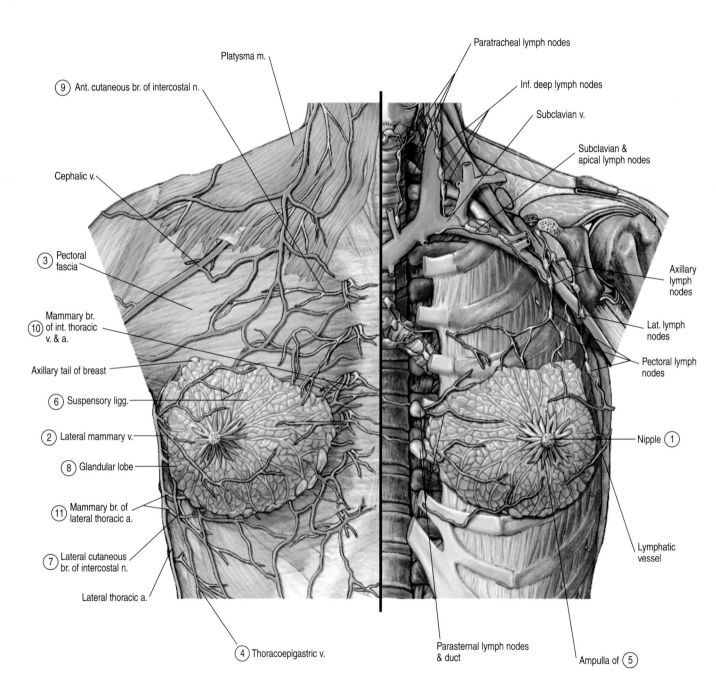

Platysma m.

Paratracheal lymph nodes

(9) Ant. cutaneous br. of intercostal n.

Inf. deep lymph nodes

Subclavian v.

Subclavian & apical lymph nodes

Cephalic v.

(3) Pectoral fascia

Axillary lymph nodes

Mammary br.
(10) of int. thoracic v. & a.

Lat. lymph nodes

Axillary tail of breast

Pectoral lymph nodes

(6) Suspensory ligg.

(2) Lateral mammary v.

Nipple (1)

(8) Glandular lobe

(11) Mammary br. of lateral thoracic a.

(7) Lateral cutaneous br. of intercostal n.

Lymphatic vessel

Lateral thoracic a.

(4) Thoracoepigastric v.

Parasternal lymph nodes & duct

Ampulla of (5)

ANTERIOR VIEW

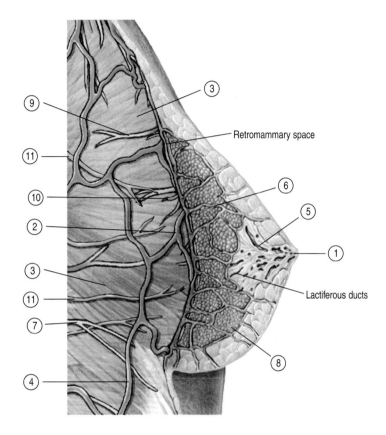

Retromammary space

Lactiferous ducts

RIGHT LATERAL VIEW OF MEDIAN SECTIONED BREAST

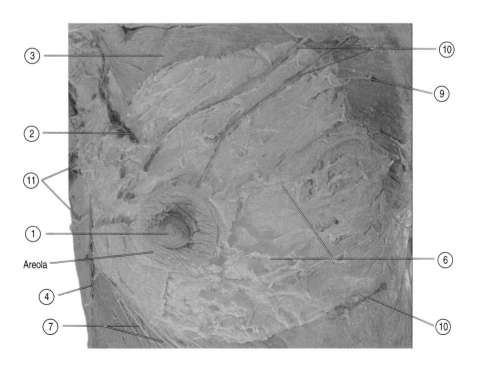

Areola

ANTERIOR VIEW OF RIGHT BREAST

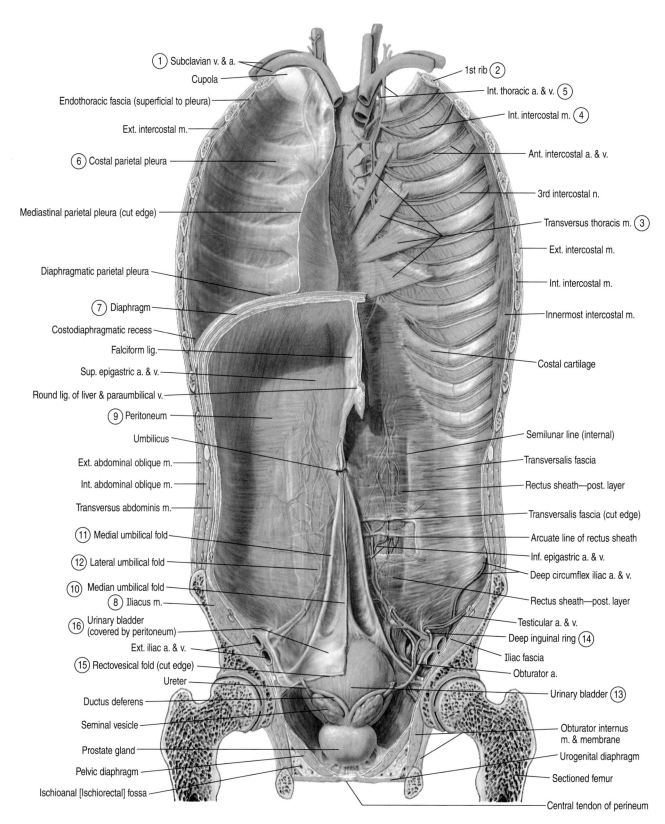

1 Subclavian v. & a.

Cupola

Endothoracic fascia (superficial to pleura)

Ext. intercostal m.

6 Costal parietal pleura

Mediastinal parietal pleura (cut edge)

Diaphragmatic parietal pleura

7 Diaphragm

Costodiaphragmatic recess

Falciform lig.

Sup. epigastric a. & v.

Round lig. of liver & paraumbilical v.

9 Peritoneum

Umbilicus

Ext. abdominal oblique m.

Int. abdominal oblique m.

Transversus abdominis m.

11 Medial umbilical fold

12 Lateral umbilical fold

10 Median umbilical fold

8 Iliacus m.

16 Urinary bladder (covered by peritoneum)

Ext. iliac a. & v.

15 Rectovesical fold (cut edge)

Ureter

Ductus deferens

Seminal vesicle

Prostate gland

Pelvic diaphragm

Ischioanal [Ischiorectal] fossa

1st rib 2

Int. thoracic a. & v. 5

Int. intercostal m. 4

Ant. intercostal a. & v.

3rd intercostal n.

Transversus thoracis m. 3

Ext. intercostal m.

Int. intercostal m.

Innermost intercostal m.

Costal cartilage

Semilunar line (internal)

Transversalis fascia

Rectus sheath—post. layer

Transversalis fascia (cut edge)

Arcuate line of rectus sheath

Inf. epigastric a. & v.

Deep circumflex iliac a. & v.

Rectus sheath—post. layer

Testicular a. & v.

Deep inguinal ring 14

Iliac fascia

Obturator a.

Urinary bladder 13

Obturator internus m. & membrane

Urogenital diaphragm

Sectioned femur

Central tendon of perineum

POSTERIOR (INTERNAL) VIEW OF ANTERIOR BODY WALL

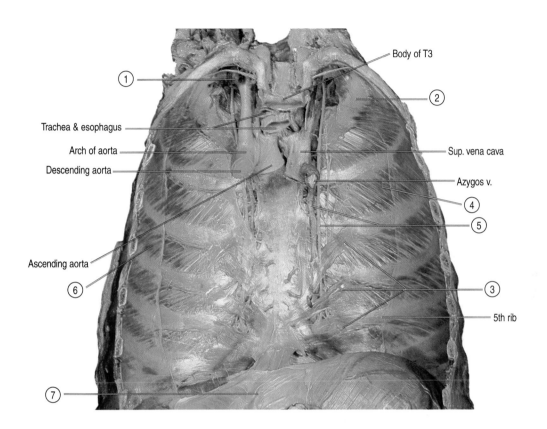

Body of T3

1

2

Trachea & esophagus

Arch of aorta — Sup. vena cava

Descending aorta — Azygos v.

4

5

Ascending aorta

6

3

5th rib

7

POSTERIOR (INTERNAL) VIEW OF ANTERIOR THORACIC WALL

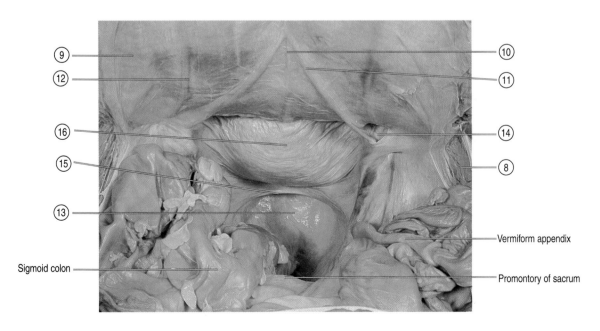

9 10

12 11

16 14

15 8

13

Vermiform appendix

Sigmoid colon — Promontory of sacrum

POSTEROSUPERIOR VIEW OF ANTERIOR ABDOMINAL WALL & PELVIC CONTENTS

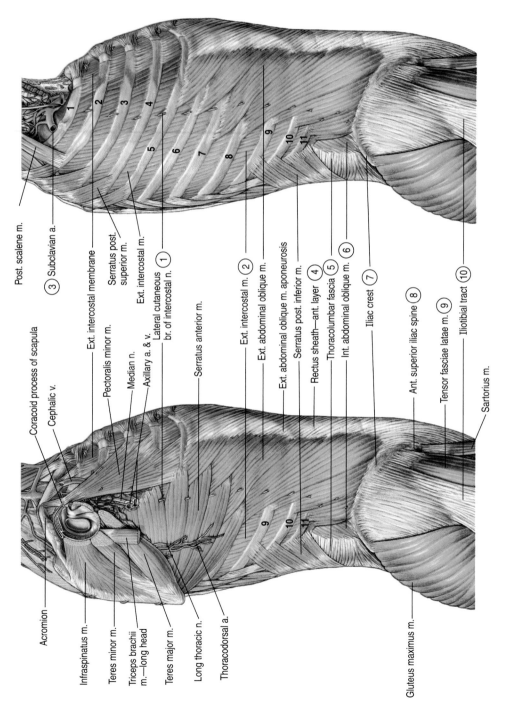

Post. scalene m.

③ Subclavian a.

Ext. intercostal membrane

Serratus post. superior m.

Ext. intercostal m.

Lateral cutaneous br. of intercostal n. ①

Ext. intercostal m. ②

Ext. abdominal oblique m.

Ext. abdominal oblique m. aponeurosis

Serratus post. inferior m.

Rectus sheath—ant. layer ④

Thoracolumbar fascia ⑤

Int. abdominal oblique m. ⑥

Iliac crest ⑦

Ant. superior iliac spine ⑧

Tensor fasciae latae m. ⑨

Iliotibial tract ⑩

Coracoid process of scapula

Cephalic v.

Pectoralis minor m.

Median n.

Axillary a. & v.

Serratus anterior m.

Acromion

Infraspinatus m.

Teres minor m.

Triceps brachii m.—long head

Teres major m.

Long thoracic n.

Thoracodorsal a.

Gluteus maximus m.

Sartorius m.

RIGHT LATERAL VIEWS

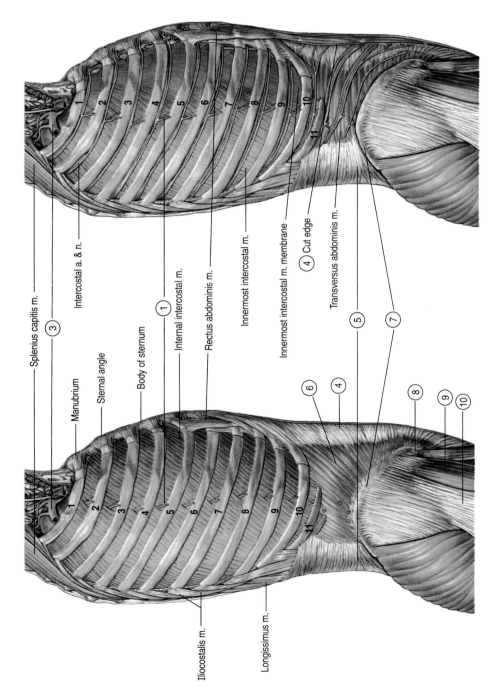

Splenius capitis m.

Intercostal a. & n.

③

Manubrium

Sternal angle

Body of sternum

①

Internal intercostal m.

Rectus abdominis m.

Innermost intercostal m.

Innermost intercostal m. membrane

④ Cut edge

Transversus abdominis m.

⑤

⑦

⑥

④

⑧

⑨

⑩

Iliocostalis m.

Longissimus m.

RIGHT LATERAL VIEWS

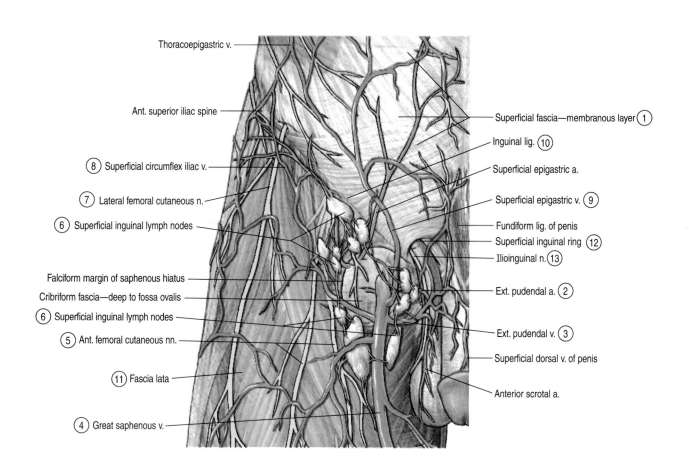

Thoracoepigastric v.

Ant. superior iliac spine

(8) Superficial circumflex iliac v.

(7) Lateral femoral cutaneous n.

(6) Superficial inguinal lymph nodes

Falciform margin of saphenous hiatus

Cribriform fascia—deep to fossa ovalis

(6) Superficial inguinal lymph nodes

(5) Ant. femoral cutaneous nn.

(11) Fascia lata

(4) Great saphenous v.

Superficial fascia—membranous layer (1)

Inguinal lig. (10)

Superficial epigastric a.

Superficial epigastric v. (9)

Fundiform lig. of penis

Superficial inguinal ring (12)

Ilioinguinal n. (13)

Ext. pudendal a. (2)

Ext. pudendal v. (3)

Superficial dorsal v. of penis

Anterior scrotal a.

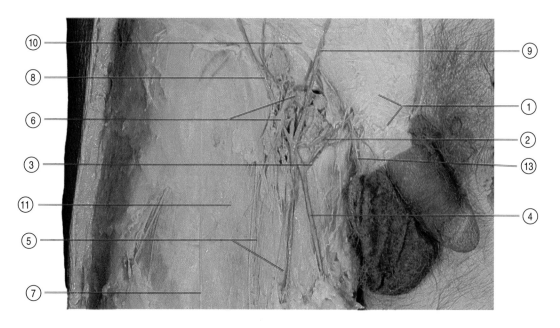

ANTERIOR VIEWS OF RIGHT SIDE

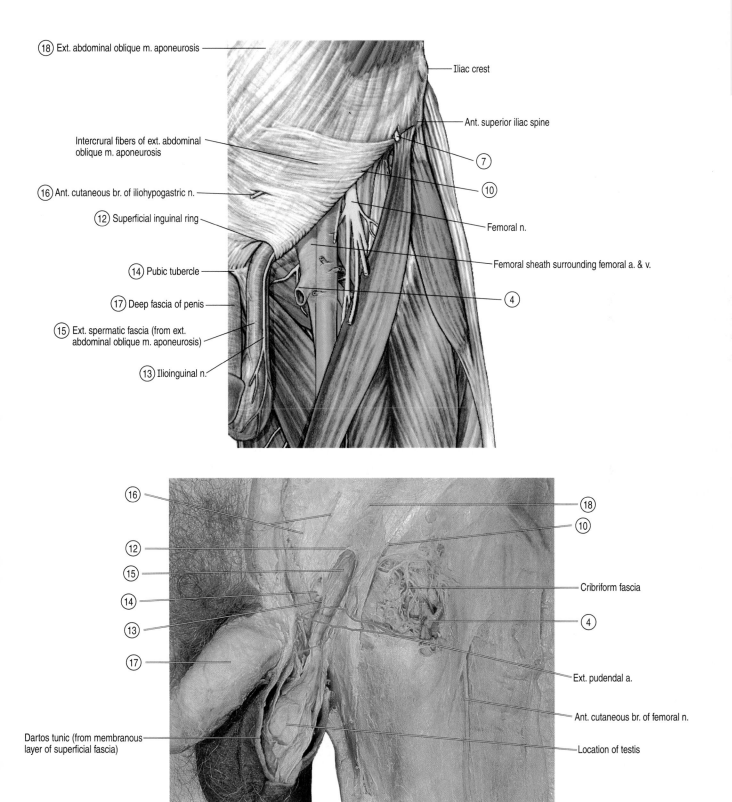

18 Ext. abdominal oblique m. aponeurosis

Iliac crest

Intercrural fibers of ext. abdominal oblique m. aponeurosis

Ant. superior iliac spine

7

10

16 Ant. cutaneous br. of iliohypogastric n.

Femoral n.

12 Superficial inguinal ring

Femoral sheath surrounding femoral a. & v.

14 Pubic tubercle

4

17 Deep fascia of penis

15 Ext. spermatic fascia (from ext. abdominal oblique m. aponeurosis)

13 Ilioinguinal n.

16

18

10

12

15

Cribriform fascia

14

13

4

17

Ext. pudendal a.

Ant. cutaneous br. of femoral n.

Dartos tunic (from membranous layer of superficial fascia)

Location of testis

ANTERIOR VIEWS OF LEFT SIDE

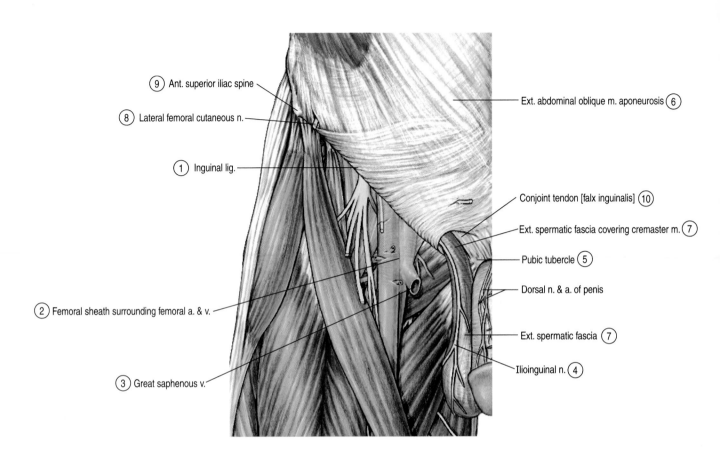

(9) Ant. superior iliac spine

(8) Lateral femoral cutaneous n.

(1) Inguinal lig.

(2) Femoral sheath surrounding femoral a. & v.

(3) Great saphenous v.

Ext. abdominal oblique m. aponeurosis (6)

Conjoint tendon [falx inguinalis] (10)

Ext. spermatic fascia covering cremaster m. (7)

Pubic tubercle (5)

Dorsal n. & a. of penis

Ext. spermatic fascia (7)

Ilioinguinal n. (4)

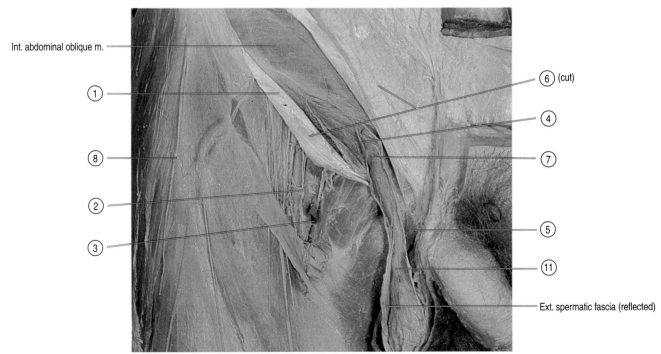

Int. abdominal oblique m.

(1)

(8)

(2)

(3)

(6) (cut)

(4)

(7)

(5)

(11)

Ext. spermatic fascia (reflected)

ANTERIOR VIEWS OF RIGHT SIDE

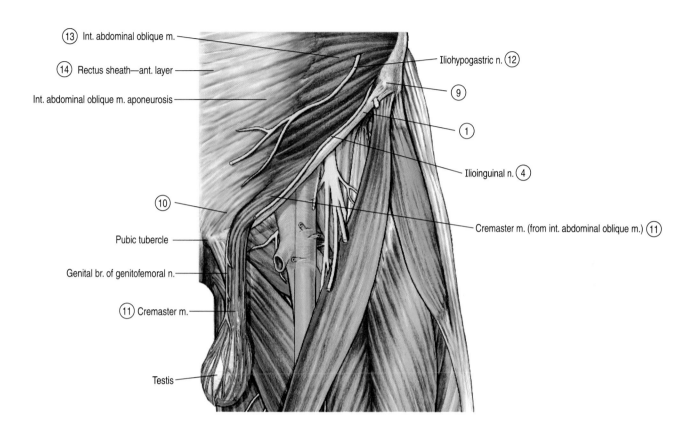

(13) Int. abdominal oblique m.

(14) Rectus sheath—ant. layer

Int. abdominal oblique m. aponeurosis

Iliohypogastric n. (12)

(9)

(1)

Ilioinguinal n. (4)

(10)

Cremaster m. (from int. abdominal oblique m.) (11)

Pubic tubercle

Genital br. of genitofemoral n.

(11) Cremaster m.

Testis

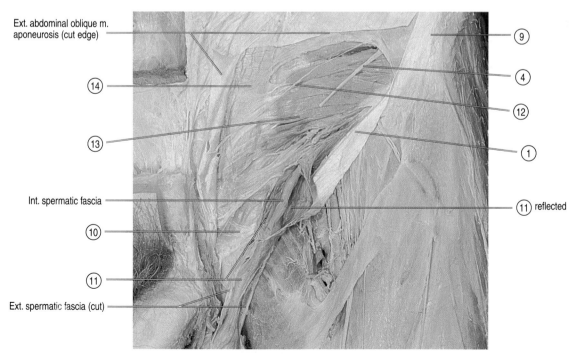

Ext. abdominal oblique m. aponeurosis (cut edge)

(9)

(4)

(14)

(12)

(13)

(1)

Int. spermatic fascia

(11) reflected

(10)

(11)

Ext. spermatic fascia (cut)

ANTERIOR VIEWS OF LEFT SIDE

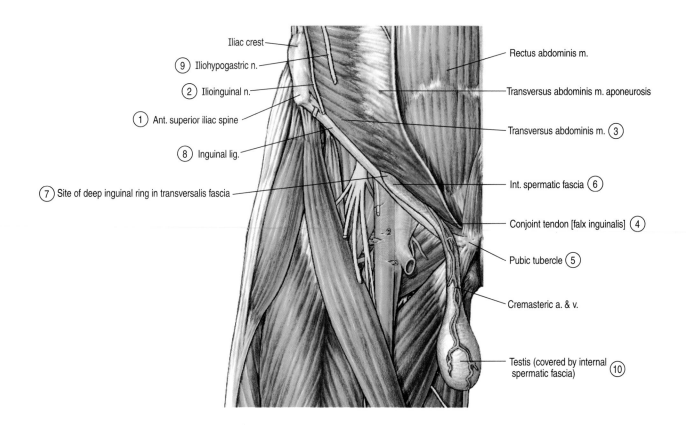

Iliac crest

⑨ Iliohypogastric n.

② Ilioinguinal n.

① Ant. superior iliac spine

⑧ Inguinal lig.

⑦ Site of deep inguinal ring in transversalis fascia

Rectus abdominis m.

Transversus abdominis m. aponeurosis

Transversus abdominis m. ③

Int. spermatic fascia ⑥

Conjoint tendon [falx inguinalis] ④

Pubic tubercle ⑤

Cremasteric a. & v.

Testis (covered by internal spermatic fascia) ⑩

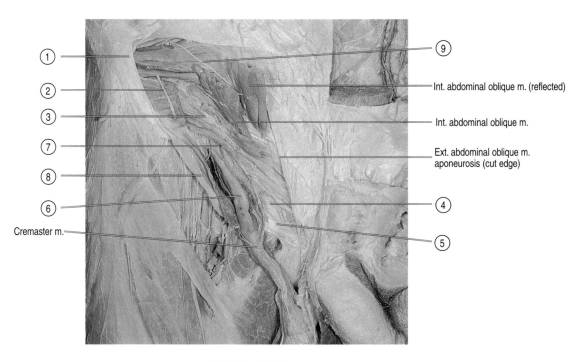

①

②

③

⑦

⑧

⑥

Cremaster m.

⑨

Int. abdominal oblique m. (reflected)

Int. abdominal oblique m.

Ext. abdominal oblique m. aponeurosis (cut edge)

④

⑤

ANTERIOR VIEWS

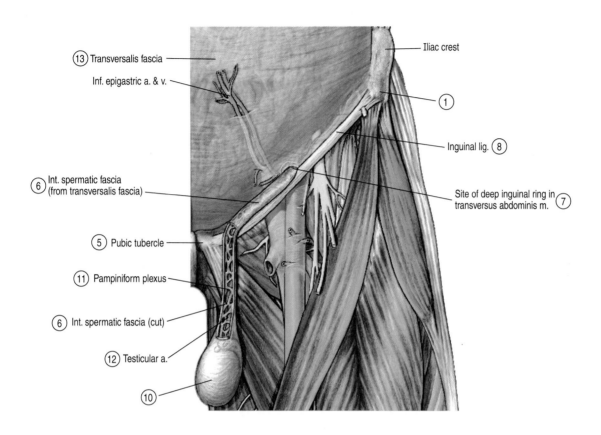

⑬ Transversalis fascia

Inf. epigastric a. & v.

Iliac crest

①

Inguinal lig. ⑧

⑥ Int. spermatic fascia
(from transversalis fascia)

Site of deep inguinal ring in
transversus abdominis m. ⑦

⑤ Pubic tubercle

⑪ Pampiniform plexus

⑥ Int. spermatic fascia (cut)

⑫ Testicular a.

⑩

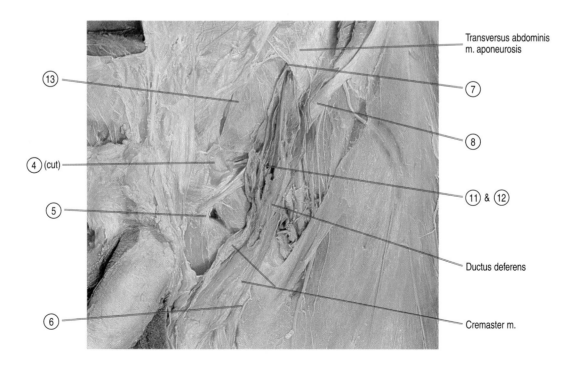

Transversus abdominis
m. aponeurosis

⑬

⑦

⑧

④ (cut)

⑪ & ⑫

⑤

Ductus deferens

⑥

Cremaster m.

ANTERIOR VIEWS

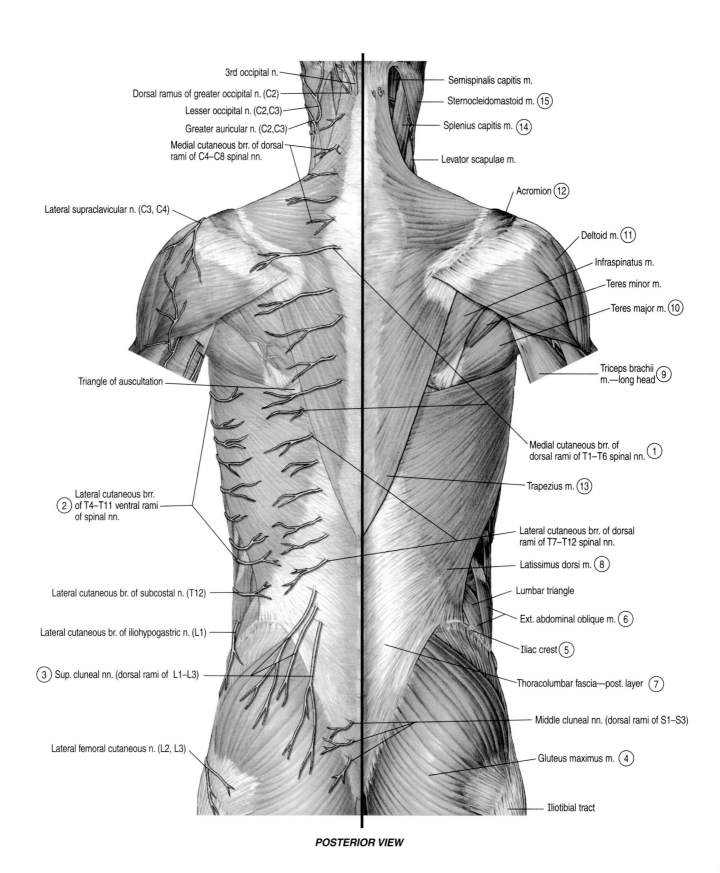

3rd occipital n.

Dorsal ramus of greater occipital n. (C2)

Lesser occipital n. (C2,C3)

Greater auricular n. (C2,C3)

Medial cutaneous brr. of dorsal rami of C4–C8 spinal nn.

Lateral supraclavicular n. (C3, C4)

Triangle of auscultation

② Lateral cutaneous brr. of T4–T11 ventral rami of spinal nn.

Lateral cutaneous br. of subcostal n. (T12)

Lateral cutaneous br. of iliohypogastric n. (L1)

③ Sup. cluneal nn. (dorsal rami of L1–L3)

Lateral femoral cutaneous n. (L2, L3)

Semispinalis capitis m.

Sternocleidomastoid m. ⑮

Splenius capitis m. ⑭

Levator scapulae m.

Acromion ⑫

Deltoid m. ⑪

Infraspinatus m.

Teres minor m.

Teres major m. ⑩

Triceps brachii m.—long head ⑨

Medial cutaneous brr. of dorsal rami of T1–T6 spinal nn. ①

Trapezius m. ⑬

Lateral cutaneous brr. of dorsal rami of T7–T12 spinal nn.

Latissimus dorsi m. ⑧

Lumbar triangle

Ext. abdominal oblique m. ⑥

Iliac crest ⑤

Thoracolumbar fascia—post. layer ⑦

Middle cluneal nn. (dorsal rami of S1–S3)

Gluteus maximus m. ④

Iliotibial tract

POSTERIOR VIEW

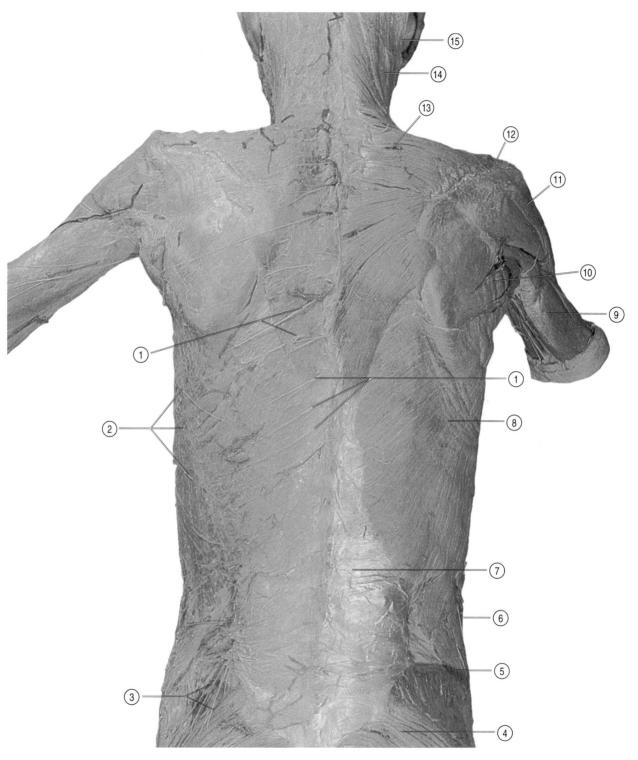

POSTERIOR VIEW

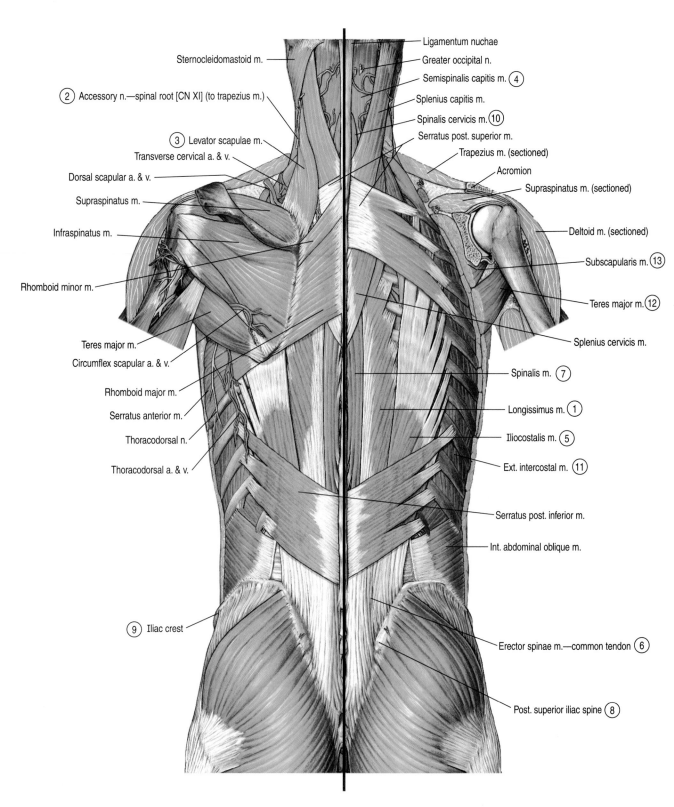

Ligamentum nuchae

Greater occipital n.

Semispinalis capitis m. ④

Splenius capitis m.

Spinalis cervicis m. ⑩

Serratus post. superior m.

Trapezius m. (sectioned)

Acromion

Supraspinatus m. (sectioned)

Deltoid m. (sectioned)

Subscapularis m. ⑬

Teres major m. ⑫

Splenius cervicis m.

Spinalis m. ⑦

Longissimus m. ①

Iliocostalis m. ⑤

Ext. intercostal m. ⑪

Serratus post. inferior m.

Int. abdominal oblique m.

Erector spinae m.—common tendon ⑥

Post. superior iliac spine ⑧

Sternocleidomastoid m.

② Accessory n.—spinal root [CN XI] (to trapezius m.)

③ Levator scapulae m.

Transverse cervical a. & v.

Dorsal scapular a. & v.

Supraspinatus m.

Infraspinatus m.

Rhomboid minor m.

Teres major m.

Circumflex scapular a. & v.

Rhomboid major m.

Serratus anterior m.

Thoracodorsal n.

Thoracodorsal a. & v.

⑨ Iliac crest

POSTERIOR VIEW

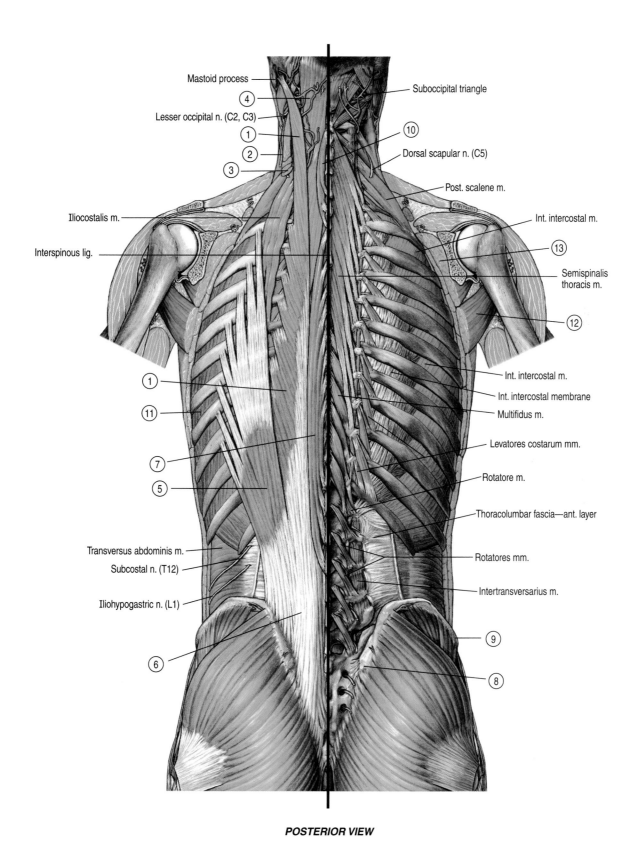

Mastoid process

Suboccipital triangle

④

Lesser occipital n. (C2, C3)

①

②

③

⑩

Dorsal scapular n. (C5)

Post. scalene m.

Iliocostalis m.

Int. intercostal m.

Interspinous lig.

⑬

Semispinalis thoracis m.

⑫

①

Int. intercostal m.

⑪

Int. intercostal membrane

Multifidus m.

⑦

Levatores costarum mm.

⑤

Rotatore m.

Thoracolumbar fascia—ant. layer

Transversus abdominis m.

Rotatores mm.

Subcostal n. (T12)

Intertransversarius m.

Iliohypogastric n. (L1)

⑨

⑥

⑧

POSTERIOR VIEW

Suboccipital Region
Plate 1.57

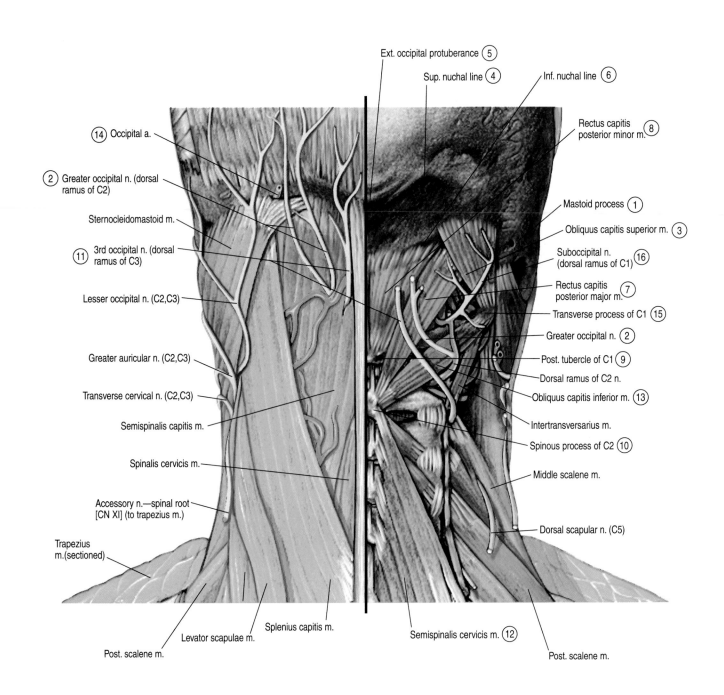

Ext. occipital protuberance (5)

Sup. nuchal line (4)

Inf. nuchal line (6)

(14) Occipital a.

Rectus capitis posterior minor m. (8)

(2) Greater occipital n. (dorsal ramus of C2)

Mastoid process (1)

Sternocleidomastoid m.

Obliquus capitis superior m. (3)

(11) 3rd occipital n. (dorsal ramus of C3)

Suboccipital n. (dorsal ramus of C1) (16)

Lesser occipital n. (C2,C3)

Rectus capitis posterior major m. (7)

Transverse process of C1 (15)

Greater occipital n. (2)

Greater auricular n. (C2,C3)

Post. tubercle of C1 (9)

Dorsal ramus of C2 n.

Transverse cervical n. (C2,C3)

Obliquus capitis inferior m. (13)

Semispinalis capitis m.

Intertransversarius m.

Spinalis cervicis m.

Spinous process of C2 (10)

Middle scalene m.

Accessory n.—spinal root [CN XI] (to trapezius m.)

Dorsal scapular n. (C5)

Trapezius m.(sectioned)

Splenius capitis m.

Semispinalis cervicis m. (12)

Levator scapulae m.

Post. scalene m.

Post. scalene m.

POSTERIOR VIEW

POSTERIOR VIEW OF CRANIAL BASE & UPPER CERVICAL REGION

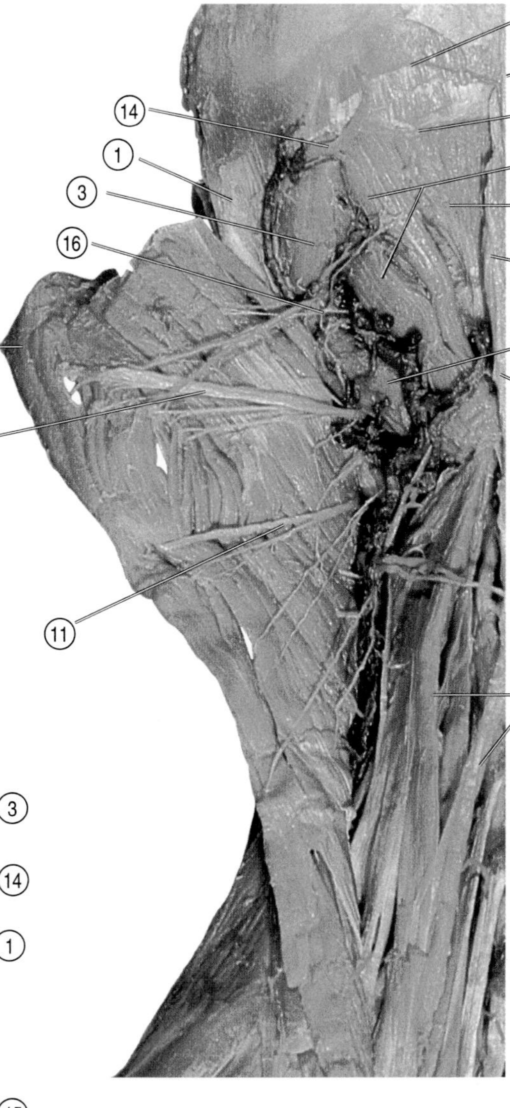

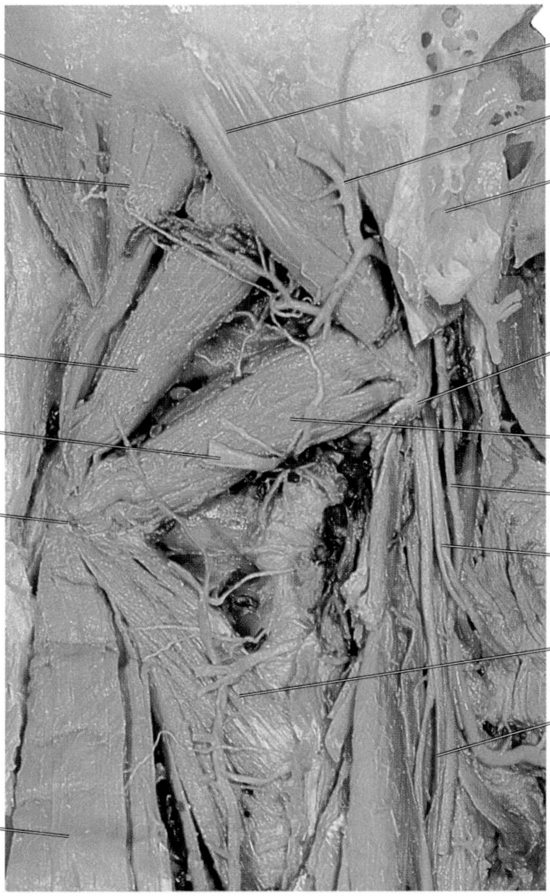

4
5
14
6
1
7
3
8
16
9
Semispinalis capitis m. (reflected)
13
10
2
11
12

6
3
L. 8
14
R. 8
1
7
15
2
13
10
14
Hypoglossal n. [CN XII]
Multifidus m.
Vagus n. [CN X]
12

POSTERIOR VIEW OF RIGHT SUBOCCIPITAL TRIANGLE

Thorax

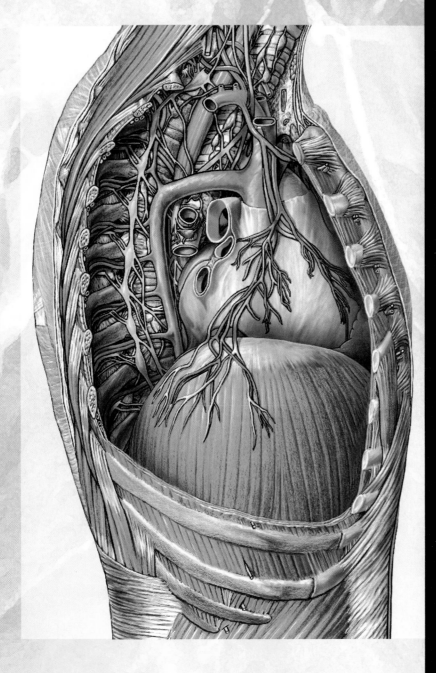

Chapter **2**

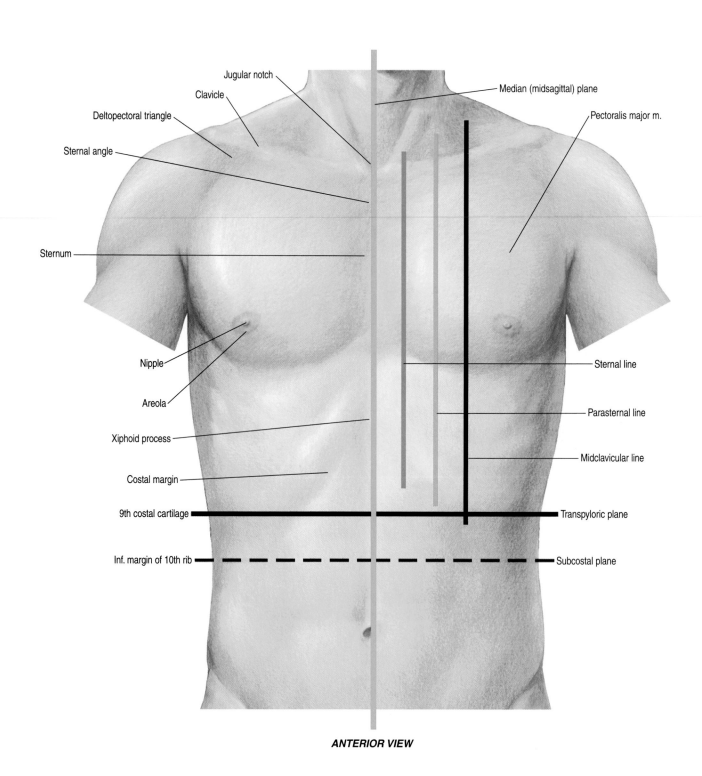

Jugular notch

Clavicle

Deltopectoral triangle

Sternal angle

Sternum

Nipple

Areola

Xiphoid process

Costal margin

9th costal cartilage

Inf. margin of 10th rib

Median (midsagittal) plane

Pectoralis major m.

Sternal line

Parasternal line

Midclavicular line

Transpyloric plane

Subcostal plane

ANTERIOR VIEW

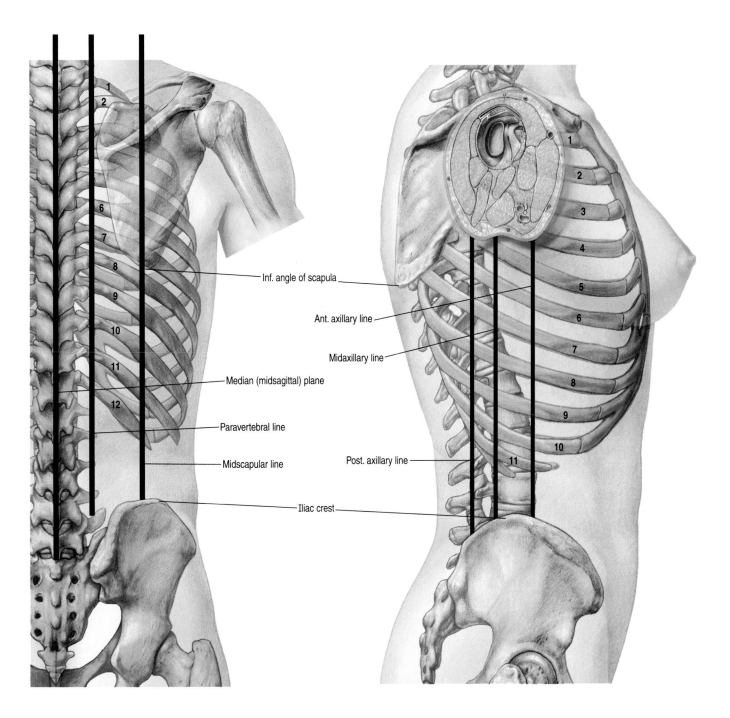

Inf. angle of scapula

Ant. axillary line

Midaxillary line

Median (midsagittal) plane

Paravertebral line

Midscapular line

Post. axillary line

Iliac crest

POSTERIOR VIEW

RIGHT LATERAL VIEW

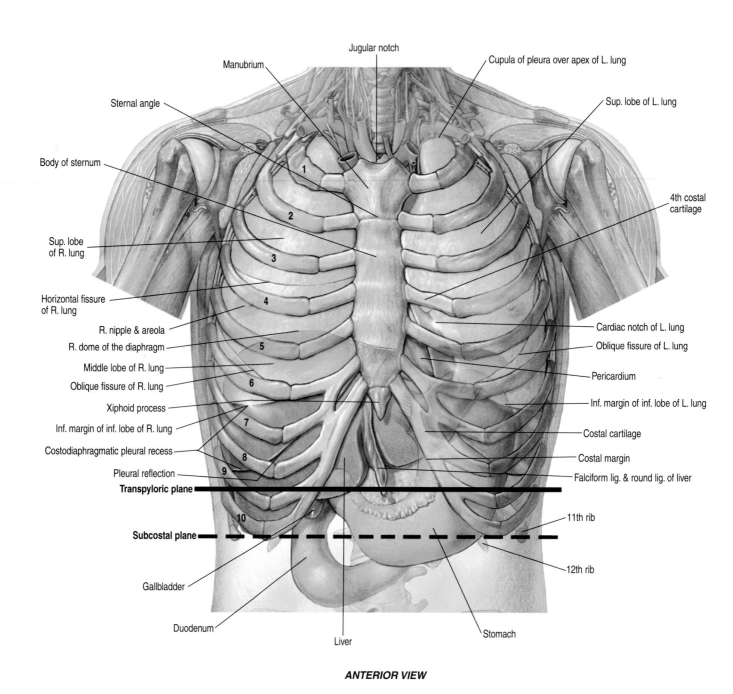

Jugular notch

Manubrium

Cupula of pleura over apex of L. lung

Sternal angle

Sup. lobe of L. lung

Body of sternum

1

4th costal cartilage

Sup. lobe of R. lung

2

3

Horizontal fissure of R. lung

4

R. nipple & areola

Cardiac notch of L. lung

R. dome of the diaphragm

5

Oblique fissure of L. lung

Middle lobe of R. lung

6

Pericardium

Oblique fissure of R. lung

Xiphoid process

Inf. margin of inf. lobe of L. lung

Inf. margin of inf. lobe of R. lung

7

Costal cartilage

Costodiaphragmatic pleural recess

8

Costal margin

Pleural reflection

9

Transpyloric plane

Falciform lig. & round lig. of liver

10

11th rib

Subcostal plane

12th rib

Gallbladder

Duodenum

Liver

Stomach

ANTERIOR VIEW

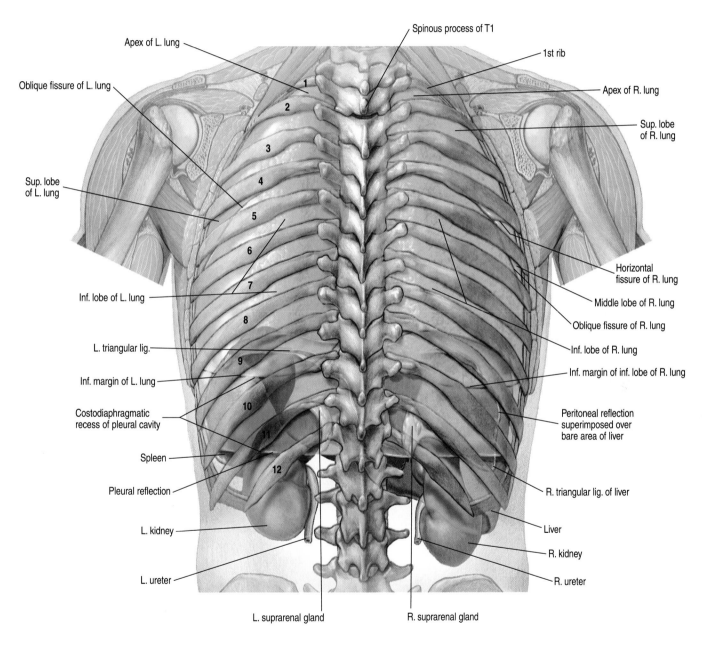

Spinous process of T1

Apex of L. lung

1st rib

Apex of R. lung

Oblique fissure of L. lung

Sup. lobe
of R. lung

Sup. lobe
of L. lung

Horizontal
fissure of R. lung

Middle lobe of R. lung

Inf. lobe of L. lung

Oblique fissure of R. lung

Inf. lobe of R. lung

L. triangular lig.

Inf. margin of inf. lobe of R. lung

Inf. margin of L. lung

Peritoneal reflection
superimposed over
bare area of liver

Costodiaphragmatic
recess of pleural cavity

Spleen

R. triangular lig. of liver

Pleural reflection

Liver

L. kidney

R. kidney

L. ureter

R. ureter

L. suprarenal gland

R. suprarenal gland

1 2 3 4 5 6 7 8 9 10 11 12

POSTERIOR VIEW

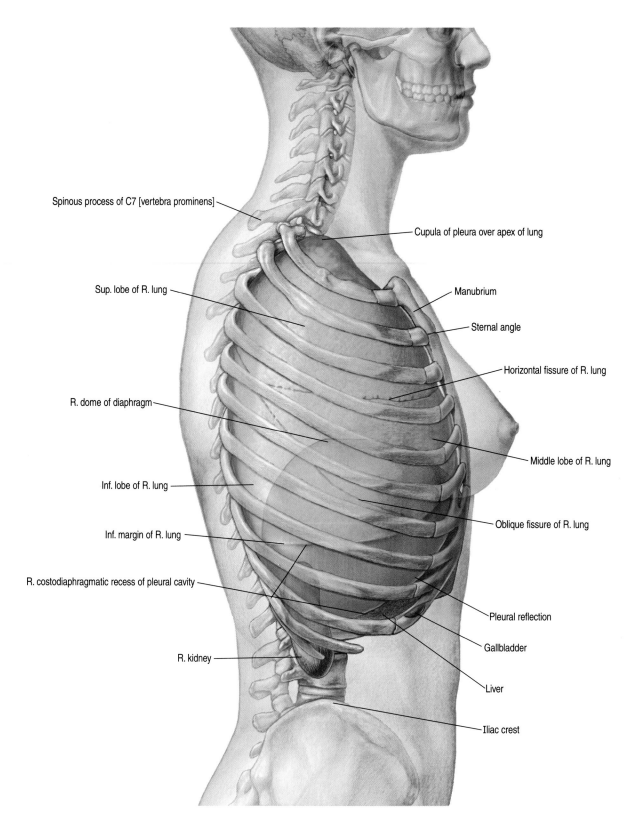

Spinous process of C7 [vertebra prominens]

Cupula of pleura over apex of lung

Sup. lobe of R. lung

Manubrium

Sternal angle

Horizontal fissure of R. lung

R. dome of diaphragm

Middle lobe of R. lung

Inf. lobe of R. lung

Inf. margin of R. lung

Oblique fissure of R. lung

R. costodiaphragmatic recess of pleural cavity

Pleural reflection

Gallbladder

R. kidney

Liver

Iliac crest

RIGHT LATERAL VIEW

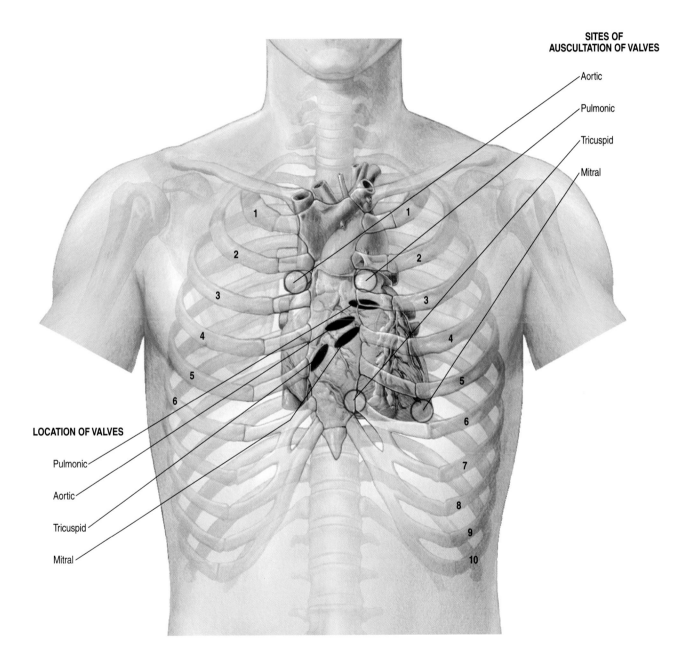

**SITES OF
AUSCULTATION OF VALVES**

Aortic

Pulmonic

Tricuspid

Mitral

LOCATION OF VALVES

Pulmonic

Aortic

Tricuspid

Mitral

ANTERIOR VIEW

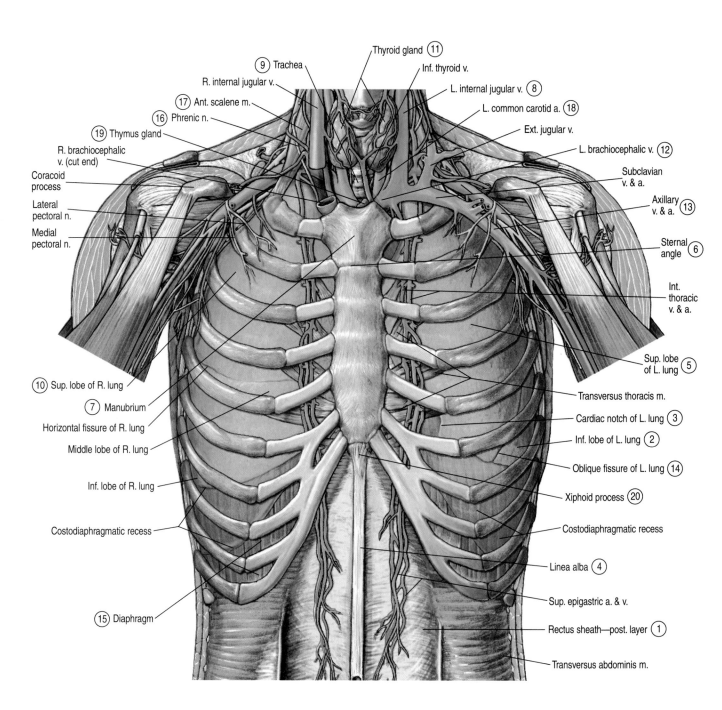

Thyroid gland ⑪
⑨ Trachea
Inf. thyroid v.
R. internal jugular v.
⑰ Ant. scalene m.
L. internal jugular v. ⑧
⑯ Phrenic n.
L. common carotid a. ⑱
⑲ Thymus gland
Ext. jugular v.
R. brachiocephalic v. (cut end)
L. brachiocephalic v. ⑫
Coracoid process
Subclavian v. & a.
Lateral pectoral n.
Axillary v. & a. ⑬
Medial pectoral n.
Sternal angle ⑥
Int. thoracic v. & a.
Sup. lobe of L. lung ⑤
⑩ Sup. lobe of R. lung
Transversus thoracis m.
⑦ Manubrium
Cardiac notch of L. lung ③
Horizontal fissure of R. lung
Inf. lobe of L. lung ②
Middle lobe of R. lung
Oblique fissure of L. lung ⑭
Xiphoid process ⑳
Inf. lobe of R. lung
Costodiaphragmatic recess
Costodiaphragmatic recess
Linea alba ④
Sup. epigastric a. & v.
⑮ Diaphragm
Rectus sheath—post. layer ①
Transversus abdominis m.

ANTERIOR VIEW

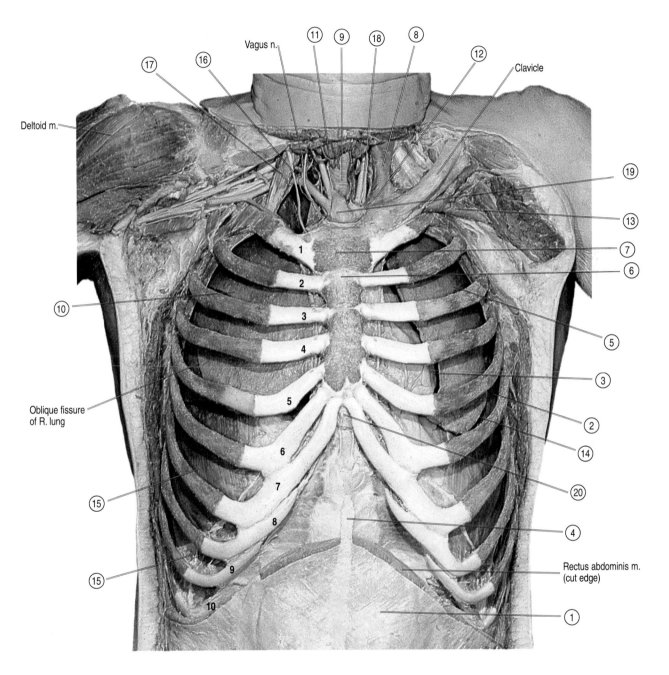

Vagus n.

Clavicle

Deltoid m.

Oblique fissure
of R. lung

Rectus abdominis m.
(cut edge)

ANTERIOR VIEW

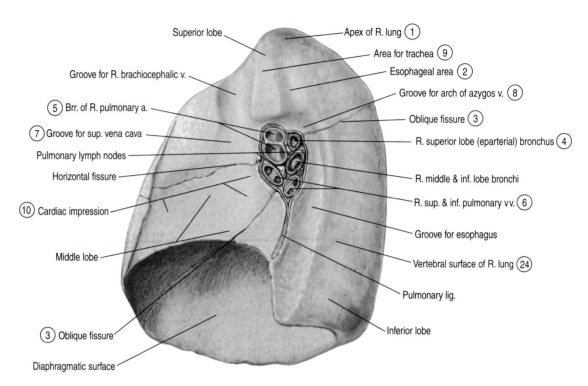

Superior lobe

Apex of R. lung ①

Area for trachea ⑨

Groove for R. brachiocephalic v.

Esophageal area ②

Groove for arch of azygos v. ⑧

⑤ Brr. of R. pulmonary a.

Oblique fissure ③

⑦ Groove for sup. vena cava

R. superior lobe (eparterial) bronchus ④

Pulmonary lymph nodes

Horizontal fissure

R. middle & inf. lobe bronchi

⑩ Cardiac impression

R. sup. & inf. pulmonary vv. ⑥

Middle lobe

Groove for esophagus

Vertebral surface of R. lung ㉔

Pulmonary lig.

③ Oblique fissure

Inferior lobe

Diaphragmatic surface

MEDIAL VIEW OF RIGHT LUNG

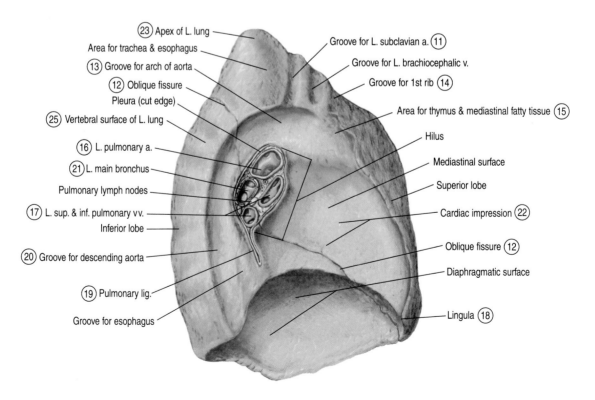

㉓ Apex of L. lung

Groove for L. subclavian a. ⑪

Area for trachea & esophagus

Groove for L. brachiocephalic v.

⑬ Groove for arch of aorta

Groove for 1st rib ⑭

⑫ Oblique fissure

Pleura (cut edge)

Area for thymus & mediastinal fatty tissue ⑮

㉕ Vertebral surface of L. lung

Hilus

⑯ L. pulmonary a.

Mediastinal surface

㉑ L. main bronchus

Superior lobe

Pulmonary lymph nodes

⑰ L. sup. & inf. pulmonary vv.

Cardiac impression ㉒

Inferior lobe

Oblique fissure ⑫

⑳ Groove for descending aorta

Diaphragmatic surface

⑲ Pulmonary lig.

Groove for esophagus

Lingula ⑱

MEDIAL VIEW OF LEFT LUNG

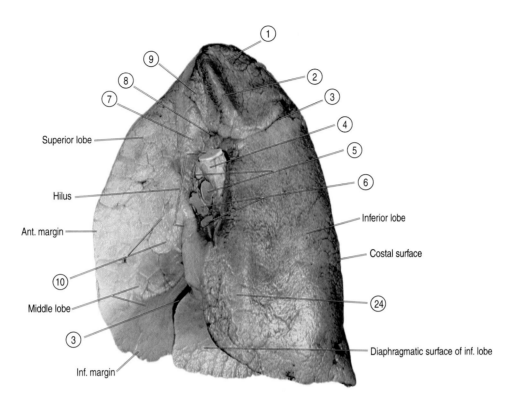

Superior lobe

Hilus

Ant. margin

Middle lobe

Inf. margin

Inferior lobe

Costal surface

Diaphragmatic surface of inf. lobe

POSTEROMEDIAL VIEW OF RIGHT LUNG

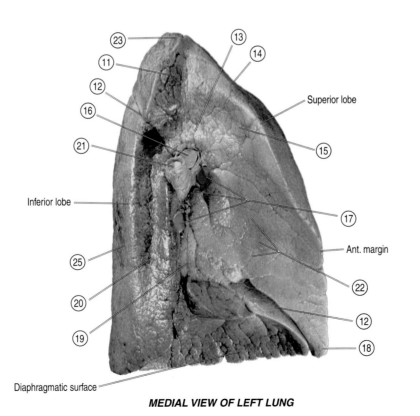

Superior lobe

Inferior lobe

Ant. margin

Diaphragmatic surface

MEDIAL VIEW OF LEFT LUNG

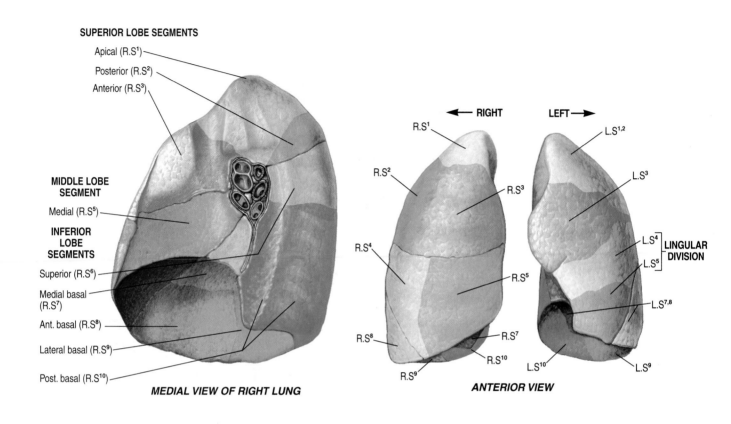

SUPERIOR LOBE SEGMENTS
Apical (R.S¹)
Posterior (R.S²)
Anterior (R.S³)

MIDDLE LOBE SEGMENT
Medial (R.S⁵)

INFERIOR LOBE SEGMENTS
Superior (R.S⁶)
Medial basal (R.S⁷)
Ant. basal (R.S⁸)
Lateral basal (R.S⁹)
Post. basal (R.S¹⁰)

MEDIAL VIEW OF RIGHT LUNG

← RIGHT   LEFT →

R.S¹
R.S²
R.S³
R.S⁴
R.S⁵
R.S⁸
R.S⁹
R.S⁷
R.S¹⁰

L.S¹,²
L.S³
L.S⁴
L.S⁵ LINGULAR DIVISION
L.S⁷,⁸
L.S¹⁰
L.S⁹

ANTERIOR VIEW

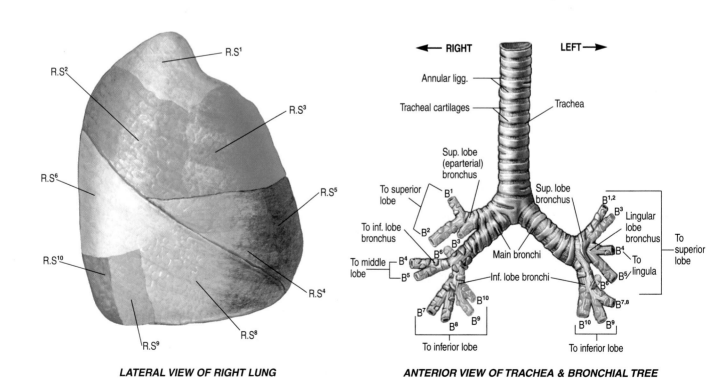

R.S¹
R.S²
R.S³
R.S⁶
R.S⁵
R.S¹⁰
R.S⁴
R.S⁸
R.S⁹

LATERAL VIEW OF RIGHT LUNG

← RIGHT   LEFT →

Annular ligg.
Tracheal cartilages
Trachea
Sup. lobe (eparterial) bronchus
Sup. lobe bronchus
To superior lobe
B¹
B²
To inf. lobe bronchus
B³
B⁶
Main bronchi
To middle lobe
B⁴
B⁵
Inf. lobe bronchi
B⁷
B⁸ B⁹ B¹⁰
To inferior lobe

B¹,²
B³ Lingular lobe bronchus
B⁴ To superior lobe
B⁵ To lingula
B⁶
B⁷,⁸
B¹⁰ B⁹
To inferior lobe

ANTERIOR VIEW OF TRACHEA & BRONCHIAL TREE

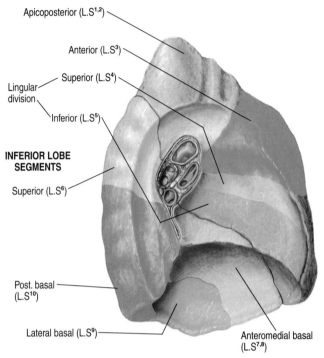

SUPERIOR LOBE SEGMENTS

Apicoposterior (L.S^{1,2})

Anterior (L.S^3)

Superior (L.S^4)

Lingular division

Inferior (L.S^5)

INFERIOR LOBE SEGMENTS

Superior (L.S^6)

Post. basal (L.S^{10})

Lateral basal (L.S^9)

Anteromedial basal (L.S^{7,8})

MEDIAL VIEW OF LEFT LUNG

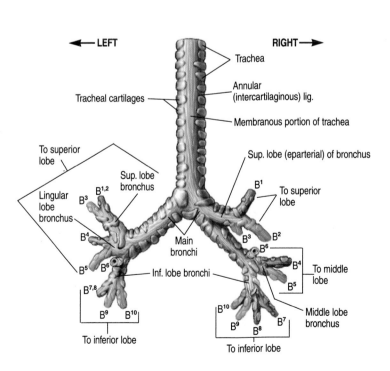

← LEFT   RIGHT →

L.S^{1,2}

L.S^3

L.S^4

L.S^6

L.S^9

L.S^{10}

R.S^1

R.S^2

R.S^6

R.S^3

R.S^4

R.S^9

R.S^{10}

POSTERIOR VIEW

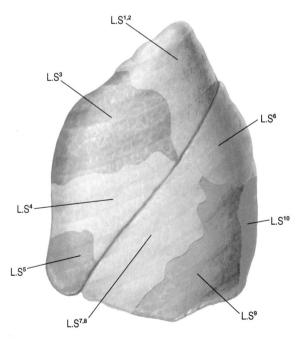

L.S^{1,2}

L.S^3

L.S^6

L.S^4

L.S^{10}

L.S^5

L.S^{7,8}

L.S^9

LATERAL VIEW OF LEFT LUNG

← LEFT   RIGHT →

Trachea

Annular (intercartilaginous) lig.

Tracheal cartilages

Membranous portion of trachea

To superior lobe

Sup. lobe bronchus

Lingular lobe bronchus

Sup. lobe (eparterial) of bronchus

B^3 B^{1,2}

B^1 To superior lobe

B^4

B^3 B^2

Main bronchi

B^5 B^6

B^6

B^4 To middle lobe

Inf. lobe bronchi

B^5

B^{7,8}

Middle lobe bronchus

B^9 B^{10}

B^{10}

To inferior lobe

B^9 B^8 B^7

To inferior lobe

POSTERIOR VIEW OF TRACHEA & BRONCHIAL TREE

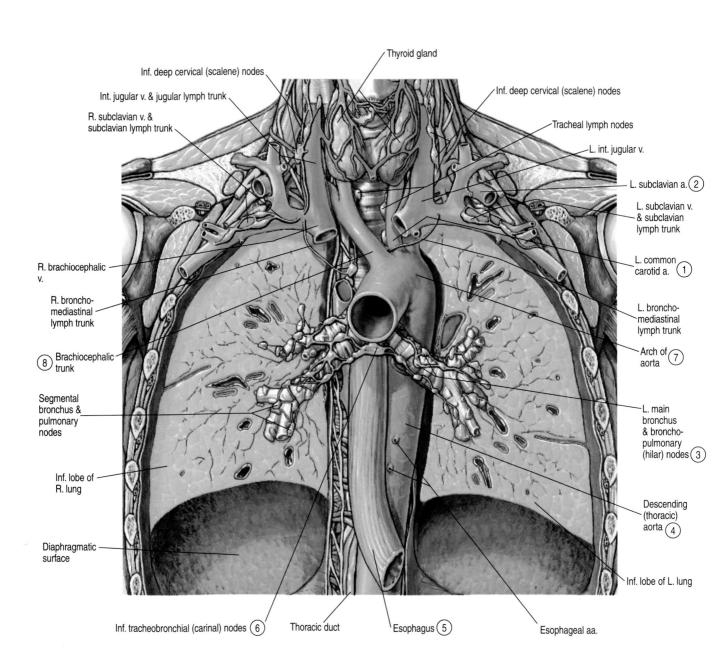

Thyroid gland

Inf. deep cervical (scalene) nodes

Int. jugular v. & jugular lymph trunk

R. subclavian v. & subclavian lymph trunk

Inf. deep cervical (scalene) nodes

Tracheal lymph nodes

L. int. jugular v.

L. subclavian a. ②

L. subclavian v. & subclavian lymph trunk

L. common carotid a. ①

R. brachiocephalic v.

R. broncho-mediastinal lymph trunk

L. broncho-mediastinal lymph trunk

Arch of ⑦ aorta

⑧ Brachiocephalic trunk

L. main bronchus & broncho-pulmonary (hilar) nodes ③

Segmental bronchus & pulmonary nodes

Inf. lobe of R. lung

Descending (thoracic) aorta ④

Diaphragmatic surface

Inf. lobe of L. lung

Inf. tracheobronchial (carinal) nodes ⑥

Thoracic duct

Esophagus ⑤

Esophageal aa.

ANTERIOR VIEW WITH CORONALLY SECTIONED LUNGS

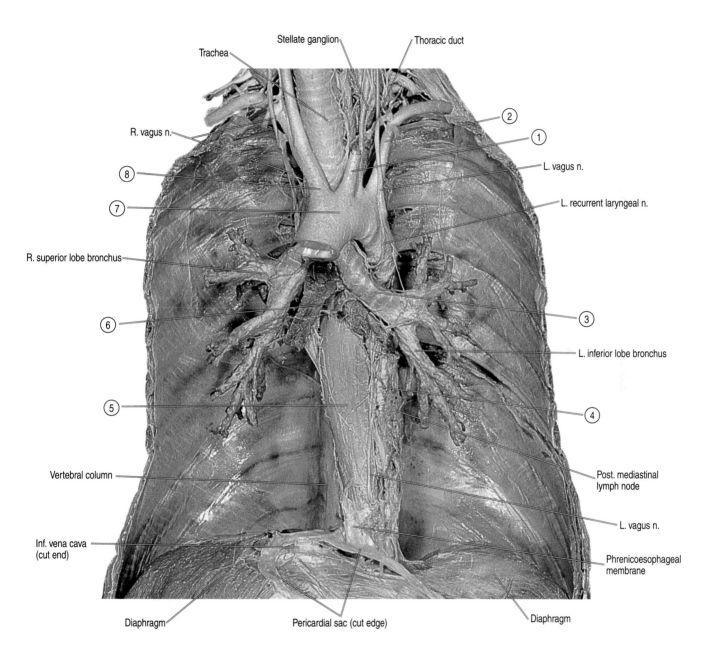

Stellate ganglion

Thoracic duct

Trachea

R. vagus n.

② ①

L. vagus n.

⑧

L. recurrent laryngeal n.

⑦

R. superior lobe bronchus

③

L. inferior lobe bronchus

⑥

⑤ ④

Vertebral column

Post. mediastinal
lymph node

Inf. vena cava
(cut end)

L. vagus n.

Phrenicoesophageal
membrane

Diaphragm

Pericardial sac (cut edge)

Diaphragm

ANTERIOR VIEW

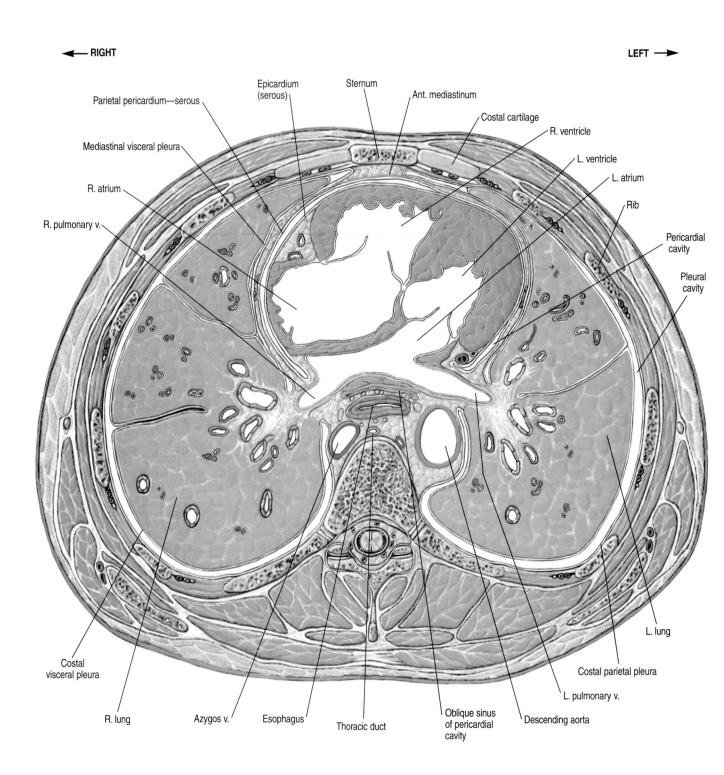

RIGHT ◄—   LEFT —►

Epicardium (serous)

Parietal pericardium—serous

Sternum

Ant. mediastinum

Mediastinal visceral pleura

Costal cartilage

R. atrium

R. ventricle

R. pulmonary v.

L. ventricle

L. atrium

Rib

Pericardial cavity

Pleural cavity

Costal visceral pleura

R. lung

Azygos v.

Esophagus

Thoracic duct

Oblique sinus of pericardial cavity

Descending aorta

L. pulmonary v.

Costal parietal pleura

L. lung

TRANSVERSE SECTION AT T8—INFERIOR VIEW

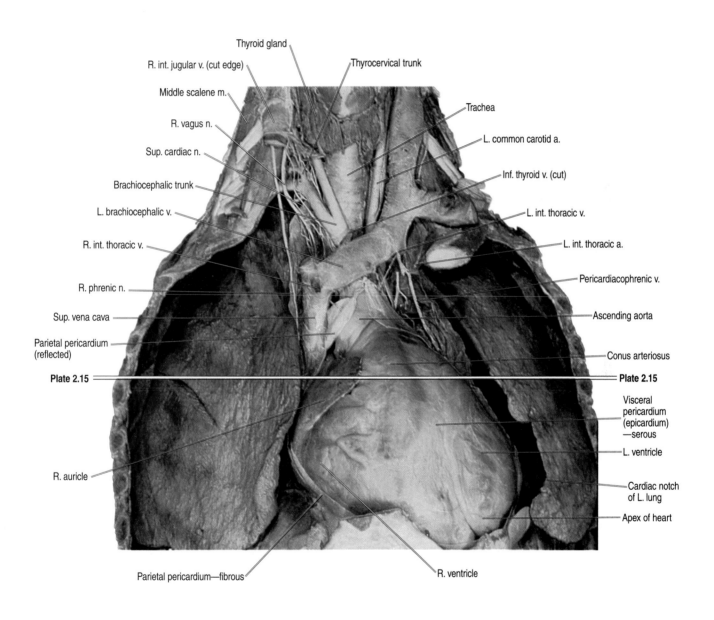

Thyroid gland

R. int. jugular v. (cut edge)

Thyrocervical trunk

Middle scalene m.

Trachea

R. vagus n.

L. common carotid a.

Sup. cardiac n.

Inf. thyroid v. (cut)

Brachiocephalic trunk

L. brachiocephalic v.

L. int. thoracic v.

R. int. thoracic v.

L. int. thoracic a.

R. phrenic n.

Pericardiacophrenic v.

Sup. vena cava

Ascending aorta

Parietal pericardium (reflected)

Conus arteriosus

Plate 2.15

Plate 2.15

Visceral pericardium (epicardium) —serous

L. ventricle

R. auricle

Cardiac notch of L. lung

Apex of heart

Parietal pericardium—fibrous

R. ventricle

ANTERIOR VIEW

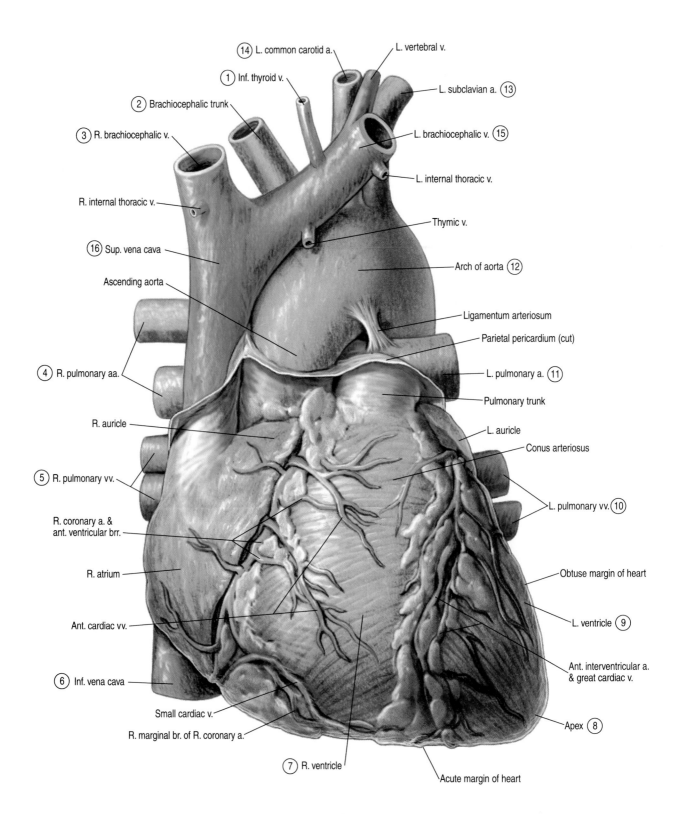

14 L. common carotid a.

1 Inf. thyroid v.

2 Brachiocephalic trunk

3 R. brachiocephalic v.

R. internal thoracic v.

16 Sup. vena cava

Ascending aorta

4 R. pulmonary aa.

R. auricle

5 R. pulmonary vv.

R. coronary a. & ant. ventricular brr.

R. atrium

Ant. cardiac vv.

6 Inf. vena cava

Small cardiac v.

R. marginal br. of R. coronary a.

7 R. ventricle

L. vertebral v.

L. subclavian a. 13

L. brachiocephalic v. 15

L. internal thoracic v.

Thymic v.

Arch of aorta 12

Ligamentum arteriosum

Parietal pericardium (cut)

L. pulmonary a. 11

Pulmonary trunk

L. auricle

Conus arteriosus

L. pulmonary vv. 10

Obtuse margin of heart

L. ventricle 9

Ant. interventricular a. & great cardiac v.

Apex 8

Acute margin of heart

ANTERIOR VIEW

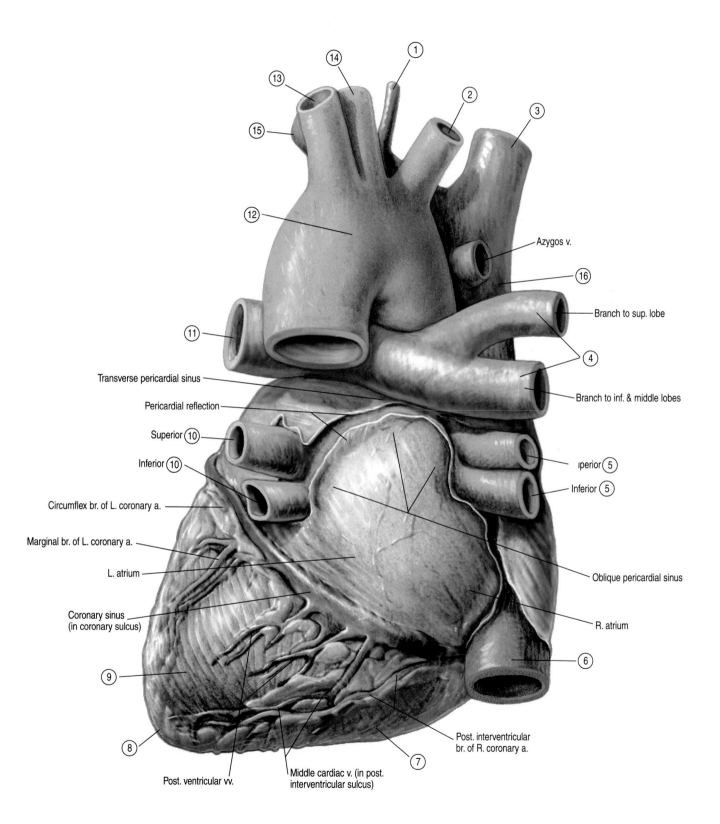

Azygos v.

Branch to sup. lobe

Branch to inf. & middle lobes

Transverse pericardial sinus

Pericardial reflection

Superior ⑩

Inferior ⑩

Circumflex br. of L. coronary a.

Marginal br. of L. coronary a.

L. atrium

Coronary sinus
(in coronary sulcus)

⑨

⑧

ıperior ⑤

Inferior ⑤

Oblique pericardial sinus

R. atrium

⑥

Post. interventricular
br. of R. coronary a.

⑦

Post. ventricular vv.

Middle cardiac v. (in post.
interventricular sulcus)

POSTERIOR VIEW

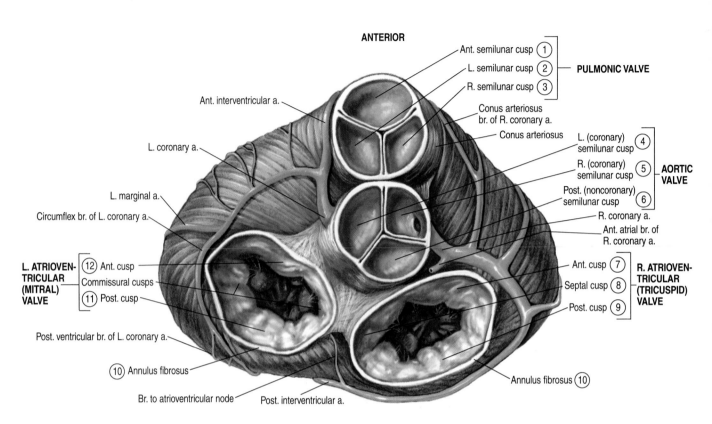

ANTERIOR

Ant. interventricular a.

L. coronary a.

L. marginal a.

Circumflex br. of L. coronary a.

L. ATRIOVEN-TRICULAR (MITRAL) VALVE
12 Ant. cusp
Commissural cusps
11 Post. cusp

Post. ventricular br. of L. coronary a.

10 Annulus fibrosus

Br. to atrioventricular node

Post. interventricular a.

Ant. semilunar cusp 1
L. semilunar cusp 2   **PULMONIC VALVE**
R. semilunar cusp 3

Conus arteriosus br. of R. coronary a.

Conus arteriosus

L. (coronary) semilunar cusp 4
R. (coronary) semilunar cusp 5   **AORTIC VALVE**
Post. (noncoronary) semilunar cusp 6

R. coronary a.

Ant. atrial br. of R. coronary a.

Ant. cusp 7   **R. ATRIOVEN-TRICULAR (TRICUSPID) VALVE**
Septal cusp 8
Post. cusp 9

Annulus fibrosus 10

HEART IN DIASTOLE VIEWED FROM BASE WITH ATRIA REMOVED

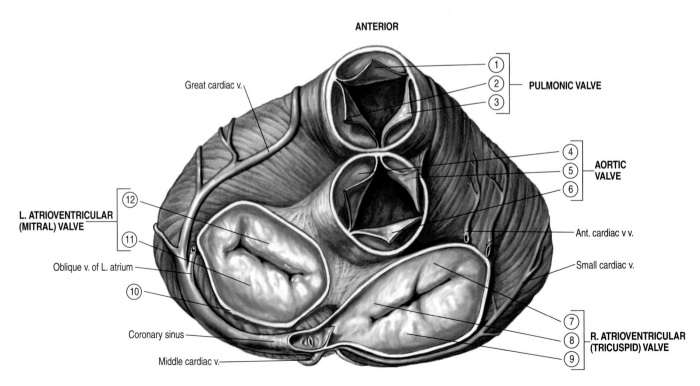

ANTERIOR

Great cardiac v.

1
2   **PULMONIC VALVE**
3

4
5   **AORTIC VALVE**
6

L. ATRIOVENTRICULAR (MITRAL) VALVE
12
11

Oblique v. of L. atrium

10

Coronary sinus

Middle cardiac v.

Ant. cardiac v v.

Small cardiac v.

7
8   **R. ATRIOVENTRICULAR (TRICUSPID) VALVE**
9

HEART IN SYSTOLE VIEWED FROM BASE WITH ATRIA REMOVED

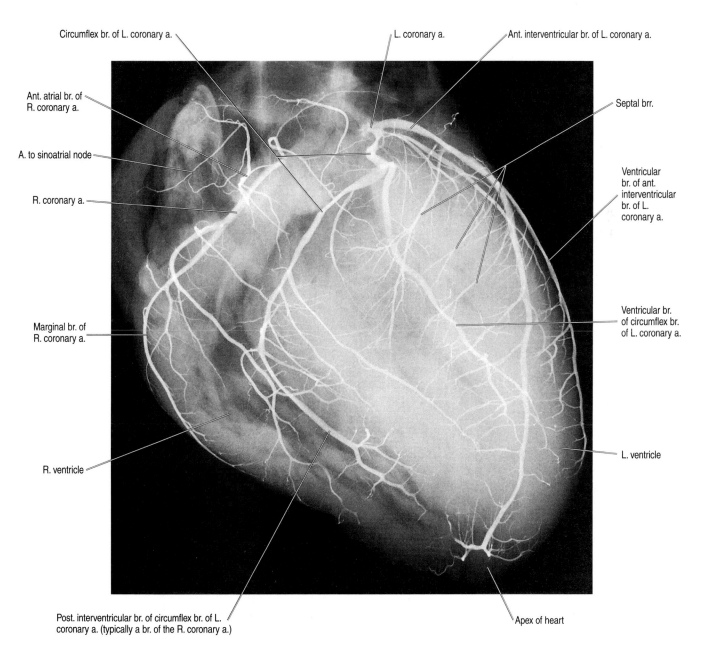

Circumflex br. of L. coronary a.

L. coronary a.

Ant. interventricular br. of L. coronary a.

Ant. atrial br. of
R. coronary a.

Septal brr.

A. to sinoatrial node

R. coronary a.

Ventricular
br. of ant.
interventricular
br. of L.
coronary a.

Marginal br. of
R. coronary a.

Ventricular br.
of circumflex br.
of L. coronary a.

R. ventricle

L. ventricle

Post. interventricular br. of circumflex br. of L.
coronary a. (typically a br. of the R. coronary a.)

Apex of heart

ANTEROPOSTERIOR VIEW

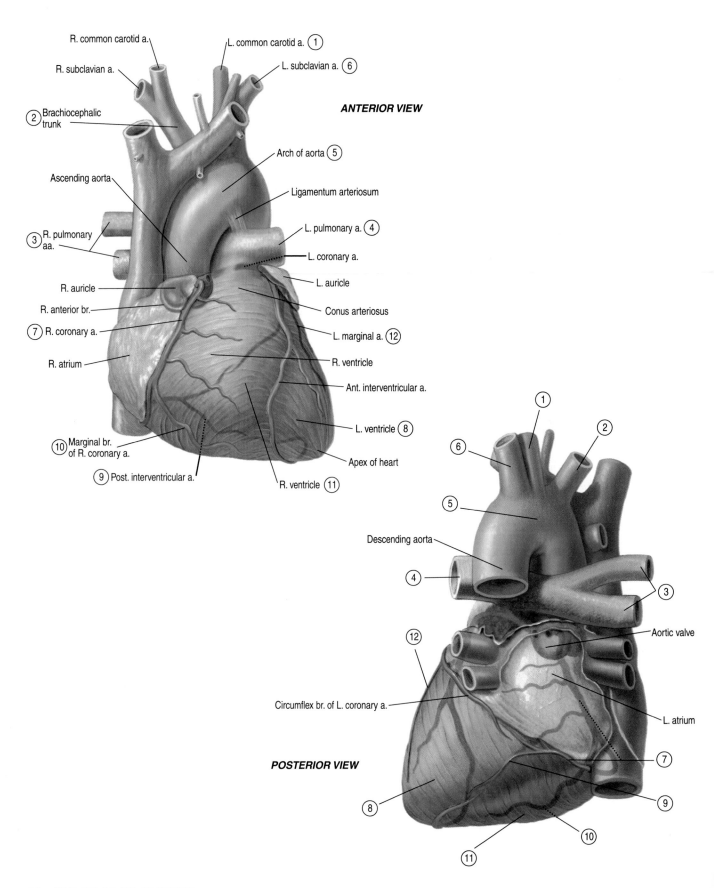

R. common carotid a.

L. common carotid a. (1)

R. subclavian a.

L. subclavian a. (6)

ANTERIOR VIEW

(2) Brachiocephalic trunk

Arch of aorta (5)

Ascending aorta

Ligamentum arteriosum

(3) R. pulmonary aa.

L. pulmonary a. (4)

L. coronary a.

R. auricle

L. auricle

R. anterior br.

Conus arteriosus

(7) R. coronary a.

L. marginal a. (12)

R. atrium

R. ventricle

Ant. interventricular a.

(10) Marginal br. of R. coronary a.

L. ventricle (8)

Apex of heart

(9) Post. interventricular a.

R. ventricle (11)

(1)

(6)

(2)

(5)

Descending aorta

(4)

(3)

(12)

Aortic valve

Circumflex br. of L. coronary a.

L. atrium

(7)

POSTERIOR VIEW

(8)

(9)

(10)

(11)

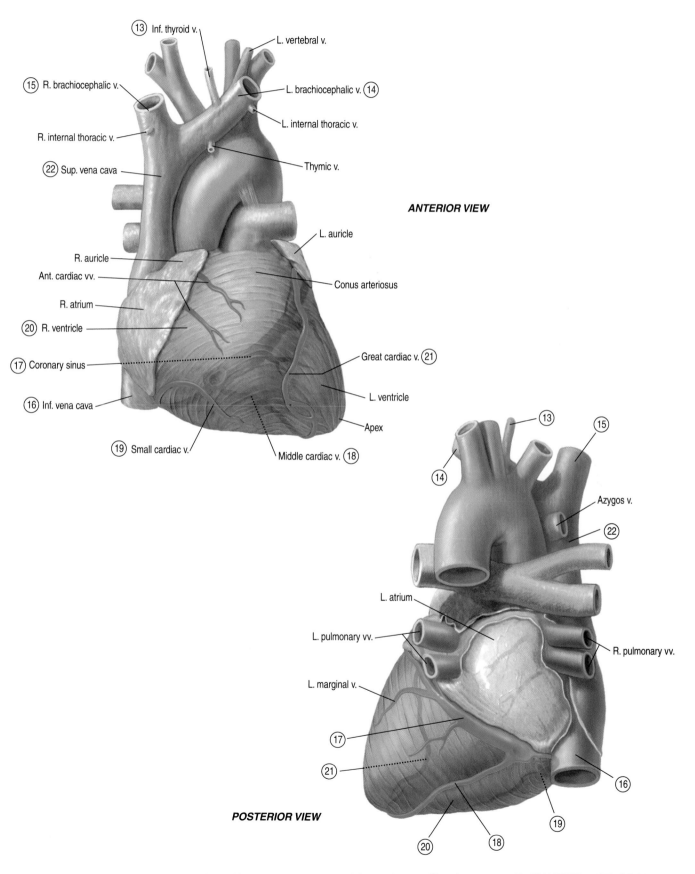

⑬ Inf. thyroid v.

L. vertebral v.

⑮ R. brachiocephalic v.

L. brachiocephalic v. ⑭

R. internal thoracic v.

L. internal thoracic v.

⑫ Sup. vena cava

Thymic v.

ANTERIOR VIEW

L. auricle

R. auricle

Ant. cardiac vv.

Conus arteriosus

R. atrium

⑳ R. ventricle

⑰ Coronary sinus

Great cardiac v. ㉑

L. ventricle

⑯ Inf. vena cava

Apex

⑲ Small cardiac v.

Middle cardiac v. ⑱

⑬

⑮

⑭

Azygos v.

㉒

L. atrium

L. pulmonary vv.

R. pulmonary vv.

L. marginal v.

⑰

㉑

⑯

⑳

⑱

⑲

POSTERIOR VIEW

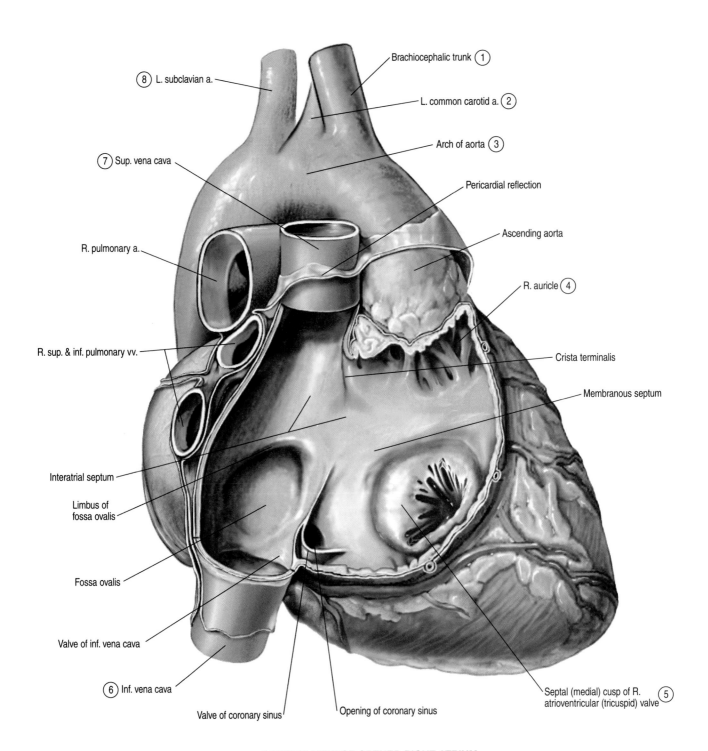

8 L. subclavian a.

Brachiocephalic trunk 1

L. common carotid a. 2

Arch of aorta 3

7 Sup. vena cava

Pericardial reflection

Ascending aorta

R. pulmonary a.

R. auricle 4

Crista terminalis

R. sup. & inf. pulmonary vv.

Membranous septum

Interatrial septum

Limbus of
fossa ovalis

Fossa ovalis

Valve of inf. vena cava

6 Inf. vena cava

Valve of coronary sinus

Opening of coronary sinus

Septal (medial) cusp of R.
atrioventricular (tricuspid) valve 5

LATERAL VIEW OF OPENED RIGHT ATRIUM

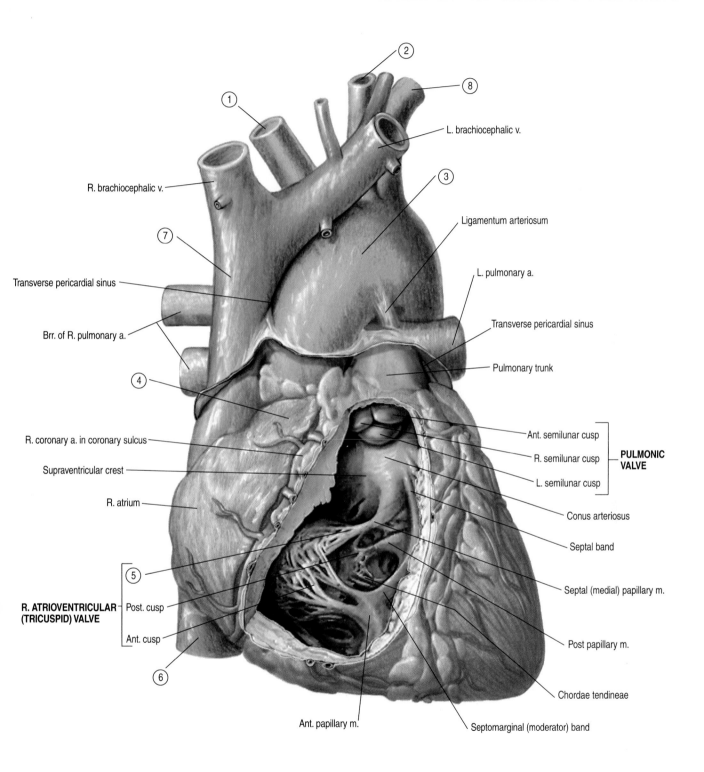

R. brachiocephalic v.

L. brachiocephalic v.

Ligamentum arteriosum

L. pulmonary a.

Transverse pericardial sinus

Transverse pericardial sinus

Brr. of R. pulmonary a.

Pulmonary trunk

R. coronary a. in coronary sulcus

Ant. semilunar cusp

R. semilunar cusp

L. semilunar cusp

PULMONIC VALVE

Supraventricular crest

Conus arteriosus

R. atrium

Septal band

Septal (medial) papillary m.

R. ATRIOVENTRICULAR (TRICUSPID) VALVE

Post. cusp

Ant. cusp

Post papillary m.

Chordae tendineae

Ant. papillary m.

Septomarginal (moderator) band

ANTERIOR VIEW OF OPENED RIGHT VENTRICLE

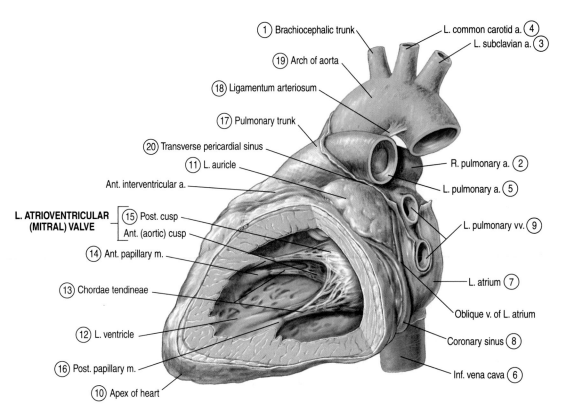

1 Brachiocephalic trunk

L. common carotid a. 4

L. subclavian a. 3

19 Arch of aorta

18 Ligamentum arteriosum

17 Pulmonary trunk

20 Transverse pericardial sinus

11 L. auricle

Ant. interventricular a.

R. pulmonary a. 2

L. pulmonary a. 5

L. ATRIOVENTRICULAR (MITRAL) VALVE

15 Post. cusp

Ant. (aortic) cusp

L. pulmonary vv. 9

14 Ant. papillary m.

13 Chordae tendineae

L. atrium 7

12 L. ventricle

Oblique v. of L. atrium

16 Post. papillary m.

Coronary sinus 8

10 Apex of heart

Inf. vena cava 6

LEFT LATERAL VIEW OF OPENED LEFT VENTRICLE

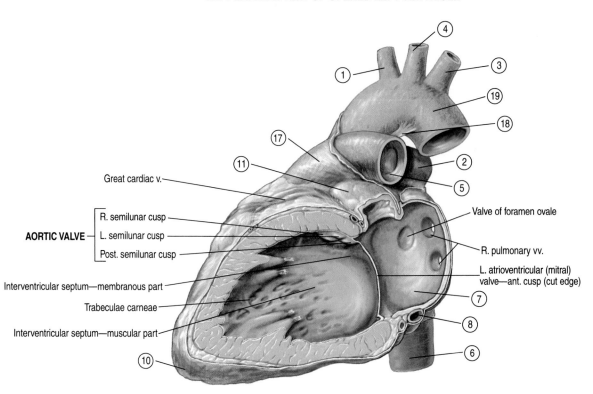

4

1

3

19

18

17

11

2

5

Great cardiac v.

Valve of foramen ovale

AORTIC VALVE

R. semilunar cusp

L. semilunar cusp

Post. semilunar cusp

R. pulmonary vv.

L. atrioventricular (mitral) valve—ant. cusp (cut edge)

Interventricular septum—membranous part

7

Trabeculae carneae

8

Interventricular septum—muscular part

6

10

LEFT LATERAL VIEW OF LEFT VENTRICLE & ATRIUM WITH MITRAL VALVE REMOVED

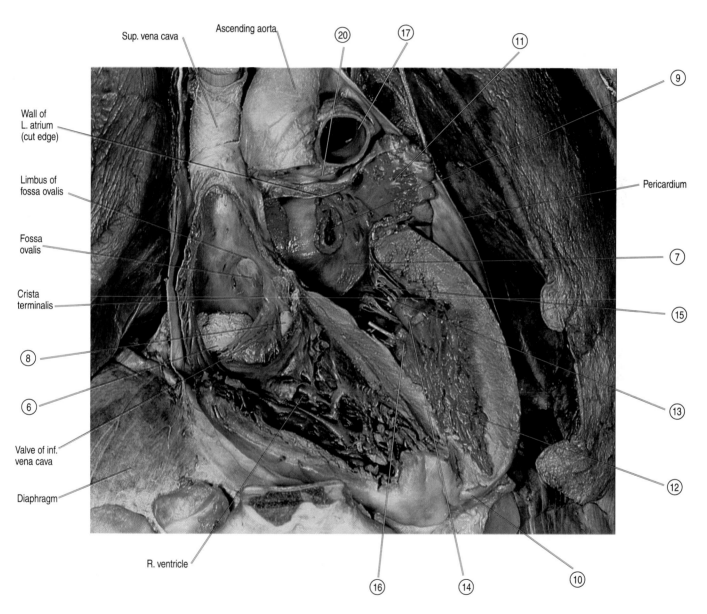

Sup. vena cava

Ascending aorta

⑳

⑰

⑪

⑨

Wall of
L. atrium
(cut edge)

Pericardium

Limbus of
fossa ovalis

Fossa
ovalis

⑦

Crista
terminalis

⑮

⑧

⑬

⑥

Valve of inf.
vena cava

⑫

Diaphragm

R. ventricle

⑯

⑭

⑩

INTERIOR OF ANTERIOR VIEW OF HEART

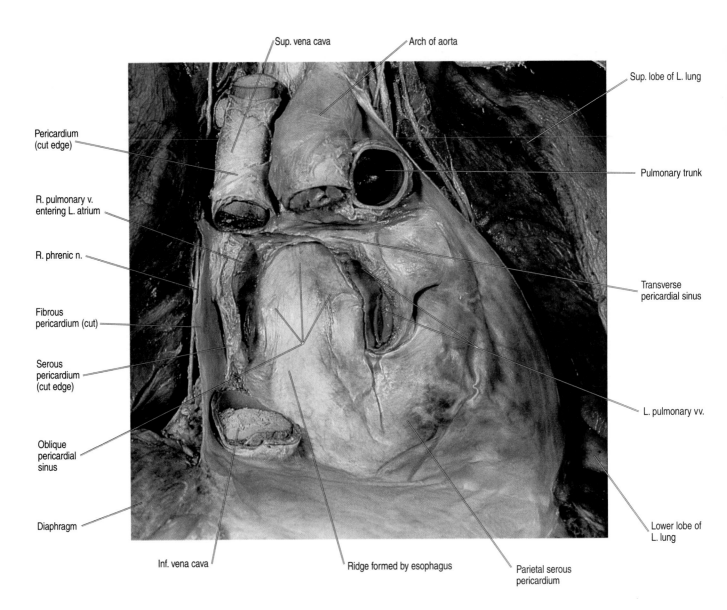

Sup. vena cava

Arch of aorta

Sup. lobe of L. lung

Pericardium
(cut edge)

Pulmonary trunk

R. pulmonary v.
entering L. atrium

R. phrenic n.

Transverse
pericardial sinus

Fibrous
pericardium (cut)

Serous
pericardium
(cut edge)

L. pulmonary vv.

Oblique
pericardial
sinus

Diaphragm

Lower lobe of
L. lung

Inf. vena cava

Ridge formed by esophagus

Parietal serous
pericardium

ANTERIOR VIEW OF PERICARDIAL CAVITY WITH HEART REMOVED

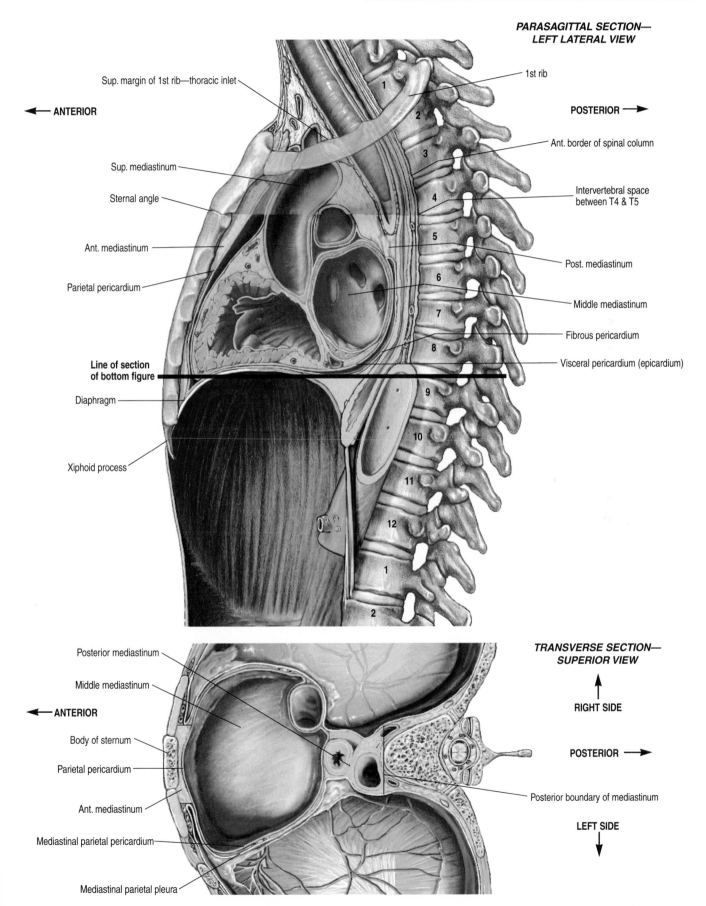

**PARASAGITTAL SECTION—
LEFT LATERAL VIEW**

Sup. margin of 1st rib—thoracic inlet

◄— **ANTERIOR**

Sup. mediastinum

Sternal angle

Ant. mediastinum

Parietal pericardium

**Line of section
of bottom figure**

Diaphragm

Xiphoid process

1st rib

POSTERIOR —►

Ant. border of spinal column

Intervertebral space
between T4 & T5

Post. mediastinum

Middle mediastinum

Fibrous pericardium

Visceral pericardium (epicardium)

**TRANSVERSE SECTION—
SUPERIOR VIEW**

Posterior mediastinum

Middle mediastinum

◄— **ANTERIOR**

RIGHT SIDE
↑

Body of sternum

Parietal pericardium

POSTERIOR —►

Ant. mediastinum

Posterior boundary of mediastinum

Mediastinal parietal pericardium

LEFT SIDE
↓

Mediastinal parietal pleura

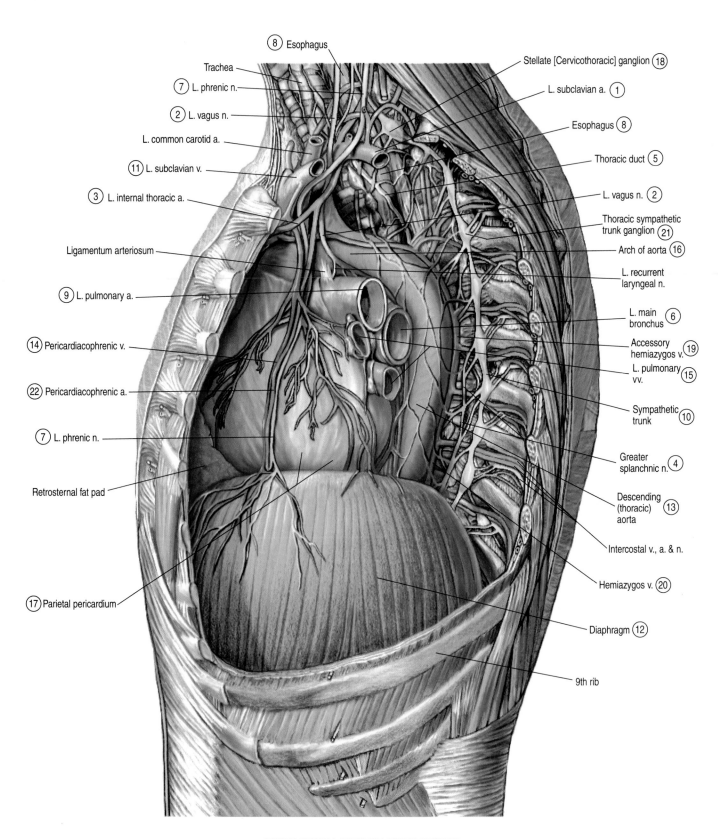

Esophagus (8)

Trachea

(7) L. phrenic n.

(2) L. vagus n.

L. common carotid a.

(11) L. subclavian v.

(3) L. internal thoracic a.

Ligamentum arteriosum

(9) L. pulmonary a.

(14) Pericardiacophrenic v.

(22) Pericardiacophrenic a.

(7) L. phrenic n.

Retrosternal fat pad

(17) Parietal pericardium

Stellate [Cervicothoracic] ganglion (18)

L. subclavian a. (1)

Esophagus (8)

Thoracic duct (5)

L. vagus n. (2)

Thoracic sympathetic trunk ganglion (21)

Arch of aorta (16)

L. recurrent laryngeal n.

L. main bronchus (6)

Accessory hemiazygos v. (19)

L. pulmonary vv. (15)

Sympathetic trunk (10)

Greater splanchnic n. (4)

Descending (thoracic) aorta (13)

Intercostal v., a. & n.

Hemiazygos v. (20)

Diaphragm (12)

9th rib

LEFT LATERAL VIEW OF MEDIASTINUM

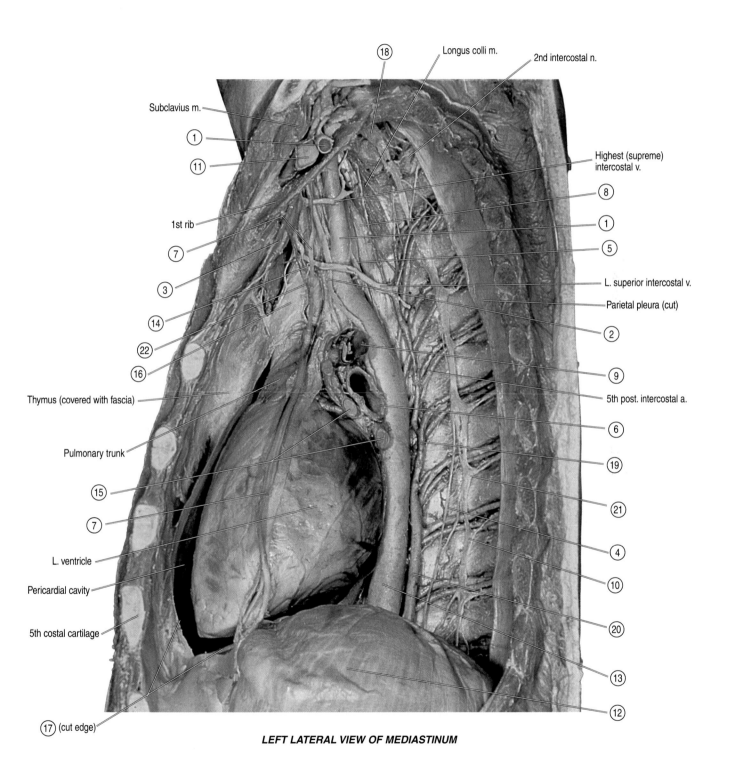

Longus colli m.

2nd intercostal n.

(18)

Subclavius m.

(1)

(11)

Highest (supreme)
intercostal v.

(8)

1st rib

(1)

(7)

(5)

(3)

L. superior intercostal v.

(14)

Parietal pleura (cut)

(22)

(2)

(16)

(9)

Thymus (covered with fascia)

5th post. intercostal a.

(6)

Pulmonary trunk

(19)

(15)

(21)

(7)

(4)

L. ventricle

(10)

Pericardial cavity

(20)

5th costal cartilage

(13)

(12)

(17) (cut edge)

LEFT LATERAL VIEW OF MEDIASTINUM

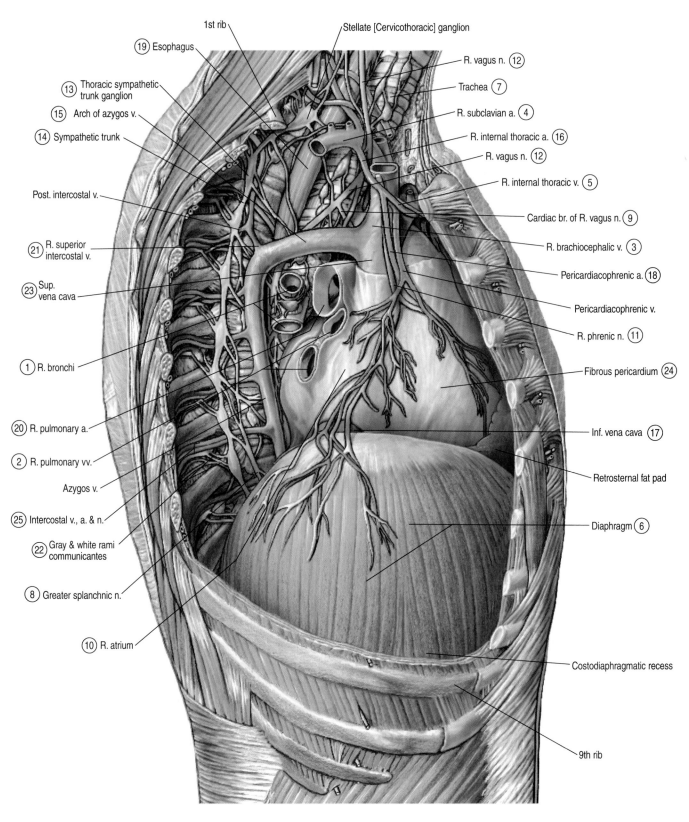

1st rib

⑲ Esophagus

Stellate [Cervicothoracic] ganglion

R. vagus n. ⑫

⑬ Thoracic sympathetic trunk ganglion

Trachea ⑦

⑮ Arch of azygos v.

R. subclavian a. ④

⑭ Sympathetic trunk

R. internal thoracic a. ⑯

R. vagus n. ⑫

Post. intercostal v.

R. internal thoracic v. ⑤

Cardiac br. of R. vagus n. ⑨

㉑ R. superior intercostal v.

R. brachiocephalic v. ③

Pericardiacophrenic a. ⑱

㉓ Sup. vena cava

Pericardiacophrenic v.

R. phrenic n. ⑪

① R. bronchi

Fibrous pericardium ㉔

⑳ R. pulmonary a.

Inf. vena cava ⑰

② R. pulmonary vv.

Retrosternal fat pad

Azygos v.

㉕ Intercostal v., a. & n.

Diaphragm ⑥

㉒ Gray & white rami communicantes

⑧ Greater splanchnic n.

⑩ R. atrium

Costodiaphragmatic recess

9th rib

RIGHT LATERAL VIEW OF MEDIASTINUM

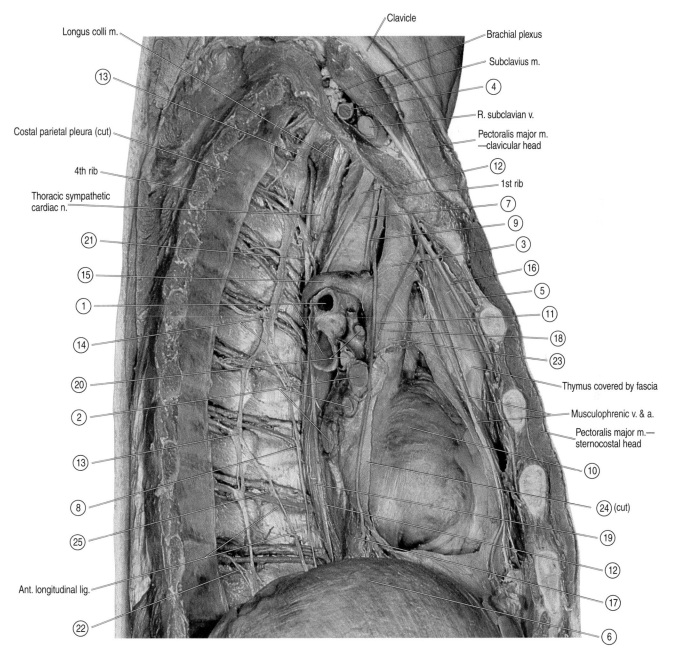

Clavicle

Longus colli m.

Brachial plexus

Subclavius m.

13

4

Costal parietal pleura (cut)

R. subclavian v.

Pectoralis major m.
—clavicular head

4th rib

12

1st rib

Thoracic sympathetic
cardiac n.

7

9

21

3

15

16

1

5

14

11

18

20

23

Thymus covered by fascia

2

Musculophrenic v. & a.

Pectoralis major m.—
sternocostal head

13

10

8

24 (cut)

25

19

12

Ant. longitudinal lig.

17

22

6

RIGHT LATERAL VIEW OF MEDIASTINUM

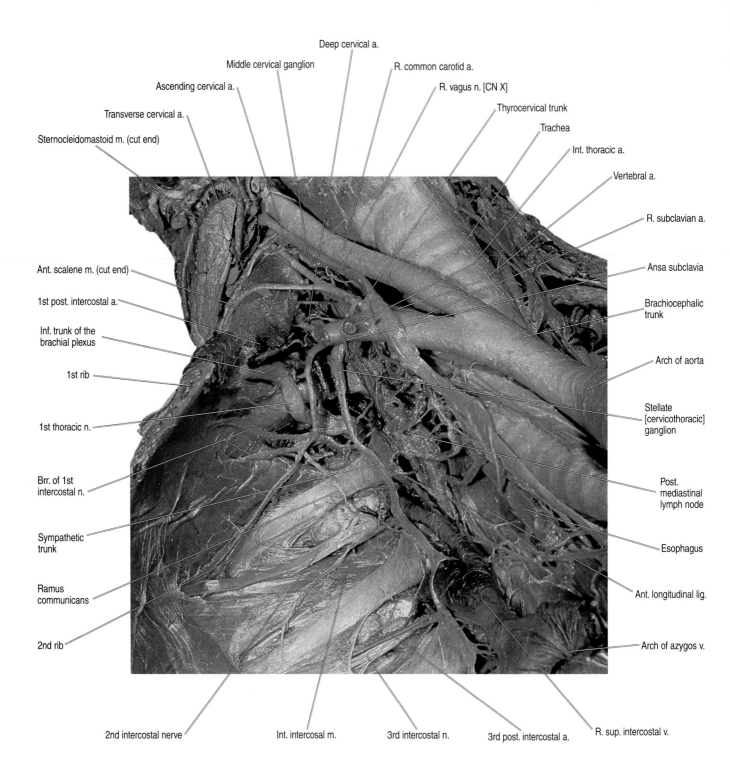

Deep cervical a.

Middle cervical ganglion

Ascending cervical a.

R. common carotid a.

R. vagus n. [CN X]

Transverse cervical a.

Thyrocervical trunk

Trachea

Sternocleidomastoid m. (cut end)

Int. thoracic a.

Vertebral a.

R. subclavian a.

Ant. scalene m. (cut end)

Ansa subclavia

1st post. intercostal a.

Brachiocephalic trunk

Inf. trunk of the brachial plexus

Arch of aorta

1st rib

Stellate [cervicothoracic] ganglion

1st thoracic n.

Brr. of 1st intercostal n.

Post. mediastinal lymph node

Sympathetic trunk

Esophagus

Ramus communicans

Ant. longitudinal lig.

2nd rib

Arch of azygos v.

2nd intercostal nerve

Int. intercosal m.

3rd intercostal n.

3rd post. intercostal a.

R. sup. intercostal v.

RIGHT ANTEROLATERAL INFERIOR OBLIQUE VIEW

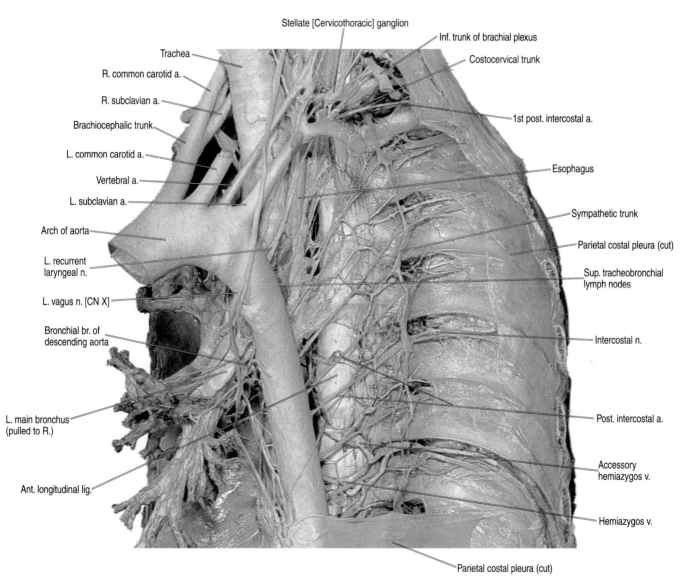

Stellate [Cervicothoracic] ganglion

Trachea

R. common carotid a.

R. subclavian a.

Brachiocephalic trunk

L. common carotid a.

Vertebral a.

L. subclavian a.

Arch of aorta

L. recurrent
laryngeal n.

L. vagus n. [CN X]

Bronchial br. of
descending aorta

L. main bronchus
(pulled to R.)

Ant. longitudinal lig.

Inf. trunk of brachial plexus

Costocervical trunk

1st post. intercostal a.

Esophagus

Sympathetic trunk

Parietal costal pleura (cut)

Sup. tracheobronchial
lymph nodes

Intercostal n.

Post. intercostal a.

Accessory
hemiazygos v.

Hemiazygos v.

Parietal costal pleura (cut)

LEFT ANTEROLATERAL VIEW

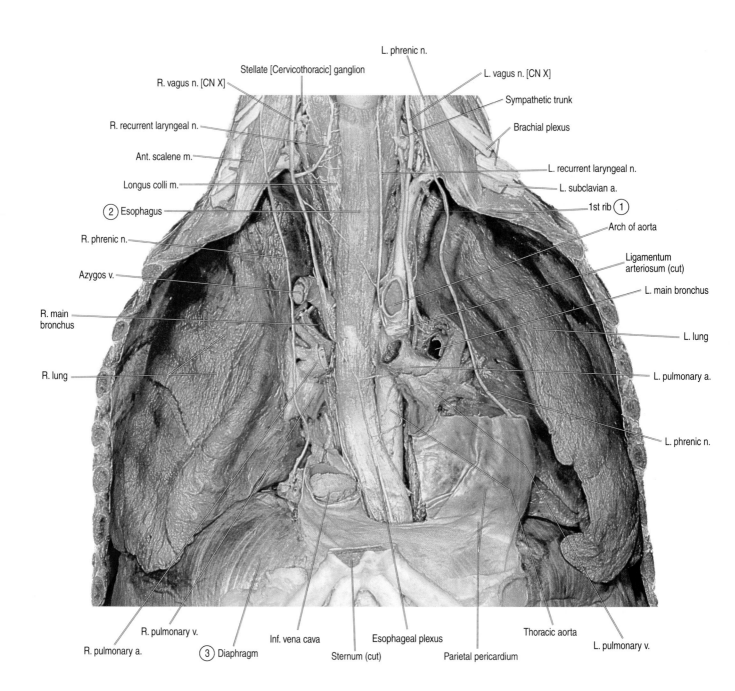

L. phrenic n.

R. vagus n. [CN X]

Stellate [Cervicothoracic] ganglion

L. vagus n. [CN X]

Sympathetic trunk

R. recurrent laryngeal n.

Brachial plexus

Ant. scalene m.

Longus colli m.

L. recurrent laryngeal n.

L. subclavian a.

2 Esophagus

1st rib 1

R. phrenic n.

Arch of aorta

Azygos v.

Ligamentum arteriosum (cut)

R. main bronchus

L. main bronchus

L. lung

R. lung

L. pulmonary a.

L. phrenic n.

R. pulmonary v.

Inf. vena cava

Esophageal plexus

Thoracic aorta

R. pulmonary a.

3 Diaphragm

Sternum (cut)

Parietal pericardium

L. pulmonary v.

ANTERIOR VIEW OF POSTERIOR MEDIASTINAL STRUCTURES

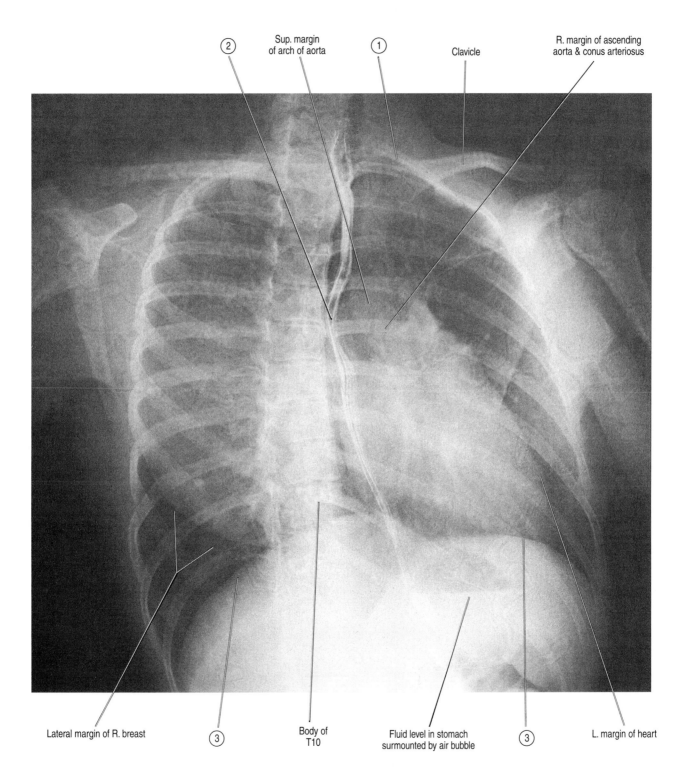

② Sup. margin
of arch of aorta

① Clavicle

R. margin of ascending
aorta & conus arteriosus

Lateral margin of R. breast

③

Body of
T10

Fluid level in stomach
surmounted by air bubble

③

L. margin of heart

RIGHT ANTERIOR OBLIQUE VIEW OF ESOPHAGUS

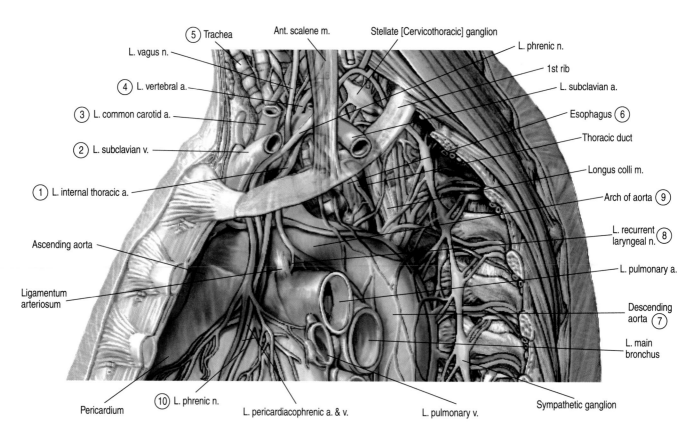

5 Trachea
L. vagus n.
Ant. scalene m.
Stellate [Cervicothoracic] ganglion
L. phrenic n.
4 L. vertebral a.
1st rib
3 L. common carotid a.
L. subclavian a.
2 L. subclavian v.
Esophagus 6
1 L. internal thoracic a.
Thoracic duct
Longus colli m.
Ascending aorta
Arch of aorta 9
L. recurrent laryngeal n. 8
Ligamentum arteriosum
L. pulmonary a.
Descending aorta 7
L. main bronchus
Pericardium
10 L. phrenic n.
L. pericardiacophrenic a. & v.
L. pulmonary v.
Sympathetic ganglion

LEFT LATERAL VIEW OF MEDIASTINUM

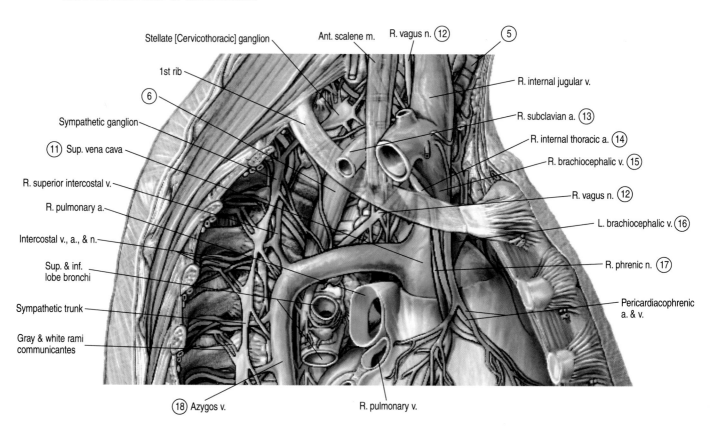

Stellate [Cervicothoracic] ganglion
Ant. scalene m.
R. vagus n. 12
5
1st rib
R. internal jugular v.
6
Sympathetic ganglion
R. subclavian a. 13
11 Sup. vena cava
R. internal thoracic a. 14
R. superior intercostal v.
R. brachiocephalic v. 15
R. pulmonary a.
R. vagus n. 12
Intercostal v., a., & n.
L. brachiocephalic v. 16
Sup. & inf. lobe bronchi
R. phrenic n. 17
Sympathetic trunk
Pericardiacophrenic a. & v.
Gray & white rami communicantes
18 Azygos v.
R. pulmonary v.

RIGHT LATERAL VIEW OF MEDIASTINUM

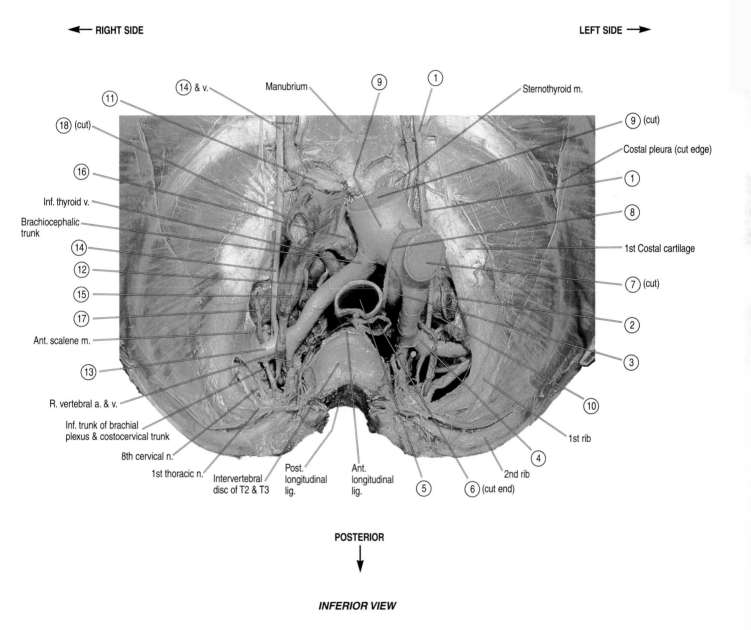

ANTERIOR

◄— RIGHT SIDE

LEFT SIDE —►

⑭ & v.   Manubrium   ⑨   ①   Sternothyroid m.

⑪

⑱ (cut)   ⑨ (cut)

Costal pleura (cut edge)

⑯   ①

Inf. thyroid v.   ⑧

Brachiocephalic
trunk   1st Costal cartilage

⑭   ⑦ (cut)

⑫

⑮   ②

⑰   ③

Ant. scalene m.

⑬   ⑩

R. vertebral a. & v.   1st rib

Inf. trunk of brachial
plexus & costocervical trunk   ④

8th cervical n.   2nd rib

1st thoracic n.   Intervertebral   Post.   Ant.   ⑤   ⑥ (cut end)
disc of T2 & T3   longitudinal   longitudinal
lig.   lig.

POSTERIOR

INFERIOR VIEW

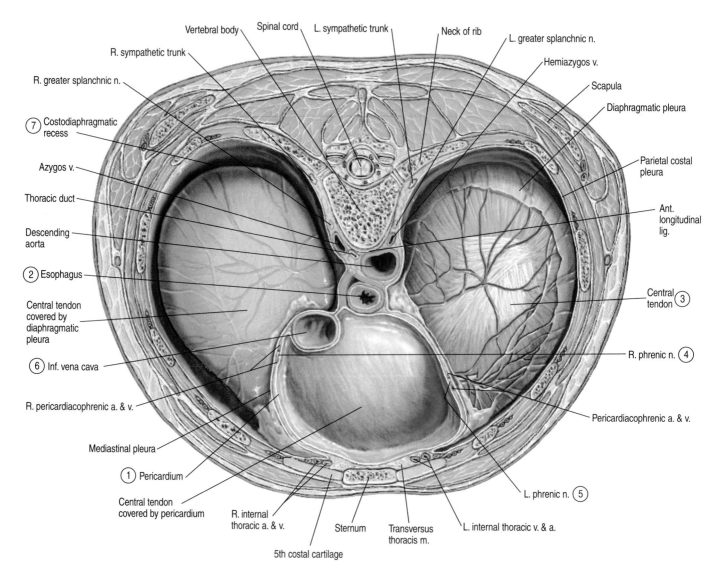

Vertebral body

Spinal cord

L. sympathetic trunk

Neck of rib

L. greater splanchnic n.

R. sympathetic trunk

Hemiazygos v.

R. greater splanchnic n.

Scapula

⑦ Costodiaphragmatic recess

Diaphragmatic pleura

Azygos v.

Parietal costal pleura

Thoracic duct

Descending aorta

Ant. longitudinal lig.

② Esophagus

Central tendon covered by diaphragmatic pleura

Central tendon ③

⑥ Inf. vena cava

R. phrenic n. ④

R. pericardiacophrenic a. & v.

Pericardiacophrenic a. & v.

Mediastinal pleura

① Pericardium

L. phrenic n. ⑤

Central tendon covered by pericardium

R. internal thoracic a. & v.

Sternum

Transversus thoracis m.

L. internal thoracic v. & a.

5th costal cartilage

SUPERIOR SURFACE

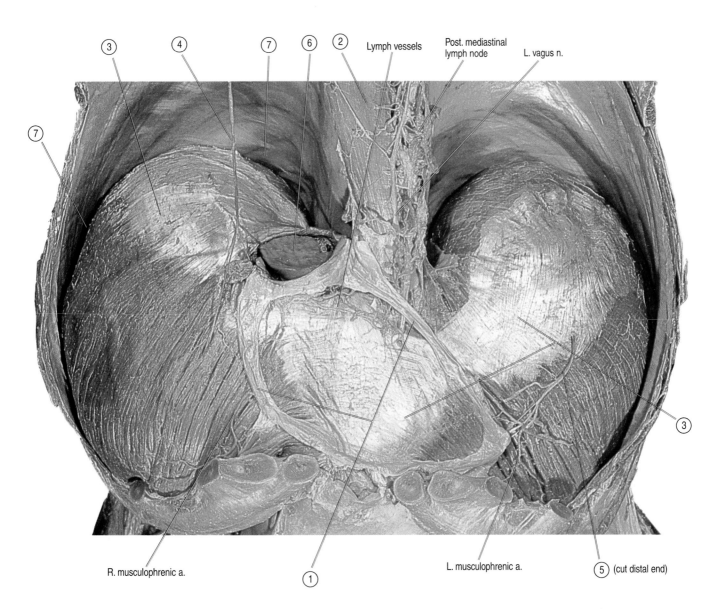

③ ④ ⑦ ⑥ ② Lymph vessels Post. mediastinal lymph node L. vagus n.

⑦

R. musculophrenic a.

L. musculophrenic a.

① ⑤ (cut distal end)

③

ANTERIOR SUPERIOR OBLIQUE VIEW OF SUPERIOR SURFACE OF DIAPHRAGM

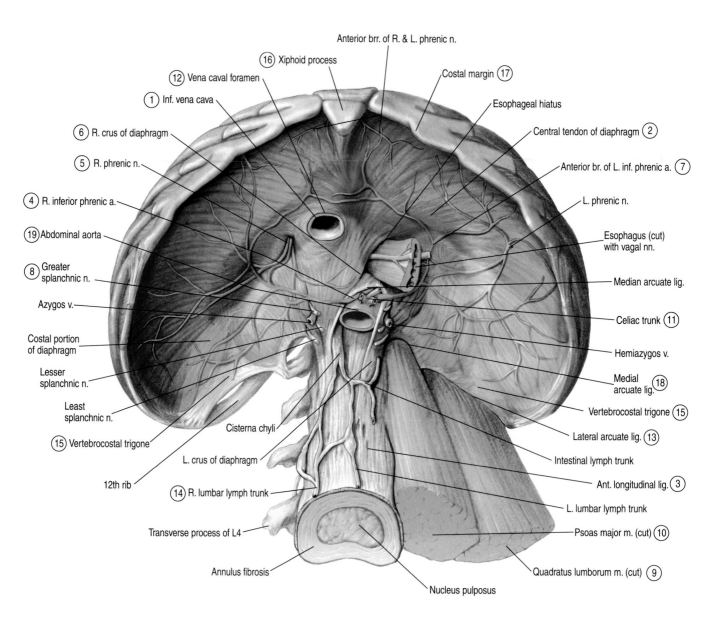

Anterior brr. of R. & L. phrenic n.

(16) Xiphoid process

(12) Vena caval foramen

Costal margin (17)

(1) Inf. vena cava

Esophageal hiatus

(6) R. crus of diaphragm

Central tendon of diaphragm (2)

(5) R. phrenic n.

Anterior br. of L. inf. phrenic a. (7)

(4) R. inferior phrenic a.

L. phrenic n.

(19) Abdominal aorta

Esophagus (cut) with vagal nn.

(8) Greater splanchnic n.

Median arcuate lig.

Azygos v.

Celiac trunk (11)

Costal portion of diaphragm

Hemiazygos v.

Lesser splanchnic n.

Medial arcuate lig. (18)

Least splanchnic n.

Vertebrocostal trigone (15)

(15) Vertebrocostal trigone

Lateral arcuate lig. (13)

Cisterna chyli

Intestinal lymph trunk

L. crus of diaphragm

Ant. longitudinal lig. (3)

12th rib

L. lumbar lymph trunk

(14) R. lumbar lymph trunk

Psoas major m. (cut) (10)

Transverse process of L4

Quadratus lumborum m. (cut) (9)

Annulus fibrosis

Nucleus pulposus

INFERIOR VIEW

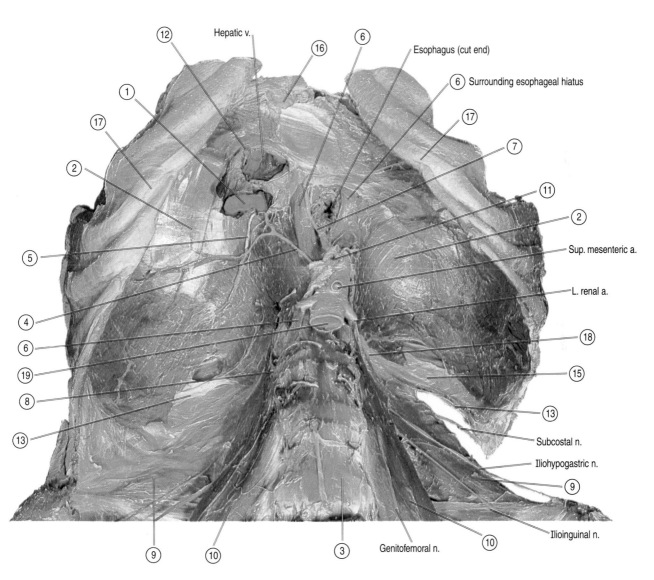

Hepatic v.

Esophagus (cut end)

Surrounding esophageal hiatus

Sup. mesenteric a.

L. renal a.

Subcostal n.

Iliohypogastric n.

Ilioinguinal n.

Genitofemoral n.

INFERIOR VIEW

Abdomen

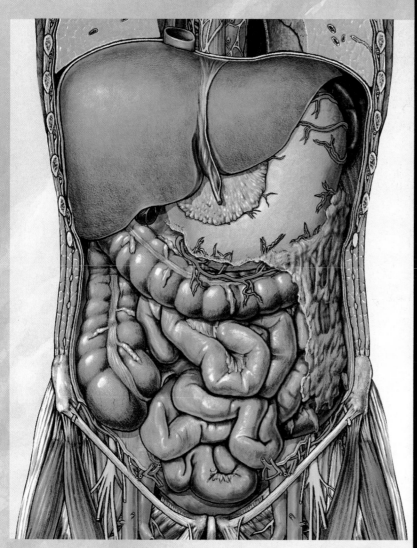

Chapter **3**

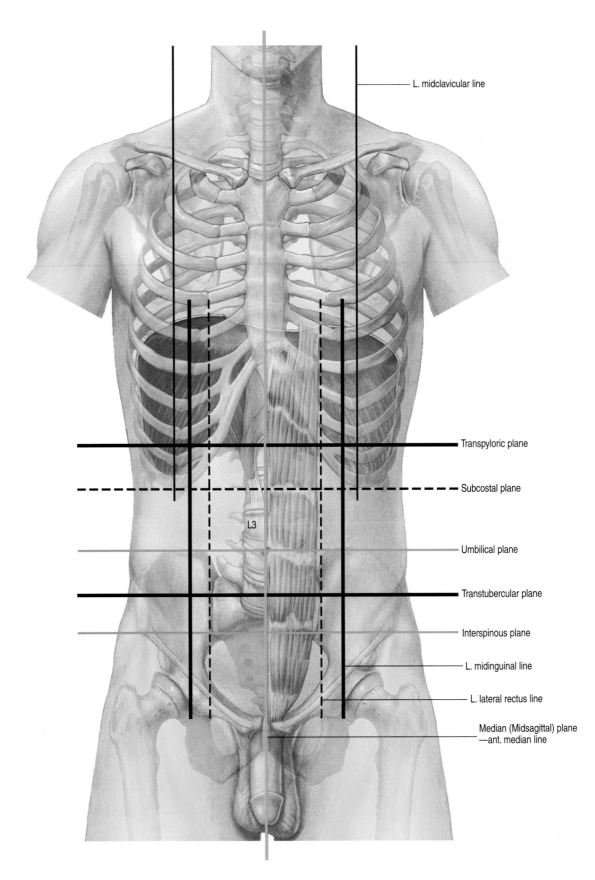

L. midclavicular line

Transpyloric plane

Subcostal plane

L3

Umbilical plane

Transtubercular plane

Interspinous plane

L. midinguinal line

L. lateral rectus line

Median (Midsagittal) plane
—ant. median line

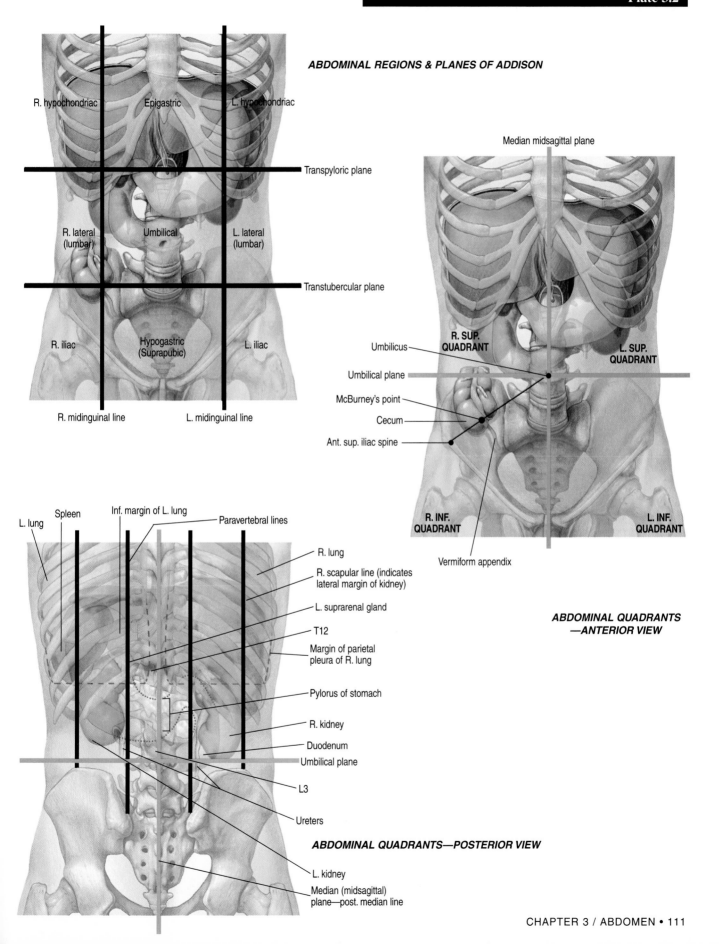

ABDOMINAL REGIONS & PLANES OF ADDISON

R. hypochondriac

Epigastric

L. hypochondriac

Transpyloric plane

R. lateral (lumbar)

Umbilical

L. lateral (lumbar)

Transtubercular plane

R. iliac

Hypogastric (Suprapubic)

L. iliac

R. midinguinal line

L. midinguinal line

Median midsagittal plane

R. SUP. QUADRANT

L. SUP. QUADRANT

Umbilicus

Umbilical plane

McBurney's point

Cecum

Ant. sup. iliac spine

R. INF. QUADRANT

L. INF. QUADRANT

Vermiform appendix

ABDOMINAL QUADRANTS —ANTERIOR VIEW

L. lung

Spleen

Inf. margin of L. lung

Paravertebral lines

R. lung

R. scapular line (indicates lateral margin of kidney)

L. suprarenal gland

T12

Margin of parietal pleura of R. lung

Pylorus of stomach

R. kidney

Duodenum

Umbilical plane

L3

Ureters

ABDOMINAL QUADRANTS—POSTERIOR VIEW

L. kidney

Median (midsagittal) plane—post. median line

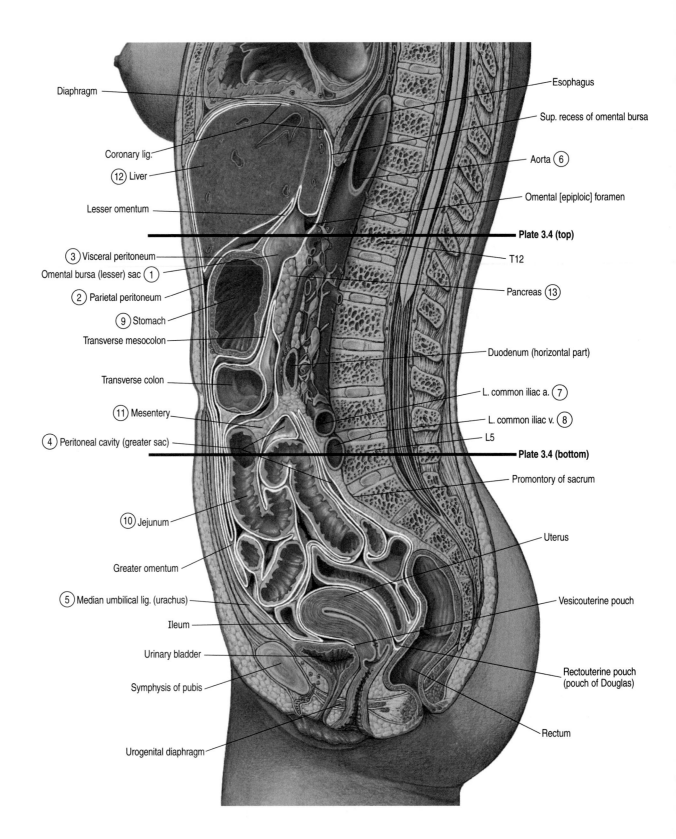

Diaphragm

Coronary lig.

(12) Liver

Lesser omentum

(3) Visceral peritoneum

Omental bursa (lesser) sac (1)

(2) Parietal peritoneum

(9) Stomach

Transverse mesocolon

Transverse colon

(11) Mesentery

(4) Peritoneal cavity (greater sac)

(10) Jejunum

Greater omentum

(5) Median umbilical lig. (urachus)

Ileum

Urinary bladder

Symphysis of pubis

Urogenital diaphragm

Esophagus

Sup. recess of omental bursa

Aorta (6)

Omental [epiploic] foramen

Plate 3.4 (top)

T12

Pancreas (13)

Duodenum (horizontal part)

L. common iliac a. (7)

L. common iliac v. (8)

L5

Plate 3.4 (bottom)

Promontory of sacrum

Uterus

Vesicouterine pouch

Rectouterine pouch
(pouch of Douglas)

Rectum

MEDIAN SECTION—LEFT LATERAL VIEW

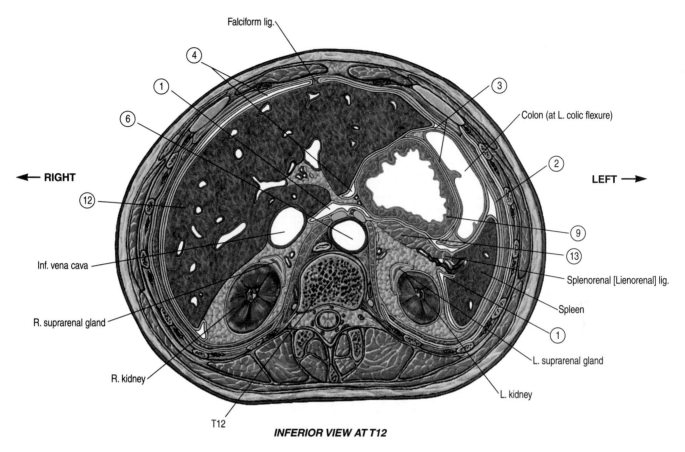

Falciform lig.

④

①

⑥

◄— **RIGHT**

⑫

③

Colon (at L. colic flexure)

②

LEFT —►

⑨

⑬

Splenorenal [Lienorenal] lig.

Spleen

①

Inf. vena cava

R. suprarenal gland

L. suprarenal gland

R. kidney

L. kidney

T12

INFERIOR VIEW AT T12

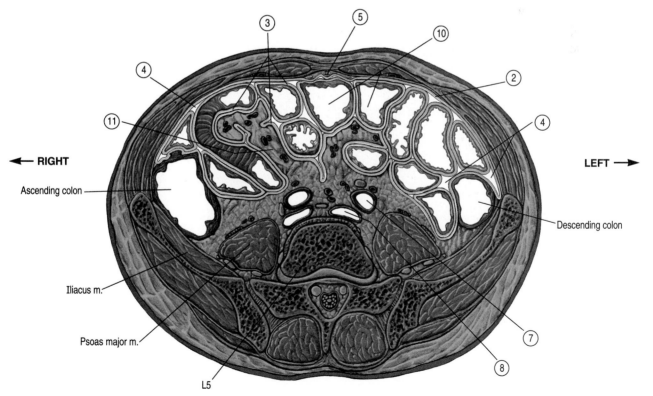

③

⑤

⑩

④

②

⑪

④

◄— **RIGHT**

LEFT —►

Ascending colon

Descending colon

Iliacus m.

Psoas major m.

⑦

L5

⑧

INFERIOR VIEW AT L5

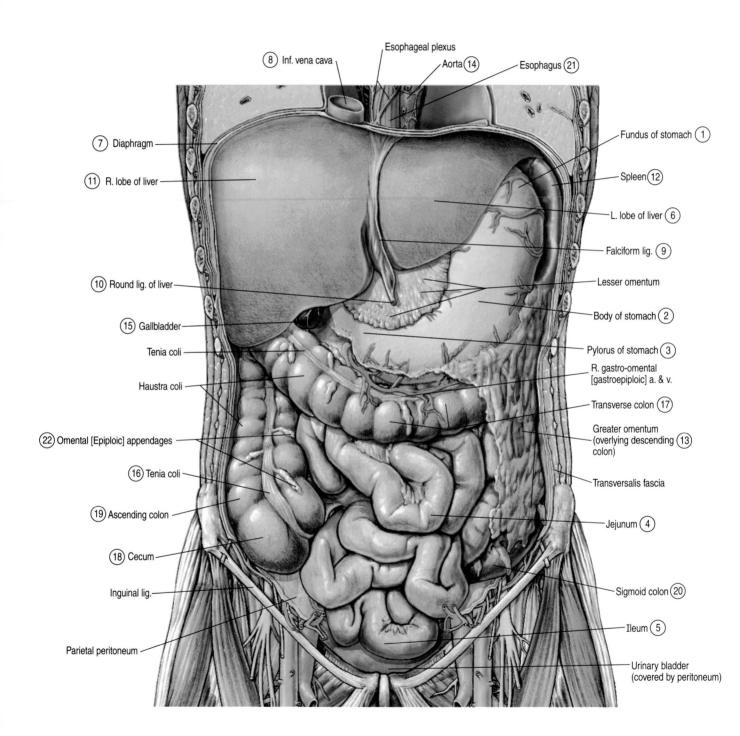

Esophageal plexus

⑧ Inf. vena cava

Aorta ⑭

Esophagus ㉑

⑦ Diaphragm

⑪ R. lobe of liver

⑩ Round lig. of liver

⑮ Gallbladder

Tenia coli

Haustra coli

㉒ Omental [Epiploic] appendages

⑯ Tenia coli

⑲ Ascending colon

⑱ Cecum

Inguinal lig.

Parietal peritoneum

Fundus of stomach ①

Spleen ⑫

L. lobe of liver ⑥

Falciform lig. ⑨

Lesser omentum

Body of stomach ②

Pylorus of stomach ③

R. gastro-omental
[gastroepiploic] a. & v.

Transverse colon ⑰

Greater omentum
(overlying descending ⑬
colon)

Transversalis fascia

Jejunum ④

Sigmoid colon ⑳

Ileum ⑤

Urinary bladder
(covered by peritoneum)

ANTERIOR VIEW

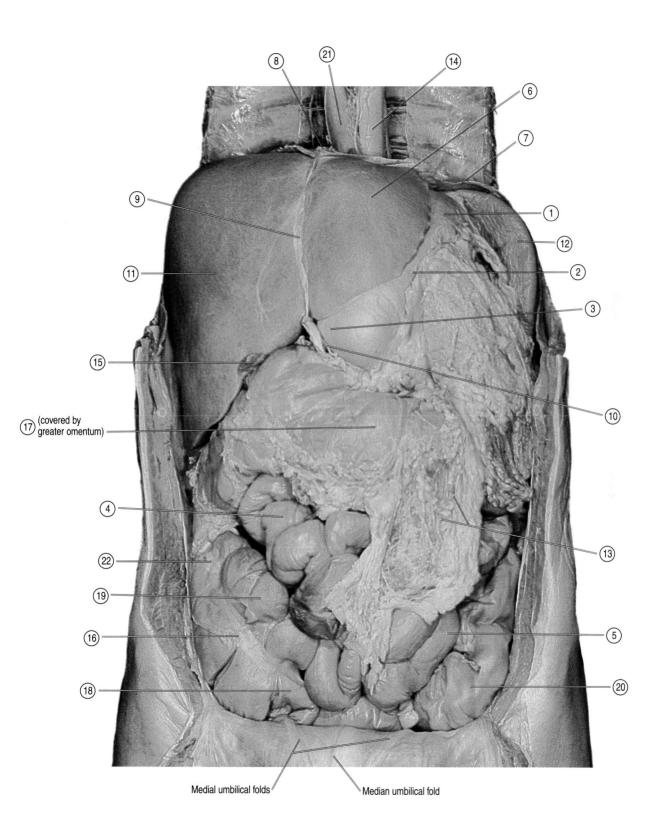

(8)   (21)   (14)

(6)

(7)

(9)

(1)

(12)

(11)

(2)

(3)

(15)

(10)

(17) (covered by
greater omentum)

(4)

(13)

(22)

(19)

(16)

(5)

(18)

(20)

Medial umbilical folds   Median umbilical fold

ANTERIOR VIEW

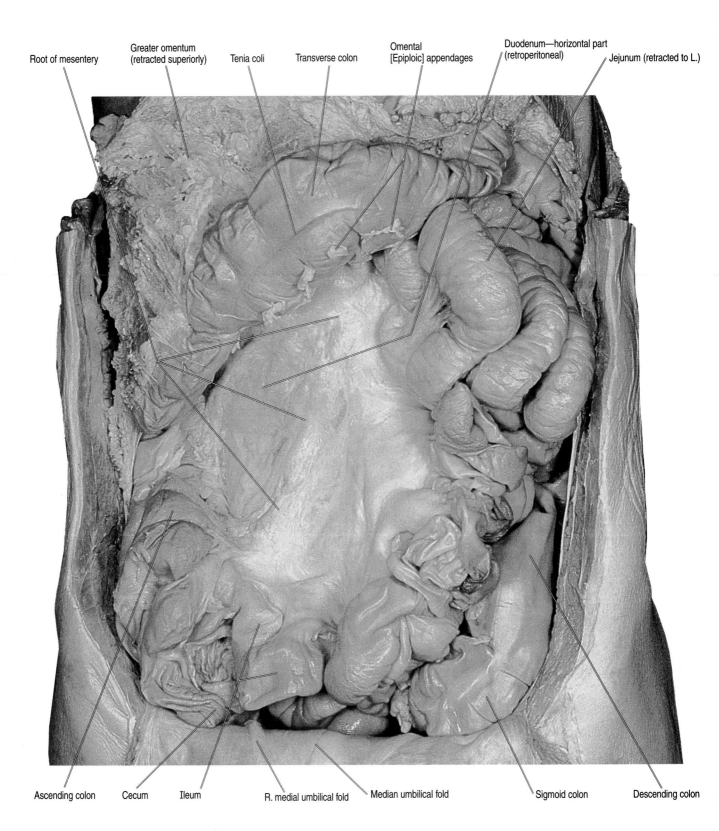

Root of mesentery

Greater omentum (retracted superiorly)

Tenia coli

Transverse colon

Omental [Epiploic] appendages

Duodenum—horizontal part (retroperitoneal)

Jejunum (retracted to L.)

Ascending colon

Cecum

Ileum

R. medial umbilical fold

Median umbilical fold

Sigmoid colon

Descending colon

ANTERIOR VIEW WITH SMALL INTESTINES RETRACTED TO LEFT

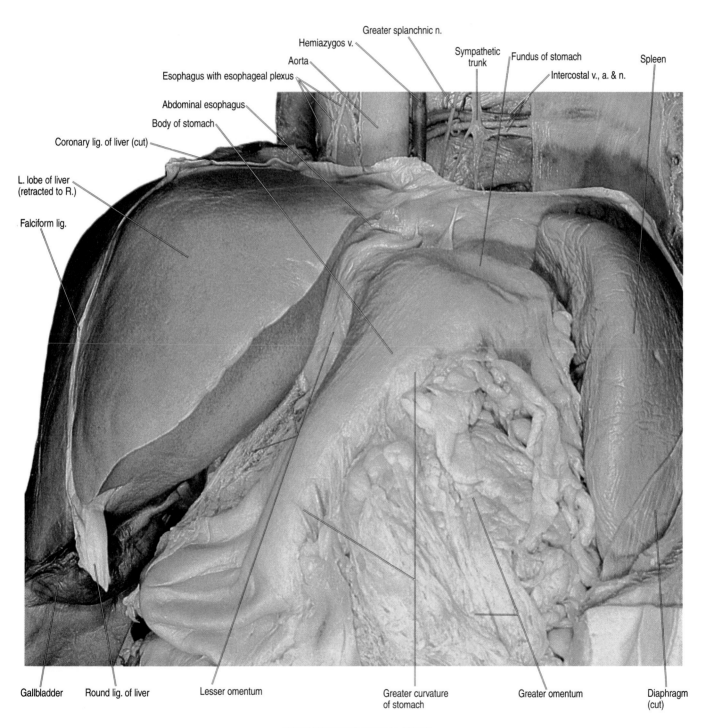

Greater splanchnic n.

Hemiazygos v.

Aorta

Esophagus with esophageal plexus

Abdominal esophagus

Body of stomach

Coronary lig. of liver (cut)

L. lobe of liver (retracted to R.)

Falciform lig.

Sympathetic trunk

Fundus of stomach

Spleen

Intercostal v., a. & n.

Gallbladder

Round lig. of liver

Lesser omentum

Greater curvature of stomach

Greater omentum

Diaphragm (cut)

LEFT ANTEROLATERAL VIEW

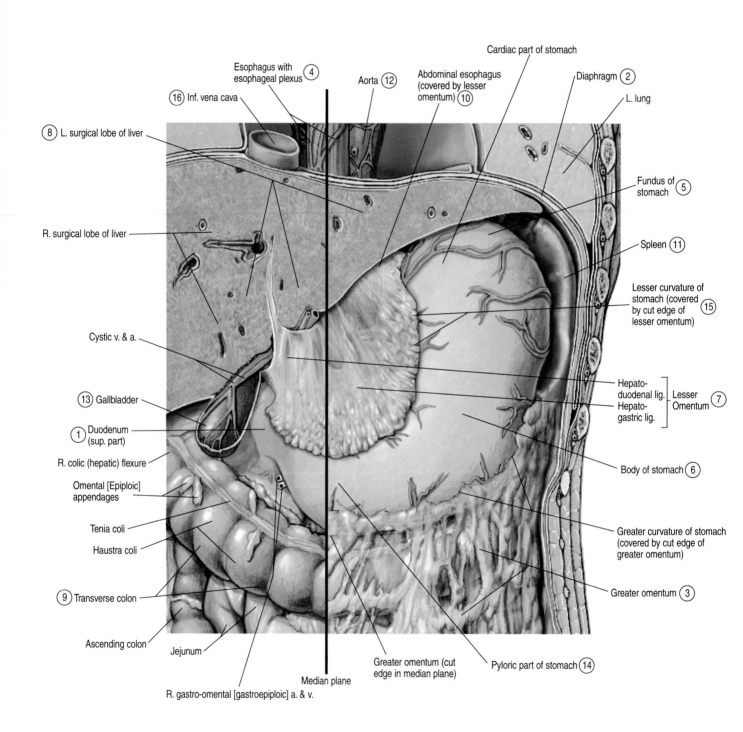

Cardiac part of stomach

Esophagus with esophageal plexus ④

Aorta ⑫

Abdominal esophagus (covered by lesser omentum) ⑩

Diaphragm ②

⑯ Inf. vena cava

L. lung

⑧ L. surgical lobe of liver

Fundus of stomach ⑤

R. surgical lobe of liver

Spleen ⑪

Lesser curvature of stomach (covered by cut edge of lesser omentum) ⑮

Cystic v. & a.

Hepato-duodenal lig.
Hepato-gastric lig.
Lesser Omentum ⑦

⑬ Gallbladder

Body of stomach ⑥

① Duodenum (sup. part)

R. colic (hepatic) flexure

Omental [Epiploic] appendages

Tenia coli

Greater curvature of stomach (covered by cut edge of greater omentum)

Haustra coli

⑨ Transverse colon

Greater omentum ③

Ascending colon

Jejunum

Pyloric part of stomach ⑭

Median plane

Greater omentum (cut edge in median plane)

R. gastro-omental [gastroepiploic] a. & v.

ANTERIOR VIEW

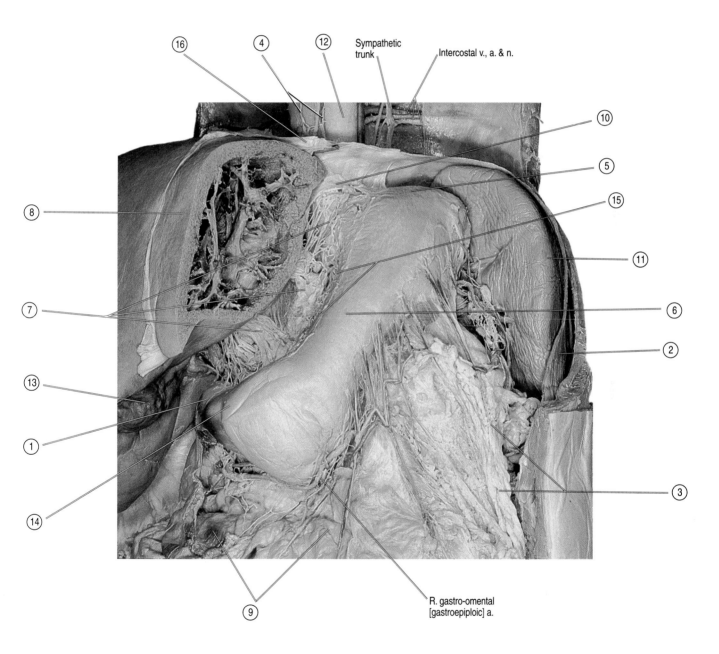

Sympathetic trunk

Intercostal v., a. & n.

R. gastro-omental [gastroepiploic] a.

LEFT ANTEROLATERAL VIEW—LATERAL SEGMENT OF L. LOBE OF LIVER PARTIALLY REMOVED

Stomach
Plate 3.11

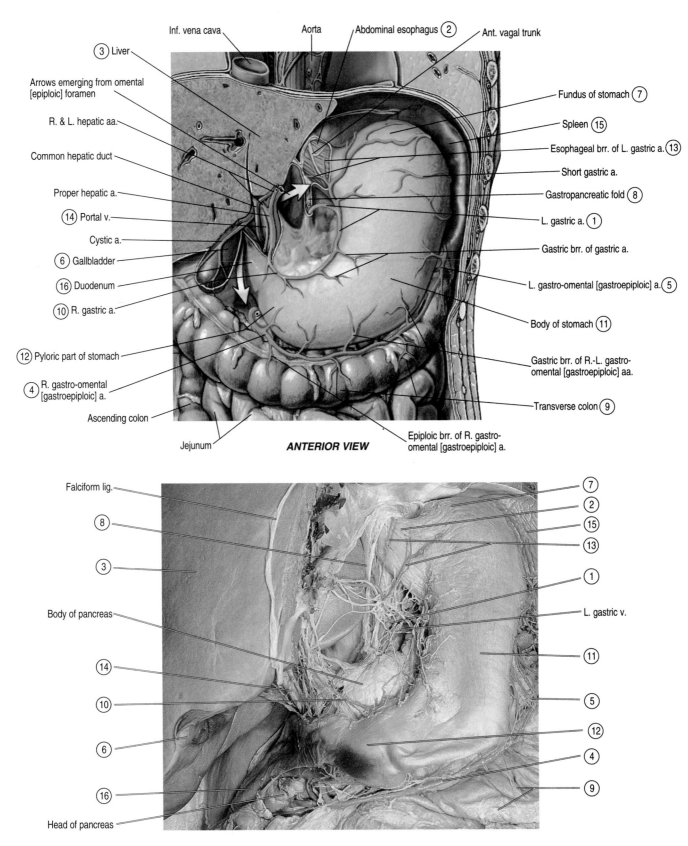

Inf. vena cava

Aorta

Abdominal esophagus ②

Ant. vagal trunk

③ Liver

Arrows emerging from omental [epiploic] foramen

R. & L. hepatic aa.

Common hepatic duct

Proper hepatic a.

⑭ Portal v.

Cystic a.

⑥ Gallbladder

⑯ Duodenum

⑩ R. gastric a.

⑫ Pyloric part of stomach

④ R. gastro-omental [gastroepiploic] a.

Ascending colon

Jejunum

Fundus of stomach ⑦

Spleen ⑮

Esophageal brr. of L. gastric a. ⑬

Short gastric a.

Gastropancreatic fold ⑧

L. gastric a. ①

Gastric brr. of gastric a.

L. gastro-omental [gastroepiploic] a. ⑤

Body of stomach ⑪

Gastric brr. of R.-L. gastro-omental [gastroepiploic] aa.

Transverse colon ⑨

Epiploic brr. of R. gastro-omental [gastroepiploic] a.

ANTERIOR VIEW

Falciform lig.

⑧

③

Body of pancreas

⑭

⑩

⑥

⑯

Head of pancreas

⑦

②

⑮

⑬

①

L. gastric v.

⑪

⑤

⑫

④

⑨

ANTERIOR VIEW—LIVER LEFT OF FALCIFORM LIG. REMOVED

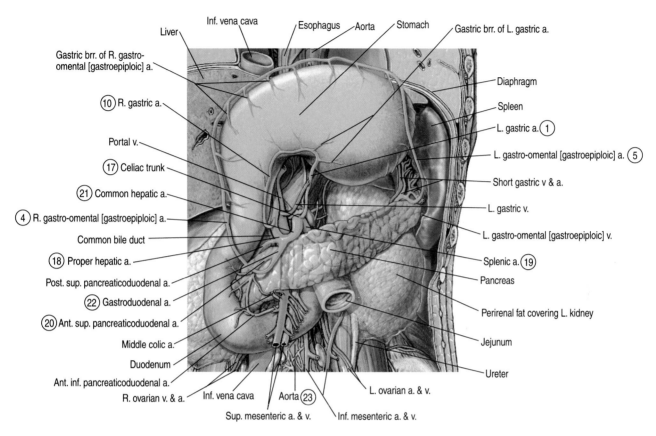

Inf. vena cava

Liver

Esophagus

Aorta

Stomach

Gastric brr. of L. gastric a.

Gastric brr. of R. gastro-omental [gastroepiploic] a.

Diaphragm

Spleen

(10) R. gastric a.

L. gastric a. (1)

Portal v.

L. gastro-omental [gastroepiploic] a. (5)

(17) Celiac trunk

Short gastric v & a.

(21) Common hepatic a.

L. gastric v.

(4) R. gastro-omental [gastroepiploic] a.

L. gastro-omental [gastroepiploic] v.

Common bile duct

Splenic a. (19)

(18) Proper hepatic a.

Pancreas

Post. sup. pancreaticoduodenal a.

Perirenal fat covering L. kidney

(22) Gastroduodenal a.

(20) Ant. sup. pancreaticoduodenal a.

Jejunum

Middle colic a.

Duodenum

Ureter

Ant. inf. pancreaticoduodenal a.

R. ovarian v. & a.

Inf. vena cava

Aorta (23)

L. ovarian a. & v.

Sup. mesenteric a. & v.

Inf. mesenteric a. & v.

**ANTERIOR VIEW—STOMACH REFLECTED SUPERIORLY
AND POSTERIOR PARIETAL PERITONEUM REMOVED**

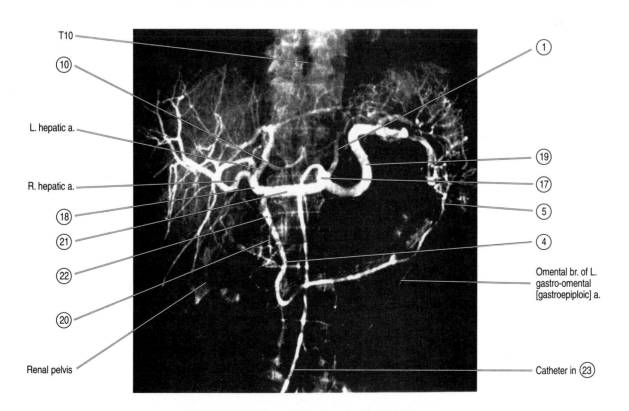

T10

(10)

(1)

L. hepatic a.

(19)

R. hepatic a.

(17)

(18)

(5)

(21)

(4)

(22)

Omental br. of L. gastro-omental [gastroepiploic] a.

(20)

Renal pelvis

Catheter in (23)

ARTERIOGRAPH OF CELIAC TRUNK & BRANCHES

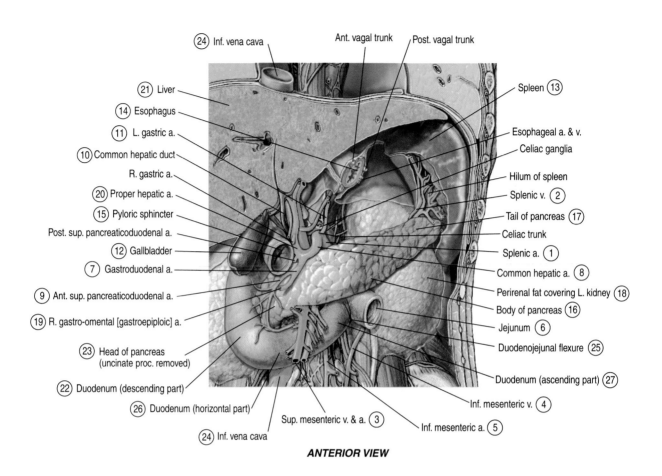

24 Inf. vena cava   Ant. vagal trunk   Post. vagal trunk

21 Liver

14 Esophagus

11 L. gastric a.

10 Common hepatic duct

R. gastric a.

20 Proper hepatic a.

15 Pyloric sphincter

Post. sup. pancreaticoduodenal a.

12 Gallbladder

7 Gastroduodenal a.

9 Ant. sup. pancreaticoduodenal a.

19 R. gastro-omental [gastroepiploic] a.

23 Head of pancreas
(uncinate proc. removed)

22 Duodenum (descending part)

26 Duodenum (horizontal part)

24 Inf. vena cava

Sup. mesenteric v. & a. 3

Inf. mesenteric a. 5

Spleen 13

Esophageal a. & v.

Celiac ganglia

Hilum of spleen

Splenic v. 2

Tail of pancreas 17

Celiac trunk

Splenic a. 1

Common hepatic a. 8

Perirenal fat covering L. kidney 18

Body of pancreas 16

Jejunum 6

Duodenojejunal flexure 25

Duodenum (ascending part) 27

Inf. mesenteric v. 4

ANTERIOR VIEW

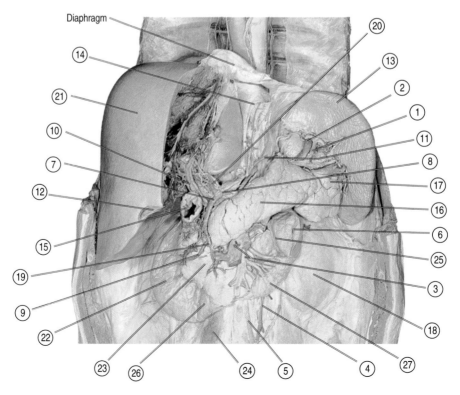

Diaphragm

14

21

10

7

12

15

19

9

22

23   26   24   5

20

13

2

1

11

8

17

16

6

25

3

18

27

ANTERIOR VIEW

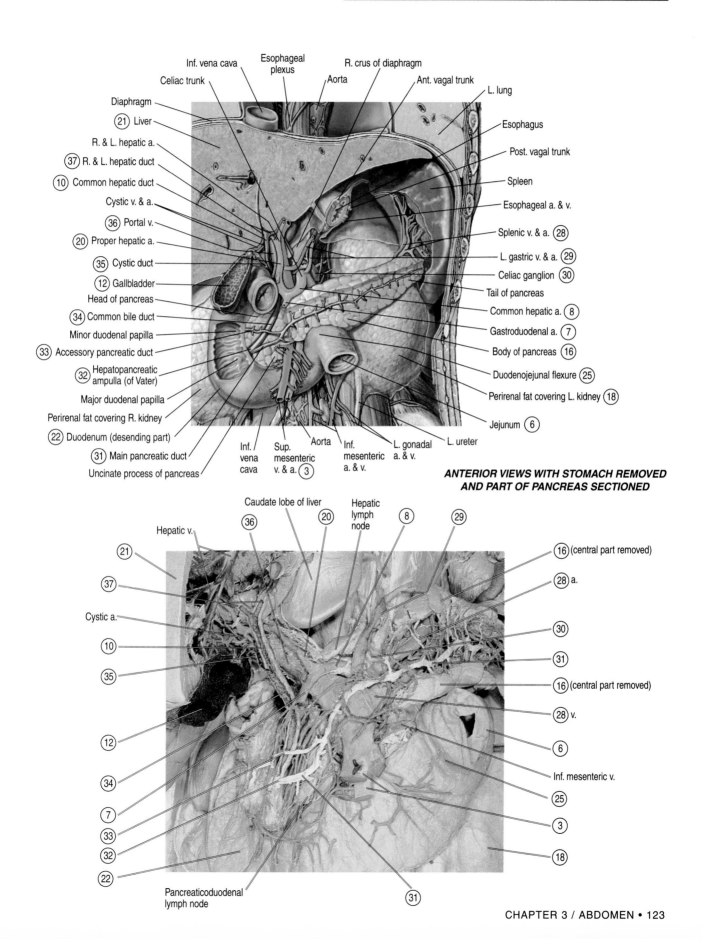

Inf. vena cava

Esophageal plexus

R. crus of diaphragm

Aorta

Ant. vagal trunk

Celiac trunk

L. lung

Diaphragm

Esophagus

㉑ Liver

Post. vagal trunk

R. & L. hepatic a.

㊲ R. & L. hepatic duct

Spleen

⑩ Common hepatic duct

Esophageal a. & v.

Cystic v. & a.

Splenic v. & a. ㉘

㊱ Portal v.

L. gastric v. & a. ㉙

⑳ Proper hepatic a.

Celiac ganglion ㉚

㉟ Cystic duct

Tail of pancreas

⑫ Gallbladder

Common hepatic a. ⑧

Head of pancreas

Gastroduodenal a. ⑦

㉞ Common bile duct

Body of pancreas ⑯

Minor duodenal papilla

Duodenojejunal flexure ㉕

㉝ Accessory pancreatic duct

㉜ Hepatopancreatic ampulla (of Vater)

Perirenal fat covering L. kidney ⑱

Major duodenal papilla

Jejunum ⑥

Perirenal fat covering R. kidney

㉒ Duodenum (desending part)

Inf. / vena cava

Sup. mesenteric v. & a. ③

Aorta

Inf. mesenteric a. & v.

L. gonadal a. & v.

L. ureter

㉛ Main pancreatic duct

Uncinate process of pancreas

ANTERIOR VIEWS WITH STOMACH REMOVED AND PART OF PANCREAS SECTIONED

Caudate lobe of liver

Hepatic lymph node

Hepatic v.

㊱ ⑳ ⑧ ㉙

㉑

⑯ (central part removed)

㊲

㉘ a.

Cystic a.

㉚

⑩

㉛

㉟

⑯ (central part removed)

㉘ v.

⑫

⑥

㉞

Inf. mesenteric v.

⑦

㉕

㉝

③

㉜

⑱

㉒

Pancreaticoduodenal lymph node

㉛

Portal Vein
Plate 3.15

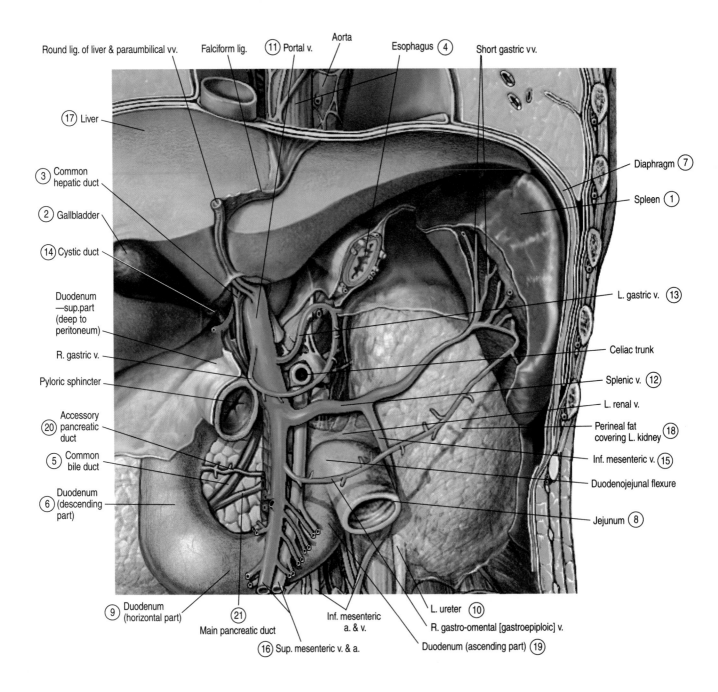

Round lig. of liver & paraumbilical vv.　Falciform lig.　⑪ Portal v.　Aorta　Esophagus ④　Short gastric vv.

⑰ Liver

③ Common hepatic duct

② Gallbladder

⑭ Cystic duct

Duodenum —sup.part (deep to peritoneum)

R. gastric v.

Pyloric sphincter

⑳ Accessory pancreatic duct

⑤ Common bile duct

⑥ Duodenum (descending part)

Diaphragm ⑦

Spleen ①

L. gastric v. ⑬

Celiac trunk

Splenic v. ⑫

L. renal v.

Perineal fat covering L. kidney ⑱

Inf. mesenteric v. ⑮

Duodenojejunal flexure

Jejunum ⑧

⑨ Duodenum (horizontal part)

㉑　Inf. mesenteric a. & v.　L. ureter ⑩

Main pancreatic duct　R. gastro-omental [gastroepiploic] v.

⑯ Sup. mesenteric v. & a.　Duodenum (ascending part) ⑲

ANTERIOR VIEW WITH STOMACH REMOVED

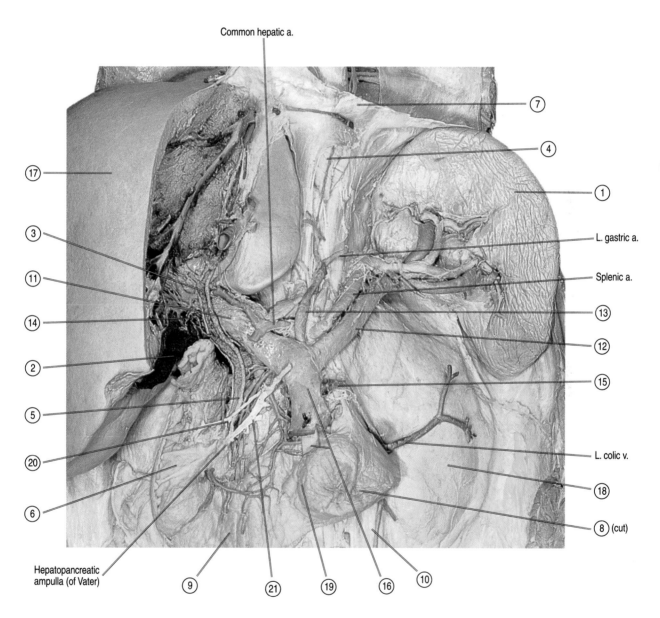

Common hepatic a.

⑦

④

⑰

①

③ L. gastric a.

⑪ Splenic a.

⑭ ⑬

② ⑫

⑤ ⑮

⑳

⑥ L. colic v.

⑱

⑧ (cut)

Hepatopancreatic
ampulla (of Vater)

⑨ ㉑ ⑲ ⑯ ⑩

**ANTERIOR VIEW WITH STOMACH, LEFT HALF OF LIVER,
AND PANCREAS REMOVED**

Liver
Plate 3.17

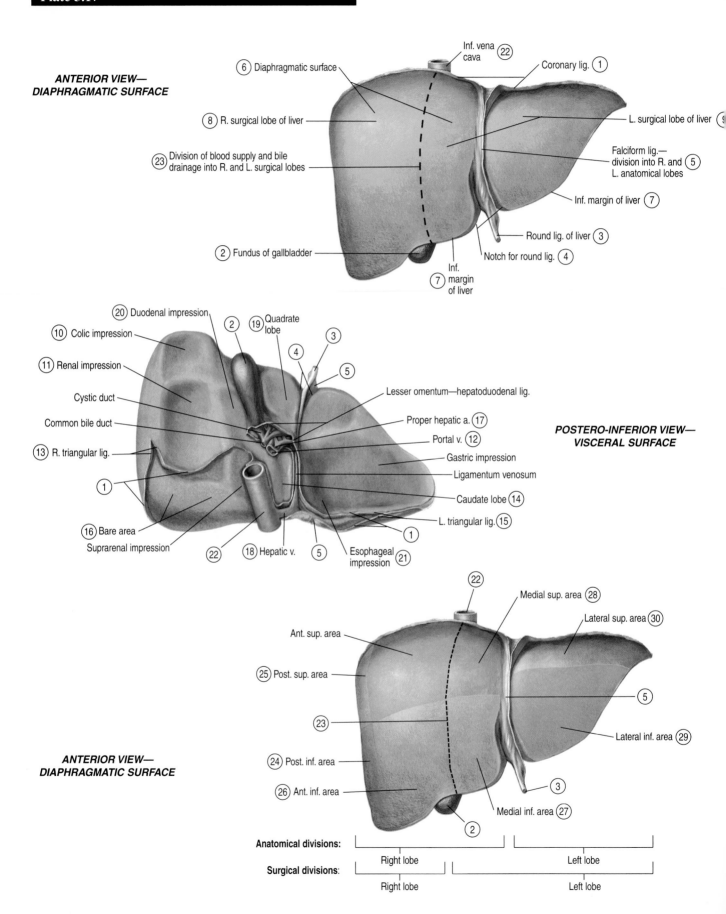

**ANTERIOR VIEW—
DIAPHRAGMATIC SURFACE**

Inf. vena cava (22)

(6) Diaphragmatic surface

Coronary lig. (1)

(8) R. surgical lobe of liver

L. surgical lobe of liver (9)

(23) Division of blood supply and bile drainage into R. and L. surgical lobes

Falciform lig.— division into R. and (5) L. anatomical lobes

Inf. margin of liver (7)

Round lig. of liver (3)

Notch for round lig. (4)

(2) Fundus of gallbladder

Inf. (7) margin of liver

(20) Duodenal impression

(2)

(19) Quadrate lobe

(3)

(10) Colic impression

(4)

(5)

(11) Renal impression

Lesser omentum—hepatoduodenal lig.

Cystic duct

Proper hepatic a. (17)

Common bile duct

Portal v. (12)

**POSTERO-INFERIOR VIEW—
VISCERAL SURFACE**

(13) R. triangular lig.

Gastric impression

Ligamentum venosum

(1)

Caudate lobe (14)

L. triangular lig. (15)

(16) Bare area

(1)

Suprarenal impression

(22)

(18) Hepatic v.

(5)

Esophageal (21) impression

(22)

Medial sup. area (28)

Lateral sup. area (30)

Ant. sup. area

(25) Post. sup. area

(5)

(23)

Lateral inf. area (29)

(24) Post. inf. area

(26) Ant. inf. area

(3)

Medial inf. area (27)

(2)

**ANTERIOR VIEW—
DIAPHRAGMATIC SURFACE**

Anatomical divisions:		
	Right lobe	Left lobe
Surgical divisions:		
	Right lobe	Left lobe

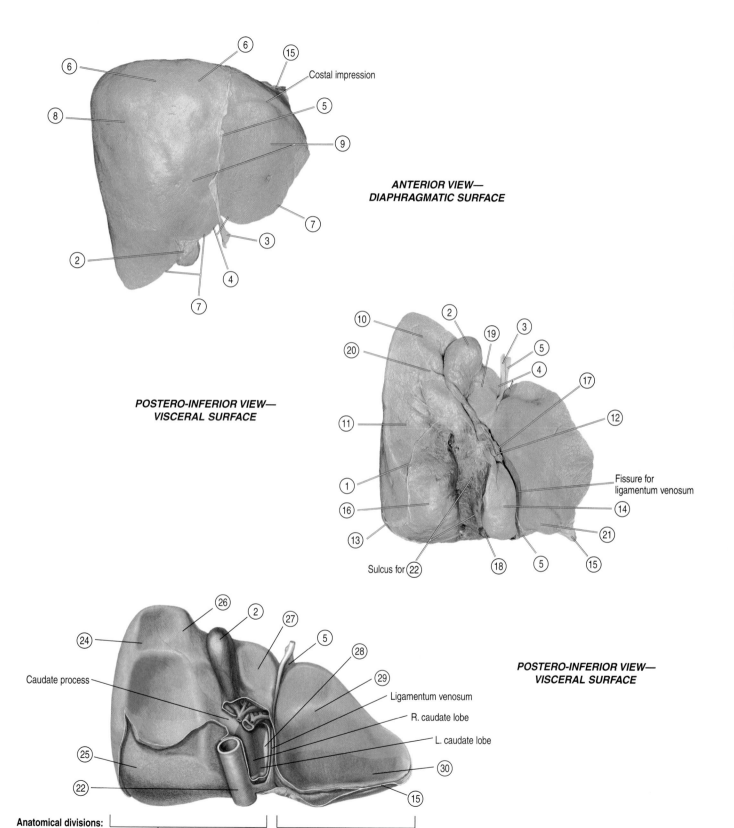

Costal impression

**ANTERIOR VIEW—
DIAPHRAGMATIC SURFACE**

**POSTERO-INFERIOR VIEW—
VISCERAL SURFACE**

Fissure for
ligamentum venosum

Sulcus for ②②

Caudate process

Ligamentum venosum

R. caudate lobe

L. caudate lobe

**POSTERO-INFERIOR VIEW—
VISCERAL SURFACE**

Anatomical divisions:			
	Right lobe		Left lobe
Surgical divisions:			
	Right lobe		Left lobe

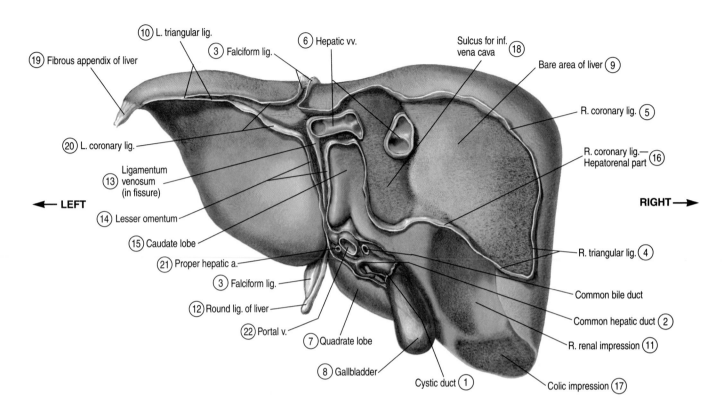

(10) L. triangular lig.

(3) Falciform lig.

(6) Hepatic vv.

Sulcus for inf. vena cava (18)

(19) Fibrous appendix of liver

Bare area of liver (9)

R. coronary lig. (5)

(20) L. coronary lig.

R. coronary lig.—Hepatorenal part (16)

(13) Ligamentum venosum (in fissure)

◄— LEFT

RIGHT —►

(14) Lesser omentum

(15) Caudate lobe

R. triangular lig. (4)

(21) Proper hepatic a.

(3) Falciform lig.

Common bile duct

(12) Round lig. of liver

Common hepatic duct (2)

(22) Portal v.

R. renal impression (11)

(7) Quadrate lobe

(8) Gallbladder

Cystic duct (1)

Colic impression (17)

POSTERIOR VIEWS—VISCERO-DIAPHRAGMATIC SURFACE

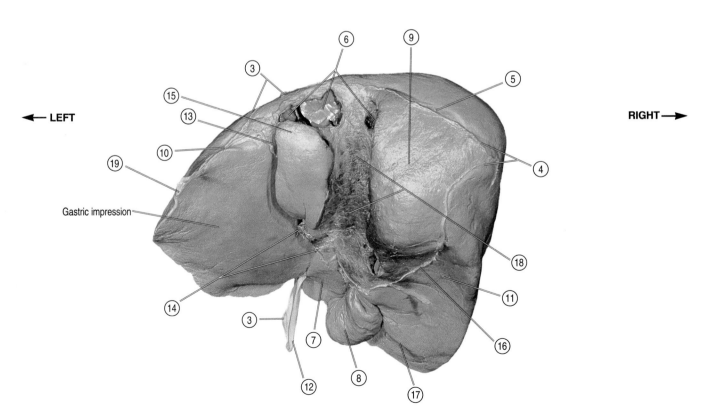

(6)

(9)

(3)

(5)

(15)

(13)

◄— LEFT

RIGHT —►

(10)

(4)

(19)

Gastric impression

(18)

(14)

(11)

(3)

(16)

(7)

(12)

(8)

(17)

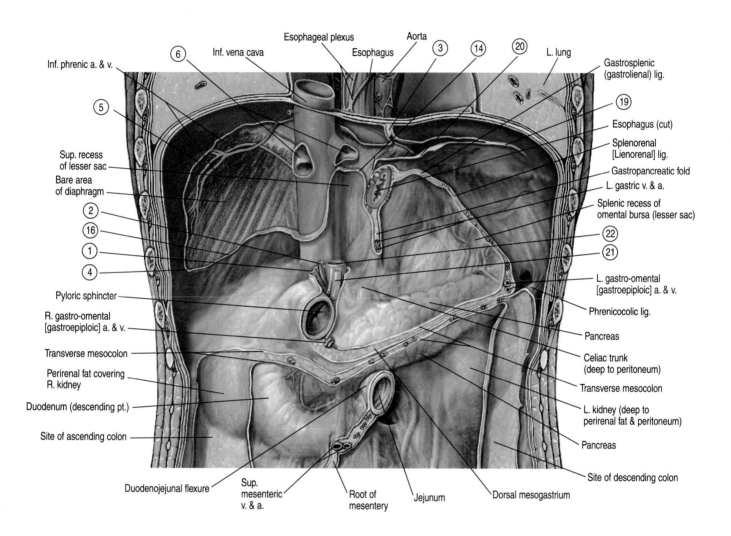

Inf. phrenic a. & v.

⑥   Inf. vena cava   Esophageal plexus   Aorta   ③   ⑭   ⑳   L. lung

Esophagus

Gastrosplenic
(gastrolienal) lig.

⑤

⑲

Esophagus (cut)

Sup. recess
of lesser sac

Splenorenal
[Lienorenal] lig.

Bare area
of diaphragm

Gastropancreatic fold

②

L. gastric v. & a.

⑯

Splenic recess of
omental bursa (lesser sac)

①

㉒

④

㉑

Pyloric sphincter

L. gastro-omental
[gastroepiploic] a. & v.

R. gastro-omental
[gastroepiploic] a. & v.

Phrenicocolic lig.

Transverse mesocolon

Pancreas

Perirenal fat covering
R. kidney

Celiac trunk
(deep to peritoneum)

Duodenum (descending pt.)

Transverse mesocolon

Site of ascending colon

L. kidney (deep to
perirenal fat & peritoneum)

Pancreas

Duodenojejunal flexure   Sup.
mesenteric
v. & a.   Root of
mesentery   Jejunum   Dorsal mesogastrium   Site of descending colon

ANTERIOR VIEW—POSTERIOR ABDOMINAL WALL

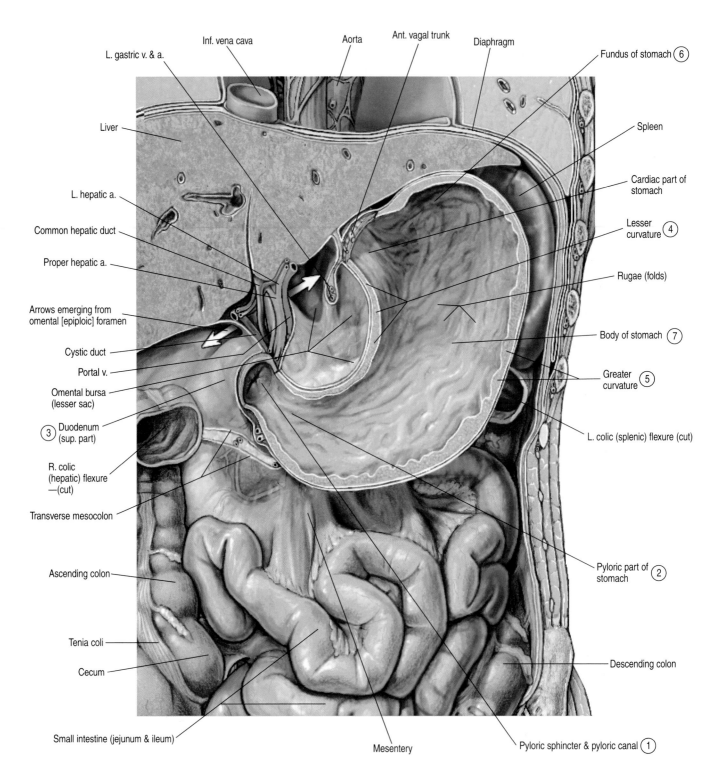

L. gastric v. & a.

Inf. vena cava

Aorta

Ant. vagal trunk

Diaphragm

Fundus of stomach ⑥

Liver

Spleen

L. hepatic a.

Cardiac part of stomach

Common hepatic duct

Lesser curvature ④

Proper hepatic a.

Rugae (folds)

Arrows emerging from omental [epiploic] foramen

Body of stomach ⑦

Cystic duct

Greater curvature ⑤

Portal v.

Omental bursa (lesser sac)

L. colic (splenic) flexure (cut)

③ Duodenum (sup. part)

R. colic (hepatic) flexure —(cut)

Transverse mesocolon

Pyloric part of stomach ②

Ascending colon

Tenia coli

Descending colon

Cecum

Small intestine (jejunum & ileum)

Mesentery

Pyloric sphincter & pyloric canal ①

ANTERIOR VIEW

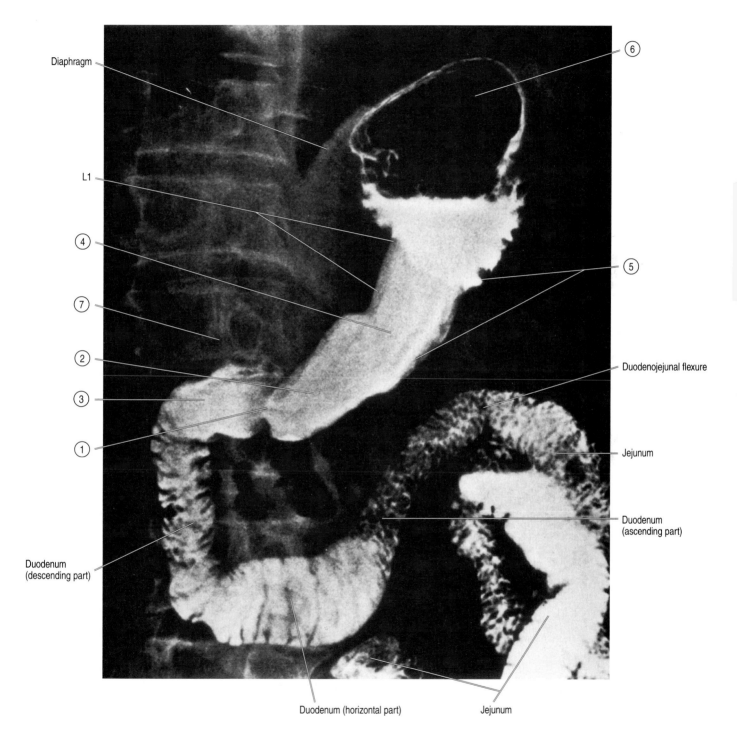

Diaphragm

L1

④

⑦

②

③

①

⑥

⑤

Duodenojejunal flexure

Jejunum

Duodenum
(ascending part)

Duodenum
(descending part)

Duodenum (horizontal part)

Jejunum

RADIOGRAPH OF UPPER G.I. TRACT FOLLOWING BARIUM SWALLOW

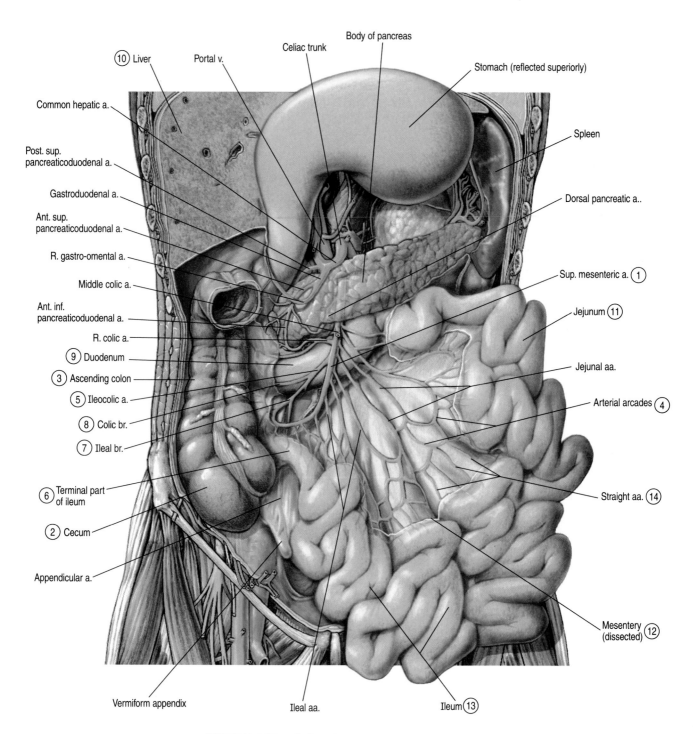

Liver ⑩

Portal v.

Celiac trunk

Body of pancreas

Stomach (reflected superiorly)

Common hepatic a.

Post. sup. pancreaticoduodenal a.

Gastroduodenal a.

Ant. sup. pancreaticoduodenal a.

R. gastro-omental a.

Middle colic a.

Ant. inf. pancreaticoduodenal a.

R. colic a.

⑨ Duodenum

③ Ascending colon

⑤ Ileocolic a.

⑧ Colic br.

⑦ Ileal br.

⑥ Terminal part of ileum

② Cecum

Appendicular a.

Vermiform appendix

Ileal aa.

Spleen

Dorsal pancreatic a..

Sup. mesenteric a. ①

Jejunum ⑪

Jejunal aa.

Arterial arcades ④

Straight aa. ⑭

Mesentery ⑫ (dissected)

Ileum ⑬

ANTERIOR VIEW—STOMACH REFLECTED SUPERIORLY

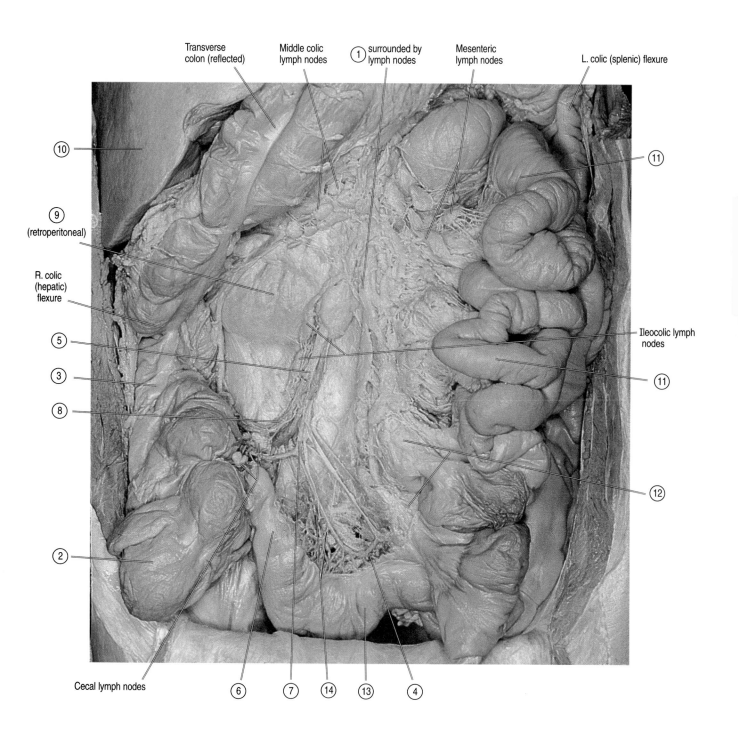

Transverse
colon (reflected)

Middle colic
lymph nodes

(1) surrounded by
lymph nodes

Mesenteric
lymph nodes

L. colic (splenic) flexure

(10)

(9)
(retroperitoneal)

R. colic
(hepatic)
flexure

(5)

(3)

(8)

(2)

(11)

Ileocolic lymph
nodes

(11)

(12)

Cecal lymph nodes

(6)   (7)   (14)   (13)   (4)

ANTERIOR VIEW—TRANSVERSE COLON REFLECTED SUPERIORLY

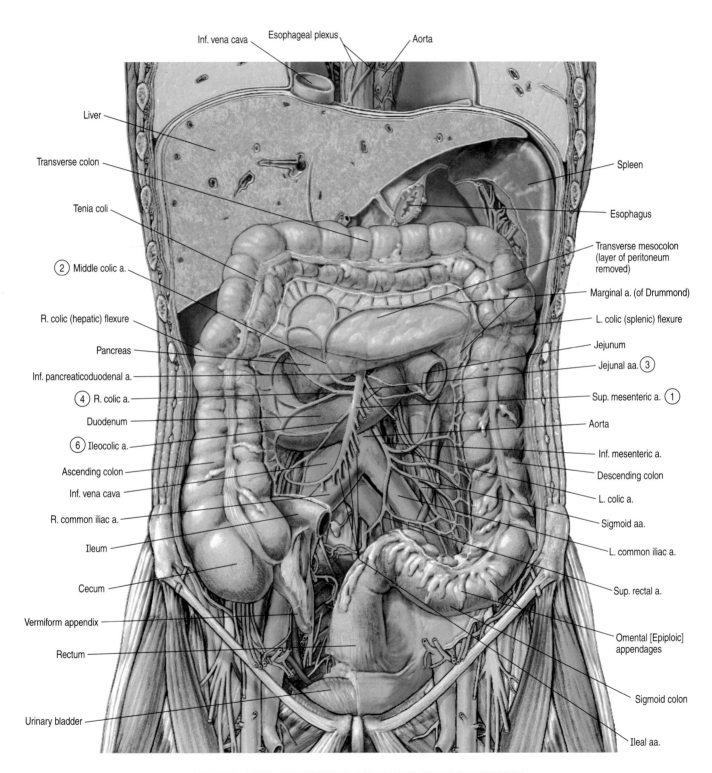

Inf. vena cava — Esophageal plexus — Aorta

Liver

Transverse colon

Tenia coli

② Middle colic a.

R. colic (hepatic) flexure

Pancreas

Inf. pancreaticoduodenal a.

④ R. colic a.

Duodenum

⑥ Ileocolic a.

Ascending colon

Inf. vena cava

R. common iliac a.

Ileum

Cecum

Vermiform appendix

Rectum

Urinary bladder

Spleen

Esophagus

Transverse mesocolon
(layer of peritoneum
removed)

Marginal a. (of Drummond)

L. colic (splenic) flexure

Jejunum

Jejunal aa. ③

Sup. mesenteric a. ①

Aorta

Inf. mesenteric a.

Descending colon

L. colic a.

Sigmoid aa.

L. common iliac a.

Sup. rectal a.

Omental [Epiploic]
appendages

Sigmoid colon

Ileal aa.

*ANTERIOR VIEW—TRANSVERSE COLON REFLECTED SUPERIORLY
& THE MESENTERY PROPER REMOVED*

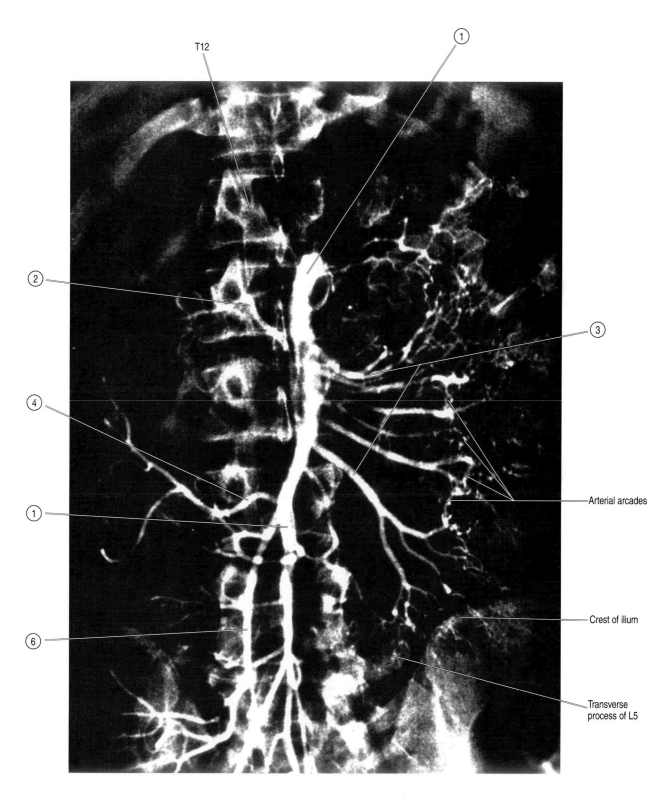

T12

② ③

④ Arterial arcades

① ⑥

Crest of ilium

Transverse process of L5

ARTERIOGRAPH OF SUPERIOR MESENTERIC ARTERY & BRANCHES

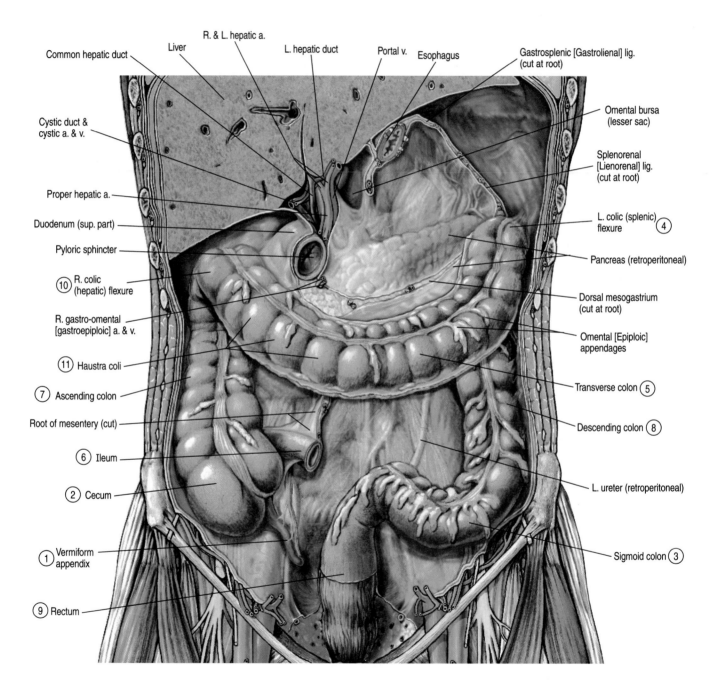

Common hepatic duct

R. & L. hepatic a.

Liver

L. hepatic duct

Portal v.

Esophagus

Gastrosplenic [Gastrolienal] lig. (cut at root)

Cystic duct & cystic a. & v.

Omental bursa (lesser sac)

Splenorenal [Lienorenal] lig. (cut at root)

Proper hepatic a.

L. colic (splenic) flexure ④

Duodenum (sup. part)

Pancreas (retroperitoneal)

Pyloric sphincter

⑩ R. colic (hepatic) flexure

Dorsal mesogastrium (cut at root)

R. gastro-omental [gastroepiploic] a. & v.

Omental [Epiploic] appendages

⑪ Haustra coli

Transverse colon ⑤

⑦ Ascending colon

Root of mesentery (cut)

Descending colon ⑧

⑥ Ileum

② Cecum

L. ureter (retroperitoneal)

① Vermiform appendix

Sigmoid colon ③

⑨ Rectum

ANTERIOR VIEW—SMALL INTESTINES REMOVED

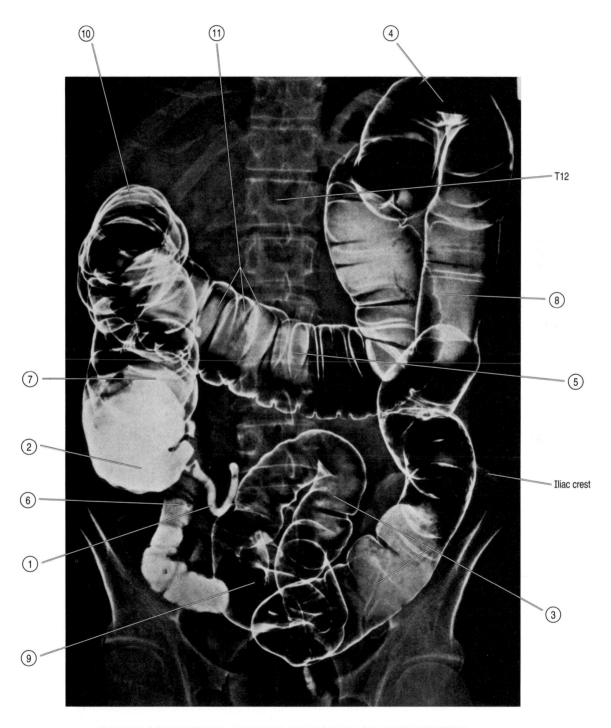

T12

8

5

Iliac crest

3

DOUBLE CONTRAST (AIR & BARIUM) RADIOGRAPH OF LARGE INTESTINE

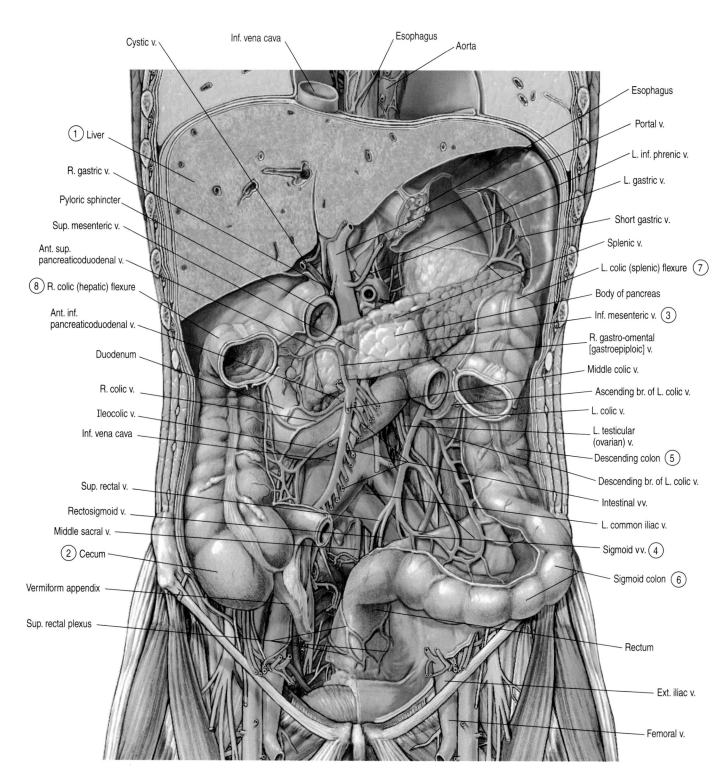

Cystic v.

Inf. vena cava

Esophagus

Aorta

Esophagus

Portal v.

(1) Liver

L. inf. phrenic v.

R. gastric v.

L. gastric v.

Pyloric sphincter

Short gastric v.

Sup. mesenteric v.

Splenic v.

Ant. sup.
pancreaticoduodenal v.

L. colic (splenic) flexure (7)

(8) R. colic (hepatic) flexure

Body of pancreas

Ant. inf.
pancreaticoduodenal v.

Inf. mesenteric v. (3)

R. gastro-omental
[gastroepiploic] v.

Duodenum

Middle colic v.

R. colic v.

Ascending br. of L. colic v.

Ileocolic v.

L. colic v.

Inf. vena cava

L. testicular
(ovarian) v.

Descending colon (5)

Sup. rectal v.

Descending br. of L. colic v.

Rectosigmoid v.

Intestinal vv.

Middle sacral v.

L. common iliac v.

(2) Cecum

Sigmoid vv. (4)

Vermiform appendix

Sigmoid colon (6)

Sup. rectal plexus

Rectum

Ext. iliac v.

Femoral v.

ANTERIOR VIEW

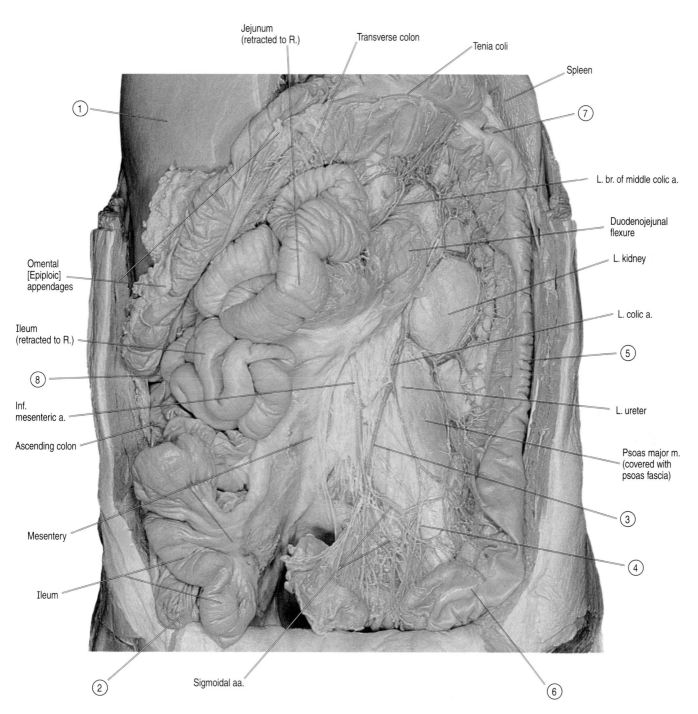

Jejunum
(retracted to R.)

Transverse colon

Tenia coli

Spleen

①

⑦

L. br. of middle colic a.

Duodenojejunal
flexure

L. kidney

Omental
[Epiploic]
appendages

L. colic a.

⑤

Ileum
(retracted to R.)

⑧

L. ureter

Inf.
mesenteric a.

Ascending colon

Psoas major m.
(covered with
psoas fascia)

③

Mesentery

④

Ileum

⑥

②

Sigmoidal aa.

ANTERIOR VIEW—TRANSVERSE COLON REFLECTED SUPERIORLY

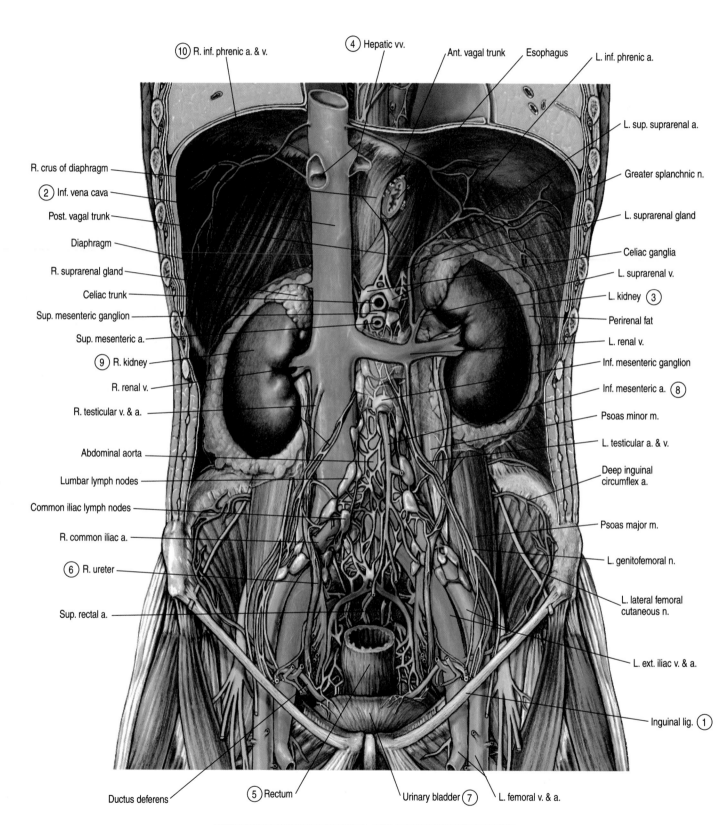

⑩ R. inf. phrenic a. & v.

④ Hepatic vv.

Ant. vagal trunk

Esophagus

L. inf. phrenic a.

R. crus of diaphragm

② Inf. vena cava

Post. vagal trunk

Diaphragm

R. suprarenal gland

Celiac trunk

Sup. mesenteric ganglion

Sup. mesenteric a.

⑨ R. kidney

R. renal v.

R. testicular v. & a.

Abdominal aorta

Lumbar lymph nodes

Common iliac lymph nodes

R. common iliac a.

⑥ R. ureter

Sup. rectal a.

L. sup. suprarenal a.

Greater splanchnic n.

L. suprarenal gland

Celiac ganglia

L. suprarenal v.

L. kidney ③

Perirenal fat

L. renal v.

Inf. mesenteric ganglion

Inf. mesenteric a. ⑧

Psoas minor m.

L. testicular a. & v.

Deep inguinal circumflex a.

Psoas major m.

L. genitofemoral n.

L. lateral femoral cutaneous n.

L. ext. iliac v. & a.

Inguinal lig. ①

Ductus deferens

⑤ Rectum

Urinary bladder ⑦

L. femoral v. & a.

ANTERIOR VIEW WITH VISCERA AND PERITONEUM REMOVED

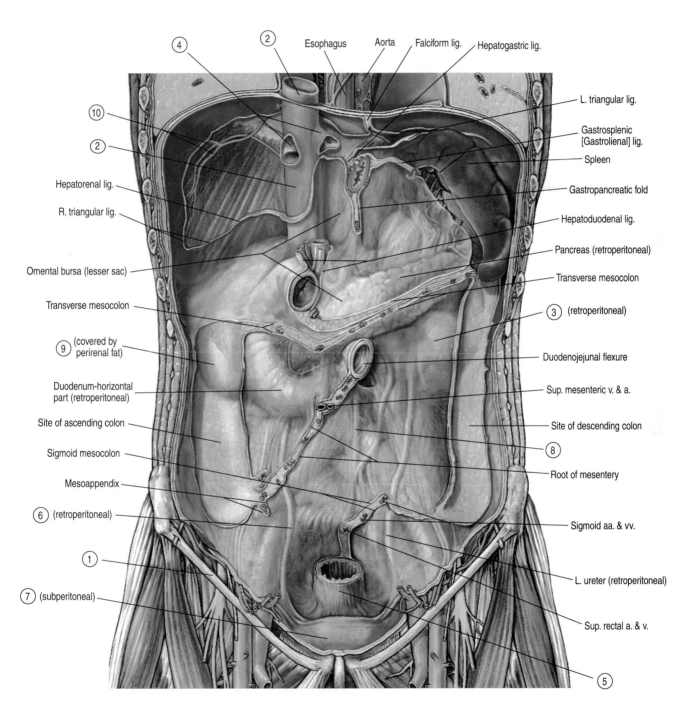

④ ② Esophagus Aorta Falciform lig. Hepatogastric lig.

L. triangular lig.

Gastrosplenic [Gastrolienal] lig.

Spleen

Gastropancreatic fold

⑩ ②

Hepatorenal lig.

R. triangular lig.

Hepatoduodenal lig.

Pancreas (retroperitoneal)

Transverse mesocolon

Omental bursa (lesser sac)

Transverse mesocolon

③ (retroperitoneal)

⑨ (covered by perirenal fat)

Duodenojejunal flexure

Sup. mesenteric v. & a.

Duodenum-horizontal part (retroperitoneal)

Site of ascending colon

Site of descending colon

⑧

Sigmoid mesocolon

Root of mesentery

Mesoappendix

⑥ (retroperitoneal)

Sigmoid aa. & vv.

①

⑦ (subperitoneal)

L. ureter (retroperitoneal)

Sup. rectal a. & v.

⑤

**ANTERIOR VIEW OF POSTERIOR ABDOMINAL WALL
SHOWING PERITONEAL COVERINGS AND MESENTERY ORIGINS**

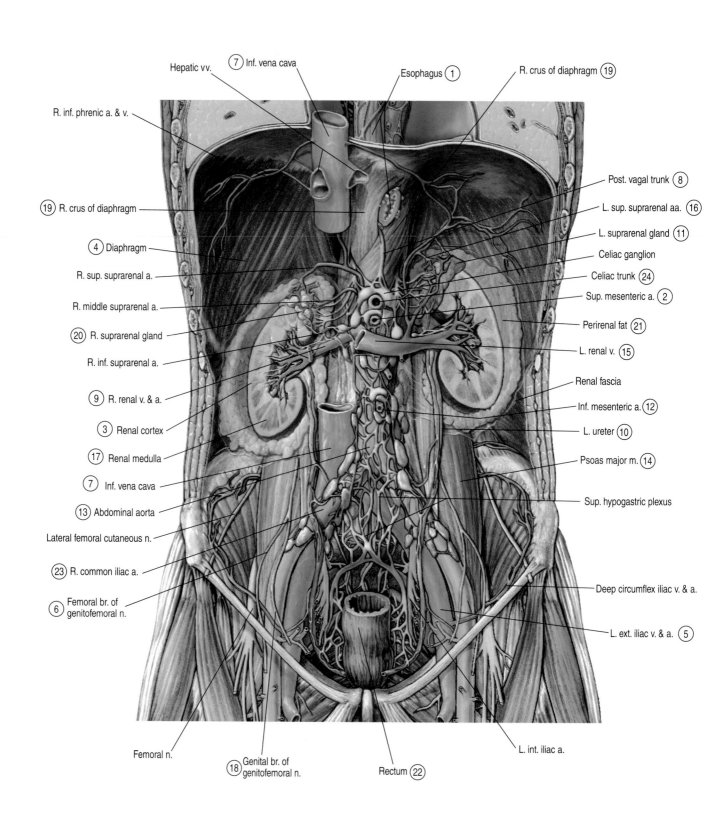

Hepatic vv.

⑦ Inf. vena cava

Esophagus ①

R. crus of diaphragm ⑲

R. inf. phrenic a. & v.

⑲ R. crus of diaphragm

④ Diaphragm

R. sup. suprarenal a.

R. middle suprarenal a.

⑳ R. suprarenal gland

R. inf. suprarenal a.

⑨ R. renal v. & a.

③ Renal cortex

⑰ Renal medulla

⑦ Inf. vena cava

⑬ Abdominal aorta

Lateral femoral cutaneous n.

㉓ R. common iliac a.

⑥ Femoral br. of genitofemoral n.

Femoral n.

⑱ Genital br. of genitofemoral n.

Rectum ㉒

Post. vagal trunk ⑧

L. sup. suprarenal aa. ⑯

L. suprarenal gland ⑪

Celiac ganglion

Celiac trunk ㉔

Sup. mesenteric a. ②

Perirenal fat ㉑

L. renal v. ⑮

Renal fascia

Inf. mesenteric a. ⑫

L. ureter ⑩

Psoas major m. ⑭

Sup. hypogastric plexus

Deep circumflex iliac v. & a.

L. ext. iliac v. & a. ⑤

L. int. iliac a.

ANTERIOR VIEW

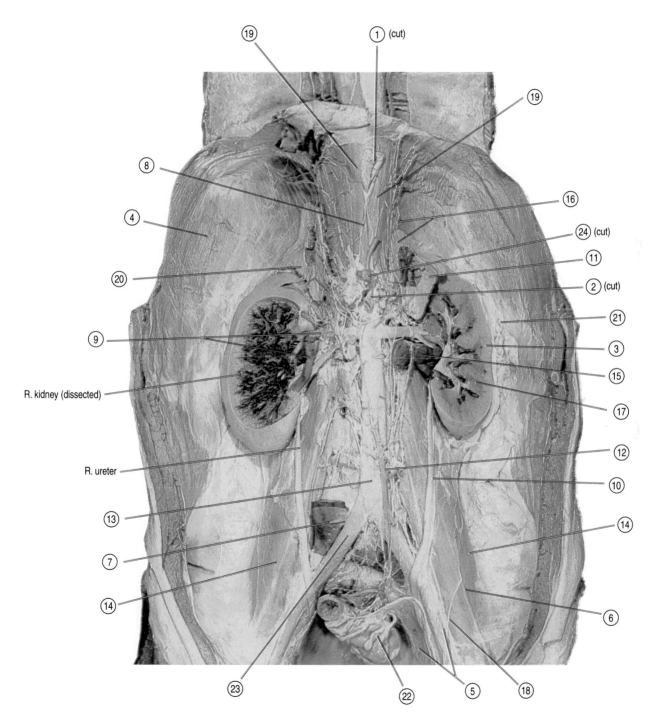

19
1 (cut)
19
8
16
4
24 (cut)
20
11
2 (cut)
9
21
3
R. kidney (dissected)
15
17
R. ureter
12
10
13
7
14
14
6
23
22
5
18

ANTERIOR VIEW

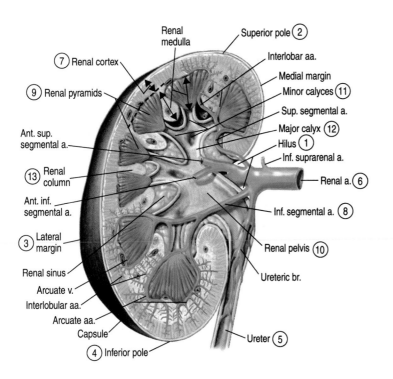

Renal medulla
Superior pole (2)
(7) Renal cortex
Interlobar aa.
(9) Renal pyramids
Medial margin
Minor calyces (11)
Sup. segmental a.
Ant. sup. segmental a.
Major calyx (12)
(13) Renal column
Hilus (1)
Inf. suprarenal a.
Ant. inf. segmental a.
Renal a. (6)
Inf. segmental a. (8)
(3) Lateral margin
Renal pelvis (10)
Renal sinus
Ureteric br.
Arcuate v.
Interlobular aa.
Arcuate aa.
Capsule
Ureter (5)
(4) Inferior pole

POSTERIOR VIEWS OF CORONALLY SECTIONED L. KIDNEY

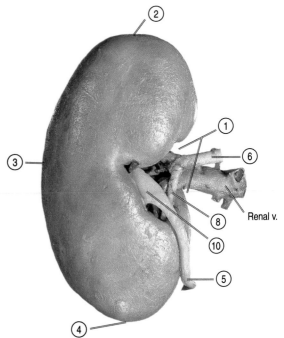

POSTERIOR SURFACE OF LEFT KIDNEY

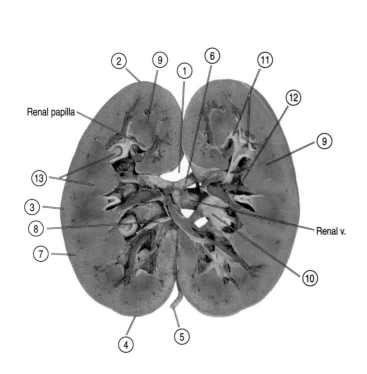

Renal papilla
Renal v.

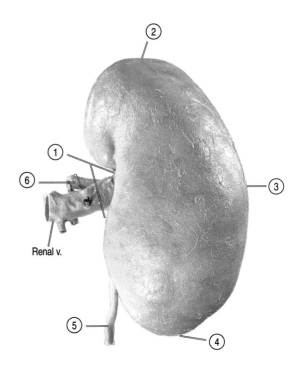

Renal v.

ANTERIOR SURFACE OF LEFT KIDNEY

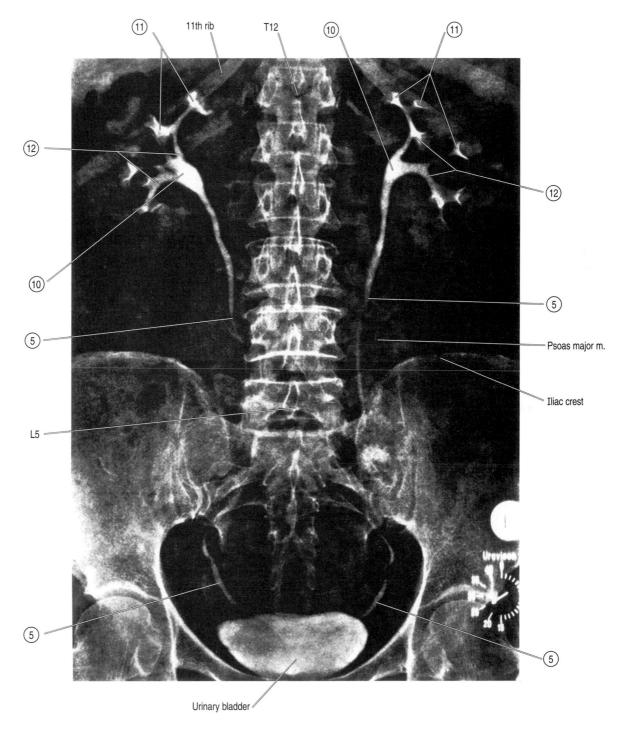

11th rib T12

11

10

11

12

12

10

5

Psoas major m.

5

Iliac crest

5

L5

5

5

Urinary bladder

INTRAVENOUS UROGRAM

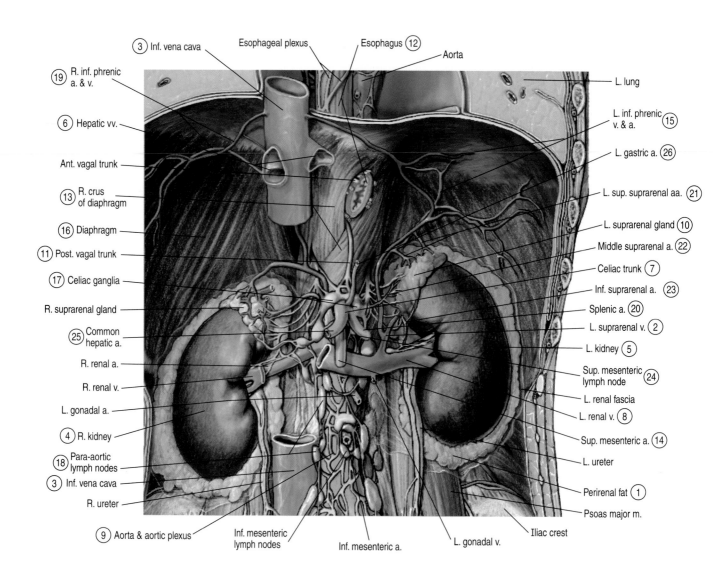

3 Inf. vena cava — Esophageal plexus — Esophagus 12 — Aorta

19 R. inf. phrenic a. & v.

6 Hepatic vv.

Ant. vagal trunk

13 R. crus of diaphragm

16 Diaphragm

11 Post. vagal trunk

17 Celiac ganglia

R. suprarenal gland

25 Common hepatic a.

R. renal a.

R. renal v.

L. gonadal a.

4 R. kidney

18 Para-aortic lymph nodes

3 Inf. vena cava

R. ureter

9 Aorta & aortic plexus — Inf. mesenteric lymph nodes — Inf. mesenteric a. — L. gonadal v.

L. lung

L. inf. phrenic v. & a. 15

L. gastric a. 26

L. sup. suprarenal aa. 21

L. suprarenal gland 10

Middle suprarenal a. 22

Celiac trunk 7

Inf. suprarenal a. 23

Splenic a. 20

L. suprarenal v. 2

L. kidney 5

Sup. mesenteric lymph node 24

L. renal fascia

L. renal v. 8

Sup. mesenteric a. 14

L. ureter

Perirenal fat 1

Psoas major m.

Iliac crest

ANTERIOR VIEW

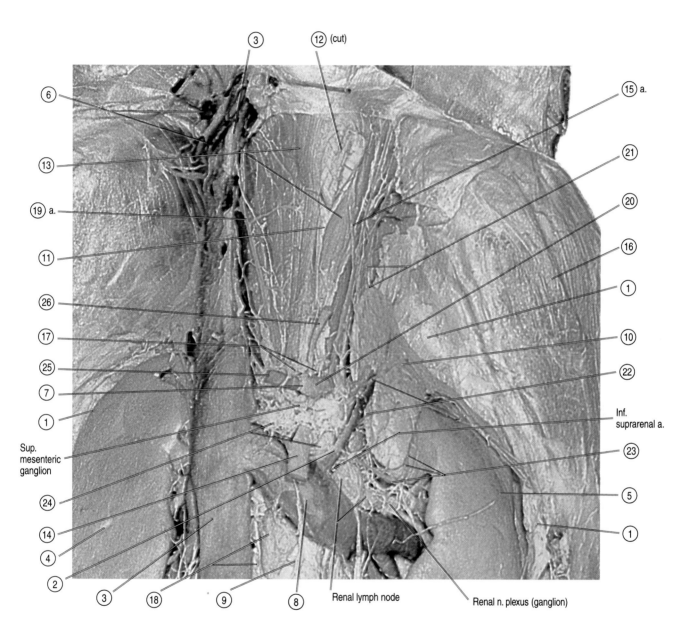

③ ⑫ (cut)

⑥

⑮ a.

⑬

⑲ a.

㉑

⑳

⑪

⑯

①

㉖

⑰

⑩

㉕

⑦

㉒

①

Inf.
suprarenal a.

Sup.
mesenteric
ganglion

㉓

⑤

㉔

①

⑭

④

②

③ ⑱ ⑨ ⑧ Renal lymph node Renal n. plexus (ganglion)

ANTERIOR VIEW OF SUPERIOR POLE OF L. KIDNEY

Pelvis and Perineum

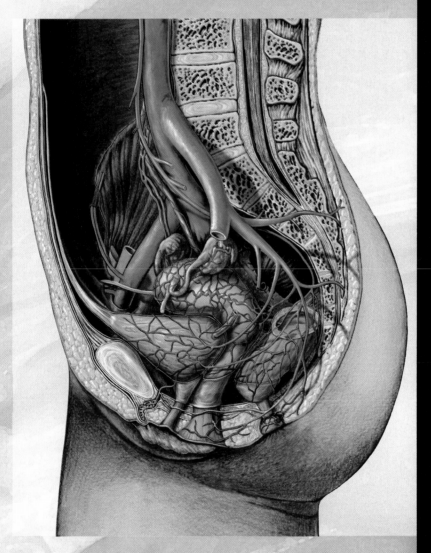

Chapter **4**

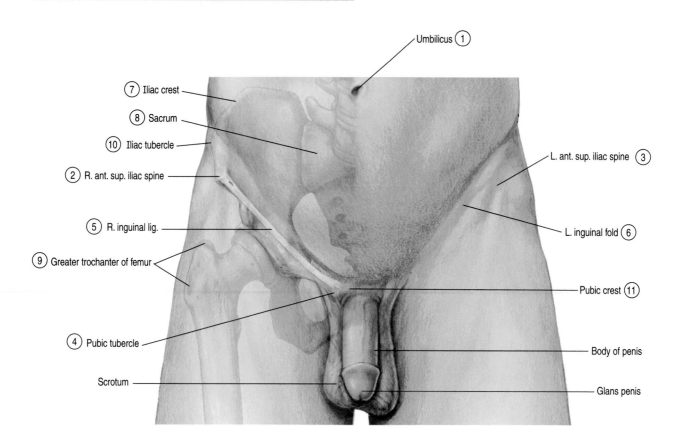

Umbilicus ⑴

⑺ Iliac crest

⑻ Sacrum

⑽ Iliac tubercle

⑵ R. ant. sup. iliac spine

⑸ R. inguinal lig.

⑼ Greater trochanter of femur

⑷ Pubic tubercle

Scrotum

L. ant. sup. iliac spine ⑶

L. inguinal fold ⑹

Pubic crest ⑾

Body of penis

Glans penis

ANTERIOR VIEW

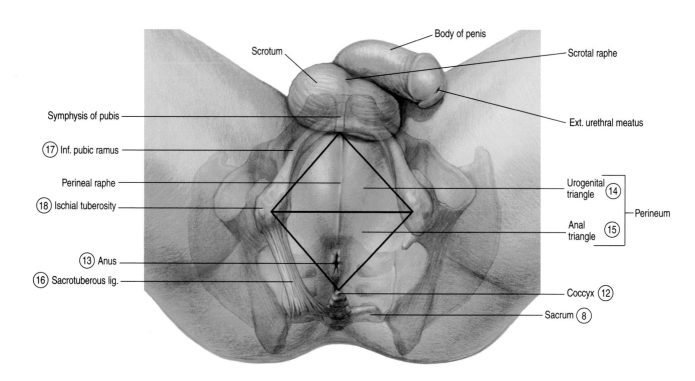

Body of penis

Scrotum

Scrotal raphe

Symphysis of pubis

⑰ Inf. pubic ramus

Perineal raphe

⑱ Ischial tuberosity

⒀ Anus

⒃ Sacrotuberous lig.

Ext. urethral meatus

Urogenital triangle ⑭

Perineum

Anal triangle ⑮

Coccyx ⑿

Sacrum ⑻

LITHOTOMY VIEW

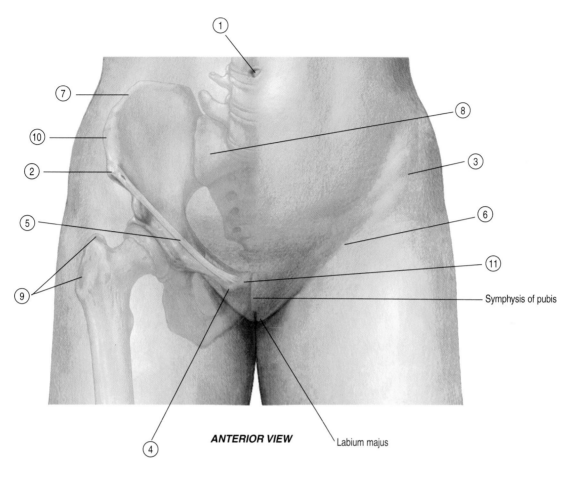

ANTERIOR VIEW

Labium majus

Symphysis of pubis

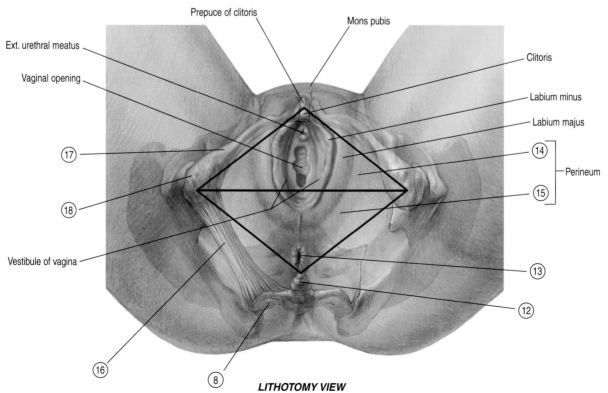

Prepuce of clitoris

Mons pubis

Ext. urethral meatus

Clitoris

Vaginal opening

Labium minus

Labium majus

Perineum

Vestibule of vagina

LITHOTOMY VIEW

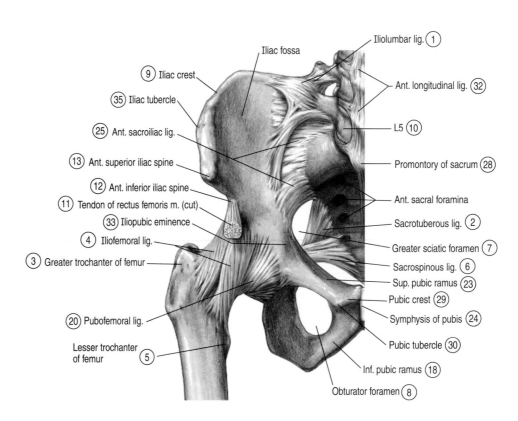

Iliac fossa

⑨ Iliac crest

㉟ Iliac tubercle

㉕ Ant. sacroiliac lig.

⑬ Ant. superior iliac spine

⑫ Ant. inferior iliac spine

⑪ Tendon of rectus femoris m. (cut)

㉝ Iliopubic eminence

④ Iliofemoral lig.

③ Greater trochanter of femur

⑳ Pubofemoral lig.

Lesser trochanter of femur ⑤

Iliolumbar lig. ①

Ant. longitudinal lig. ㉜

L5 ⑩

Promontory of sacrum ㉘

Ant. sacral foramina

Sacrotuberous lig. ②

Greater sciatic foramen ⑦

Sacrospinous lig. ⑥

Sup. pubic ramus ㉓

Pubic crest ㉙

Symphysis of pubis ㉔

Pubic tubercle ㉚

Inf. pubic ramus ⑱

Obturator foramen ⑧

ANTERIOR VIEW

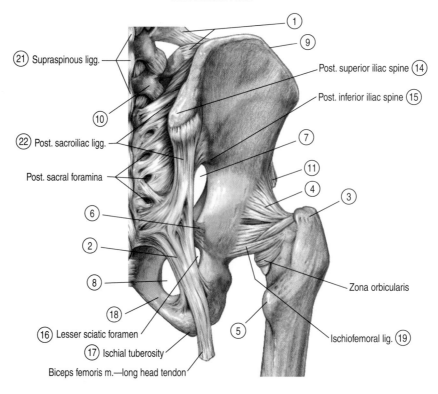

①

⑨

Post. superior iliac spine ⑭

Post. inferior iliac spine ⑮

㉑ Supraspinous ligg.

⑩

㉒ Post. sacroiliac ligg.

Post. sacral foramina

⑥

②

⑦

⑪

④

③

⑧

⑱

Zona orbicularis

⑯ Lesser sciatic foramen

⑰ Ischial tuberosity

Biceps femoris m.—long head tendon

⑤

Ischiofemoral lig. ⑲

POSTERIOR VIEW

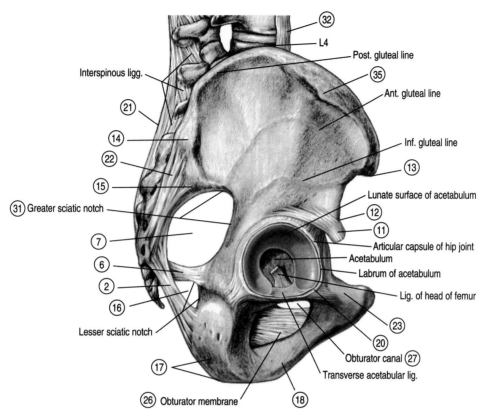

③② ─ ③②
──── L4
Post. gluteal line
③⑤
Interspinous ligg.
Ant. gluteal line
②①
⑭
Inf. gluteal line
②②
⑬
⑮
Lunate surface of acetabulum
③① Greater sciatic notch
⑫
⑪
⑦
Articular capsule of hip joint
⑥
Acetabulum
②
Labrum of acetabulum
⑯
Lig. of head of femur
Lesser sciatic notch
②③
②⓪
⑰
Obturator canal ②⑦
Transverse acetabular lig.
②⑥ Obturator membrane
⑱

RIGHT LATERAL VIEW

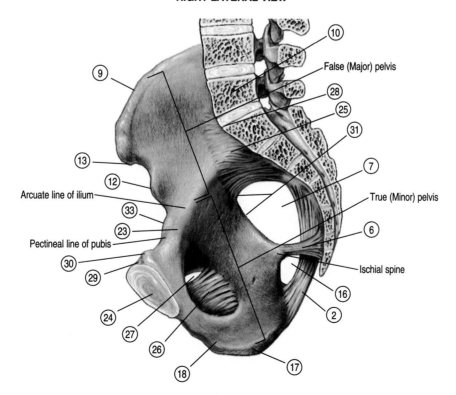

⑩
⑨
False (Major) pelvis
②⑧
②⑤
③①
⑬
⑦
⑫
True (Minor) pelvis
Arcuate line of ilium
③③
②③
⑥
Pectineal line of pubis
③⓪
Ischial spine
②⑨
⑯
②④
②
②⑦
⑰
②⑥
⑱

RIGHT SIDE OF HEMISECTED PELVIS—MEDIAL VIEW

Bony Pelvis—Male
Plate 4.5

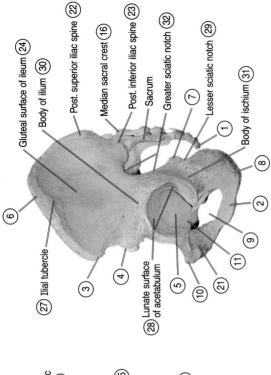

Left Lateral View

27 Iliac tubercle
6
3
4
28 Lunate surface of acetabulum
5
10
21
11
9
2
8
1
Body of ischium 31
Lesser sciatic notch 29
7
Greater sciatic notch 32
Sacrum
Post. inferior iliac spine 23
Median sacral crest 16
Post. superior iliac spine 22
Body of ilium 30
Gluteal surface of ileum 24

Superior View

6
19
12
17
16
35 Sacral canal
37
1
7
27
6
18
3
4
20
14
10
34
13
15

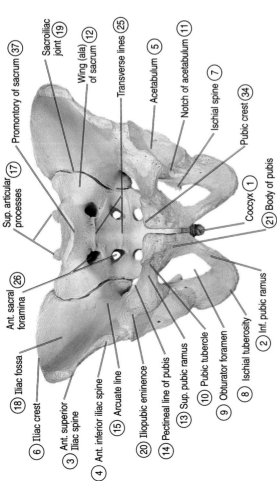

Anterior View

Promontory of sacrum 37
Sacroiliac joint 19
Wing (ala) 12 of sacrum
Transverse lines 25
Acetabulum 5
Notch of acetabulum 11
Ischial spine 7
Pubic crest 34
Body of pubis 1
Coccyx 1
21 Body of pubis
2 Inf. pubic ramus
8 Ischial tuberosity
9 Obturator foramen
10 Pubic tubercle
13 Sup. pubic ramus
14 Pectineal line of pubis
20 Iliopubic eminence
15 Arcuate line
4 Ant. inferior iliac spine
3 Ant. superior iliac spine
6 Iliac crest
18 Iliac fossa
26 Ant. sacral foramina
17 Sup. articular processes

Inferior View

Sacral hiatus 33
Sacral cornua 38
Coccygeal cornua 36
16
6
3
4
5
1
7
8
2
20
5
24
32
23
22

154 • PDR ATLAS OF ANATOMY

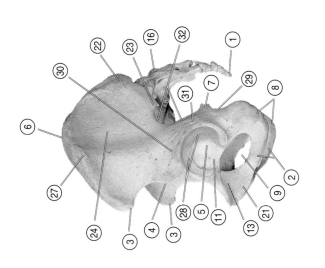

LEFT LATERAL VIEW

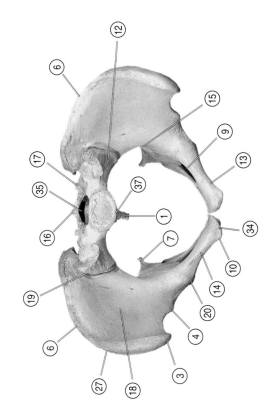
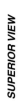

SUPERIOR VIEW

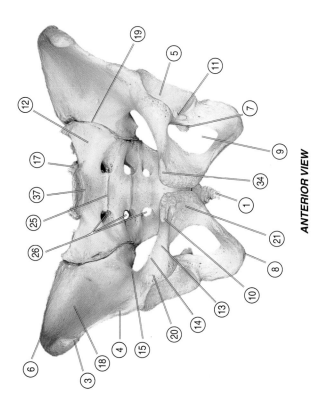

ANTERIOR VIEW

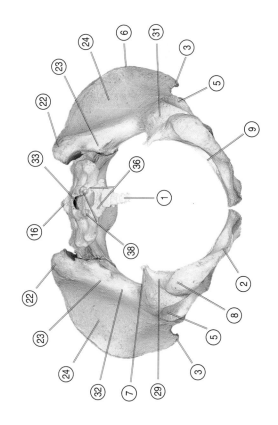

INFERIOR VIEW

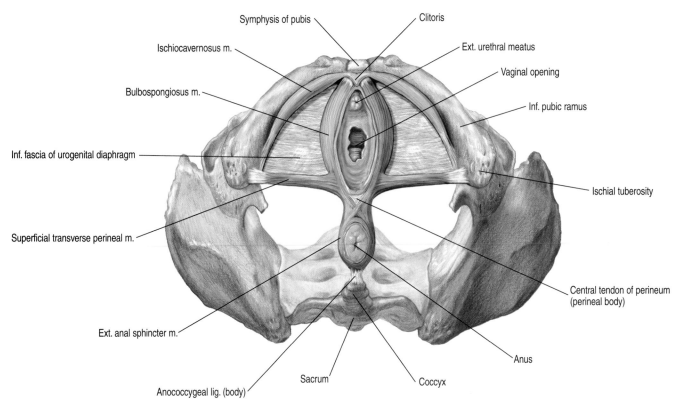

Symphysis of pubis

Clitoris

Ischiocavernosus m.

Ext. urethral meatus

Bulbospongiosus m.

Vaginal opening

Inf. pubic ramus

Inf. fascia of urogenital diaphragm

Ischial tuberosity

Superficial transverse perineal m.

Central tendon of perineum
(perineal body)

Ext. anal sphincter m.

Anus

Anococcygeal lig. (body)

Sacrum

Coccyx

FEMALE—INFERIOR VIEW

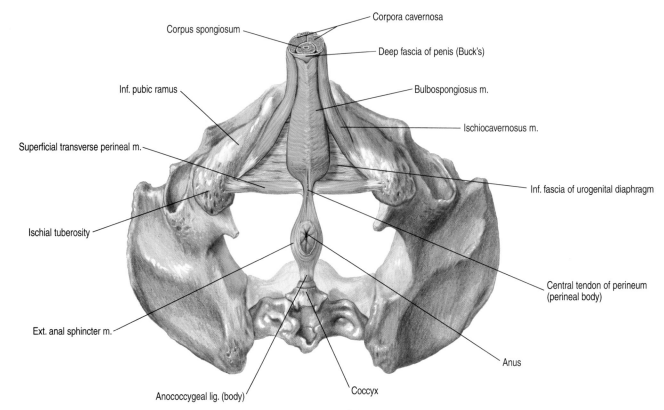

Corpora cavernosa

Corpus spongiosum

Deep fascia of penis (Buck's)

Inf. pubic ramus

Bulbospongiosus m.

Ischiocavernosus m.

Superficial transverse perineal m.

Inf. fascia of urogenital diaphragm

Ischial tuberosity

Central tendon of perineum
(perineal body)

Ext. anal sphincter m.

Anus

Anococcygeal lig. (body)

Coccyx

MALE—INFERIOR VIEW

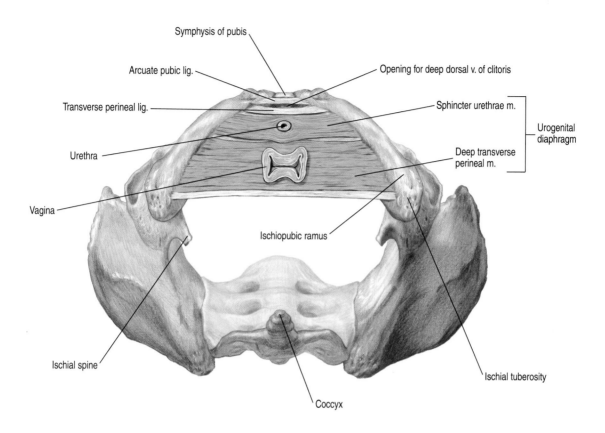

Symphysis of pubis

Arcuate pubic lig.

Opening for deep dorsal v. of clitoris

Transverse perineal lig.

Sphincter urethrae m.

Urogenital diaphragm

Urethra

Deep transverse perineal m.

Vagina

Ischiopubic ramus

Ischial spine

Ischial tuberosity

Coccyx

FEMALE—INFERIOR VIEW

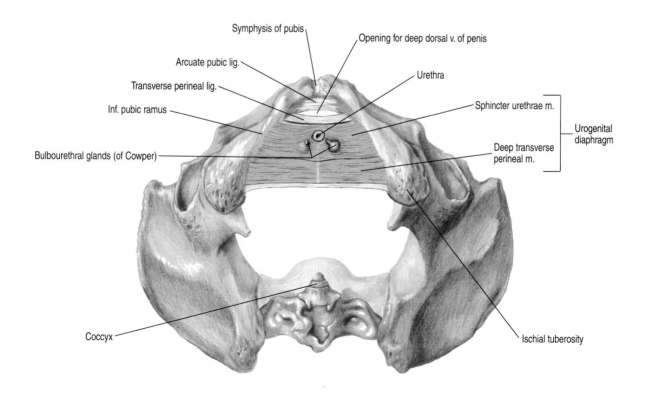

Symphysis of pubis

Arcuate pubic lig.

Opening for deep dorsal v. of penis

Transverse perineal lig.

Urethra

Inf. pubic ramus

Sphincter urethrae m.

Urogenital diaphragm

Deep transverse perineal m.

Bulbourethral glands (of Cowper)

Coccyx

Ischial tuberosity

MALE—INFERIOR VIEW

Pelvic Muscles—Pelvic Diaphragm
Plate 4.9

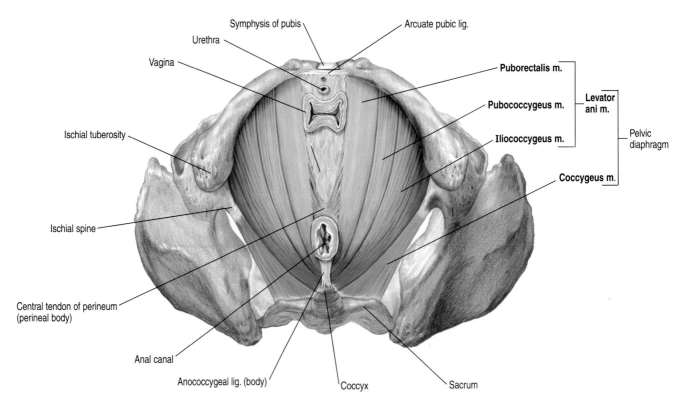

FEMALE—INFERIOR VIEW

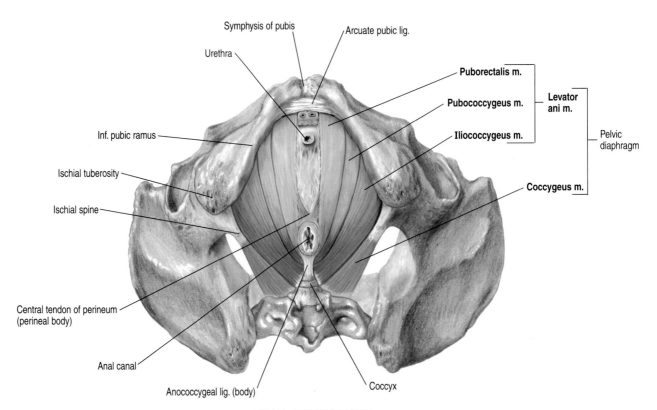

MALE—INFERIOR VIEW

Muscle	Superior or Lateral Attachment	Inferior or Medial Attachment	Innervation	Action(s)
Ischiocavernosus	Int. surface of ischial ramus & tuberosity laterally	Sides & ventrum of crus of penis in ♂ or clitoris medially in ♀	Perineal brr. of pudendal n. (S2–4)	Maintains erection of penis or clitoris
Bulbospongiosus	Dorsum of clitoris in ♀; inf. fascia of urogenital diaphragm, sides & dorsum of penile bulb in ♂	Perineal body, inf. fascia of urogenital diaphragm & median raphe of penile bulb in ♂	Perineal brr. of pudendal n. (S2–4)	Compresses vaginal orifice & erection of clitoris in ♀; compresses urethra, assist in erection & ejaculation in ♂
Superficial transverse perineal	Int. surface of ischial tuberosity laterally	Perineal body (central perineal tendon) medially	Perineal brr. of pudendal n. (S2–4)	Supports pelvic viscera
Ext. anal sphincter	Anococcygeal lig. to coccyx & int. anal sphincter m. superiorly	Perineal body anteriorly & skin superficially	Inf. rectal n. (S2–3) and perineal br. of S4 spinal n.	Compresses anus
Sphincter urethrae	Inf. pubic ramus laterally	Perineal body posteriorly & fibers from opposite side medially	Perineal brr. of pudendal n. (S2–4)	Compresses urethra in ♂ & ♀ & vagina in ♀
Deep transverse perineal	Ischial ramus laterally	Perineal body medially	Perineal brr. of pudendal n. (S2–4)	Supports pelvic viscera

FEMALE PERINEUM & MUSCLES— LEFT LATERAL VIEW

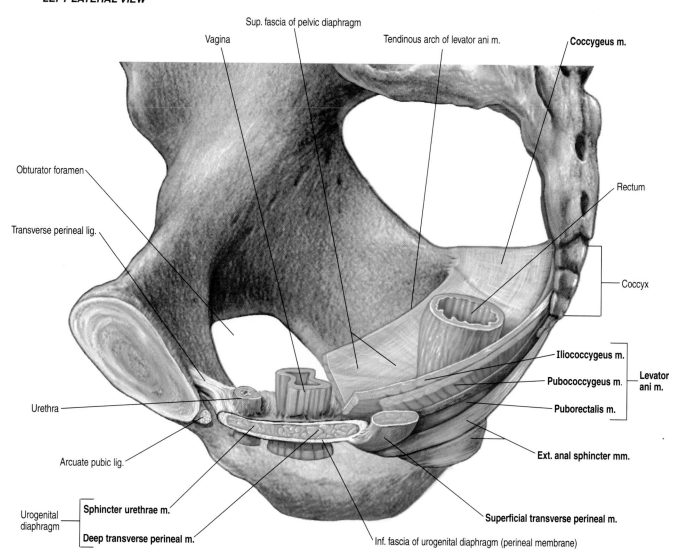

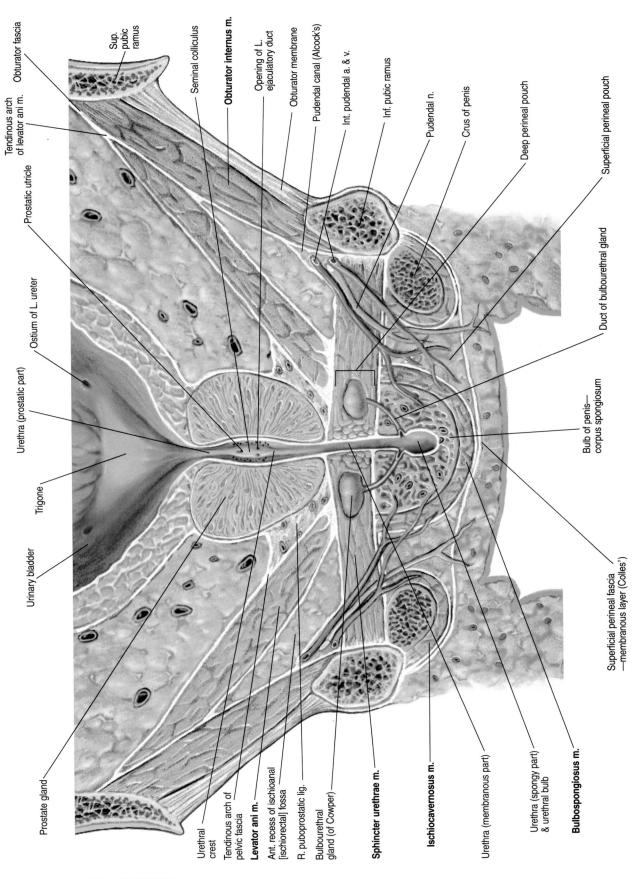

Obturator fascia

Sup. pubic ramus

Tendinous arch of levator ani m.

Seminal colliculus

Obturator internus m.

Opening of L. ejaculatory duct

Obturator membrane

Pudendal canal (Alcock's)

Int. pudendal a. & v.

Inf. pubic ramus

Pudendal n.

Crus of penis

Deep perineal pouch

Superficial perineal pouch

Prostatic utricle

Ostium of L. ureter

Urethra (prostatic part)

Trigone

Urinary bladder

Prostate gland

Urethral crest

Tendinous arch of pelvic fascia

Levator ani m.

Ant. recess of ischioanal [ischiorectal] fossa

R. puboprostatic lig.

Bulbourethral gland (of Cowper)

Sphincter urethrae m.

Ischiocavernosus m.

Urethra (membranous part)

Urethra (spongy part) & urethral bulb

Bulbospongiosus m.

Superficial perineal fascia —membranous layer (Colles')

Bulb of penis— corpus spongiosum

Duct of bulbourethral gland

MALE CORONAL SECTION—ANTERIOR VIEW

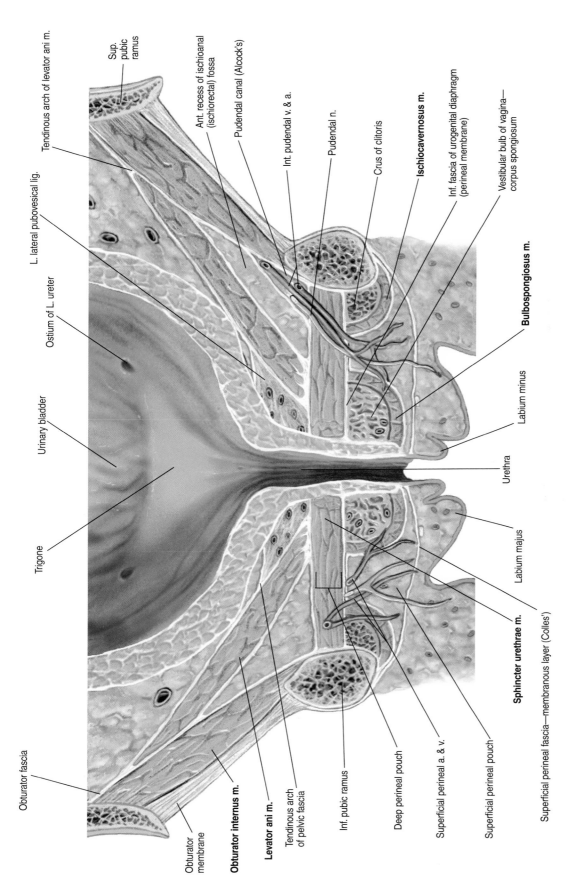

Sup. pubic ramus

Tendinous arch of levator ani m.

Ant. recess of ischioanal (ischiorectal) fossa

Pudendal canal (Alcock's)

Int. pudendal v. & a.

Pudendal n.

Crus of clitoris

Ischiocavernosus m.

Inf. fascia of urogenital diaphragm (perineal membrane)

Vestibular bulb of vagina—corpus spongiosum

Bulbospongiosus m.

L. lateral pubovesical lig.

Ostium of L. ureter

Urinary bladder

Trigone

Labium minus

Labium majus

Urethra

Obturator fascia

Obturator membrane

Obturator internus m.

Levator ani m.

Tendinous arch of pelvic fascia

Inf. pubic ramus

Deep perineal pouch

Superficial perineal a. & v.

Superficial perineal pouch

Sphincter urethrae m.

Superficial perineal fascia—membranous layer (Colles')

FEMALE CORONAL SECTION—ANTERIOR VIEW

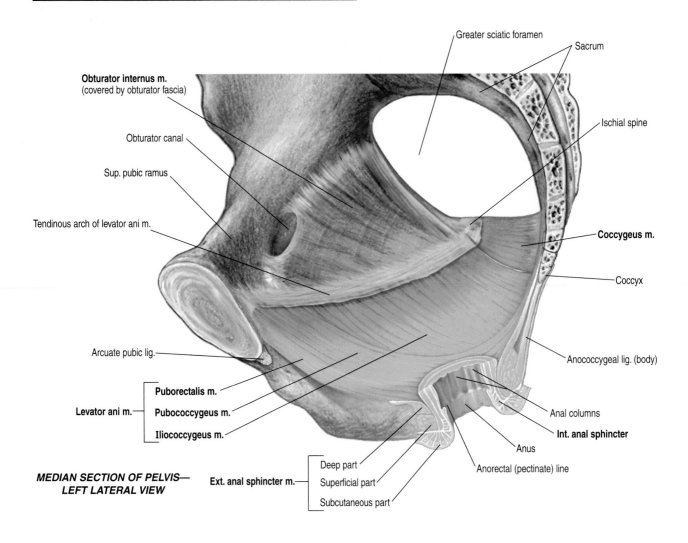

Greater sciatic foramen

Sacrum

Obturator internus m.
(covered by obturator fascia)

Ischial spine

Obturator canal

Sup. pubic ramus

Coccygeus m.

Tendinous arch of levator ani m.

Coccyx

Arcuate pubic lig.

Anococcygeal lig. (body)

Puborectalis m.

Levator ani m. — **Pubococcygeus m.**

Iliococcygeus m.

Anal columns

Int. anal sphincter

Anus

Anorectal (pectinate) line

MEDIAN SECTION OF PELVIS—LEFT LATERAL VIEW

Ext. anal sphincter m. — Deep part
Superficial part
Subcutaneous part

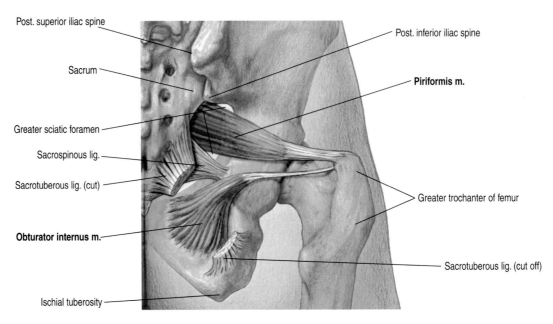

Post. superior iliac spine

Post. inferior iliac spine

Sacrum

Piriformis m.

Greater sciatic foramen

Sacrospinous lig.

Sacrotuberous lig. (cut)

Greater trochanter of femur

Obturator internus m.

Sacrotuberous lig. (cut off)

Ischial tuberosity

RIGHT GLUTEAL REGION—POSTERIOR VIEW

Muscles of the Pelvic Diaphragm

Muscle	Superior or Lateral Attachment	Inferior or Medial Attachment	Innervation	Action(s)
Puborectalis	Body of pubis anteriorly	Fibers of opposite side post. to rectum	Inf. rectal n. (S2, 3) & perineal brr. of S3, 4 spinal n.	Maintains anorectal flexure by drawing anal canal anteriorly
Pubococcygeus	Body of pubis and obturator fascia anteriorly	Coccyx & anococcygeal lig. posteriorly	Inf. rectal n. (S2, 3) & perineal brr. of S3, 4 spinal n.	Supports pelvic viscera
Iliococcygeus	Ischial spine & tendinous arch of pelvic fascia laterally	Coccyx & anococcygeal lig. posteriorly	Inf. rectal n. (S2, 3) & perineal brr. of S3, 4 spinal n.	Supports pelvic viscera
Coccygeus	Ischial spine & sacrospinous lig. laterally	Coccyx & S5 vertebra medially	Brr. of S3–5 spinal nn.	Supports pelvic viscera

Muscles of the Pelvic Walls

Muscle	Superior or Medial Attachment	Inferior or Lateral Attachment	Innervation	Action(s)
Obturator internus	Pelvic surfaces of ilium & ischium; obturator membrane	Greater trochanter of femur	N. to obturator internus (L5–S2)	Rotates thigh laterally
Piriformis	Pelvic surface of 2nd–4th sacral segments; sup. margin of greater sciatic notch, & sacrotuberous lig.	Greater trochanter of femur	Ventral rami of S1 & S2	Rotates thigh laterally

MEDIAN VIEW—RIGHT SIDE OF MEDIAL SECTION

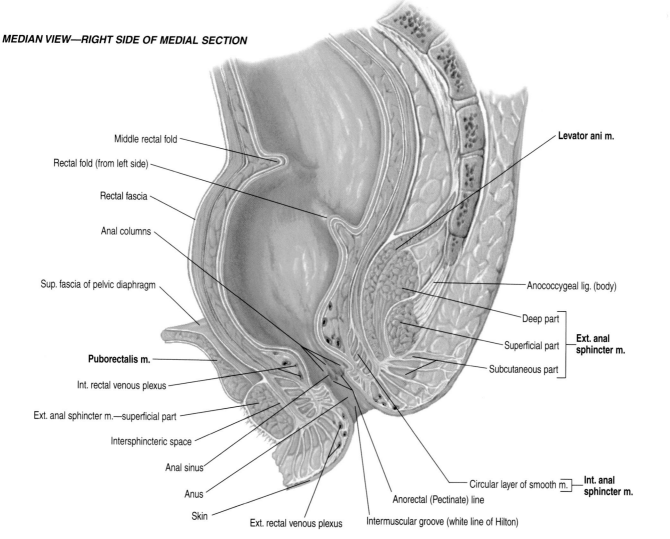

Middle rectal fold

Rectal fold (from left side)

Rectal fascia

Anal columns

Sup. fascia of pelvic diaphragm

Puborectalis m.

Int. rectal venous plexus

Ext. anal sphincter m.—superficial part

Intersphincteric space

Anal sinus

Anus

Skin

Ext. rectal venous plexus

Anorectal (Pectinate) line

Intermuscular groove (white line of Hilton)

Circular layer of smooth m.

Int. anal sphincter m.

Levator ani m.

Anococcygeal lig. (body)

Deep part

Superficial part — Ext. anal sphincter m.

Subcutaneous part

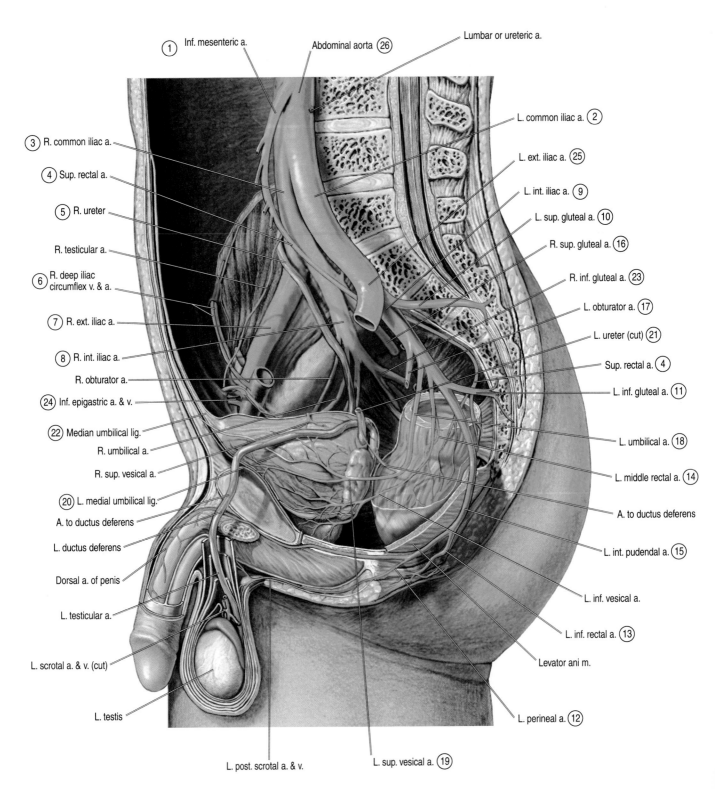

Inf. mesenteric a. ①

Abdominal aorta ㉖

Lumbar or ureteric a.

③ R. common iliac a.

④ Sup. rectal a.

⑤ R. ureter

R. testicular a.

⑥ R. deep iliac circumflex v. & a.

⑦ R. ext. iliac a.

⑧ R. int. iliac a.

R. obturator a.

㉔ Inf. epigastric a. & v.

㉒ Median umbilical lig.

R. umbilical a.

R. sup. vesical a.

⑳ L. medial umbilical lig.

A. to ductus deferens

L. ductus deferens

Dorsal a. of penis

L. testicular a.

L. scrotal a. & v. (cut)

L. testis

L. post. scrotal a. & v.

L. sup. vesical a. ⑲

L. common iliac a. ②

L. ext. iliac a. ㉕

L. int. iliac a. ⑨

L. sup. gluteal a. ⑩

R. sup. gluteal a. ⑯

R. inf. gluteal a. ㉓

L. obturator a. ⑰

L. ureter (cut) ㉑

Sup. rectal a. ④

L. inf. gluteal a. ⑪

L. umbilical a. ⑱

L. middle rectal a. ⑭

A. to ductus deferens

L. int. pudendal a. ⑮

L. inf. vesical a.

L. inf. rectal a. ⑬

Levator ani m.

L. perineal a. ⑫

MEDIAL VIEW WITH PERITONEUM REMOVED

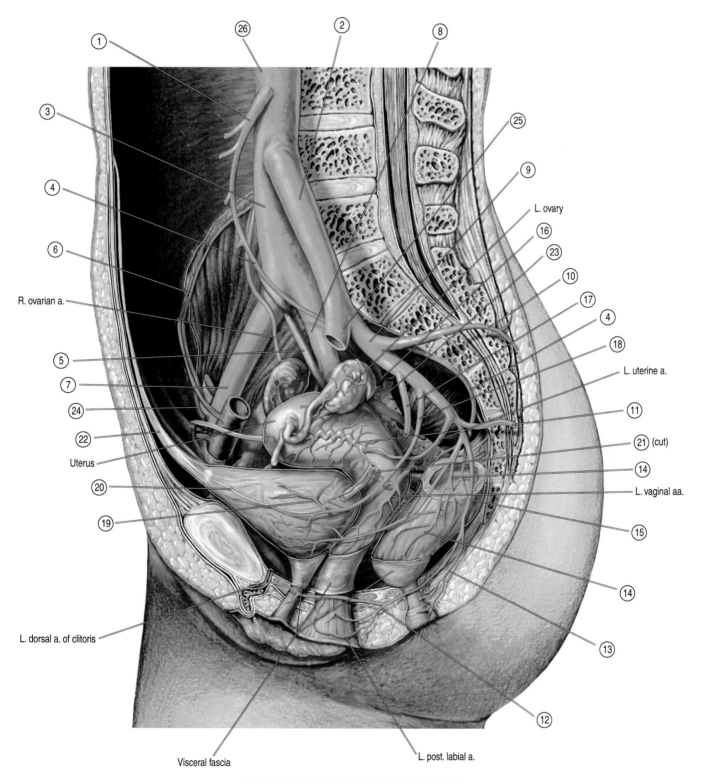

MEDIAL VIEW WITH PERITONEUM REMOVED

Labels visible in figure:
26, 2, 8, 1, 3, 4, 6, R. ovarian a., 5, 7, 24, 22, Uterus, 20, 19, L. dorsal a. of clitoris, Visceral fascia, L. post. labial a., 25, 9, L. ovary, 16, 23, 10, 17, 4, 18, L. uterine a., 11, 21 (cut), 14, L. vaginal aa., 15, 14, 13, 12

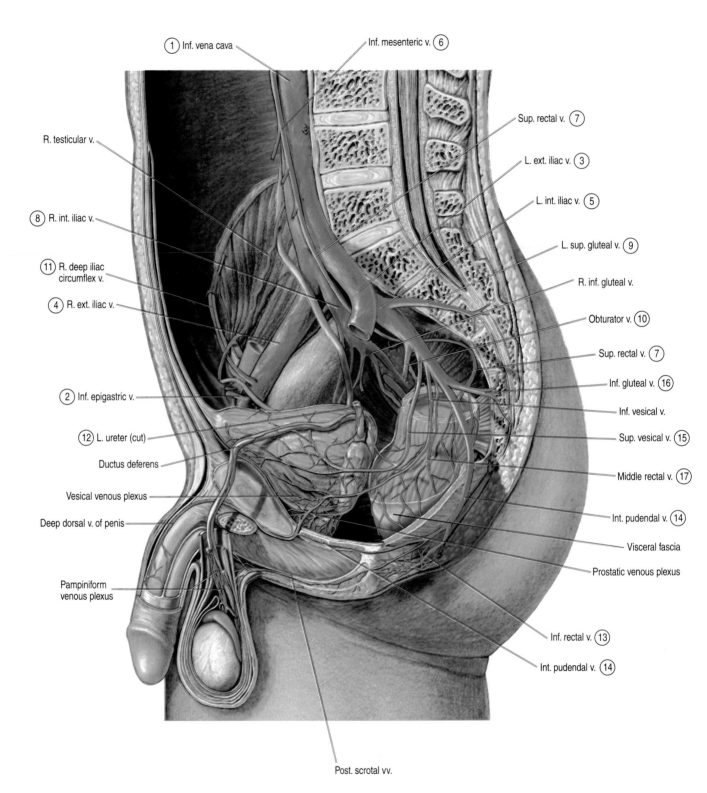

① Inf. vena cava

Inf. mesenteric v. ⑥

R. testicular v.

⑧ R. int. iliac v.

⑪ R. deep iliac circumflex v.

④ R. ext. iliac v.

② Inf. epigastric v.

⑫ L. ureter (cut)

Ductus deferens

Vesical venous plexus

Deep dorsal v. of penis

Pampiniform venous plexus

Sup. rectal v. ⑦

L. ext. iliac v. ③

L. int. iliac v. ⑤

L. sup. gluteal v. ⑨

R. inf. gluteal v.

Obturator v. ⑩

Sup. rectal v. ⑦

Inf. gluteal v. ⑯

Inf. vesical v.

Sup. vesical v. ⑮

Middle rectal v. ⑰

Int. pudendal v. ⑭

Visceral fascia

Prostatic venous plexus

Inf. rectal v. ⑬

Int. pudendal v. ⑭

Post. scrotal vv.

MEDIAL VIEW WITH PERITONEUM REMOVED

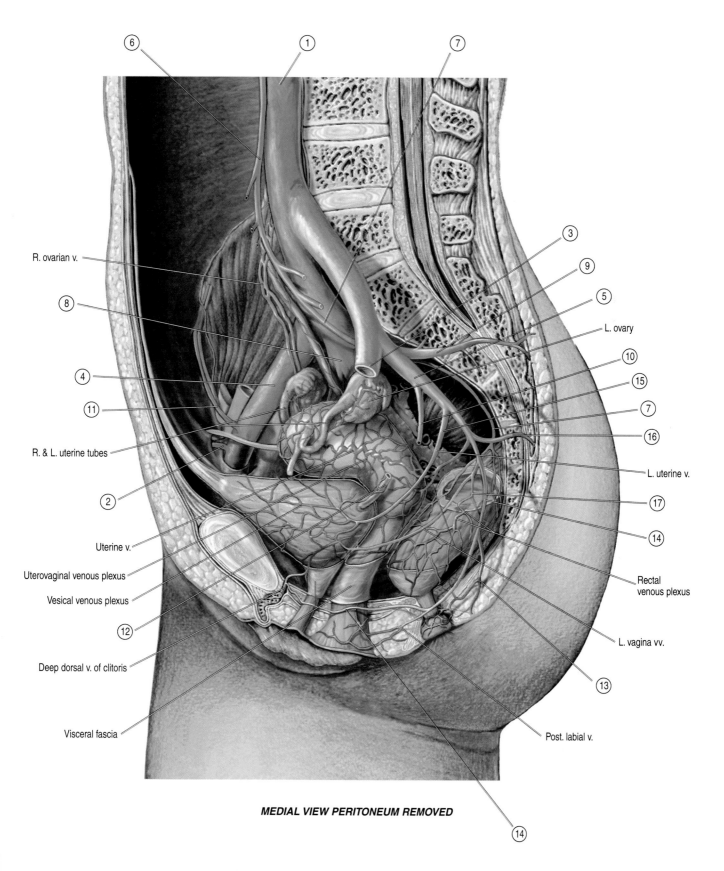

R. ovarian v.

L. ovary

L. uterine v.

R. & L. uterine tubes

Uterine v.

Rectal venous plexus

Uterovaginal venous plexus

Vesical venous plexus

L. vagina vv.

Deep dorsal v. of clitoris

Post. labial v.

Visceral fascia

MEDIAL VIEW PERITONEUM REMOVED

Dermatomes & Cutaneous Nerves—Male
Plate 4.17

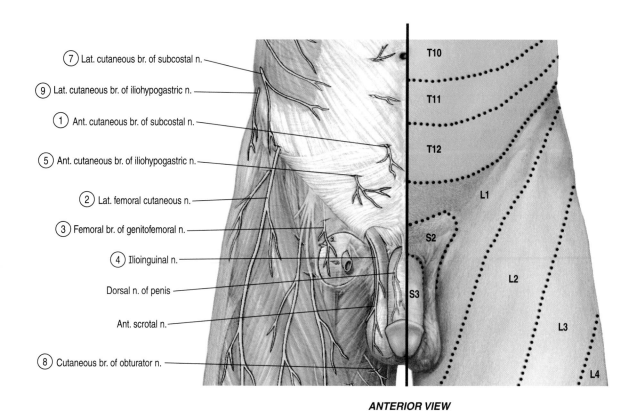

(7) Lat. cutaneous br. of subcostal n.

(9) Lat. cutaneous br. of iliohypogastric n.

(1) Ant. cutaneous br. of subcostal n.

(5) Ant. cutaneous br. of iliohypogastric n.

(2) Lat. femoral cutaneous n.

(3) Femoral br. of genitofemoral n.

(4) Ilioinguinal n.

Dorsal n. of penis

Ant. scrotal n.

(8) Cutaneous br. of obturator n.

T10
T11
T12
L1
S2
L2
S3
L3
L4

ANTERIOR VIEW

Genital br. of genitofemoral n.

Ant. scrotal n.

Post. scrotal nn.

(12) Medial br. of ant. femoral cutaneous n.

(8) Cutaneous br. of obturator n.

(13) Perineal br. of post. femoral cutaneous n.

(14) Post. femoral cutaneous n.

(6) Inf. rectal nn.

(15) Inf. cluneal nn.

(11) Medial cluneal n.

(10) Anococcygeal nn.

L3
L2
L1
S2
S5 S4 S3 S1
L5
Co1

LITHOTOMY VIEW

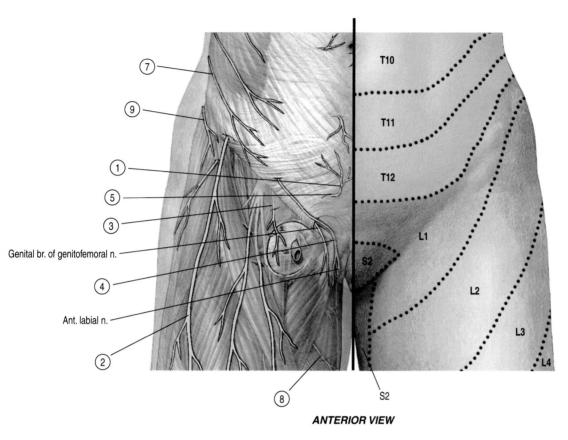

Genital br. of genitofemoral n.

Ant. labial n.

T10
T11
T12
L1
S2
L2
L3
L4

S2

ANTERIOR VIEW

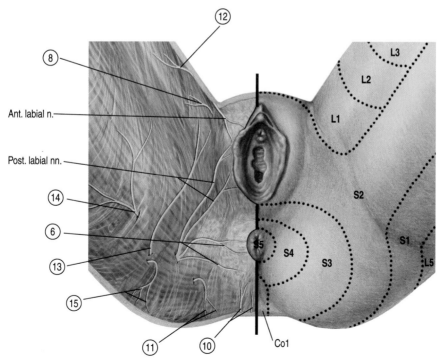

Ant. labial n.

Post. labial nn.

L3
L2
L1
S2
S1
L5
S5
S4
S3

Co1

LITHOTOMY VIEW

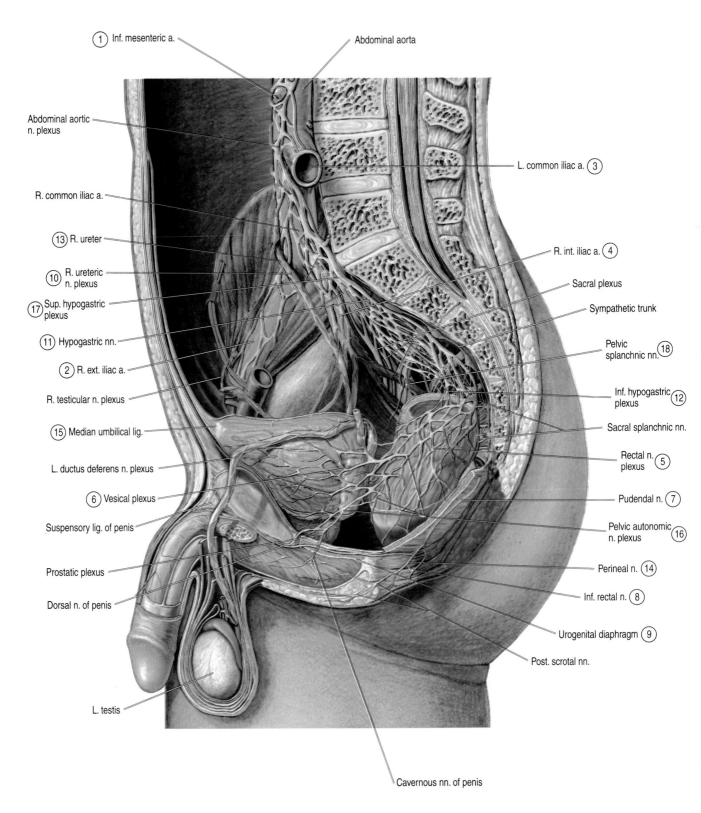

① Inf. mesenteric a.

Abdominal aorta

Abdominal aortic n. plexus

L. common iliac a. ③

R. common iliac a.

⑬ R. ureter

⑩ R. ureteric n. plexus

R. int. iliac a. ④

Sacral plexus

Sympathetic trunk

⑰ Sup. hypogastric plexus

⑪ Hypogastric nn.

Pelvic splanchnic nn. ⑱

② R. ext. iliac a.

Inf. hypogastric plexus ⑫

R. testicular n. plexus

Sacral splanchnic nn.

⑮ Median umbilical lig.

Rectal n. plexus ⑤

L. ductus deferens n. plexus

Pudendal n. ⑦

⑥ Vesical plexus

Pelvic autonomic n. plexus ⑯

Suspensory lig. of penis

Perineal n. ⑭

Prostatic plexus

Inf. rectal n. ⑧

Dorsal n. of penis

Urogenital diaphragm ⑨

Post. scrotal nn.

L. testis

Cavernous nn. of penis

MEDIAL VIEW WITH PERITONEUM REMOVED

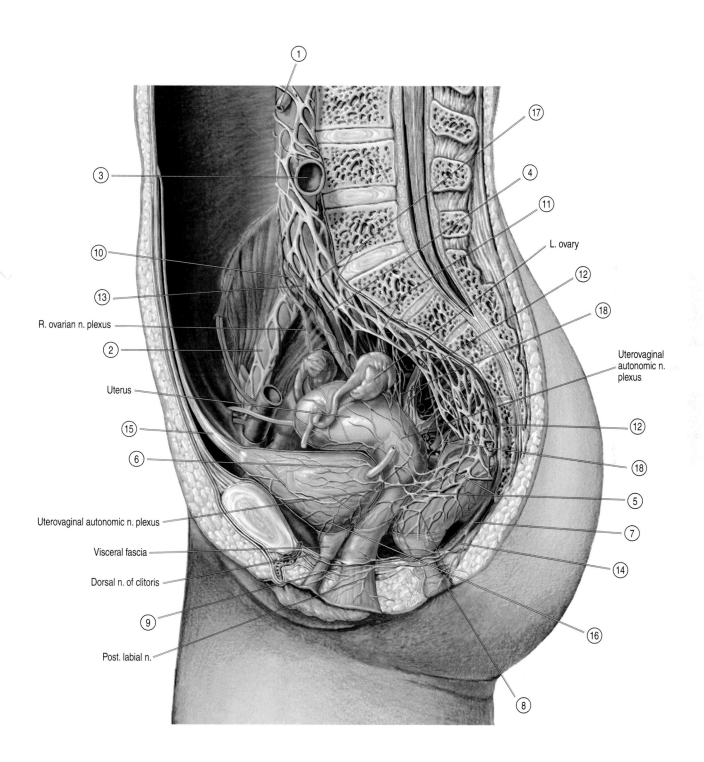

①

③

⑩

⑬

R. ovarian n. plexus

②

Uterus

⑮

⑥

Uterovaginal autonomic n. plexus

Visceral fascia

Dorsal n. of clitoris

⑨

Post. labial n.

⑰

④

⑪

L. ovary

⑫

⑱

Uterovaginal autonomic n. plexus

⑫

⑱

⑤

⑦

⑭

⑯

⑧

MEDIAL VIEW PERITONEUM REMOVED

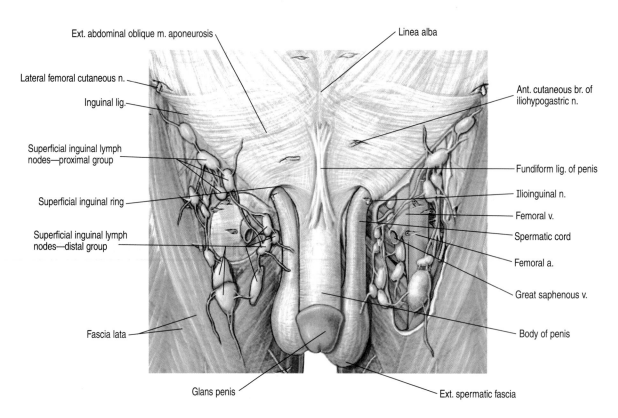

Ext. abdominal oblique m. aponeurosis

Linea alba

Lateral femoral cutaneous n.

Inguinal lig.

Ant. cutaneous br. of iliohypogastric n.

Superficial inguinal lymph nodes—proximal group

Fundiform lig. of penis

Superficial inguinal ring

Ilioinguinal n.

Femoral v.

Superficial inguinal lymph nodes—distal group

Spermatic cord

Femoral a.

Great saphenous v.

Fascia lata

Body of penis

Glans penis

Ext. spermatic fascia

MALE ANTERIOR VIEW

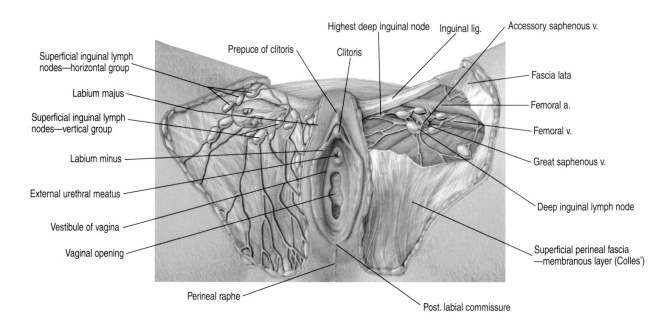

Highest deep inguinal node

Inguinal lig.

Accessory saphenous v.

Prepuce of clitoris

Clitoris

Superficial inguinal lymph nodes—horizontal group

Fascia lata

Labium majus

Femoral a.

Superficial inguinal lymph nodes—vertical group

Femoral v.

Labium minus

Great saphenous v.

External urethral meatus

Vestibule of vagina

Deep inguinal lymph node

Vaginal opening

Superficial perineal fascia —membranous layer (Colles')

Perineal raphe

Post. labial commissure

FEMALE LITHOTOMY VIEW

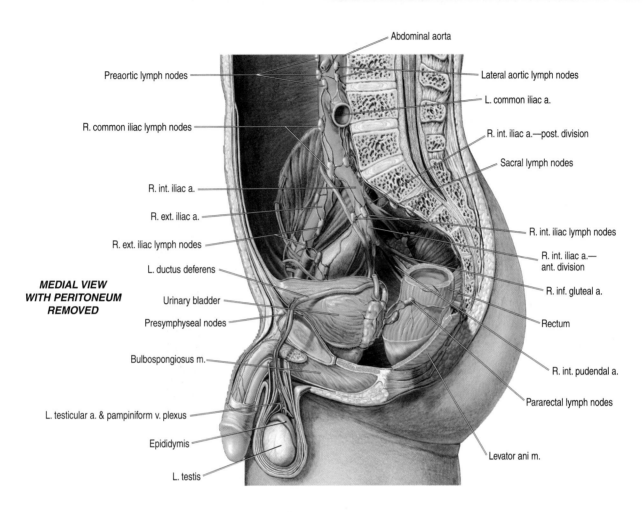

Abdominal aorta

Preaortic lymph nodes

Lateral aortic lymph nodes

R. common iliac lymph nodes

L. common iliac a.

R. int. iliac a.—post. division

Sacral lymph nodes

R. int. iliac a.

R. ext. iliac a.

R. int. iliac lymph nodes

R. ext. iliac lymph nodes

R. int. iliac a.—ant. division

L. ductus deferens

R. inf. gluteal a.

MEDIAL VIEW WITH PERITONEUM REMOVED

Urinary bladder

Presymphyseal nodes

Rectum

Bulbospongiosus m.

R. int. pudendal a.

Pararectal lymph nodes

L. testicular a. & pampiniform v. plexus

Epididymis

Levator ani m.

L. testis

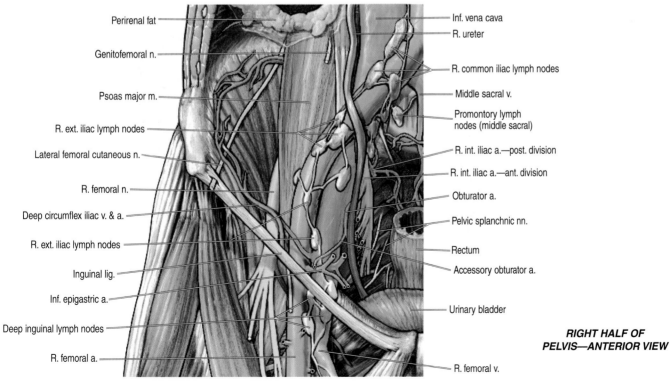

Perirenal fat

Inf. vena cava

R. ureter

Genitofemoral n.

R. common iliac lymph nodes

Psoas major m.

Middle sacral v.

Promontory lymph nodes (middle sacral)

R. ext. iliac lymph nodes

R. int. iliac a.—post. division

Lateral femoral cutaneous n.

R. int. iliac a.—ant. division

R. femoral n.

Obturator a.

Deep circumflex iliac v. & a.

Pelvic splanchnic nn.

R. ext. iliac lymph nodes

Rectum

Inguinal lig.

Accessory obturator a.

Inf. epigastric a.

Urinary bladder

Deep inguinal lymph nodes

RIGHT HALF OF PELVIS—ANTERIOR VIEW

R. femoral a.

R. femoral v.

♀ = **Characteristic Female Structures**

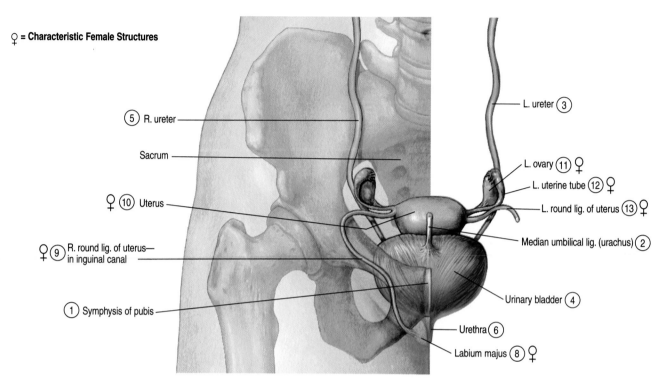

⑤ R. ureter

Sacrum

♀ ⑩ Uterus

♀ ⑨ R. round lig. of uterus— in inguinal canal

① Symphysis of pubis

L. ureter ③

L. ovary ⑪ ♀

L. uterine tube ⑫ ♀

L. round lig. of uterus ⑬ ♀

Median umbilical lig. (urachus) ②

Urinary bladder ④

Urethra ⑥

Labium majus ⑧ ♀

ANTERIOR VIEW

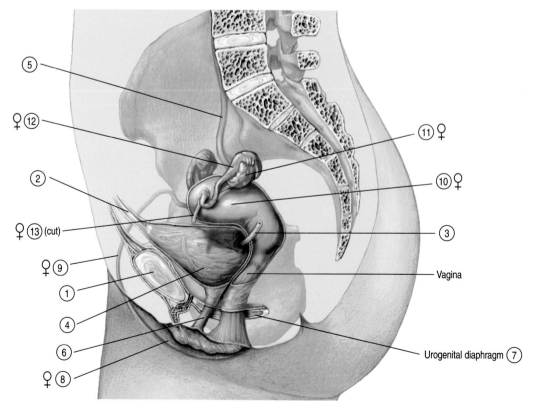

⑤

♀ ⑫

②

♀ ⑬ (cut)

♀ ⑨

①

④

⑥

♀ ⑧

⑪ ♀

⑩ ♀

③

Vagina

Urogenital diaphragm ⑦

MEDIAL VIEW

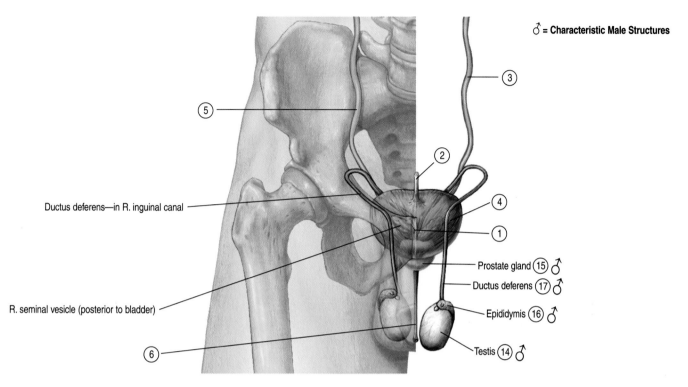

♂ = **Characteristic Male Structures**

Ductus deferens—in R. inguinal canal

Prostate gland (15) ♂

Ductus deferens (17) ♂

R. seminal vesicle (posterior to bladder)

Epididymis (16) ♂

Testis (14) ♂

ANTERIOR VIEW

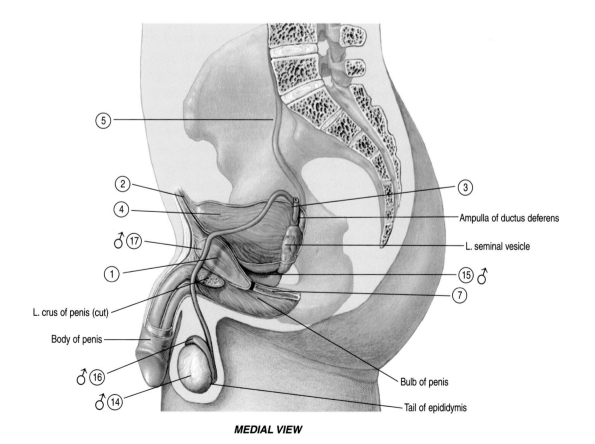

Ampulla of ductus deferens

L. seminal vesicle

L. crus of penis (cut)

Body of penis

Bulb of penis

Tail of epididymis

MEDIAL VIEW

Pelvic Contents—Female
Plate • 4.25

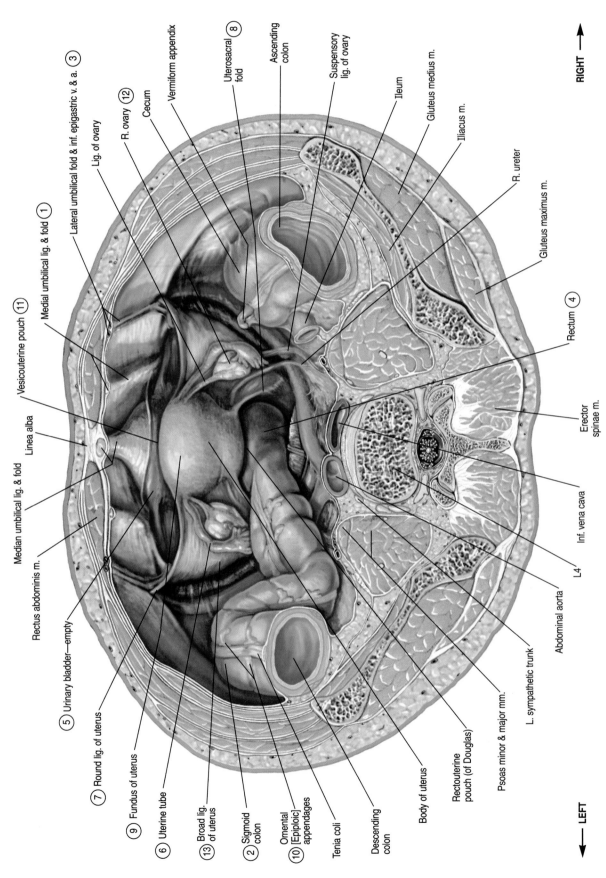

Lateral umbilical fold & inf. epigastric v. & a. ③

Medial umbilical lig. & fold ①

Vesicouterine pouch ⑪

Median umbilical lig. & fold

Linea alba

Rectus abdominis m.

⑤ Urinary bladder—empty

⑦ Round lig. of uterus

⑨ Fundus of uterus

⑥ Uterine tube

⑬ Broad lig. of uterus

② Sigmoid colon

⑩ Omental [Epiploic] appendages

Tenia coli

Descending colon

Body of uterus

Rectouterine pouch (of Douglas)

Psoas minor & major mm.

L. sympathetic trunk

Abdominal aorta

Inf. vena cava

⑫ R. ovary

Lig. of ovary

Cecum

Vermiform appendix

Uterosacral fold ⑧

Ascending colon

Suspensory lig. of ovary

Ileum

Gluteus medius m.

Iliacus m.

R. ureter

Gluteus maximus m.

Rectum ④

Erector spinae m.

L4

TRANSVERSE SECTION AT L4—SUPERIOR VIEW

RIGHT →

← LEFT

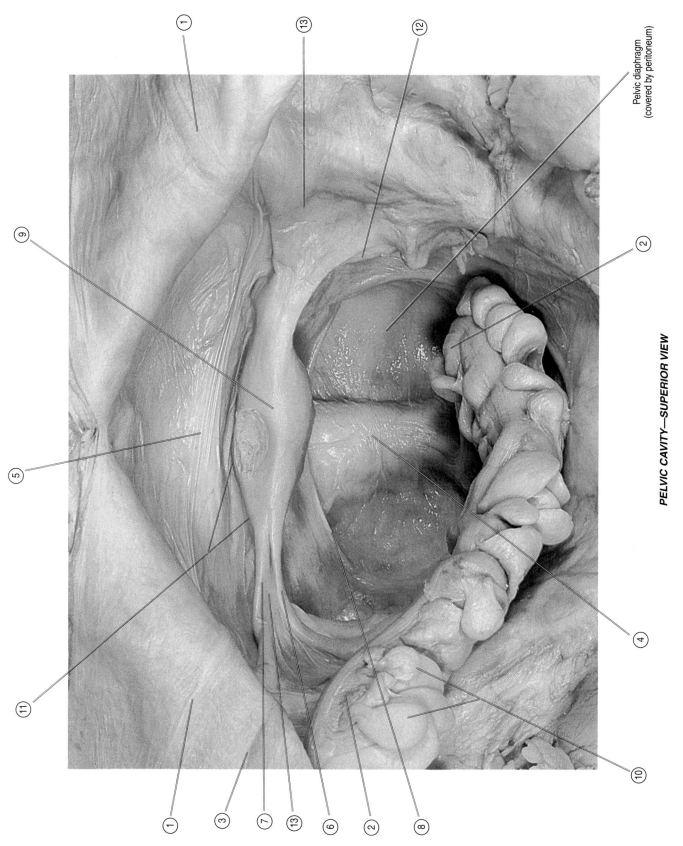

Pelvic diaphragm
(covered by peritoneum)

PELVIC CAVITY—SUPERIOR VIEW

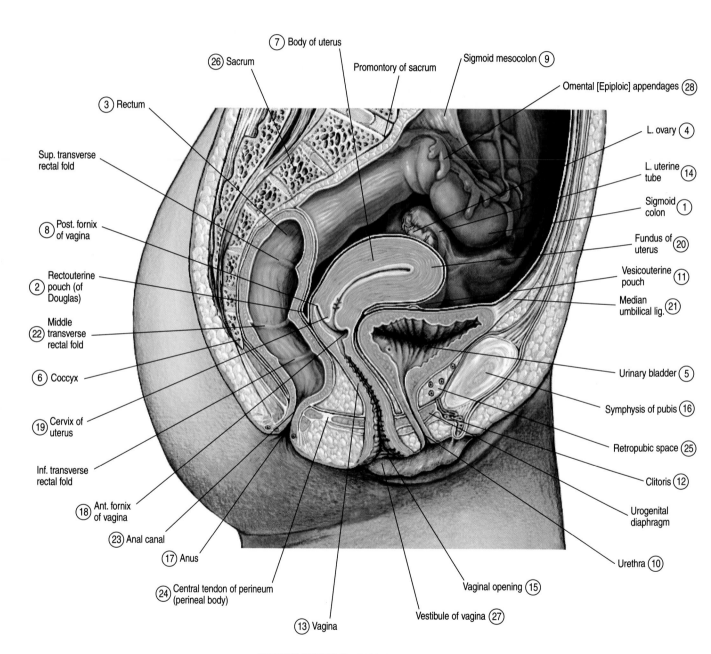

⑦ Body of uterus

㉖ Sacrum

Promontory of sacrum

Sigmoid mesocolon ⑨

Omental [Epiploic] appendages ㉘

③ Rectum

Sup. transverse rectal fold

L. ovary ④

L. uterine tube ⑭

Sigmoid colon ①

⑧ Post. fornix of vagina

Fundus of uterus ⑳

② Rectouterine pouch (of Douglas)

Vesicouterine pouch ⑪

㉒ Middle transverse rectal fold

Median umbilical lig. ㉑

⑥ Coccyx

Urinary bladder ⑤

⑲ Cervix of uterus

Symphysis of pubis ⑯

Inf. transverse rectal fold

Retropubic space ㉕

⑱ Ant. fornix of vagina

Clitoris ⑫

㉓ Anal canal

Urogenital diaphragm

⑰ Anus

Urethra ⑩

㉔ Central tendon of perineum (perineal body)

Vaginal opening ⑮

⑬ Vagina

Vestibule of vagina ㉗

MEDIAN SECTION—RIGHT LATERAL VIEW

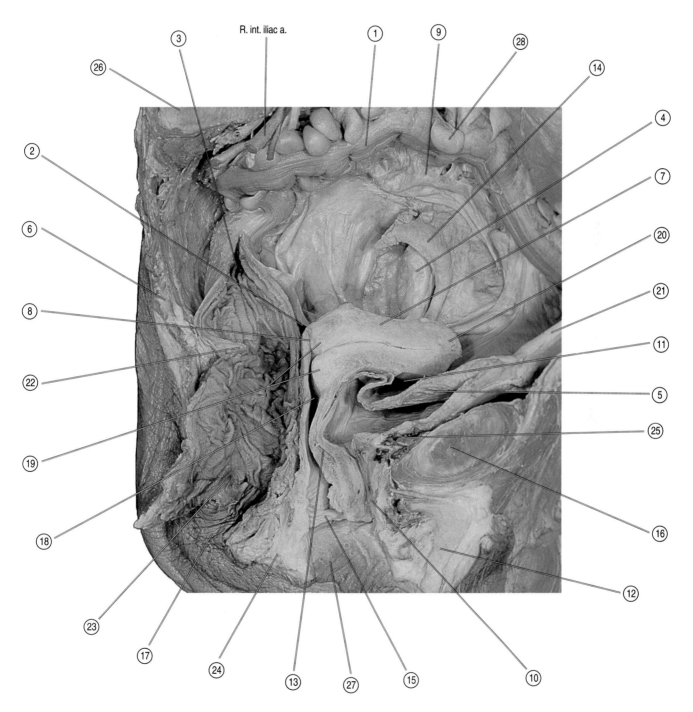

R. int. iliac a.

MEDIAN SECTION—RIGHT LATERAL VIEW OF LEFT PELVIS

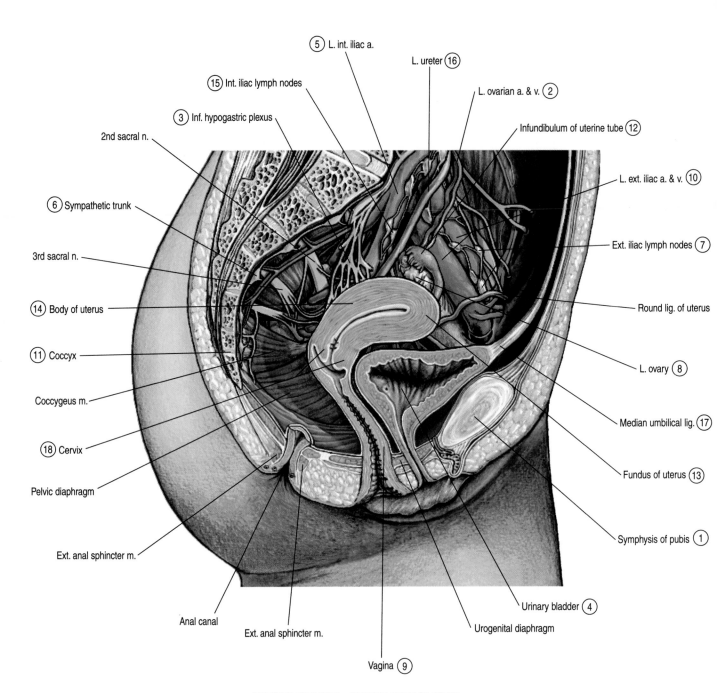

⑤ L. int. iliac a.

⑮ Int. iliac lymph nodes

L. ureter ⑯

③ Inf. hypogastric plexus

L. ovarian a. & v. ②

2nd sacral n.

Infundibulum of uterine tube ⑫

⑥ Sympathetic trunk

L. ext. iliac a. & v. ⑩

3rd sacral n.

Ext. iliac lymph nodes ⑦

⑭ Body of uterus

Round lig. of uterus

⑪ Coccyx

L. ovary ⑧

Coccygeus m.

Median umbilical lig. ⑰

⑱ Cervix

Fundus of uterus ⑬

Pelvic diaphragm

Symphysis of pubis ①

Ext. anal sphincter m.

Urinary bladder ④

Anal canal

Urogenital diaphragm

Ext. anal sphincter m.

Vagina ⑨

MEDIAN SECTION—RIGHT LATERAL VIEW

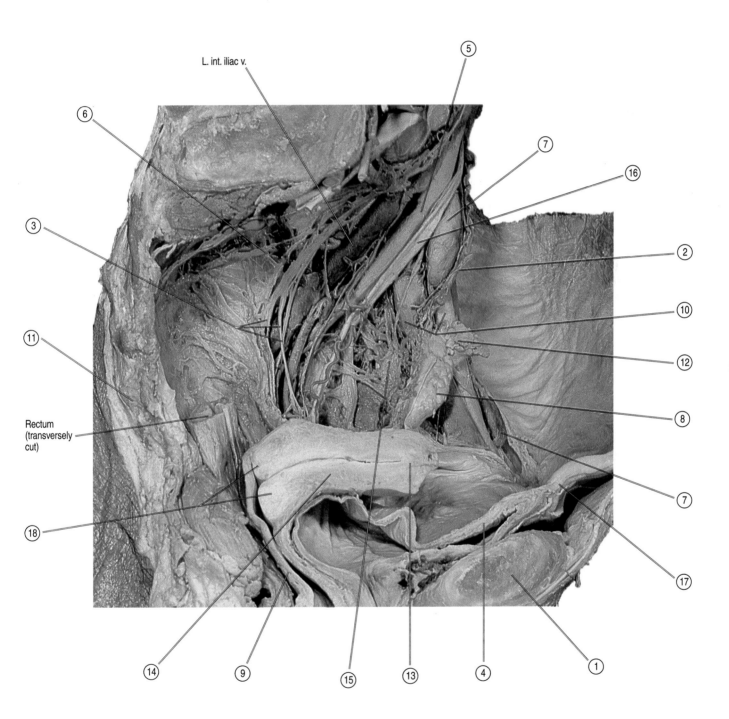

L. int. iliac v.

Rectum
(transversely
cut)

LEFT HALF OF HEMISECTED PELVIS—MEDIAL VIEW

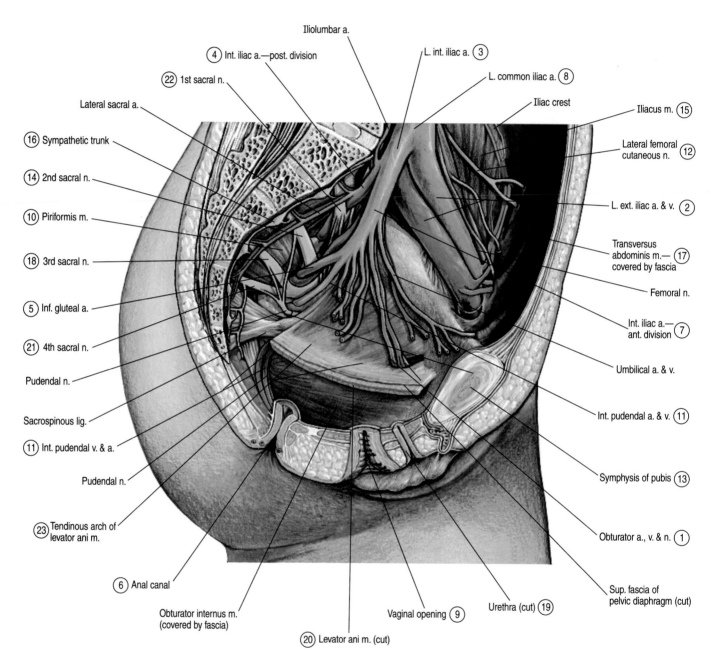

Iliolumbar a.

④ Int. iliac a.—post. division

㉒ 1st sacral n.

L. int. iliac a. ③

L. common iliac a. ⑧

Iliac crest

Iliacus m. ⑮

Lateral sacral a.

⑯ Sympathetic trunk

Lateral femoral cutaneous n. ⑫

⑭ 2nd sacral n.

L. ext. iliac a. & v. ②

⑩ Piriformis m.

Transversus abdominis m.— ⑰ covered by fascia

⑱ 3rd sacral n.

Femoral n.

⑤ Inf. gluteal a.

Int. iliac a.— ⑦ ant. division

㉑ 4th sacral n.

Umbilical a. & v.

Pudendal n.

Int. pudendal a. & v. ⑪

Sacrospinous lig.

⑪ Int. pudendal v. & a.

Symphysis of pubis ⑬

Pudendal n.

Obturator a., v. & n. ①

㉓ Tendinous arch of levator ani m.

Sup. fascia of pelvic diaphragm (cut)

⑥ Anal canal

Obturator internus m. (covered by fascia)

Vaginal opening ⑨

Urethra (cut) ⑲

㉒ Levator ani m. (cut)

MEDIAN SECTION—RIGHT LATERAL VIEW

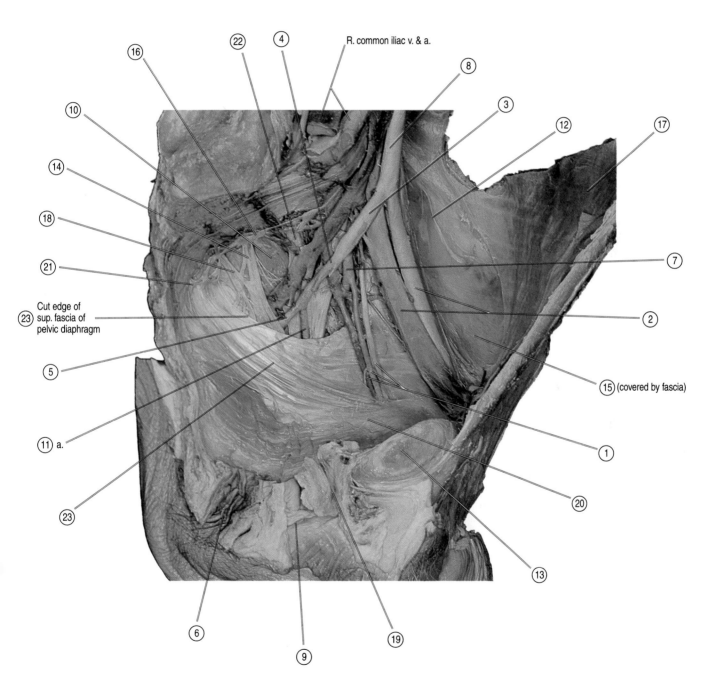

R. common iliac v. & a.

Cut edge of
sup. fascia of
pelvic diaphragm

(15) (covered by fascia)

MEDIAN SECTION—RIGHT LATERAL VIEW

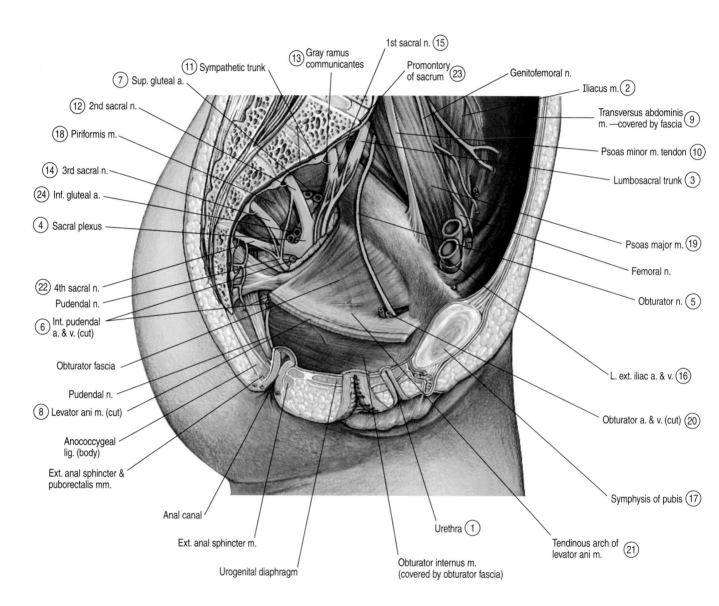

1st sacral n. (15)

(13) Gray ramus communicantes

(11) Sympathetic trunk

Promontory of sacrum (23)

Genitofemoral n.

(7) Sup. gluteal a.

Iliacus m. (2)

(12) 2nd sacral n.

Transversus abdominis m. —covered by fascia (9)

(18) Piriformis m.

Psoas minor m. tendon (10)

(14) 3rd sacral n.

Lumbosacral trunk (3)

(24) Inf. gluteal a.

(4) Sacral plexus

Psoas major m. (19)

Femoral n.

(22) 4th sacral n.
Pudendal n.

Obturator n. (5)

(6) Int. pudendal a. & v. (cut)

Obturator fascia

L. ext. iliac a. & v. (16)

Pudendal n.

(8) Levator ani m. (cut)

Obturator a. & v. (cut) (20)

Anococcygeal lig. (body)

Ext. anal sphincter & puborectalis mm.

Symphysis of pubis (17)

Anal canal

Urethra (1)

Ext. anal sphincter m.

Tendinous arch of levator ani m. (21)

Urogenital diaphragm

Obturator internus m. (covered by obturator fascia)

MEDIAN SECTION—RIGHT LATERAL VIEW

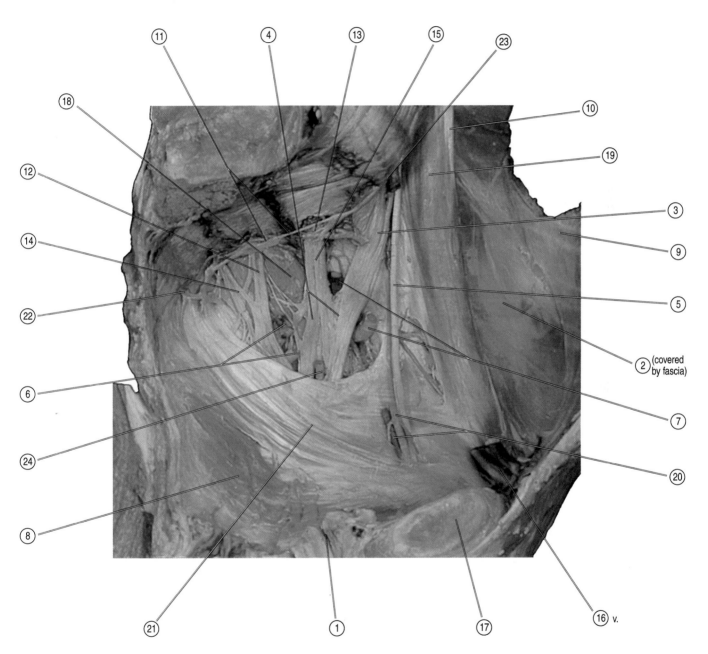

MEDIAN SECTION—RIGHT LATERAL VIEW

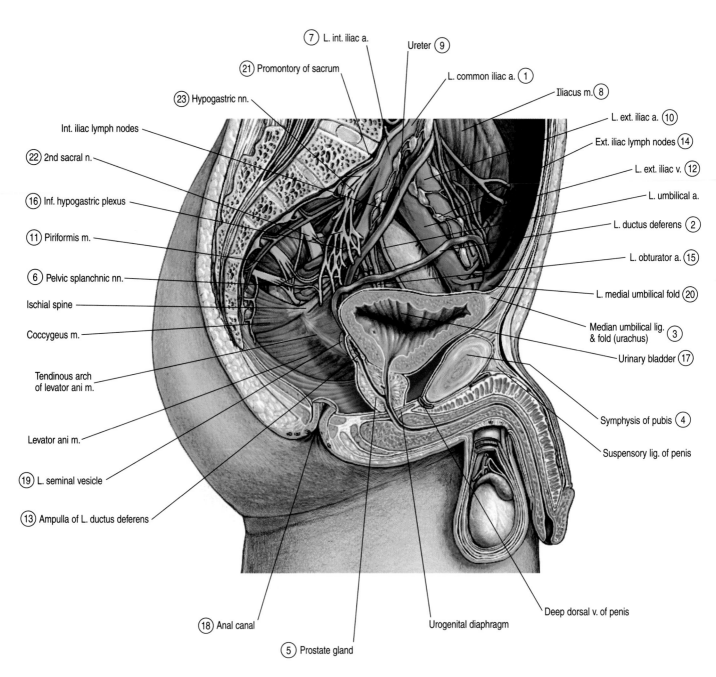

⑦ L. int. iliac a.

Ureter ⑨

㉑ Promontory of sacrum

L. common iliac a. ①

㉓ Hypogastric nn.

Iliacus m. ⑧

Int. iliac lymph nodes

L. ext. iliac a. ⑩

Ext. iliac lymph nodes ⑭

㉒ 2nd sacral n.

L. ext. iliac v. ⑫

⑯ Inf. hypogastric plexus

L. umbilical a.

L. ductus deferens ②

⑪ Piriformis m.

L. obturator a. ⑮

⑥ Pelvic splanchnic nn.

L. medial umbilical fold ⑳

Ischial spine

Median umbilical lig.
& fold (urachus) ③

Coccygeus m.

Urinary bladder ⑰

Tendinous arch
of levator ani m.

Levator ani m.

Symphysis of pubis ④

Suspensory lig. of penis

⑲ L. seminal vesicle

⑬ Ampulla of L. ductus deferens

Deep dorsal v. of penis

⑱ Anal canal

Urogenital diaphragm

⑤ Prostate gland

MEDIAN SECTION—RIGHT LATERAL VIEW

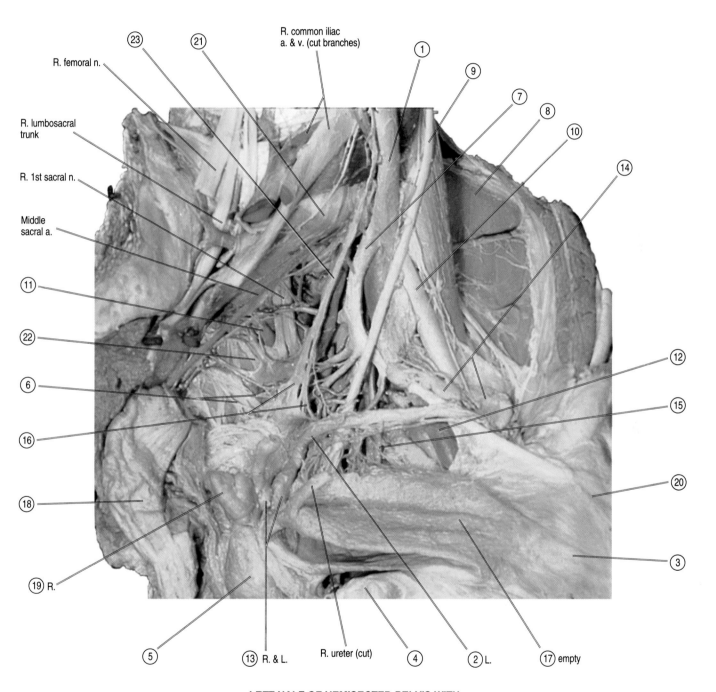

R. common iliac
a. & v. (cut branches)

R. femoral n.

R. lumbosacral
trunk

R. 1st sacral n.

Middle
sacral a.

R. ureter (cut)

R. & L.

L.

empty

R.

**LEFT HALF OF HEMISECTED PELVIS WITH
BLADDER PULLED ANTERIORLY—MEDIAL VIEW**

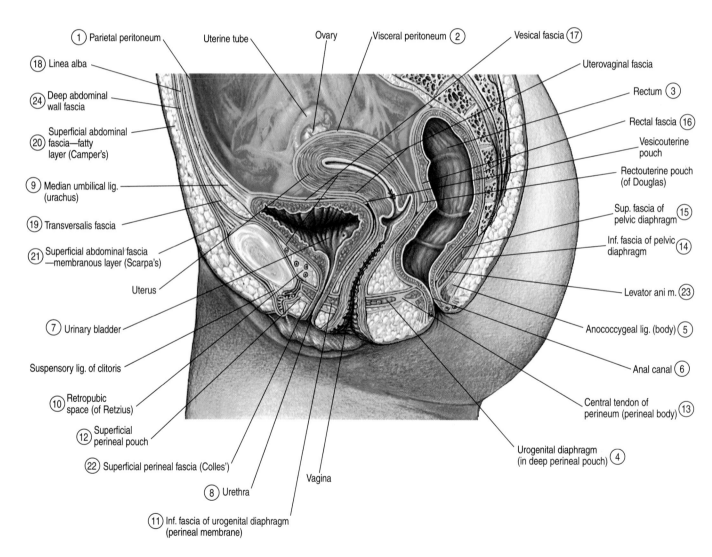

1 Parietal peritoneum

Uterine tube

Ovary

Visceral peritoneum 2

Vesical fascia 17

18 Linea alba

24 Deep abdominal wall fascia

20 Superficial abdominal fascia—fatty layer (Camper's)

9 Median umbilical lig. (urachus)

19 Transversalis fascia

21 Superficial abdominal fascia—membranous layer (Scarpa's)

Uterus

7 Urinary bladder

Suspensory lig. of clitoris

10 Retropubic space (of Retzius)

12 Superficial perineal pouch

22 Superficial perineal fascia (Colles')

Vagina

8 Urethra

11 Inf. fascia of urogenital diaphragm (perineal membrane)

Uterovaginal fascia

Rectum 3

Rectal fascia 16

Vesicouterine pouch

Rectouterine pouch (of Douglas)

Sup. fascia of pelvic diaphragm 15

Inf. fascia of pelvic diaphragm 14

Levator ani m. 23

Anococcygeal lig. (body) 5

Anal canal 6

Central tendon of perineum (perineal body) 13

Urogenital diaphragm (in deep perineal pouch) 4

MEDIAN SECTION—LEFT LATERAL VIEW

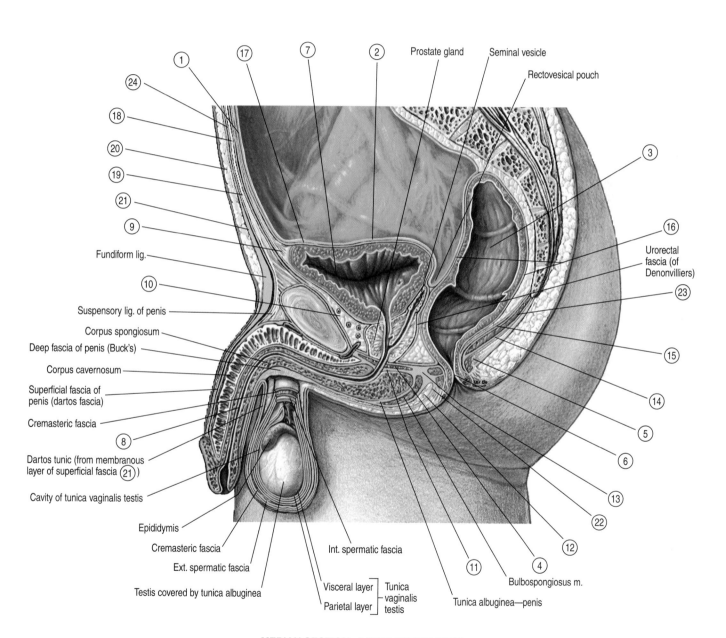

Prostate gland

Seminal vesicle

Rectovesical pouch

① ⑰ ⑦ ②

㉔

⑱

⑳

⑲

③

㉑

⑨

Fundiform lig.

⑯

Urorectal
fascia (of
Denonvilliers)

⑩

Suspensory lig. of penis

Corpus spongiosum

㉓

Deep fascia of penis (Buck's)

Corpus cavernosum

⑮

Superficial fascia of
penis (dartos fascia)

Cremasteric fascia

⑭

⑧

⑤

Dartos tunic (from membranous
layer of superficial fascia ㉑)

⑥

Cavity of tunica vaginalis testis

⑬

Epididymis

㉒

Cremasteric fascia

⑫

Ext. spermatic fascia

Int. spermatic fascia

⑪ ④

Bulbospongiosus m.

Testis covered by tunica albuginea

Visceral layer ⎤ Tunica
⎟ vaginalis
Parietal layer ⎦ testis

Tunica albuginea—penis

MEDIAN SECTION—LEFT LATERAL VIEW

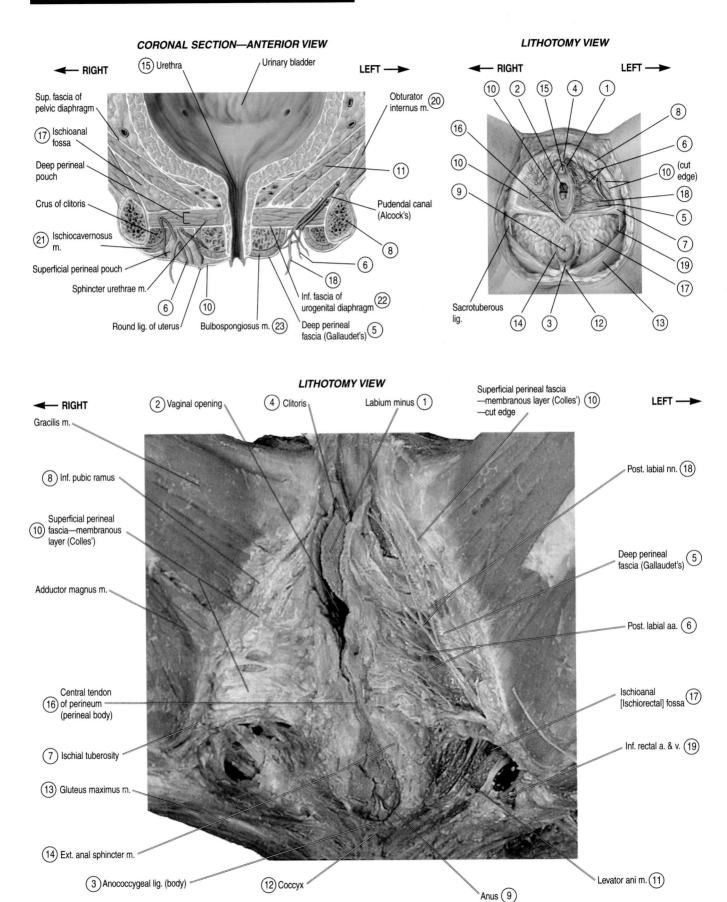

CORONAL SECTION—ANTERIOR VIEW

← RIGHT   (15) Urethra   Urinary bladder   LEFT →

Sup. fascia of pelvic diaphragm

(17) Ischioanal fossa

Deep perineal pouch

Crus of clitoris

(21) Ischiocavernosus m.

Superficial perineal pouch

Sphincter urethrae m.

Round lig. of uterus   Bulbospongiosus m. (23)

(6)   (10)

Obturator internus m. (20)

(11)

Pudendal canal (Alcock's)

(8)

(6)

(18)

Inf. fascia of urogenital diaphragm (22)

Deep perineal fascia (Gallaudet's) (5)

LITHOTOMY VIEW

← RIGHT   LEFT →

(10) (2) (15) (4) (1)

(16)

(10)

(9)

(8)

(6)

(10) (cut edge)

(18)

(5)

(7)

(19)

(17)

Sacrotuberous lig.

(14) (3) (12) (13)

LITHOTOMY VIEW

← RIGHT

(2) Vaginal opening   (4) Clitoris   Labium minus (1)   Superficial perineal fascia —membranous layer (Colles') (10) —cut edge   LEFT →

Gracilis m.

(8) Inf. pubic ramus

(10) Superficial perineal fascia—membranous layer (Colles')

Adductor magnus m.

Central tendon (16) of perineum (perineal body)

(7) Ischial tuberosity

(13) Gluteus maximus m.

(14) Ext. anal sphincter m.

(3) Anococcygeal lig. (body)   (12) Coccyx   Anus (9)

Post. labial nn. (18)

Deep perineal fascia (Gallaudet's) (5)

Post. labial aa. (6)

Ischioanal [Ischiorectal] fossa (17)

Inf. rectal a. & v. (19)

Levator ani m. (11)

LITHOTOMY VIEW

← RIGHT   LEFT →

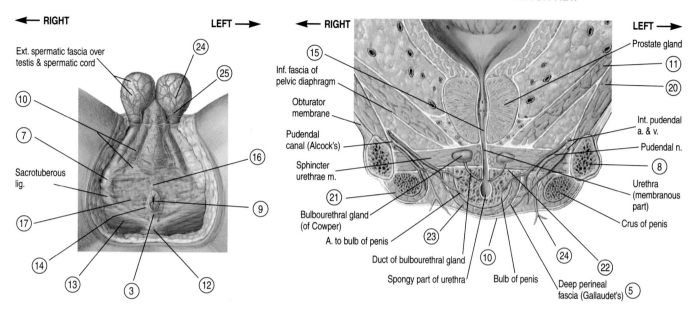

Ext. spermatic fascia over testis & spermatic cord

24

25

10

7

Sacrotuberous lig.

16

17

9

14

13

3

12

CORONAL SECTION—ANTERIOR VIEW

← RIGHT   LEFT →

15

Inf. fascia of pelvic diaphragm

Obturator membrane

Pudendal canal (Alcock's)

Sphincter urethrae m.

Bulbourethral gland (of Cowper)

A. to bulb of penis

21

23

Duct of bulbourethral gland

Spongy part of urethra

Bulb of penis

10

Prostate gland

11

20

Int. pudendal a. & v.

Pudendal n.

8

Urethra (membranous part)

Crus of penis

24

22

Deep perineal fascia (Gallaudet's)

5

LITHOTOMY VIEW

← RIGHT   LEFT →

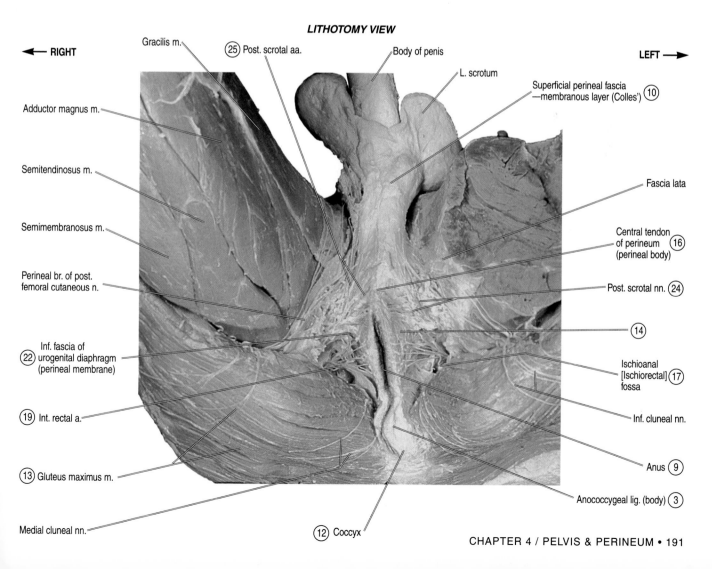

Gracilis m.

25 Post. scrotal aa.

Body of penis

L. scrotum

Superficial perineal fascia —membranous layer (Colles') 10

Adductor magnus m.

Semitendinosus m.

Semimembranosus m.

Fascia lata

Central tendon of perineum (perineal body) 16

Perineal br. of post. femoral cutaneous n.

Post. scrotal nn. 24

14

Inf. fascia of
22 urogenital diaphragm (perineal membrane)

Ischioanal [Ischiorectal] 17 fossa

Inf. cluneal nn.

19 Int. rectal a.

Anus 9

13 Gluteus maximus m.

Anococcygeal lig. (body) 3

Medial cluneal nn.

12 Coccyx

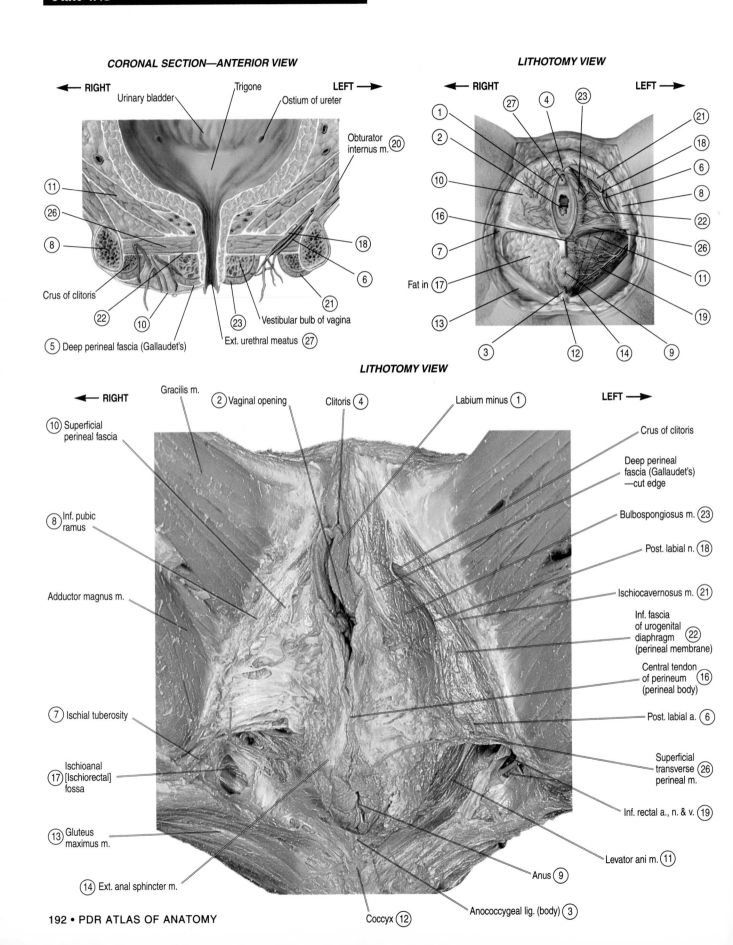

CORONAL SECTION—ANTERIOR VIEW

← RIGHT   LEFT →

Urinary bladder
Trigone
Ostium of ureter
Obturator internus m. ⑳
⑪
㉖
⑧
Crus of clitoris
㉒
⑩
⑱
⑥
㉓
Vestibular bulb of vagina
Ext. urethral meatus ㉗
⑤ Deep perineal fascia (Gallaudet's)
㉑

LITHOTOMY VIEW

← RIGHT   LEFT →

㉗ ④ ㉓
① ㉑
② ⑱
⑩ ⑥
⑯ ⑧
⑦ ㉒
Fat in ⑰ ㉖
⑬ ⑪
⑲
③ ⑫ ⑭ ⑨

LITHOTOMY VIEW

← RIGHT   LEFT →

Gracilis m.
② Vaginal opening
Clitoris ④
Labium minus ①

⑩ Superficial perineal fascia
Crus of clitoris
Deep perineal fascia (Gallaudet's) —cut edge
Bulbospongiosus m. ㉓
⑧ Inf. pubic ramus
Post. labial n. ⑱
Ischiocavernosus m. ㉑
Adductor magnus m.
Inf. fascia of urogenital diaphragm ㉒ (perineal membrane)
Central tendon of perineum ⑯ (perineal body)
Post. labial a. ⑥
⑦ Ischial tuberosity
Superficial transverse ㉖ perineal m.
Ischioanal ⑰ [Ischiorectal] fossa
Inf. rectal a., n. & v. ⑲
⑬ Gluteus maximus m.
Levator ani m. ⑪
Anus ⑨
⑭ Ext. anal sphincter m.
Anococcygeal lig. (body) ③
Coccyx ⑫

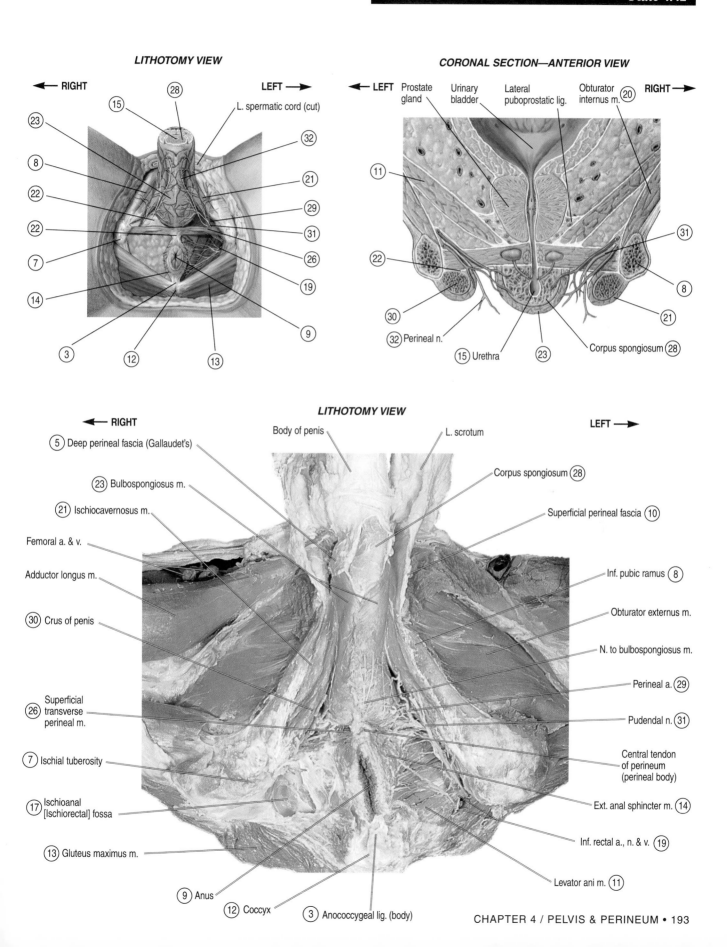

LITHOTOMY VIEW

← RIGHT LEFT →

(28)
(15)
(23)
(8)
(22)
(22)
(7)
(14)
L. spermatic cord (cut)
(32)
(21)
(29)
(31)
(26)
(19)
(9)
(3)
(12)
(13)

CORONAL SECTION—ANTERIOR VIEW

← LEFT Prostate gland Urinary bladder Lateral puboprostatic lig. Obturator internus m. (20) RIGHT →

(11)
(22)
(30)
(32) Perineal n.
(15) Urethra
(23)
Corpus spongiosum (28)
Corpus spongiosum (28)
(31)
(8)
(21)

LITHOTOMY VIEW

← RIGHT Body of penis L. scrotum LEFT →

(5) Deep perineal fascia (Gallaudet's)
(23) Bulbospongiosus m.
(21) Ischiocavernosus m.
Femoral a. & v.
Adductor longus m.
(30) Crus of penis
(26) Superficial transverse perineal m.
(7) Ischial tuberosity
(17) Ischioanal [Ischiorectal] fossa
(13) Gluteus maximus m.
(9) Anus
(12) Coccyx
(3) Anococcygeal lig. (body)

Corpus spongiosum (28)
Superficial perineal fascia (10)
Inf. pubic ramus (8)
Obturator externus m.
N. to bulbospongiosus m.
Perineal a. (29)
Pudendal n. (31)
Central tendon of perineum (perineal body)
Ext. anal sphincter m. (14)
Inf. rectal a., n. & v. (19)
Levator ani m. (11)

Perineum—Female III
Plate 4.43

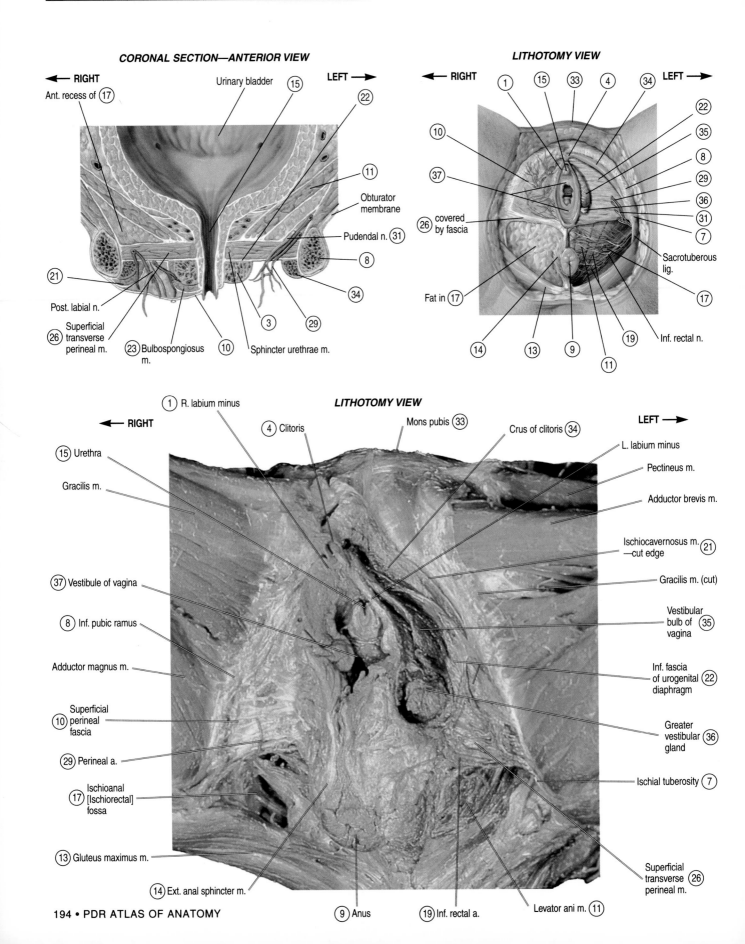

CORONAL SECTION—ANTERIOR VIEW

← RIGHT LEFT →

Urinary bladder 15

Ant. recess of 17

22

11

Obturator membrane

Pudendal n. 31

8

21

Post. labial n.

34

26 Superficial transverse perineal m.

23 Bulbospongiosus m.

3

29

10

Sphincter urethrae m.

LITHOTOMY VIEW

← RIGHT LEFT →

1 15 33 4 34

10

22

35

8

29

36

31

7

37

26 covered by fascia

Sacrotuberous lig.

Fat in 17

17

Inf. rectal n.

14 13 9 19

11

LITHOTOMY VIEW

1 R. labium minus

4 Clitoris

Mons pubis 33

Crus of clitoris 34

← RIGHT LEFT →

15 Urethra

L. labium minus

Gracilis m.

Pectineus m.

Adductor brevis m.

Ischiocavernosus m. 21 —cut edge

Gracilis m. (cut)

37 Vestibule of vagina

8 Inf. pubic ramus

Vestibular bulb of 35 vagina

Adductor magnus m.

Inf. fascia of urogenital 22 diaphragm

10 Superficial perineal fascia

Greater vestibular 36 gland

29 Perineal a.

17 Ischioanal [Ischiorectal] fossa

Ischial tuberosity 7

13 Gluteus maximus m.

Superficial transverse 26 perineal m.

14 Ext. anal sphincter m.

9 Anus

19 Inf. rectal a.

Levator ani m. 11

LITHOTOMY VIEW

← RIGHT   LEFT →

⑮ Corpus cavernosum

Deep fascia of penis

㉘

Spermatic cord (cut)

㉓

㉑

⑧

㉛

⑦

⑲

㉚

㉘

㉒

⑪

㊳

⑨   ⑭

CORONAL SECTION—ANTERIOR VIEW

← RIGHT   Urinary bladder   LEFT →

Prostate gland   Urogenital diaphragm

⑪   ⑪

⑪   ㉛

Ant. recess of ⑰

⑧   ㉙

㉚   Urethra ⑮

㉑

㉔ Post. scrotal n.   Post. scrotal a. ㉕

㉒ ㉓ ㉘

Bulbourethral gland (of Cowper)

LITHOTOMY VIEW

← RIGHT   LEFT →

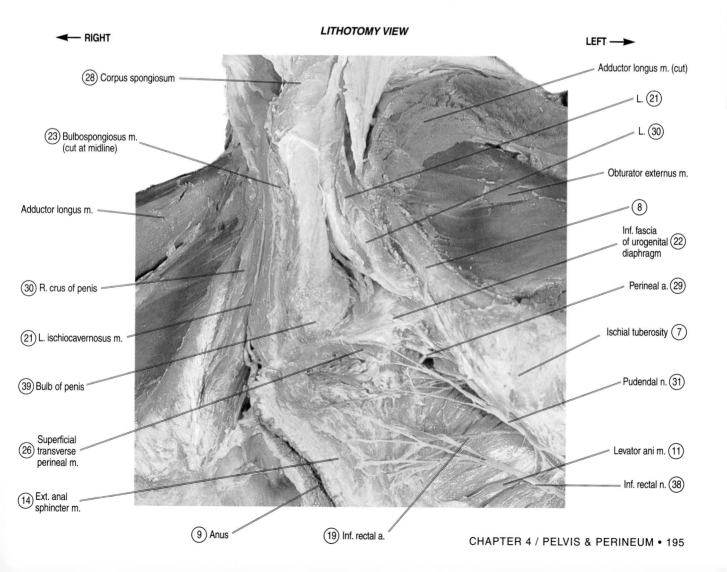

㉘ Corpus spongiosum   Adductor longus m. (cut)

L. ㉑

㉓ Bulbospongiosus m. (cut at midline)   L. ㉚

Obturator externus m.

Adductor longus m.   ⑧

Inf. fascia of urogenital ㉒ diaphragm

㉚ R. crus of penis   Perineal a. ㉙

㉑ L. ischiocavernosus m.   Ischial tuberosity ⑦

⑲ Bulb of penis   Pudendal n. ㉛

㉖ Superficial transverse perineal m.   Levator ani m. ⑪

⑭ Ext. anal sphincter m.   Inf. rectal n. ㊳

⑨ Anus   ⑲ Inf. rectal a.

CORONAL SECTION—ANTERIOR VIEW

← **RIGHT**   **LEFT** →

Urinary bladder

(15)

Obturator internus m.

(11)

(17)

(8)

(34) Crus of clitoris

(21)

(22)

(10)

(40)

(41)

Vestibular bulb of vagina (35)

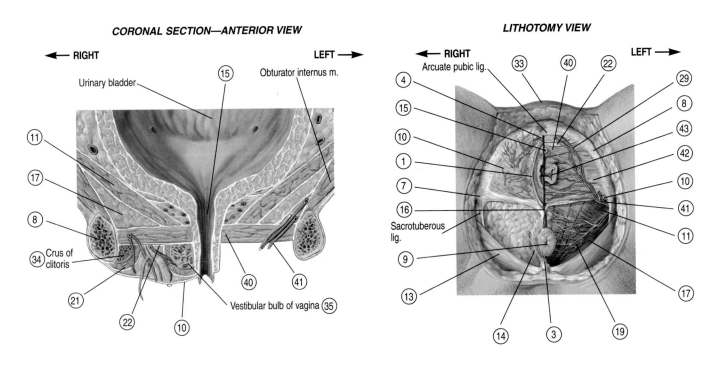

LITHOTOMY VIEW

← **RIGHT**   **LEFT** →

Arcuate pubic lig.

(33) (40) (22)

(4)

(15)

(10)

(1)

(7)

(16)

Sacrotuberous lig.

(9)

(13)

(29)

(8)

(43)

(42)

(10)

(41)

(11)

(17)

(14) (3) (19)

LITHOTOMY VIEW

← **RIGHT**   **LEFT** →

(4) Clitoris   Suspensory lig. of clitoris   Mons pubis (33)

Adductor longus m.

Gracilis m.

(1) R. labium minus

(15) Urethra

(21) Ischiocavernosus m. (visible through investing fascia)

(43) Vagina

(10) Superficial perineal fascia

(7) Ischial tuberosity

(17) Ischioanal [Ischiorectal] fossa

(13) Gluteus maximus m.

Intercavernosus septum

Inf. fascia of urogenital diaphragm (22) (cut & reflected)

Sphincter urethrae m. portion of (40) urogenital diaphragm

Inf. pubic ramus (8)

Perineal a. (29)

Inf. pudendal a. (41)

Deep transverse perineal m. (42)

Central tendon of perineum (16) (perineal body)

Levator ani m. (11)

Inf. rectal a. (19)

(9) Anus   Anococcygeal lig. (body) (3)   Ext. anal sphincter m. (14)

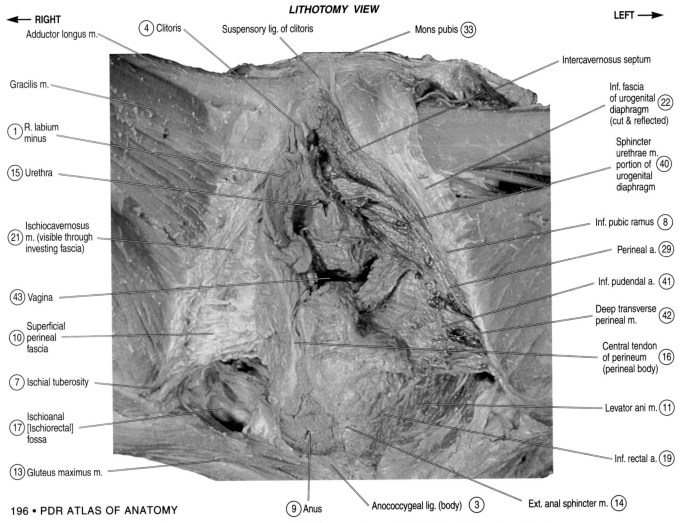

LITHOTOMY VIEW

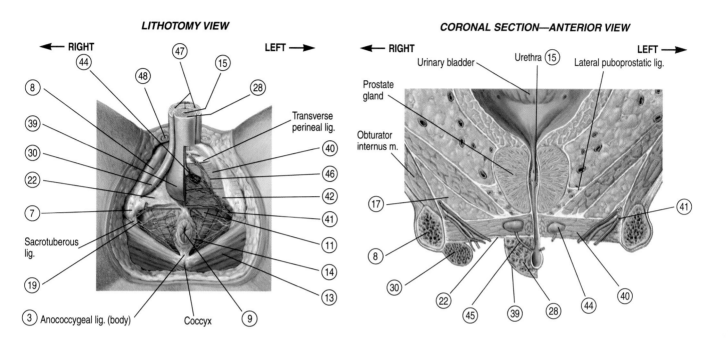

← RIGHT   47   LEFT →
44   15
8   48   28
39   Transverse
30   perineal lig.
22   40
7   46
Sacrotuberous   42
lig.   41
19   11
14
13
3 Anococcygeal lig. (body)   Coccyx   9

CORONAL SECTION—ANTERIOR VIEW

← RIGHT   Urethra 15   LEFT →
Urinary bladder   Lateral puboprostatic lig.
Prostate
gland
Obturator
internus m.
17   41
8   30   22   45   39   28   44   40

LITHOTOMY VIEW

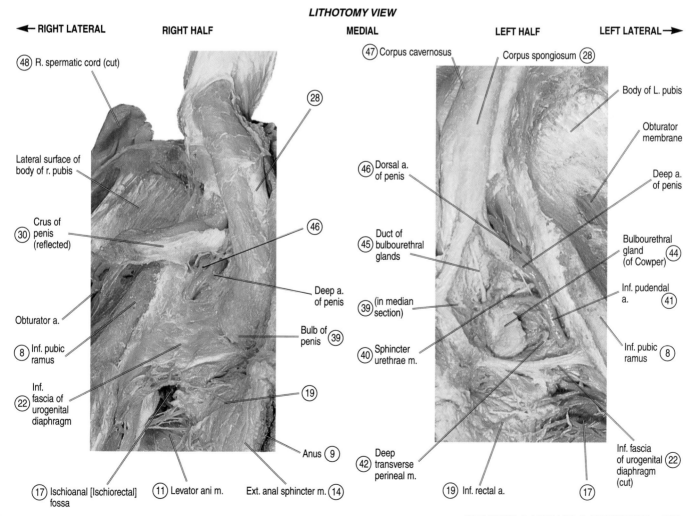

← RIGHT LATERAL   RIGHT HALF   MEDIAL   LEFT HALF   LEFT LATERAL →
47 Corpus cavernosus   Corpus spongiosum 28
48 R. spermatic cord (cut)   Body of L. pubis
28
Lateral surface of   Obturator
body of r. pubis   membrane
46 Dorsal a.   Deep a.
Crus of   of penis   of penis
30 penis   46
(reflected)   Duct of   Bulbourethral
45 bulbourethral   gland
glands   (of Cowper) 44
Deep a.
Obturator a.   of penis   39 (in median   Inf. pudendal
section)   a. 41
8 Inf. pubic   Bulb of
ramus   penis 39   40 Sphincter   Inf. pubic
urethrae m.   ramus 8
Inf.
22 fascia of   19
urogenital   Inf. fascia
diaphragm   42 Deep   of urogenital 22
transverse   diaphragm
Anus 9   perineal m.   (cut)
17 Ischioanal [Ischiorectal]   11 Levator ani m.   Ext. anal sphincter m. 14   19 Inf. rectal a.   17
fossa

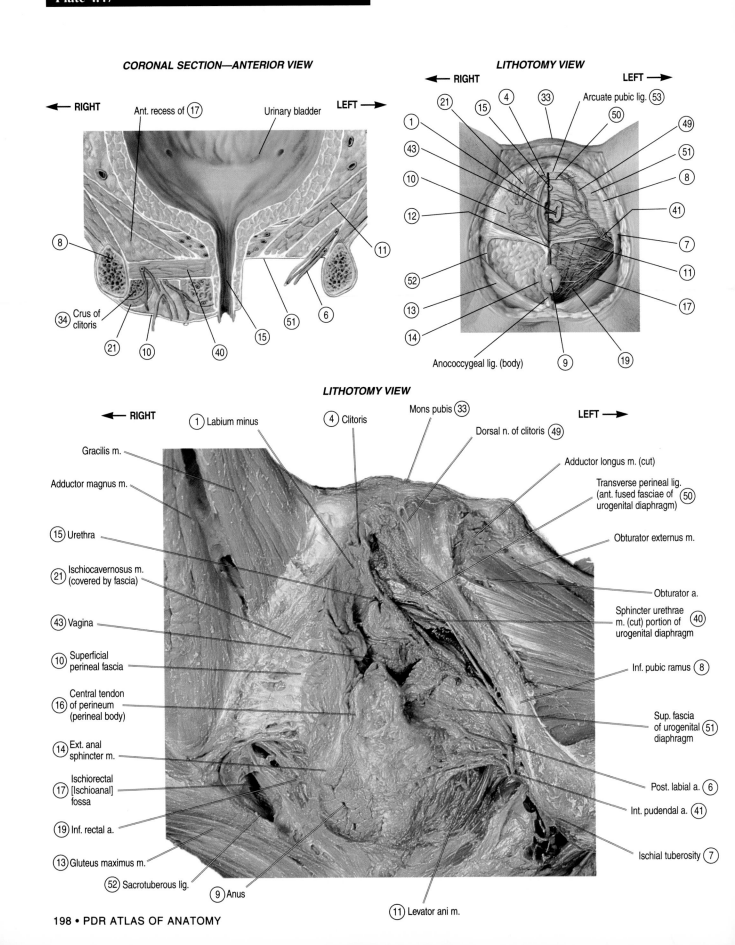

CORONAL SECTION—ANTERIOR VIEW

← RIGHT

Ant. recess of ⑰

Urinary bladder

LEFT →

⑧

⑪

Crus of clitoris ㉞

⑤

⑩

㊵

⑮

⑥

⑤

LITHOTOMY VIEW

← RIGHT

LEFT →

㉑ ⑮ ④ ㉝ Arcuate pubic lig. ㊿

① ㊿ ㊾

㊸ ㊿

⑩ ㊿

⑫ ㊸

⑧

㊶

⑦

⑪

㊼ ⑰

⑬

⑭

Anococcygeal lig. (body) ⑨ ⑲

LITHOTOMY VIEW

← RIGHT

① Labium minus

④ Clitoris

Mons pubis ㉝

Dorsal n. of clitoris ㊾

LEFT →

Gracilis m.

Adductor magnus m.

Adductor longus m. (cut)

Transverse perineal lig. (ant. fused fasciae of ㊿ urogenital diaphragm)

⑮ Urethra

Obturator externus m.

㉑ Ischiocavernosus m. (covered by fascia)

Obturator a.

㊸ Vagina

Sphincter urethrae m. (cut) portion of ㊵ urogenital diaphragm

⑩ Superficial perineal fascia

Inf. pubic ramus ⑧

⑯ Central tendon of perineum (perineal body)

Sup. fascia of urogenital ㊿ diaphragm

⑭ Ext. anal sphincter m.

⑰ Ischiorectal [Ischioanal] fossa

Post. labial a. ⑥

⑲ Inf. rectal a.

Int. pudendal a. ㊶

⑬ Gluteus maximus m.

Ischial tuberosity ⑦

㊼ Sacrotuberous lig.

⑨ Anus

⑪ Levator ani m.

LITHOTOMY VIEW

← RIGHT   LEFT →

CORONAL SECTION—ANTERIOR VIEW

← RIGHT   LEFT →

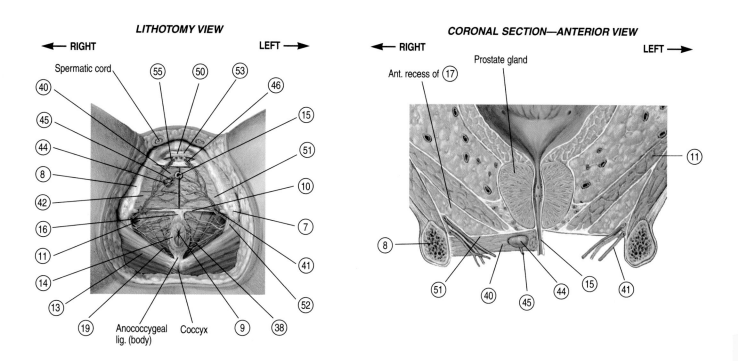

Spermatic cord — 55 50 53 46

40 45 44 8 42 16 11 14 13

15 51 10 7 41 52

19   Anococcygeal lig. (body)   Coccyx   9   38

Ant. recess of 17   Prostate gland   11

8

51   40   45   44   15   41

LITHOTOMY VIEWS

← RIGHT LATERAL   RIGHT HALF   MEDIAL   LEFT HALF   LEFT LATERAL →

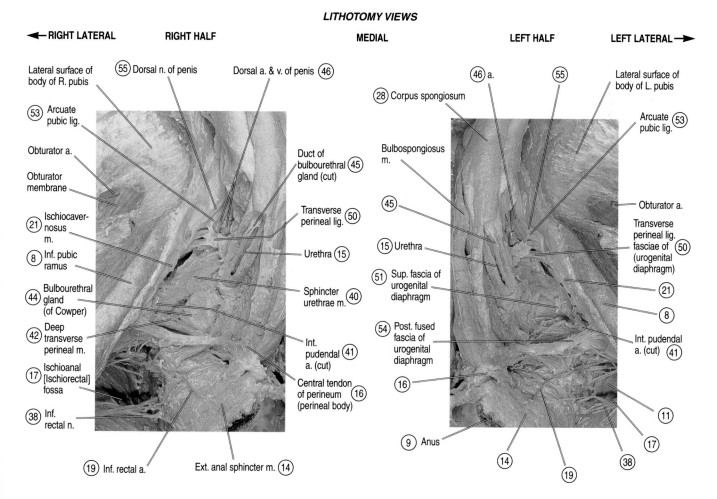

Lateral surface of body of R. pubis

55 Dorsal n. of penis   Dorsal a. & v. of penis 46

53 Arcuate pubic lig.

Obturator a.

Obturator membrane

21 Ischiocaver- nosus m.

8 Inf. pubic ramus

44 Bulbourethral gland (of Cowper)

42 Deep transverse perineal m.

17 Ischioanal [Ischiorectal] fossa

38 Inf. rectal n.

19 Inf. rectal a.

Duct of bulbourethral 45 gland (cut)

Transverse 50 perineal lig.

Urethra 15

Sphincter 40 urethrae m.

Int. pudendal 41 a. (cut)

Central tendon of perineum 16 (perineal body)

Ext. anal sphincter m. 14

46 a.   55

28 Corpus spongiosum

Bulbospongiosus m.

45

15 Urethra

51 Sup. fascia of urogenital diaphragm

54 Post. fused fascia of urogenital diaphragm

16

9 Anus

14   19   38

Lateral surface of body of L. pubis

Arcuate 53 pubic lig.

Obturator a.

Transverse perineal lig. fasciae of 50 (urogenital diaphragm)

21

8

Int. pudendal a. (cut) 41

11

17

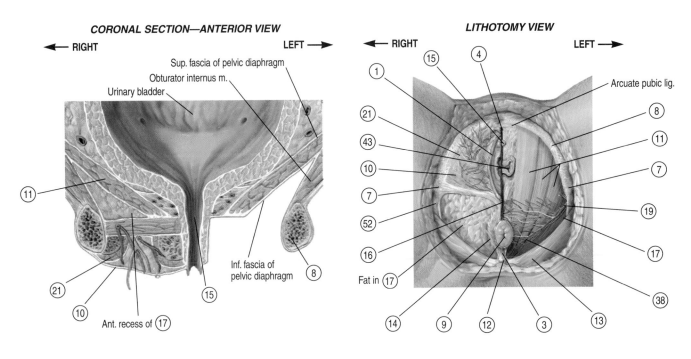

CORONAL SECTION—ANTERIOR VIEW

← RIGHT   LEFT →

Sup. fascia of pelvic diaphragm
Obturator internus m.
Urinary bladder

⑪

⑪ Inf. fascia of
pelvic diaphragm

⑧

㉑

⑩

Ant. recess of ⑰

⑮

LITHOTOMY VIEW

← RIGHT   LEFT →

⑮   ④

①   Arcuate pubic lig.

㉑   ⑧

㊸   ⑪

⑩   ⑦

⑦   ⑲

㊱   ⑰

⑯   ㊳

Fat in ⑰

⑭   ⑨   ⑫   ③   ⑬

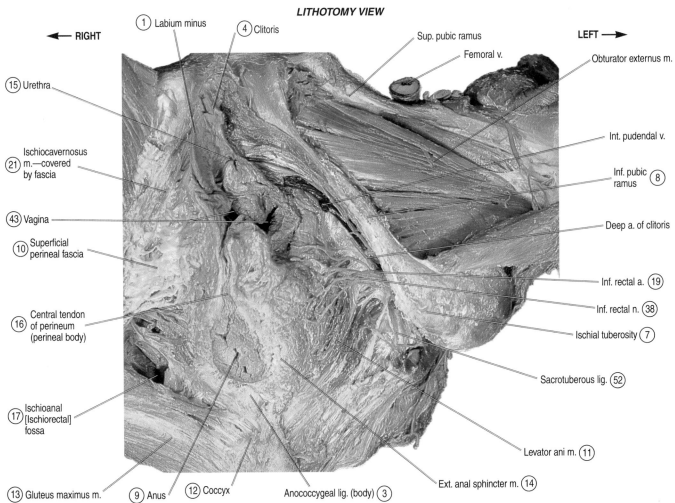

LITHOTOMY VIEW

① Labium minus   ④ Clitoris   Sup. pubic ramus   LEFT →

Femoral v.

Obturator externus m.

⑮ Urethra

Int. pudendal v.

㉑ Ischiocavernosus
m.—covered
by fascia

Inf. pubic ⑧
ramus

㊸ Vagina

Deep a. of clitoris

⑩ Superficial
perineal fascia

Inf. rectal a. ⑲

⑯ Central tendon
of perineum
(perineal body)

Inf. rectal n. ㊳

Ischial tuberosity ⑦

⑰ Ischioanal
[Ischiorectal]
fossa

Sacrotuberous lig. ㊷

Levator ani m. ⑪

⑬ Gluteus maximus m.   ⑨ Anus   ⑫ Coccyx   Anococcygeal lig. (body) ③   Ext. anal sphincter m. ⑭

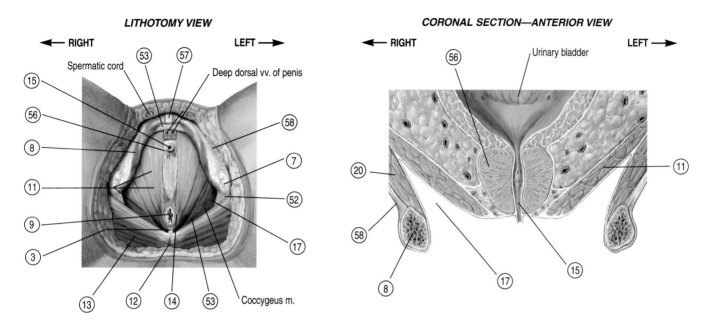

LITHOTOMY VIEW

← RIGHT   LEFT →

53 57
Spermatic cord   Deep dorsal vv. of penis
15
56   58
8   7
11   52
9   17
3
13 12 14 53 Coccygeus m.

CORONAL SECTION—ANTERIOR VIEW

← RIGHT   LEFT →

56   Urinary bladder
20   11
58
8   17   15

LITHOTOMY VIEW

← RIGHT   Puboprostatic m.   57 Pubic symphysis   Arcuate pubic lig. 53   LEFT →

15 Urethra   Obturator membrane 58

Obturator canal

56 Prostate gland

Puborectalis
m. part of 11

11 Levator ani m.

Inf. pubic
ramus 8

Obturator
internus
m. fascia

20 Obturator
internus m.

16 Central tendon
of perineum
(perineal body)

Ischial tuberosity 7

Ischioanal
[Ischiorectal] 17
fossa

52 Sacrotuberous lig.

Pubococcygeal
m. part of 11

14 Ext. anal sphincter m.

Iliococcygeal
m. part of 11

9 Anus

Coccyx 12   Anococcygeal lig. (body) 3

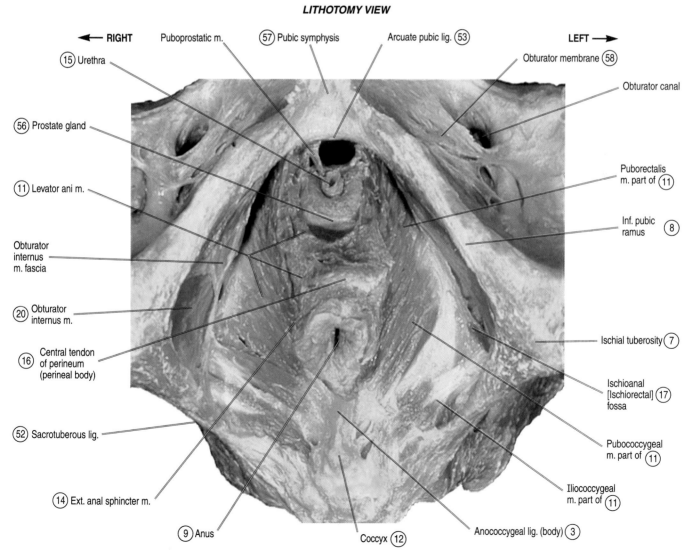

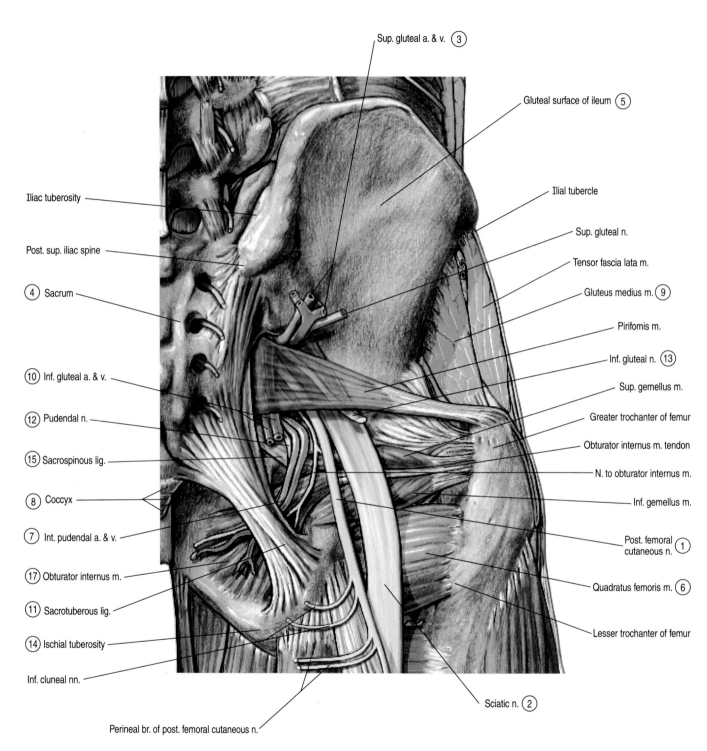

Sup. gluteal a. & v. ③

Gluteal surface of ileum ⑤

Ilial tubercle

Iliac tuberosity

Sup. gluteal n.

Tensor fascia lata m.

Post. sup. iliac spine

Gluteus medius m. ⑨

④ Sacrum

Pirifomis m.

Inf. gluteal n. ⑬

⑩ Inf. gluteal a. & v.

Sup. gemellus m.

⑫ Pudendal n.

Greater trochanter of femur

Obturator internus m. tendon

⑮ Sacrospinous lig.

N. to obturator internus m.

⑧ Coccyx

Inf. gemellus m.

⑦ Int. pudendal a. & v.

Post. femoral ①
cutaneous n.

⑰ Obturator internus m.

⑪ Sacrotuberous lig.

Quadratus femoris m. ⑥

⑭ Ischial tuberosity

Lesser trochanter of femur

Inf. cluneal nn.

Sciatic n. ②

Perineal br. of post. femoral cutaneous n.

GLUTEAL REGION—POSTERIOR VIEW

MIDLINE

RIGHT ⟶

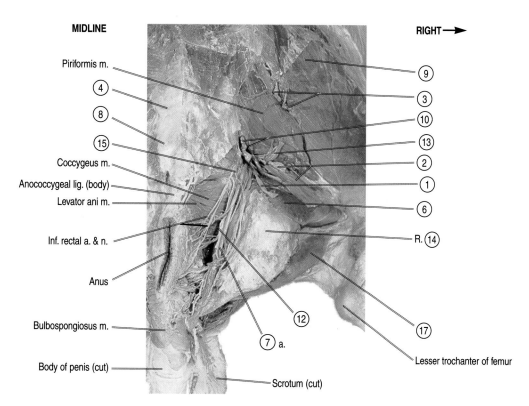

Piriformis m.

④

⑧

⑮

Coccygeus m.

Anococcygeal lig. (body)

Levator ani m.

Inf. rectal a. & n.

Anus

Bulbospongiosus m.

Body of penis (cut)

⑨

③

⑩

⑬

②

①

⑥

R. ⑭

⑦ a.

⑫

⑰

Lesser trochanter of femur

Scrotum (cut)

INFERIOR OBLIQUE VIEW OF RIGHT MALE PERINEUM & PUDENDAL CANAL

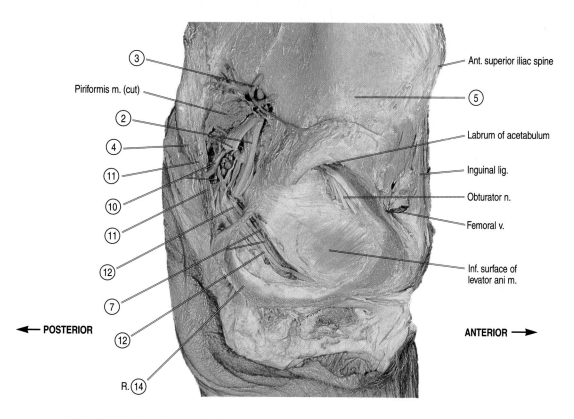

③

Piriformis m. (cut)

②

④

⑪

⑩

⑪

⑫

⑦

⑫

Ant. superior iliac spine

⑤

Labrum of acetabulum

Inguinal lig.

Obturator n.

Femoral v.

Inf. surface of
levator ani m.

⟵ POSTERIOR

ANTERIOR ⟶

R. ⑭

DISSECTION OF FEMALE PERINEUM FROM LATERAL APPROACH (ACETABULUM REMOVED)

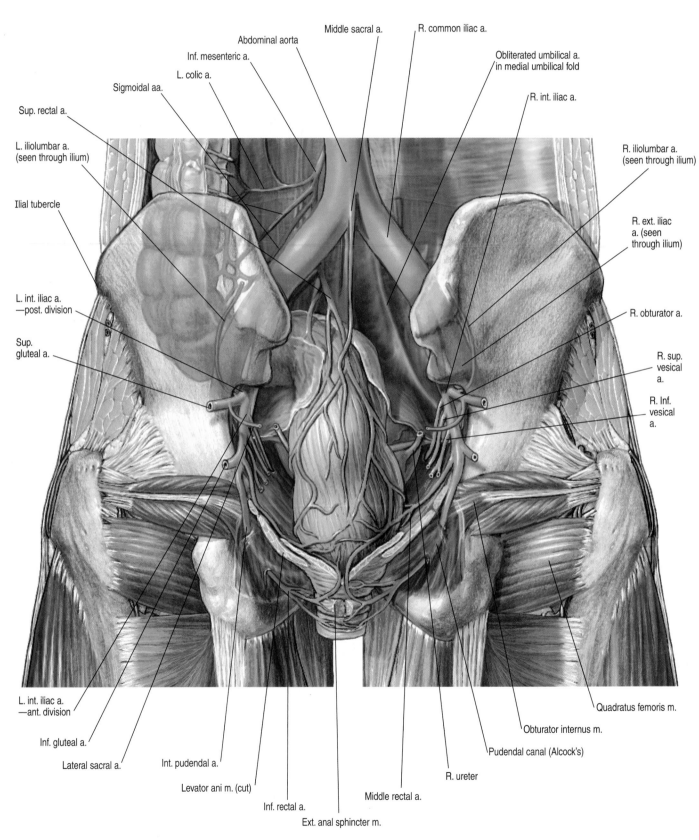

Middle sacral a.

R. common iliac a.

Abdominal aorta

Inf. mesenteric a.

Obliterated umbilical a. in medial umbilical fold

L. colic a.

Sigmoidal aa.

R. int. iliac a.

Sup. rectal a.

L. iliolumbar a. (seen through ilium)

R. iliolumbar a. (seen through ilium)

Ilial tubercle

R. ext. iliac a. (seen through ilium)

L. int. iliac a. —post. division

R. obturator a.

Sup. gluteal a.

R. sup. vesical a.

R. Inf. vesical a.

L. int. iliac a. —ant. division

Quadratus femoris m.

Inf. gluteal a.

Obturator internus m.

Lateral sacral a.

Pudendal canal (Alcock's)

Int. pudendal a.

R. ureter

Levator ani m. (cut)

Middle rectal a.

Inf. rectal a.

Ext. anal sphincter m.

POSTERIOR VIEW WITH SACRUM REMOVED

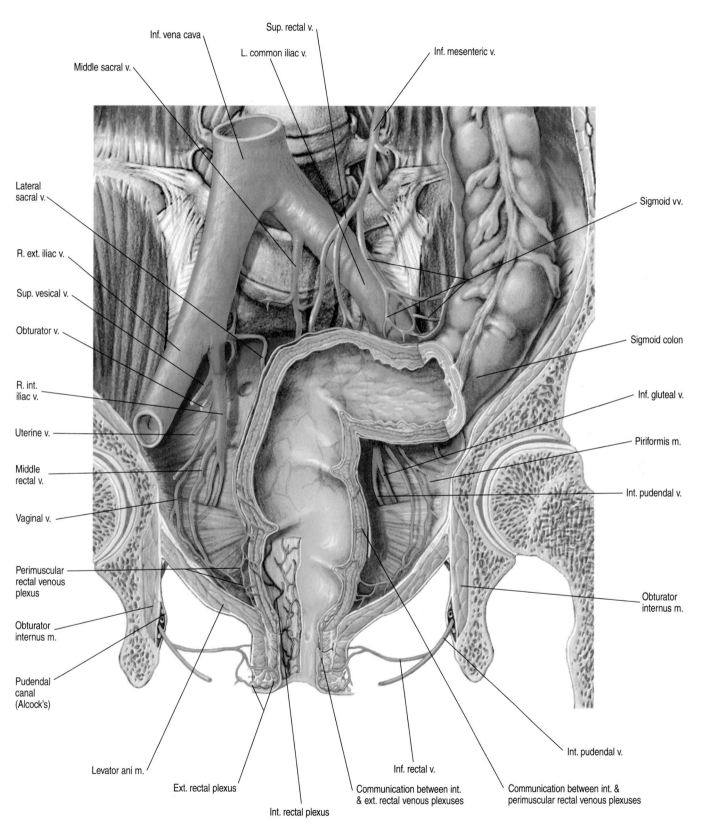

Inf. vena cava

Sup. rectal v.

Middle sacral v.

L. common iliac v.

Inf. mesenteric v.

Sigmoid vv.

Lateral sacral v.

R. ext. iliac v.

Sup. vesical v.

Obturator v.

Sigmoid colon

R. int. iliac v.

Inf. gluteal v.

Uterine v.

Piriformis m.

Middle rectal v.

Int. pudendal v.

Vaginal v.

Perimuscular rectal venous plexus

Obturator internus m.

Obturator internus m.

Pudendal canal (Alcock's)

Int. pudendal v.

Levator ani m.

Ext. rectal plexus

Inf. rectal v.

Communication between int. & ext. rectal venous plexuses

Communication between int. & perimuscular rectal venous plexuses

Int. rectal plexus

CORONAL SECTION—ANTERIOR VIEW

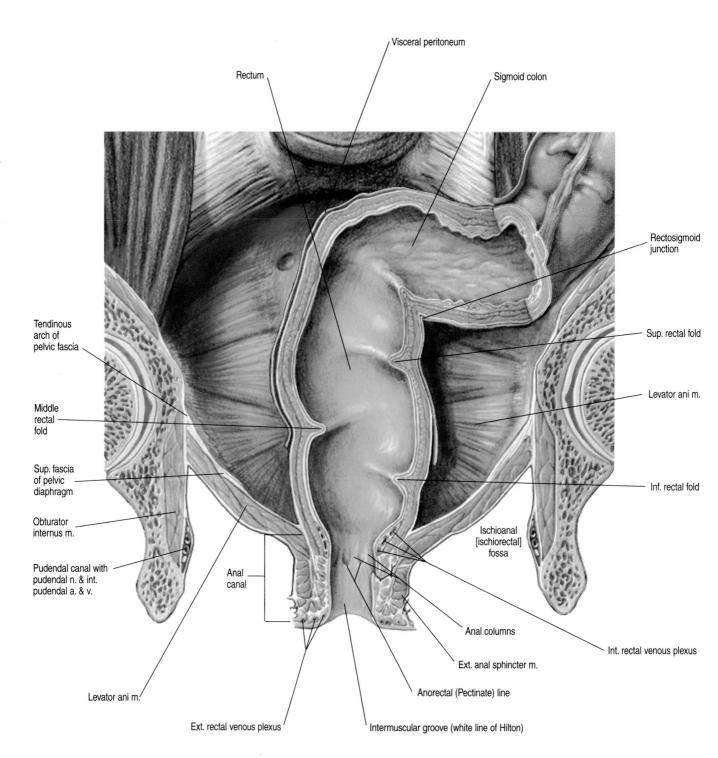

Visceral peritoneum

Rectum

Sigmoid colon

Rectosigmoid junction

Tendinous arch of pelvic fascia

Sup. rectal fold

Middle rectal fold

Levator ani m.

Sup. fascia of pelvic diaphragm

Inf. rectal fold

Obturator internus m.

Pudendal canal with pudendal n. & int. pudendal a. & v.

Anal canal

Ischioanal [ischiorectal] fossa

Anal columns

Int. rectal venous plexus

Levator ani m.

Ext. anal sphincter m.

Ext. rectal venous plexus

Anorectal (Pectinate) line

Intermuscular groove (white line of Hilton)

CORONAL SECTION—ANTERIOR VIEW

Lower Limb

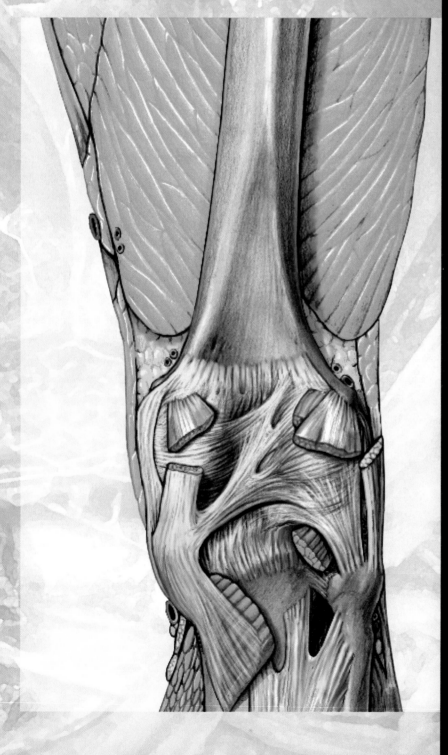

Chapter 5

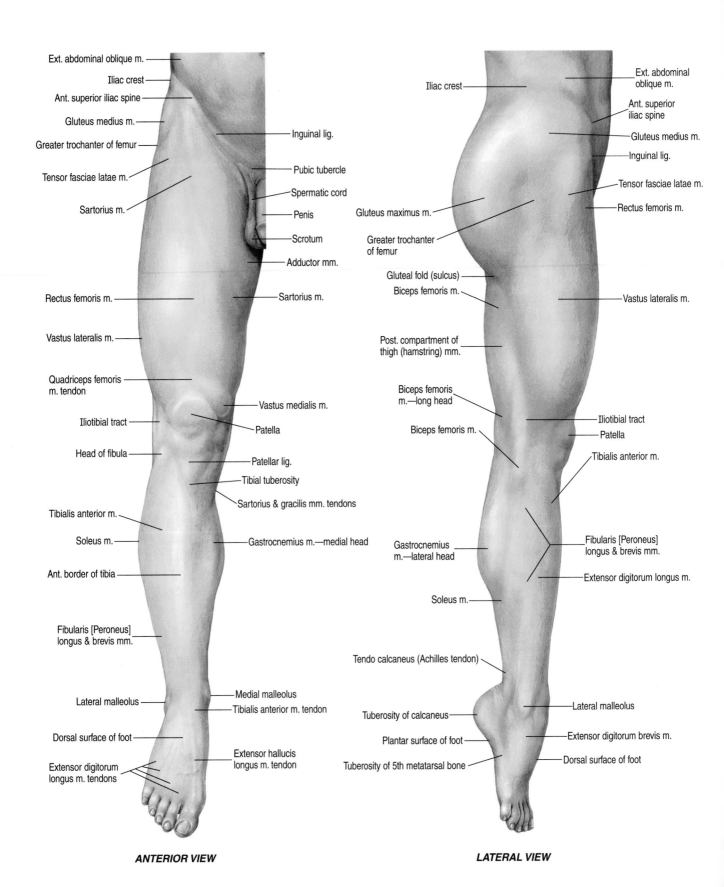

Ext. abdominal oblique m.
Iliac crest
Ant. superior iliac spine
Gluteus medius m.
Greater trochanter of femur
Tensor fasciae latae m.
Sartorius m.
Rectus femoris m.
Vastus lateralis m.
Quadriceps femoris m. tendon
Iliotibial tract
Head of fibula
Tibialis anterior m.
Soleus m.
Ant. border of tibia
Fibularis [Peroneus] longus & brevis mm.
Lateral malleolus
Dorsal surface of foot
Extensor digitorum longus m. tendons

Inguinal lig.
Pubic tubercle
Spermatic cord
Penis
Scrotum
Adductor mm.
Sartorius m.
Vastus medialis m.
Patella
Patellar lig.
Tibial tuberosity
Sartorius & gracilis mm. tendons
Gastrocnemius m.—medial head
Medial malleolus
Tibialis anterior m. tendon
Extensor hallucis longus m. tendon

ANTERIOR VIEW

Iliac crest
Gluteus maximus m.
Greater trochanter of femur
Gluteal fold (sulcus)
Biceps femoris m.
Post. compartment of thigh (hamstring) mm.
Biceps femoris m.—long head
Biceps femoris m.
Gastrocnemius m.—lateral head
Soleus m.
Tendo calcaneus (Achilles tendon)
Tuberosity of calcaneus
Plantar surface of foot
Tuberosity of 5th metatarsal bone

Ext. abdominal oblique m.
Ant. superior iliac spine
Gluteus medius m.
Inguinal lig.
Tensor fasciae latae m.
Rectus femoris m.
Vastus lateralis m.
Iliotibial tract
Patella
Tibialis anterior m.
Fibularis [Peroneus] longus & brevis mm.
Extensor digitorum longus m.
Lateral malleolus
Extensor digitorum brevis m.
Dorsal surface of foot

LATERAL VIEW

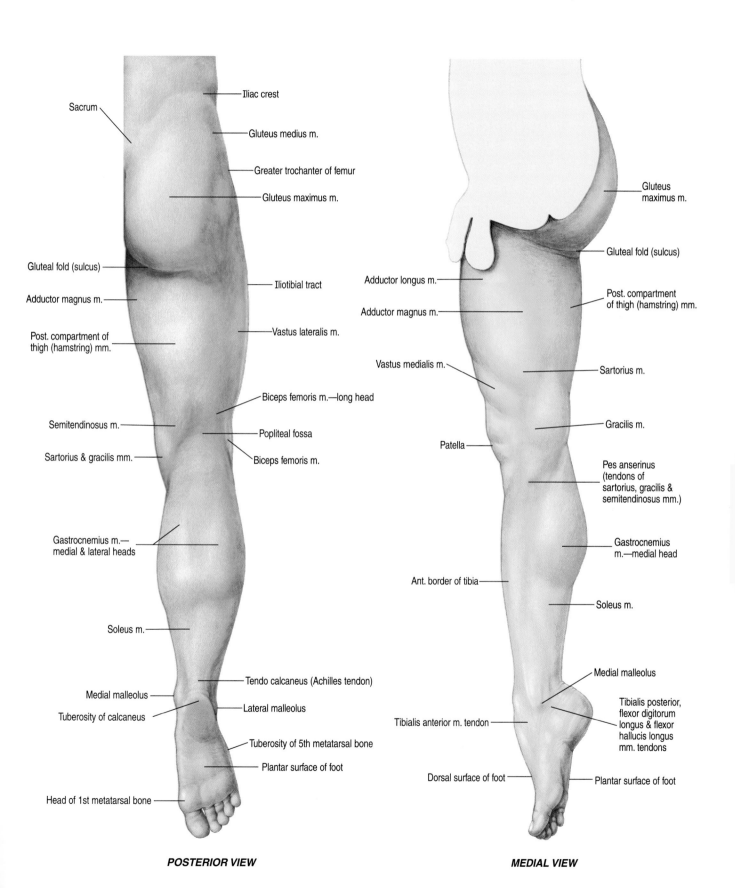

Iliac crest

Sacrum

Gluteus medius m.

Greater trochanter of femur

Gluteus maximus m.

Gluteal fold (sulcus)

Adductor magnus m.

Post. compartment of thigh (hamstring) mm.

Iliotibial tract

Vastus lateralis m.

Biceps femoris m.—long head

Semitendinosus m.

Popliteal fossa

Sartorius & gracilis mm.

Biceps femoris m.

Gastrocnemius m.— medial & lateral heads

Soleus m.

Medial malleolus

Tuberosity of calcaneus

Tendo calcaneus (Achilles tendon)

Lateral malleolus

Tuberosity of 5th metatarsal bone

Plantar surface of foot

Head of 1st metatarsal bone

POSTERIOR VIEW

Gluteus maximus m.

Gluteal fold (sulcus)

Adductor longus m.

Post. compartment of thigh (hamstring) mm.

Adductor magnus m.

Vastus medialis m.

Sartorius m.

Gracilis m.

Patella

Pes anserinus (tendons of sartorius, gracilis & semitendinosus mm.)

Gastrocnemius m.—medial head

Ant. border of tibia

Soleus m.

Medial malleolus

Tibialis posterior, flexor digitorum longus & flexor hallucis longus mm. tendons

Tibialis anterior m. tendon

Dorsal surface of foot

Plantar surface of foot

MEDIAL VIEW

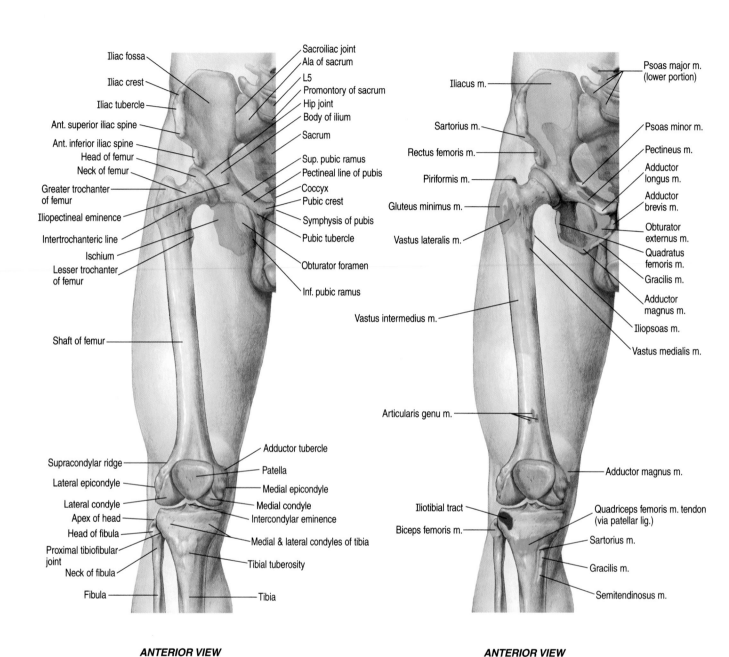

Iliac fossa
Iliac crest
Iliac tubercle
Ant. superior iliac spine
Ant. inferior iliac spine
Head of femur
Neck of femur
Greater trochanter of femur
Iliopectineal eminence
Intertrochanteric line
Ischium
Lesser trochanter of femur

Sacroiliac joint
Ala of sacrum
L5
Promontory of sacrum
Hip joint
Body of ilium
Sacrum
Sup. pubic ramus
Pectineal line of pubis
Coccyx
Pubic crest
Symphysis of pubis
Pubic tubercle
Obturator foramen
Inf. pubic ramus

Shaft of femur

Supracondylar ridge
Lateral epicondyle
Lateral condyle
Apex of head
Head of fibula
Proximal tibiofibular joint
Neck of fibula
Fibula

Adductor tubercle
Patella
Medial epicondyle
Medial condyle
Intercondylar eminence
Medial & lateral condyles of tibia
Tibial tuberosity
Tibia

ANTERIOR VIEW

Iliacus m.
Sartorius m.
Rectus femoris m.
Piriformis m.
Gluteus minimus m.
Vastus lateralis m.

Psoas major m. (lower portion)
Psoas minor m.
Pectineus m.
Adductor longus m.
Adductor brevis m.
Obturator externus m.
Quadratus femoris m.
Gracilis m.
Adductor magnus m.
Iliopsoas m.
Vastus medialis m.

Vastus intermedius m.

Articularis genu m.

Iliotibial tract
Biceps femoris m.

Adductor magnus m.
Quadriceps femoris m. tendon (via patellar lig.)
Sartorius m.
Gracilis m.
Semitendinosus m.

ANTERIOR VIEW

- Gluteus minimus
- Vastus lateralis
- Vastus medialis
- Iliopsoas
- Vastus intermedius
- Obturator externus

- Adductor longus
- Iliotibial tract
- Piriformis
- Articularis genu
- Patellar ligament
- Sartorius

- Gracilis
- Adductor brevis
- Quadratus femoris
- Biceps femoris
- Semitendinosus
- Iliacus

- Psoas major
- Rectus femoris
- Psoas minor
- Adductor magnus
- Pectineus

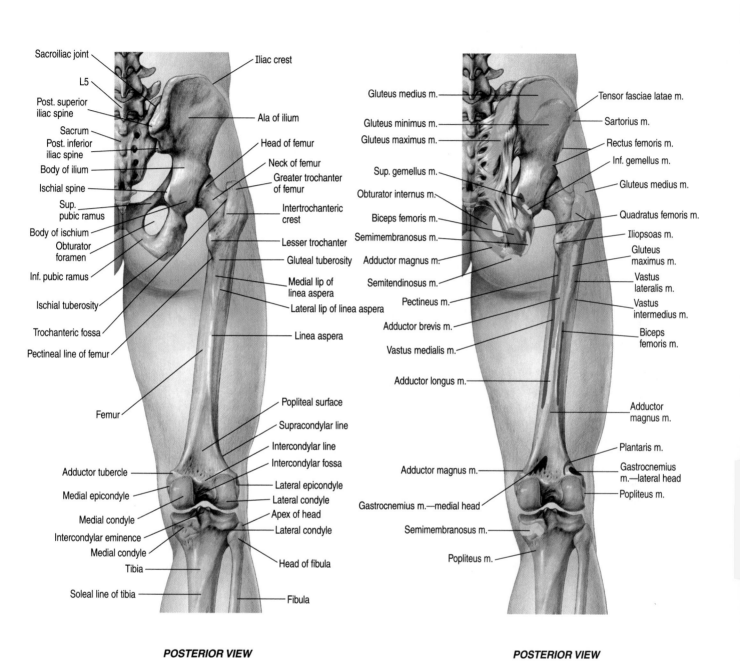

Sacroiliac joint
L5
Post. superior iliac spine
Sacrum
Post. inferior iliac spine
Body of ilium
Ischial spine
Sup. pubic ramus
Body of ischium
Obturator foramen
Inf. pubic ramus
Ischial tuberosity
Trochanteric fossa
Pectineal line of femur
Femur
Adductor tubercle
Medial epicondyle
Medial condyle
Intercondylar eminence
Medial condyle
Tibia
Soleal line of tibia

Iliac crest
Ala of ilium
Head of femur
Neck of femur
Greater trochanter of femur
Intertrochanteric crest
Lesser trochanter
Gluteal tuberosity
Medial lip of linea aspera
Lateral lip of linea aspera
Linea aspera
Popliteal surface
Supracondylar line
Intercondylar line
Intercondylar fossa
Lateral epicondyle
Lateral condyle
Apex of head
Lateral condyle
Head of fibula
Fibula

POSTERIOR VIEW

Gluteus medius m.
Gluteus minimus m.
Gluteus maximus m.
Sup. gemellus m.
Obturator internus m.
Biceps femoris m.
Semimembranosus m.
Adductor magnus m.
Semitendinosus m.
Pectineus m.
Adductor brevis m.
Vastus medialis m.
Adductor longus m.
Adductor magnus m.
Gastrocnemius m.—medial head
Semimembranosus m.
Popliteus m.

Tensor fasciae latae m.
Sartorius m.
Rectus femoris m.
Inf. gemellus m.
Gluteus medius m.
Quadratus femoris m.
Iliopsoas m.
Gluteus maximus m.
Vastus lateralis m.
Vastus intermedius m.
Biceps femoris m.
Adductor magnus m.
Plantaris m.
Gastrocnemius m.—lateral head
Popliteus m.

POSTERIOR VIEW

○ **Sartorius**
○ **Rectus femoris**
○ **Tensor fasciae latae**
○ **Gluteus medius**
○ **Gluteus minimus**
○ **Obturator internus**

○ **Semimembranosus**
○ **Popliteus**
○ **Adductor magnus**
○ **Gluteus maximus**
○ **Quadratus femoris**
○ **Inferior gemellus**

○ **Superior gemellus**
○ **Semitendinosus**
○ **Biceps femoris**
○ **Gastrocnemius**
○ **Iliopsoas**
○ **Pectineus**

○ **Vastus medialis**
○ **Adductor brevis**
○ **Adductor longus**
○ **Vastus lateralis**
○ **Vastus intermedius**
○ **Plantaris**

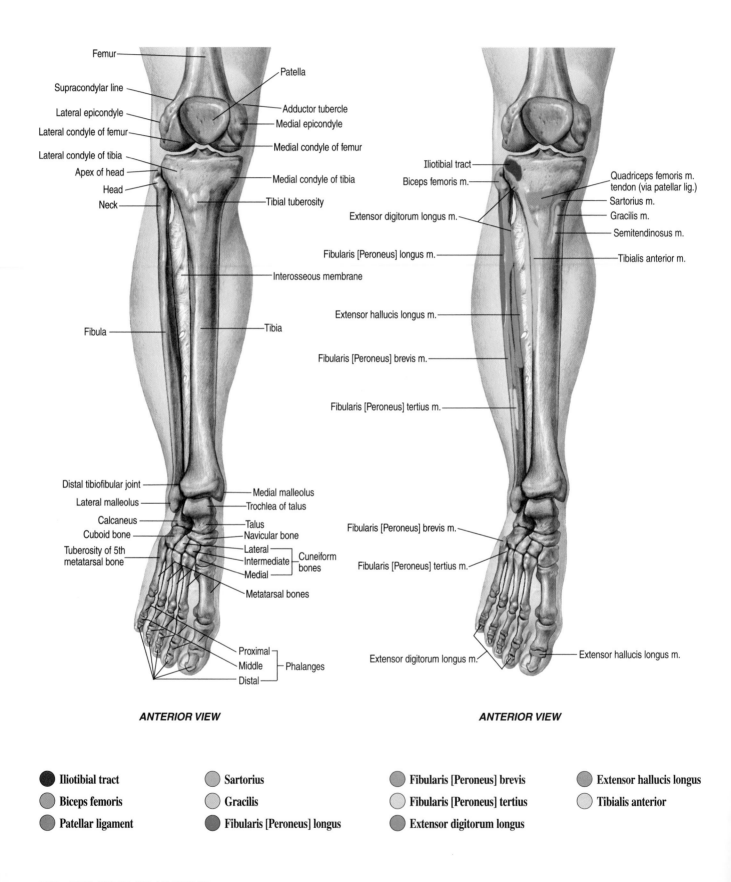

Femur

Supracondylar line

Lateral epicondyle

Lateral condyle of femur

Lateral condyle of tibia

Apex of head

Head

Neck

Fibula

Distal tibiofibular joint

Lateral malleolus

Calcaneus

Cuboid bone

Tuberosity of 5th metatarsal bone

Patella

Adductor tubercle

Medial epicondyle

Medial condyle of femur

Medial condyle of tibia

Tibial tuberosity

Interosseous membrane

Tibia

Medial malleolus

Trochlea of talus

Talus

Navicular bone

Lateral

Intermediate — Cuneiform bones

Medial

Metatarsal bones

Proximal

Middle — Phalanges

Distal

ANTERIOR VIEW

Iliotibial tract

Biceps femoris m.

Extensor digitorum longus m.

Fibularis [Peroneus] longus m.

Extensor hallucis longus m.

Fibularis [Peroneus] brevis m.

Fibularis [Peroneus] tertius m.

Fibularis [Peroneus] brevis m.

Fibularis [Peroneus] tertius m.

Extensor digitorum longus m.

Quadriceps femoris m. tendon (via patellar lig.)

Sartorius m.

Gracilis m.

Semitendinosus m.

Tibialis anterior m.

Extensor hallucis longus m.

ANTERIOR VIEW

- Iliotibial tract
- Biceps femoris
- Patellar ligament
- Sartorius
- Gracilis
- Fibularis [Peroneus] longus
- Fibularis [Peroneus] brevis
- Fibularis [Peroneus] tertius
- Extensor digitorum longus
- Extensor hallucis longus
- Tibialis anterior

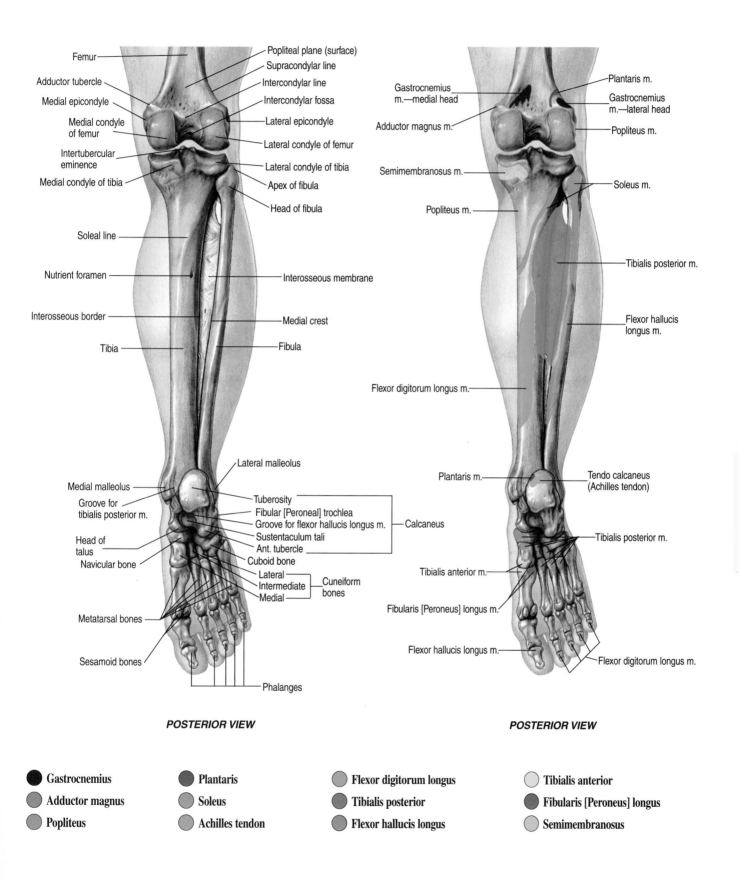

Femur

Popliteal plane (surface)

Adductor tubercle

Supracondylar line

Medial epicondyle

Intercondylar line

Medial condyle of femur

Intercondylar fossa

Intertubercular eminence

Lateral epicondyle

Medial condyle of tibia

Lateral condyle of femur

Lateral condyle of tibia

Apex of fibula

Head of fibula

Soleal line

Nutrient foramen

Interosseous membrane

Interosseous border

Medial crest

Tibia

Fibula

Lateral malleolus

Medial malleolus

Tuberosity

Groove for tibialis posterior m.

Fibular [Peroneal] trochlea

Groove for flexor hallucis longus m.

Calcaneus

Head of talus

Sustentaculum tali

Ant. tubercle

Navicular bone

Cuboid bone

Lateral

Intermediate

Cuneiform bones

Medial

Metatarsal bones

Sesamoid bones

Phalanges

Gastrocnemius m.—medial head

Plantaris m.

Gastrocnemius m.—lateral head

Adductor magnus m.

Popliteus m.

Semimembranosus m.

Soleus m.

Popliteus m.

Tibialis posterior m.

Flexor hallucis longus m.

Flexor digitorum longus m.

Plantaris m.

Tendo calcaneus (Achilles tendon)

Tibialis posterior m.

Tibialis anterior m.

Fibularis [Peroneus] longus m.

Flexor hallucis longus m.

Flexor digitorum longus m.

POSTERIOR VIEW

POSTERIOR VIEW

● **Gastrocnemius**

● **Adductor magnus**

● **Popliteus**

● **Plantaris**

● **Soleus**

● **Achilles tendon**

● **Flexor digitorum longus**

● **Tibialis posterior**

● **Flexor hallucis longus**

○ **Tibialis anterior**

● **Fibularis [Peroneus] longus**

○ **Semimembranosus**

Anterior Thigh Muscles
Table 5.1

Muscle	Proximal Attachment	Distal Attachment	Innervation	Main Actions
Iliopsoas **Psoas major**	Sides of T12 to L5 vertebral bodies, intervertebral discs between them & transverse processes of L1–L5	Lesser trochanter of femur	Ventral rami of lumbar nn. (**L1, L2** & L3)[a]	Act conjointly in flexing thigh at hip joint and in stabilizing this joint.
Psoas minor	Sides of T12 & L1 vertebrae & intervertebral disc	Pectineal line, iliopectineal eminence via iliopectineal arch lig.	Ventral rami of lumbar nn. (L1 & L2)	
Iliacus	Iliac crest, iliac fossa, ala of sacrum, ant. sacroiliac ligg. & capsule of hip joint	Tendon of psoas major & body of femur, inf. to lesser trochanter	Femoral n. (**L2** & L3)	
Tensor fasciae latae	Ant. sup. iliac spine & ant. part of ext. lip of iliac crest	Anterolateral aspect of lateral tibial condyle via iliotibial tract	Sup. gluteal n. (L4 & L5)	Abducts, medially rotates, and flexes thigh; helps to keep knee extended
Sartorius	Ant. sup. iliac spine & sup. part of notch inf. to it	Sup. part of medial surface of tibia	Femoral n. (L2 & L3)	Flexes, abducts & laterally rotates thigh at hip joint & flexes leg at knee joint
Quadriceps femoris **Rectus femoris**	Ant. inf. iliac spine & groove sup. to acetabulum	Base of patella & via patellar lig. to tibial tuberosity	Femoral n. (L2, **L3** & **L4**)	Extend leg at knee joint; rectus femoris also helps iliopsoas to flex thigh
Vastus lateralis	Greater trochanter & lateral lip of linea aspera of femur			
Vastus medialis	Intertrochanteric line & medial lip of linea aspera of femur			
Vastus intermedius	Ant. & lateral surfaces of shaft of femur			

[a]In this and subsequent tables, the numbers indicate the spinal cord segmental innervation of the nerves. For example, **L1**, **L2**, and L3 indicate that the nerves supplying the psoas major muscle are derived from the first three lumbar segments of the spinal cord; the boldface (**L1, L2**) indicates the main segmental innervation. Damage to one or more of these spinal cord segments or to the motor nerve roots arising from them results in paralysis of the muscles concerned.

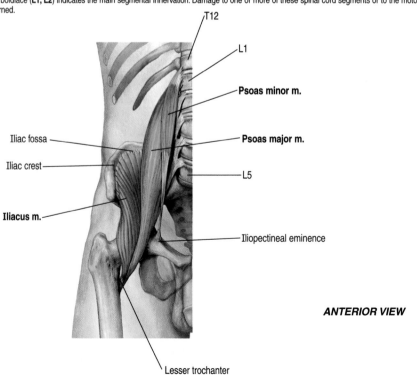

T12

L1

Psoas minor m.

Psoas major m.

Iliac fossa

Iliac crest

L5

Iliacus m.

Iliopectineal eminence

Lesser trochanter

ANTERIOR VIEW

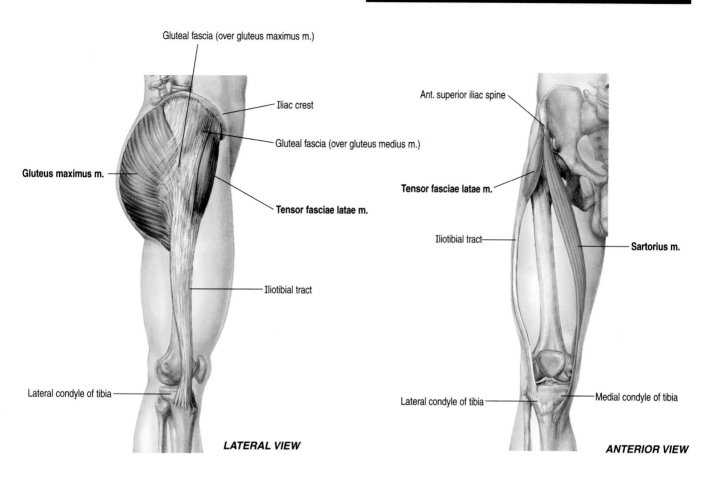

Gluteal fascia (over gluteus maximus m.)

Iliac crest

Gluteal fascia (over gluteus medius m.)

Gluteus maximus m.

Tensor fasciae latae m.

Iliotibial tract

Lateral condyle of tibia

LATERAL VIEW

Ant. superior iliac spine

Tensor fasciae latae m.

Iliotibial tract

Sartorius m.

Lateral condyle of tibia

Medial condyle of tibia

ANTERIOR VIEW

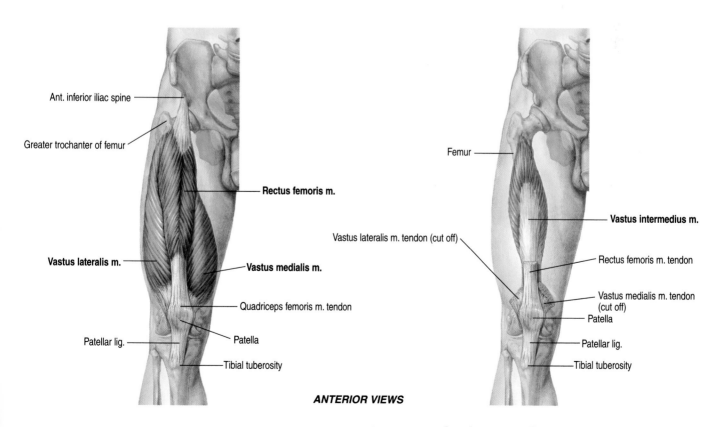

Ant. inferior iliac spine

Greater trochanter of femur

Rectus femoris m.

Vastus lateralis m.

Vastus medialis m.

Quadriceps femoris m. tendon

Patellar lig.

Patella

Tibial tuberosity

Femur

Vastus intermedius m.

Vastus lateralis m. tendon (cut off)

Rectus femoris m. tendon

Vastus medialis m. tendon (cut off)

Patella

Patellar lig.

Tibial tuberosity

ANTERIOR VIEWS

Gluteal & Posterior Thigh Muscles
Table 5.2

Gluteal Muscle	Proximal Attachment	Distal Attachment	Innervation	Main Actions
Gluteus maximus	Ext. surface of ala of ilium, including iliac crest, dorsal surface of sacrum & coccyx, and sacrotuberous lig.	Most fibers end in iliotibial tract which inserts into lateral condyle of tibia; some fibers insert on gluteal tuberosity of femur	Inf. gluteal n. (L5, **S1** & **S2**)	Extends thigh & assists in its lat. rotation; also assists in raising trunk from flexed position
Gluteus medius	Ext. surface of ilium between ant. & post. gluteal lines	Lateral surface of greater trochanter of femur	Sup. gluteal n. (**L5** & S1)	Abduct & medially rotate thigh; steady pelvis
Gluteus minimus	Ext. surface of ilium between ant. & inf. gluteal lines	Ant. surface of greater trochanter of femur		
Piriformis	Ant. surface of sacrum between S2 & S4	Superior border of greater trochanter of femur	Brr. from ventral rami of **S1** & S2	
Obturator internus	Pelvic surface of obturator membrane & surrounding bones	Trochanteric fossa[a]	N. to obturator internus (L5 & **S1**)	Laterally rotate extended thigh & abduct flexed thigh
Gemelli, superior & inferior	*Sup.:* ischial spine *Inf.:* ischial tuberosity		*Sup. gemellus,* same nerve supply as obturator internus *Inf. gemellus,* same nerve supply as quadratus femoris	
Quadratus femoris	Lateral border of ischial tuberosity	Quadrate tubercle on intertrochanteric crest of femur & inf. to it	N. to quadratus femoris (L5 & S1)	Laterally rotates thigh[b]

[a]The gemelli muscles blend with the tendon of the obturator internus muscle as it attaches to the trochanteric fossa.
[b]There are six lateral rotators of the thigh: piriformis, obturator internus, gemelli (superior and inferior), quadratus femoris, and obturator externus. These muscles also stabilize the hip joint.

Post. Thigh Muscle	Proximal Attachment	Distal Attachment	Innervation	Main Actions
Semitendinosus	Ischial tuberosity	Medial surface of sup. part of tibia	Tibial division of sciatic n. (**L5, S1** & **S2**)	Extend thigh; flex leg and rotate it medially; when thigh & leg are flexed, they can extend trunk
Semimembranous		Post. part of medial condyle of tibia		
Biceps femoris	*Long head:* Ischial tuberosity *Short head:* Lateral lip of distal half of linea aspera & lateral supracondylar line	Lateral side of head of fibular	*Long head:* Tibial division of sciatic n. (L5, **S1** & **S2**) *Short head:* Common fibular (peroneal) division of sciatic n. (L5, **S1** & **S2**)	Flexes leg & rotates it laterally; extends thigh (*e.g.,* when starting to walk)

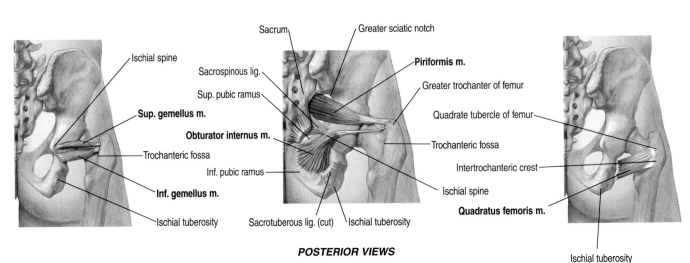

POSTERIOR VIEWS

POSTERIOR VIEW

LATERAL VIEWS

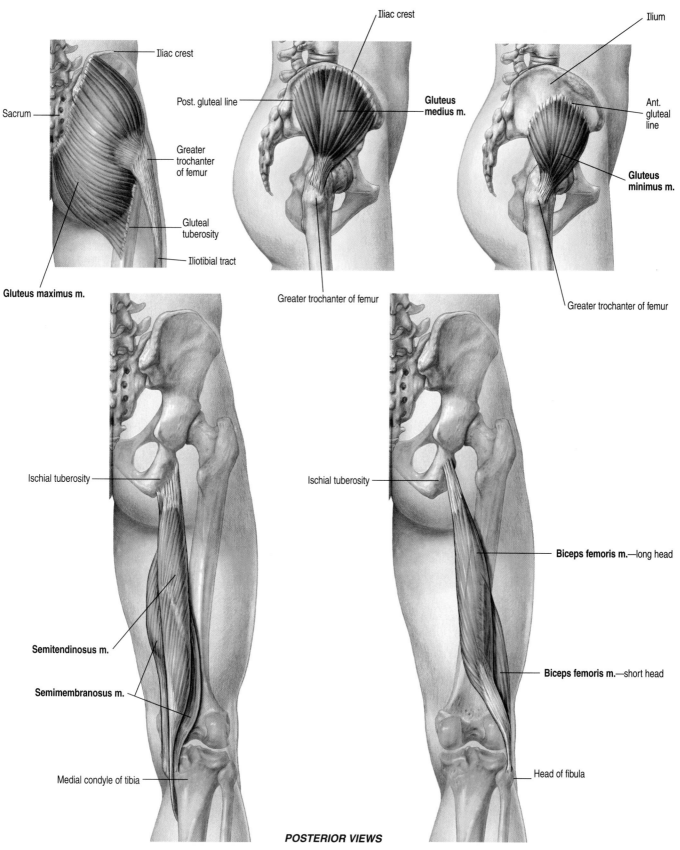

Iliac crest

Iliac crest

Ilium

Sacrum

Post. gluteal line

Gluteus medius m.

Ant. gluteal line

Greater trochanter of femur

Gluteus minimus m.

Gluteal tuberosity

Iliotibial tract

Gluteus maximus m.

Greater trochanter of femur

Greater trochanter of femur

Ischial tuberosity

Ischial tuberosity

Biceps femoris m.—long head

Semitendinosus m.

Semimembranosus m.

Biceps femoris m.—short head

Medial condyle of tibia

Head of fibula

POSTERIOR VIEWS

Medial Thigh Muscles
Table 5.3

Muscle[a]	Proximal Attachment	Distal Attachment	Innervation	Main Actions
Pectineus	Pecten pubis	Pectineal line of femur	Femoral nerve (**L2** & L3) & br. from obturator n. (L2, L3)	Adducts; flexes & laterally rotates thigh
Adductor longus	Body of pubis, inf. to pubic crest	Middle third of linea aspera of femur	Obturator n. ant. br. (L2, **L3** & L4)	Adducts thigh
Adductor brevis	Body & inf. ramus of pubis	Pectineal line & proximal part of linea aspera of femur	Obturator n. (L2, **L3** & L4)	Adducts thigh & to some extent flexes it
Adductor magnus	Inf. ramus of pubis, ramus of ischium (adductor part) & ischial tuberosity	Gluteal tuberosity, linea aspera med., supracondylar line (adductor part) & adductor tubercle of femur (hamstring part)	*Adductor part*, obturator n. (L2, **L3** & L4) *Hamstring part*, tibial portion of sciatic n. (**L4**)	Adducts thigh; its adductor part also flexes thigh & its hamstring part extends it
Gracilis	Body & inf. ramus of pubis	Sup. part of med. surface of tibia	Obturator n. (**L2**, L3 & L4)	Adducts thigh, flexes leg & helps to rotate it medially
Obturator externus	Margins of obturator foramen & ext. surface of obturator membrane	Trochanteric fossa of femur	Obturator n. (L3 & **L4**)	Laterally rotates thigh

[a]Collectively, the first five muscles listed are known as the *adductors of the thigh*, but their actions are more complex than this, *e.g.*, they act as *fixors of the hip* during flexion of the knee joint and are active during walking.

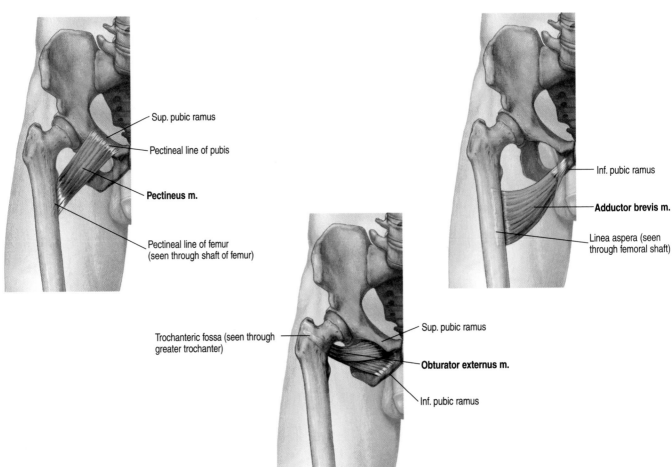

Sup. pubic ramus

Pectineal line of pubis

Pectineus m.

Pectineal line of femur (seen through shaft of femur)

Inf. pubic ramus

Adductor brevis m.

Linea aspera (seen through femoral shaft)

Trochanteric fossa (seen through greater trochanter)

Sup. pubic ramus

Obturator externus m.

Inf. pubic ramus

ANTERIOR VIEWS

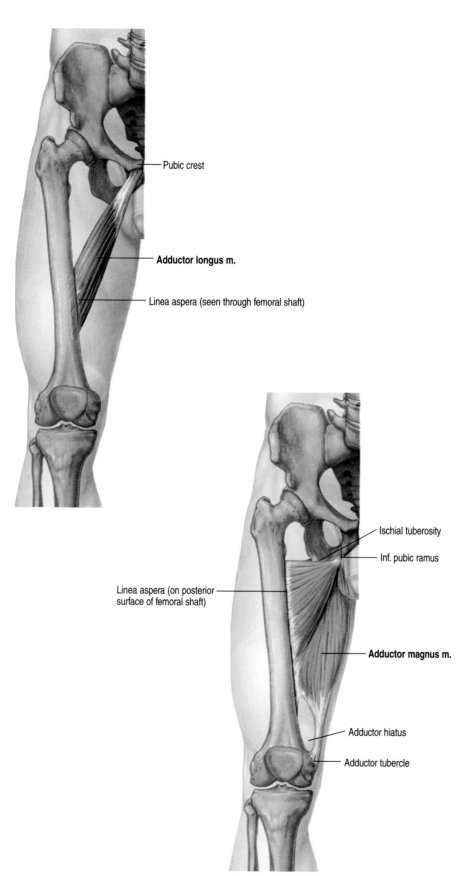

Pubic crest

Adductor longus m.

Linea aspera (seen through femoral shaft)

Ischial tuberosity

Inf. pubic ramus

Linea aspera (on posterior
surface of femoral shaft)

Adductor magnus m.

Adductor hiatus

Adductor tubercle

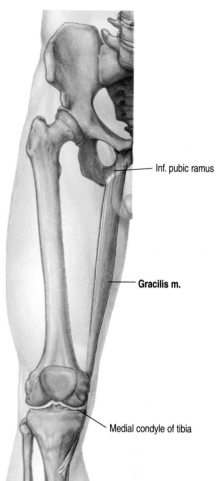

Inf. pubic ramus

Gracilis m.

Medial condyle of tibia

ANTERIOR VIEWS

Anterior & Lateral Leg Muscles
Table 5.4

Anterior Muscle	Proximal Attachment	Distal Attachment	Innervation	Main Actions
Tibialis anterior	Lateral condyle & sup. half of lateral surface of tibia	Medial & inf. surfaces of medial cuneiform bone & base of 1st metatarsal bone	Deep fibular [peroneal] n. (**L4** & L5)	Dorsiflexes & inverts foot
Extensor hallucis longus	Middle part of ant. surface of fibula & interosseous membrane	Dorsal aspect of base of distal phalanx of 1st digit (hallux)	Deep fibular [peroneal] n. (L5 & S1)	Extends 1st digit & dorsiflexes foot
Extensor digitorum longus	Lateral condyle of tibia, sup. 3/4 of ant. surface of fibula & interosseous membrane	Middle & distal phalanges of lateral 4 digits		Extends lateral 4 digits dorsiflexes foot
Fibularis [Peroneus] tertius	Inferior third of ant. surface of fibula & interosseous membrane	Dorsum of base of 5th metatarsal bone		Dorsiflexes foot & aids in eversion of it

Lateral Muscle[a]	Proximal Attachment	Distal Attachment	Innervation	Main Actions
Fibularis [Peroneus] longus	Head & sup. 2/3 of lateral surface of fibula	Base of metatarsal 1st bone & medial cuneiform bone	Superficial fibular (peroneal) n. (**L5**, **S1** & S2)	Everts & plantar flexes foot
Fibularis [Peroneus] brevis	Inf. 2/3 of lateral surface of fibula	Dorsal surface of tuberosity of 5th metatarsal bone		Everts foot & weakly plantarflexes foot

[a]The fibularis [peroneus] longus and brevis were named because their proximal attachment is to the fibula. *Peroneus* is the Greek word for the Latin term *fibula* and was formerly used to describe these muscles.

ANTERIOR VIEWS

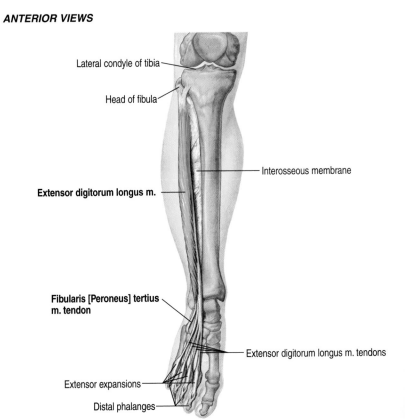

Lateral condyle of tibia
Tibialis anterior m.
Medial cuneiform bone
Base of 1st metatarsal bone

Lateral condyle of tibia
Head of fibula
Interosseous membrane
Extensor digitorum longus m.
Fibularis [Peroneus] tertius m. tendon
Extensor digitorum longus m. tendons
Extensor expansions
Distal phalanges

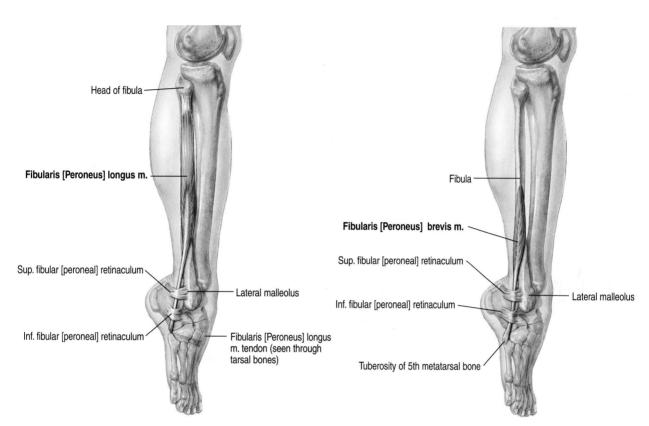

Head of fibula

Fibularis [Peroneus] longus m.

Sup. fibular [peroneal] retinaculum

Lateral malleolus

Inf. fibular [peroneal] retinaculum

Fibularis [Peroneus] longus
m. tendon (seen through
tarsal bones)

Fibula

Fibularis [Peroneus] brevis m.

Sup. fibular [peroneal] retinaculum

Inf. fibular [peroneal] retinaculum

Lateral malleolus

Tuberosity of 5th metatarsal bone

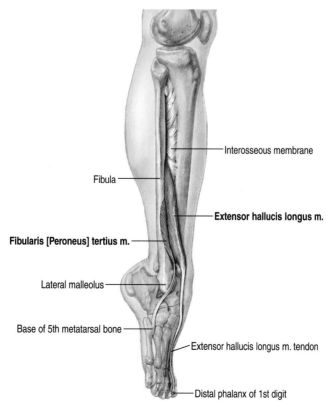

Interosseous membrane

Fibula

Extensor hallucis longus m.

Fibularis [Peroneus] tertius m.

Lateral malleolus

Base of 5th metatarsal bone

Extensor hallucis longus m. tendon

Distal phalanx of 1st digit

LATERAL VIEWS

Posterior Leg Muscles
Table 5.5

Superficial Muscle	Proximal Attachment	Distal Attachment	Innervation	Main Actions
Gastrocnemius	*Lateral head:* Lateral aspect of lateral condyle of femur *Medial head:* Popliteal surface of femur, sup. to medial condyle	Post. surface of tuberosity of calcaneus via tendo calcaneus	Tibial n. (L5, S1 & **S2**)	Plantarflexes foot, raises heel during walking & flexes knee joint
Soleus	Post. aspect of head of fibula, sup. 4th of post. surface of fibula, soleal line & medial border of tibia			Plantarflexes foot
Plantaris	Inf. end of lat. supracondylar line of femur & oblique popliteal lig.	Medial side of tendo calcaneus		Weakly assists gastrocnemius in plantarflexing foot & flexing knee joint

Deep Muscle	Proximal Attachment	Distal Attachment	Innervation	Main Actions
Popliteus	Lateral epicondyle of femur & lateral meniscus	Post. surface of tibia, sup. to soleal line	Tibial n. (**L4, L5** & S1)	Weakly flexes knee & unlocks it
Flexor hallucis longus	Inf. 2/3 of post. surface of fibula & inf. part of interosseous membrane	Base of distal phalanx of 1st digit (hallux)	Tibial n. (**S2**–S3)	Flexes 1st digit at all joints and plantarflexes foot
Flexor digitorum longus	Medial part of post. surface of tibia, inf. to soleal line & by a broad aponeurosis to fibula	Bases of distal phalanges of lateral 4 digits		Flexes 4 digits & plantarflexes foot
Tibialis posterior	Interosseous membrane, post. surface of tibia inf. to soleal line & post. surface of fibula	Tuberosity of navicular, cuneiform & cuboid bones, & bases of 2nd, 3rd & 4th metatarsal bones	Tibial n. (L4–L5)	Plantarflexes & inverts foot

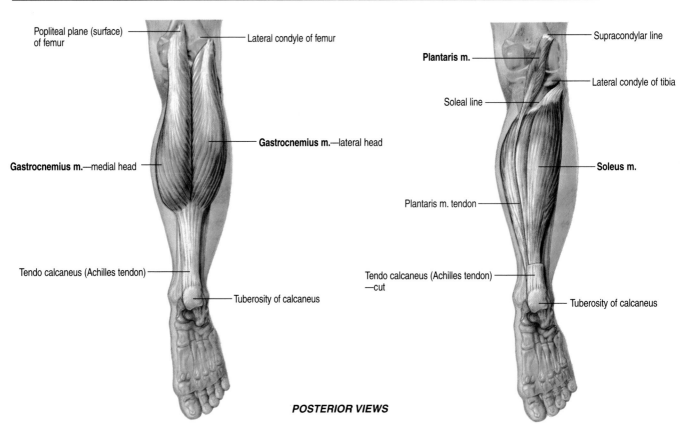

POSTERIOR VIEWS

Popliteal plane (surface) of femur — Lateral condyle of femur — Gastrocnemius m.—lateral head — Gastrocnemius m.—medial head — Tendo calcaneus (Achilles tendon) — Tuberosity of calcaneus

Plantaris m. — Supracondylar line — Soleal line — Lateral condyle of tibia — Plantaris m. tendon — Soleus m. — Tendo calcaneus (Achilles tendon) —cut — Tuberosity of calcaneus

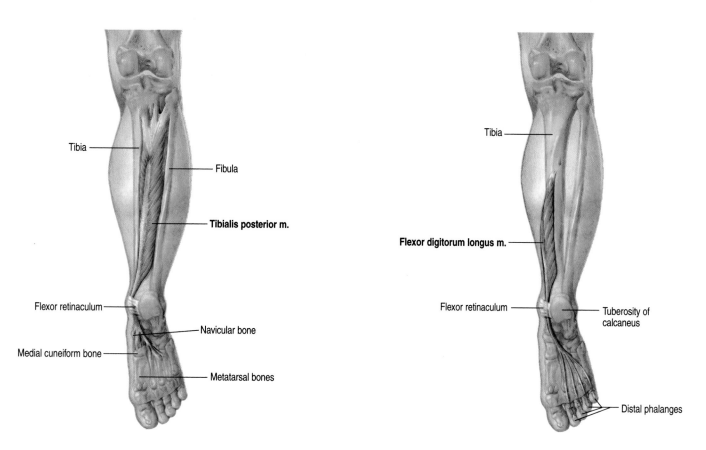

Tibia

Fibula

Tibialis posterior m.

Flexor retinaculum

Navicular bone

Medial cuneiform bone

Metatarsal bones

Tibia

Flexor digitorum longus m.

Flexor retinaculum

Tuberosity of calcaneus

Distal phalanges

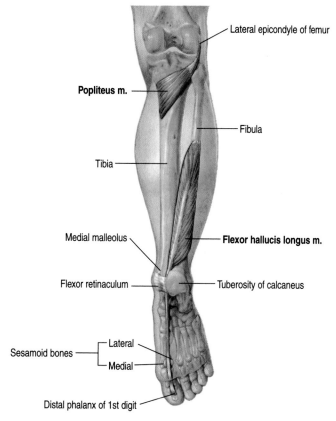

Lateral epicondyle of femur

Popliteus m.

Fibula

Tibia

Medial malleolus

Flexor hallucis longus m.

Flexor retinaculum

Tuberosity of calcaneus

Sesamoid bones — Lateral

Medial

Distal phalanx of 1st digit

POSTERIOR VIEWS

Intrinsic Foot Muscles
Table 5.6

Muscle	Proximal Attachment	Distal Attachment	Innervation	Main Actions
FIRST LAYER[a]				
Abductor hallucis	Medial process of tuber calcanei, flexor retinaculum & plantar aponeurosis	Medial side of base of proximal phalanx & medial sesamoid bone of 1st digit (hallux)	Medial plantar n. (S2 & **S3**)	Abducts & flexes 1st digit
Flexor digitorum brevis	Medial process of tuber calcanei, plantar aponeurosis & intermuscular septa	Both sides of middle phalanges of lateral 4 digits		Flexes lateral 4 digits (toes)
Abductor digiti minimi	Medial & lateral processes of tuber calcanei, plantar aponeurosis & intermuscular septa	Lateral side of base of proximal phalanx of 5th digit (little toe)	Lateral plantar n. (S2 & **S3**)	Abducts & flexes 5th digit
SECOND LAYER				
Quadratus plantae	Medial surface & lateral margin of plantar surface of calcaneus	Posterolateral margin of tendon of flexor digitorum longus	Lateral plantar n. (S2 & **S3**)	Assists flexor digitorum longus in flexing lateral 4 digits
Lumbricalis	Tendons of flexor digitorum longus	Medial sides of bases of proximal phalanges of lateral 4 digits & extensor expansions of tendons of extensor digitorum longus	*Medial one:* medial plantar n. (S2 & **S3**) *Lateral three:* lateral plantar n. (S2 & **S3**)	Flex proximal phalanges & extend middle & distal phalanges of lateral 4 digits
THIRD LAYER				
Flexor hallucis brevis	Plantar surfaces of cuboid & lateral cuneiform bones	Both sides of base of proximal phalanx of 1st digit	Medial plantar n. (S2 & **S3**)	Flexes proximal phalanx of 1st digit (hallux)
Adductor hallucis	*Oblique head:* Bases of metatarsal bones 2–4 *Transverse head:* Plantar ligg. of metatarsophalangeal joints 2–5	*Tendons of both heads* attached to lateral side of base of proximal phalanx & lat. sesamoid bone of 1st digit (hallux)	Deep br. of lateral plantar n. (S2 & **S3**)	Adducts 1st digit; assists in maintaining transverse arch of foot
Flexor digiti minimi brevis	Base of 5th metatarsal bone	Base of proximal phalanx of 5th digit	Superficial br. of lateral plantar n. (S2 & **S3**)	Flexes proximal phalanx of 5th digit, thereby assisting with its flexion
FOURTH LAYER				
Plantar interossei (3 muscles)	Bases & medial sides of metatarsal bones 3–5	Medial sides of bases of proximal phalanges of digits 3–5	Lateral plantar n. (S2 & **S3**)	Adduct digits (2–4) & flex metatarsophalangeal joints
Dorsal interossei (4 muscles)	Adjacent side of metatarsal bones 1–5	*1st:* medial side of proximal phalanx of 2nd digit *2nd–4th:* lateral sides of digits 2–4		Abduct digits (2–4) & flex metatarsorphalangeal joints

[a]In spite of the individual actions ascribed to them, the primary function of the first layer of intrinsic muscles of the foot is to provide dynamic support of the longitudinal arch of the foot (i.e., resisting forces tending to spread or flatten it).

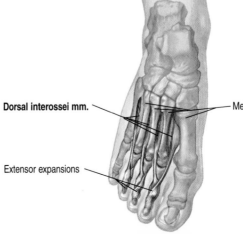

Dorsal interossei mm.

Metatarsal bones

Extensor expansions

DORSAL SURFACE VIEW

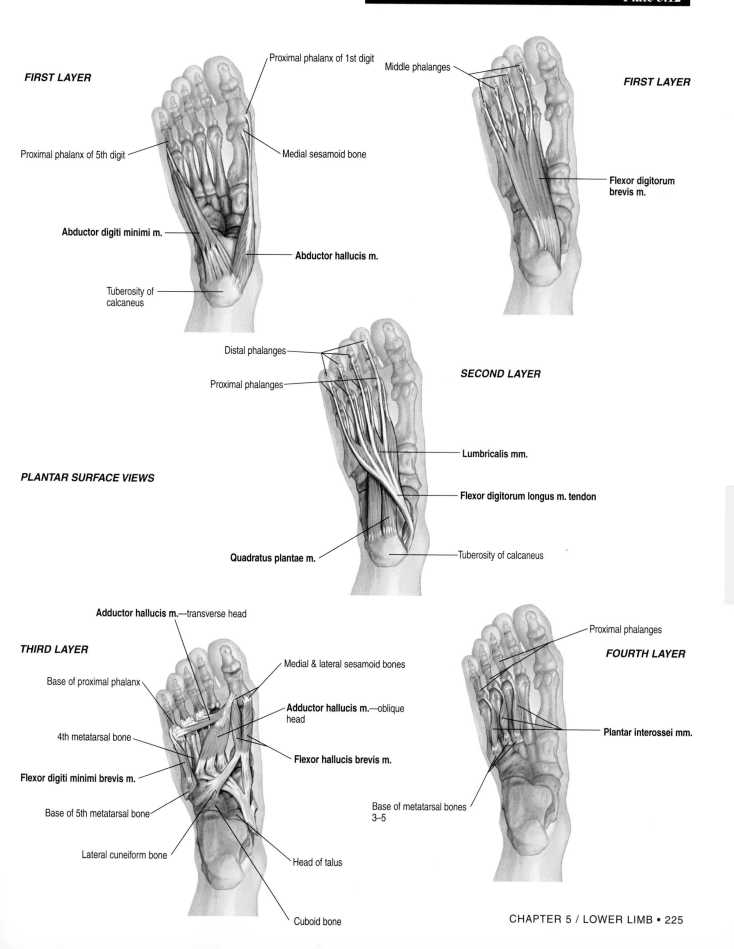

FIRST LAYER

Proximal phalanx of 1st digit

Middle phalanges

FIRST LAYER

Proximal phalanx of 5th digit

Medial sesamoid bone

Flexor digitorum
brevis m.

Abductor digiti minimi m.

Abductor hallucis m.

Tuberosity of
calcaneus

Distal phalanges

SECOND LAYER

Proximal phalanges

PLANTAR SURFACE VIEWS

Lumbricalis mm.

Flexor digitorum longus m. tendon

Quadratus plantae m.

Tuberosity of calcaneus

Adductor hallucis m.—transverse head

THIRD LAYER

Medial & lateral sesamoid bones

Proximal phalanges

FOURTH LAYER

Base of proximal phalanx

Adductor hallucis m.—oblique
head

4th metatarsal bone

Flexor hallucis brevis m.

Plantar interossei mm.

Flexor digiti minimi brevis m.

Base of 5th metatarsal bone

Base of metatarsal bones
3–5

Lateral cuneiform bone

Head of talus

Cuboid bone

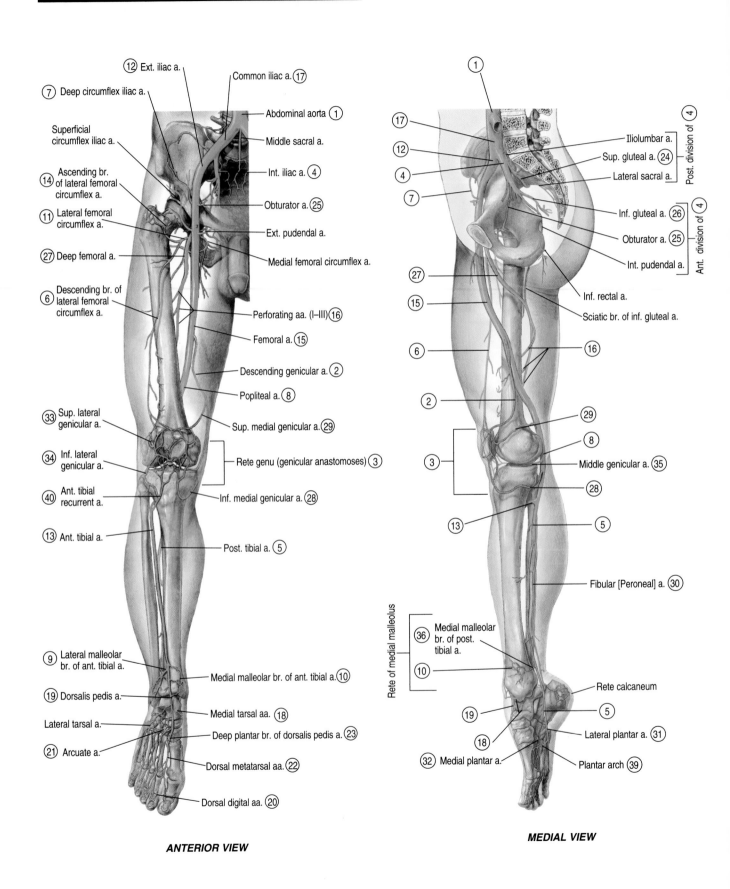

⑫ Ext. iliac a.

Common iliac a. ⑰

⑦ Deep circumflex iliac a.

Abdominal aorta ①

Superficial circumflex iliac a.

Middle sacral a.

⑭ Ascending br. of lateral femoral circumflex a.

Int. iliac a. ④

⑪ Lateral femoral circumflex a.

Obturator a. ㉕

⑦ Deep femoral a.

Ext. pudendal a.

⑥ Descending br. of lateral femoral circumflex a.

Medial femoral circumflex a.

Perforating aa. (I–III) ⑯

Femoral a. ⑮

Descending genicular a. ②

Popliteal a. ⑧

㉝ Sup. lateral genicular a.

Sup. medial genicular a. ㉙

㉞ Inf. lateral genicular a.

Rete genu (genicular anastomoses) ③

⑳ Ant. tibial recurrent a.

Inf. medial genicular a. ㉘

⑬ Ant. tibial a.

Post. tibial a. ⑤

⑨ Lateral malleolar br. of ant. tibial a.

Medial malleolar br. of ant. tibial a. ⑩

⑲ Dorsalis pedis a.

Medial tarsal aa. ⑱

Lateral tarsal a.

Deep plantar br. of dorsalis pedis a. ㉓

㉑ Arcuate a.

Dorsal metatarsal aa. ㉒

Dorsal digital aa. ⑳

ANTERIOR VIEW

①

⑰

⑫

Iliolumbar a.

Sup. gluteal a. ㉔

④

Lateral sacral a.

⑦

Post. division of ④

Inf. gluteal a. ㉖

Obturator a. ㉕

Int. pudendal a.

Ant. division of ④

㉗

⑮

Inf. rectal a.

Sciatic br. of inf. gluteal a.

⑥

⑯

②

㉙

③

⑧

Middle genicular a. ㉟

㉘

⑬

⑤

Fibular [Peroneal] a. ㉚

Rete of medial malleolus

㊱ Medial malleolar br. of post. tibial a.

⑩

Rete calcaneum

⑲

⑤

⑱

Lateral plantar a. ㉛

㉜ Medial plantar a.

Plantar arch ㊴

MEDIAL VIEW

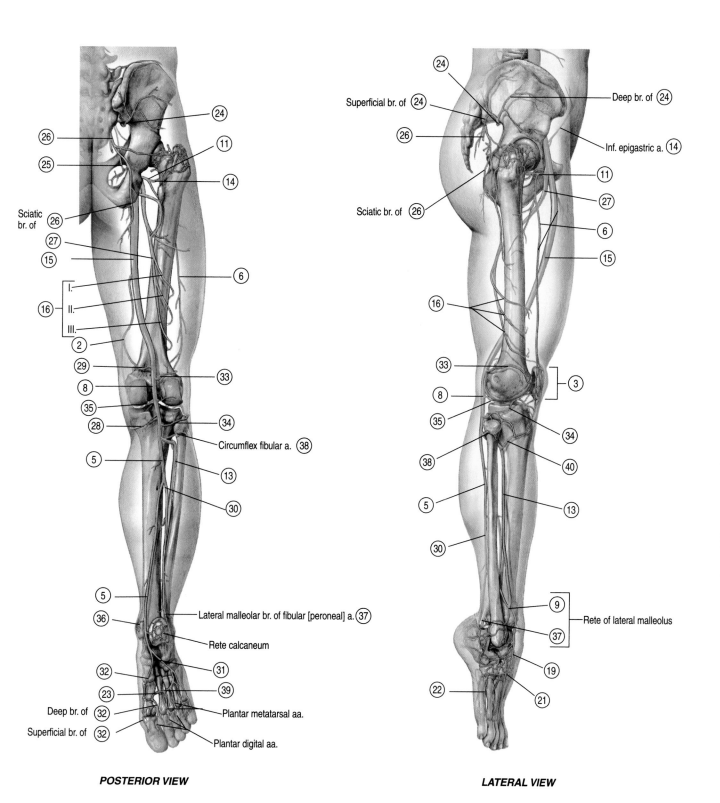

Superficial br. of (24)

(26)

Sciatic br. of (26)

(24)

Deep br. of (24)

Inf. epigastric a. (14)

(11)

(27)

(6)

(15)

(16)

(33)

(3)

(8)

(35)

(34)

(40)

(38)

(5)

(13)

(30)

(9)

Rete of lateral malleolus

(37)

(19)

(22)

(21)

(24)

(26)

(25)

Sciatic
br. of (26)

(27)

(15)

(24)

(11)

(14)

I.
II.
III.
(2)

(16)

(6)

(29)

(8)

(35)

(28)

(33)

(34)

Circumflex fibular a. (38)

(5)

(13)

(30)

(5)

(36)

Lateral malleolar br. of fibular [peroneal] a. (37)

Rete calcaneum

(32)

(31)

(23)

(39)

Deep br. of (32)

Plantar metatarsal aa.

Superficial br. of (32)

Plantar digital aa.

POSTERIOR VIEW

LATERAL VIEW

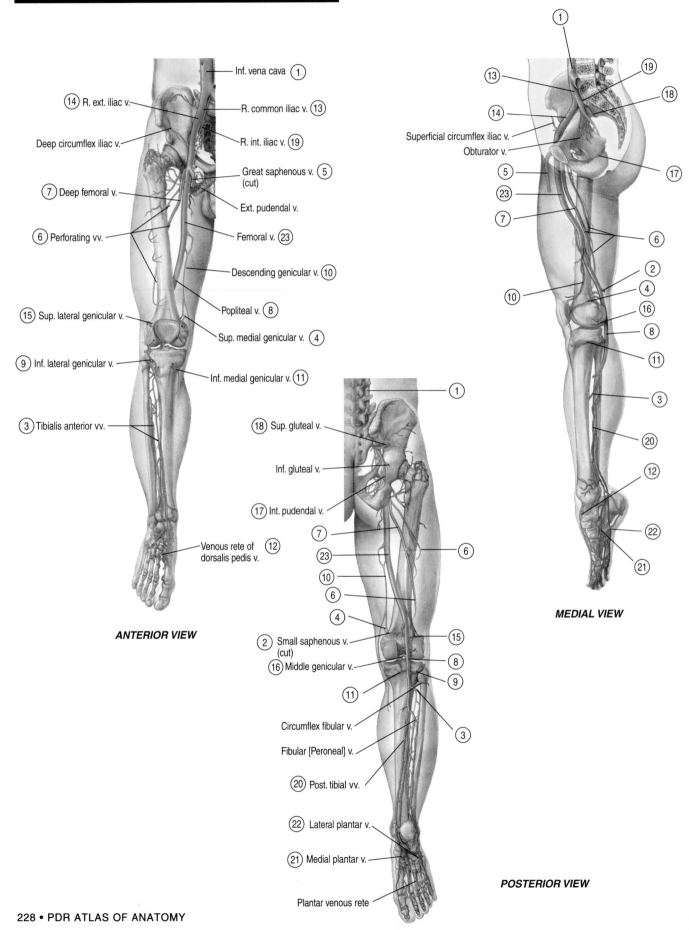

Inf. vena cava ①

⑭ R. ext. iliac v.

R. common iliac v. ⑬

Deep circumflex iliac v.

R. int. iliac v. ⑲

Great saphenous v. ⑤ (cut)

⑦ Deep femoral v.

Ext. pudendal v.

⑥ Perforating vv.

Femoral v. ㉓

Descending genicular v. ⑩

⑮ Sup. lateral genicular v.

Popliteal v. ⑧

Sup. medial genicular v. ④

⑨ Inf. lateral genicular v.

Inf. medial genicular v. ⑪

③ Tibialis anterior vv.

Venous rete of ⑫ dorsalis pedis v.

ANTERIOR VIEW

①
⑬
⑭ Superficial circumflex iliac v.
Obturator v.
⑤
㉓
⑦
⑲
⑱
⑰
⑥
②
④
⑯
⑧
⑪
⑩
③
⑳
⑫
㉒
㉑

MEDIAL VIEW

①
⑱ Sup. gluteal v.

Inf. gluteal v.

⑰ Int. pudendal v.

⑦
㉓
⑩
⑥
④
⑥

② Small saphenous v. (cut)

⑯ Middle genicular v.

⑪
⑮
⑧
⑨
③

Circumflex fibular v.

Fibular [Peroneal] v.

⑳ Post. tibial vv.

㉒ Lateral plantar v.

㉑ Medial plantar v.

Plantar venous rete

POSTERIOR VIEW

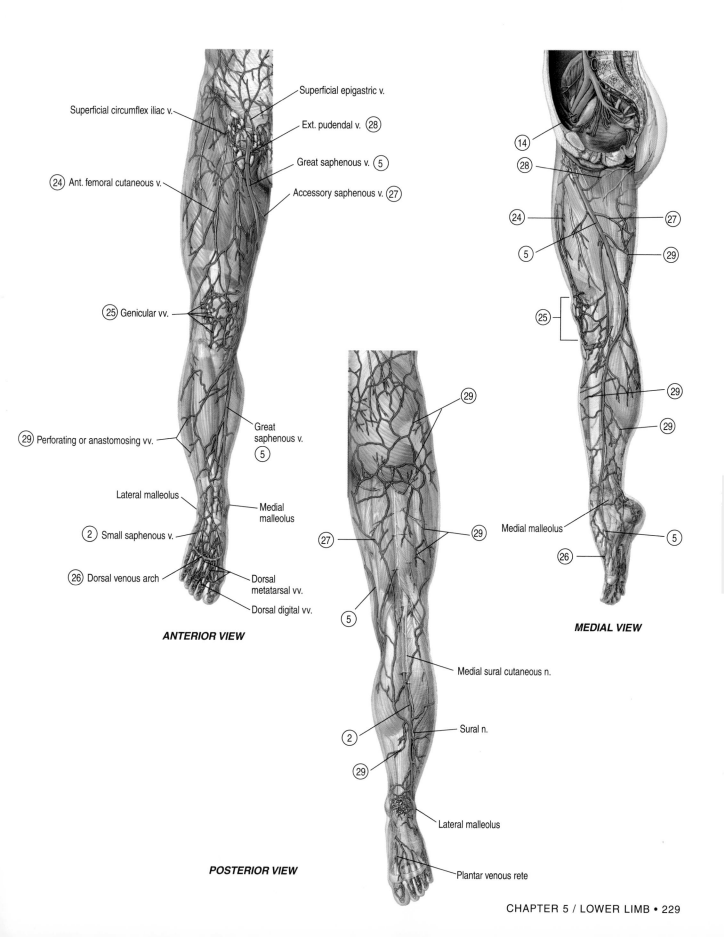

Superficial circumflex iliac v.

Superficial epigastric v.

Ext. pudendal v. (28)

Great saphenous v. (5)

Accessory saphenous v. (27)

(24) Ant. femoral cutaneous v.

(14)

(28)

(24)

(27)

(5)

(29)

(25) Genicular vv.

(25)

(29)

(29)

(29)

(29)

(29) Perforating or anastomosing vv.

Great
saphenous v.
(5)

(27)

(29)

Medial malleolus

(5)

Lateral malleolus

Medial
malleolus

(26)

(2) Small saphenous v.

(5)

MEDIAL VIEW

(26) Dorsal venous arch

Dorsal
metatarsal vv.

Dorsal digital vv.

ANTERIOR VIEW

Medial sural cutaneous n.

Sural n.

(2)

(29)

Lateral malleolus

POSTERIOR VIEW

Plantar venous rete

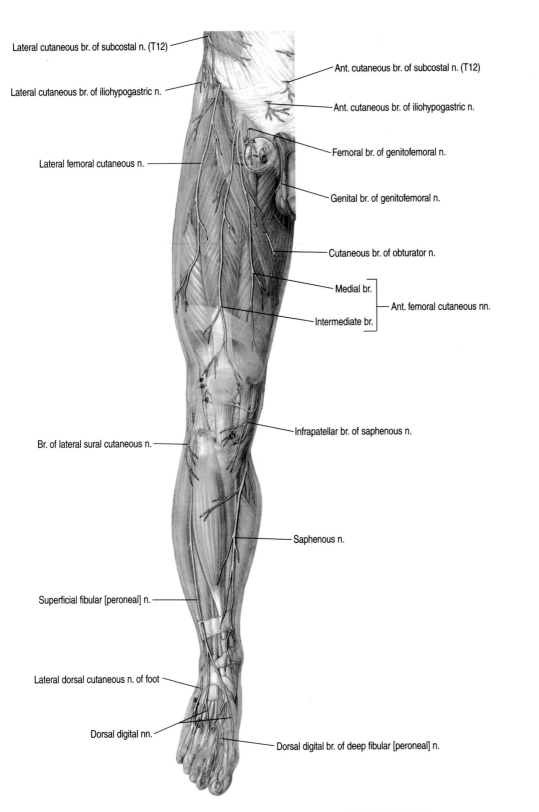

Lateral cutaneous br. of subcostal n. (T12)

Lateral cutaneous br. of iliohypogastric n.

Lateral femoral cutaneous n.

Ant. cutaneous br. of subcostal n. (T12)

Ant. cutaneous br. of iliohypogastric n.

Femoral br. of genitofemoral n.

Genital br. of genitofemoral n.

Cutaneous br. of obturator n.

Medial br.

Intermediate br.

Ant. femoral cutaneous nn.

Infrapatellar br. of saphenous n.

Br. of lateral sural cutaneous n.

Saphenous n.

Superficial fibular [peroneal] n.

Lateral dorsal cutaneous n. of foot

Dorsal digital nn.

Dorsal digital br. of deep fibular [peroneal] n.

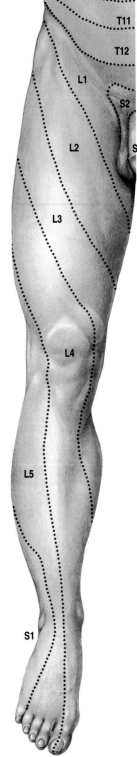

T10
T11
T12
L1
S2
L2
S3
L3
L4
L5
S1

ANTERIOR VIEWS

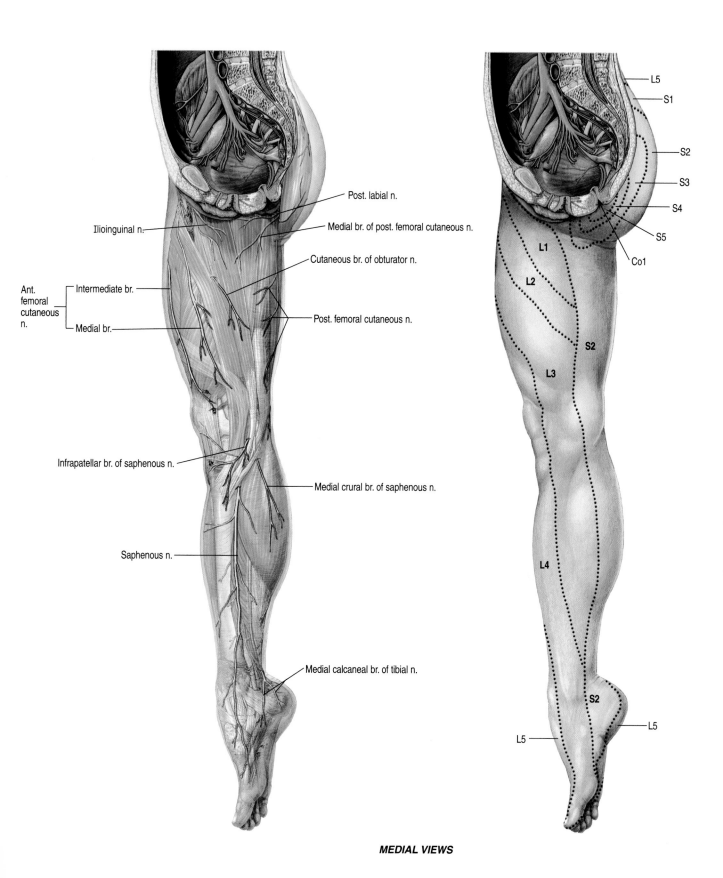

Post. labial n.

Ilioinguinal n.

Medial br. of post. femoral cutaneous n.

Cutaneous br. of obturator n.

Ant.
femoral
cutaneous
n.

Intermediate br.

Post. femoral cutaneous n.

Medial br.

Infrapatellar br. of saphenous n.

Medial crural br. of saphenous n.

Saphenous n.

Medial calcaneal br. of tibial n.

L5
S1
S2
S3
S4
S5
Co1

L1
L2
S2
L3
L4
S2
L5
L5

MEDIAL VIEWS

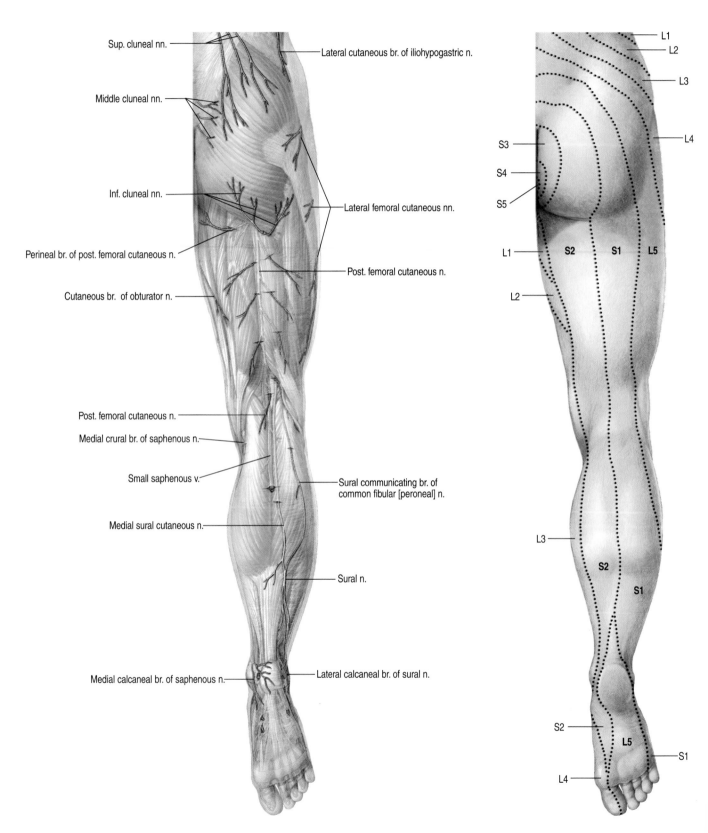

Sup. cluneal nn.

Lateral cutaneous br. of iliohypogastric n.

Middle cluneal nn.

Inf. cluneal nn.

Lateral femoral cutaneous nn.

Perineal br. of post. femoral cutaneous n.

Post. femoral cutaneous n.

Cutaneous br. of obturator n.

Post. femoral cutaneous n.

Medial crural br. of saphenous n.

Small saphenous v.

Sural communicating br. of common fibular [peroneal] n.

Medial sural cutaneous n.

Sural n.

Medial calcaneal br. of saphenous n.

Lateral calcaneal br. of sural n.

L1
L2
L3
L4

S3
S4
S5

L1
L2
S2 S1 L5

L3
S2
S1

L3

S2
L5

S2
L4
L5
S1

POSTERIOR VIEWS

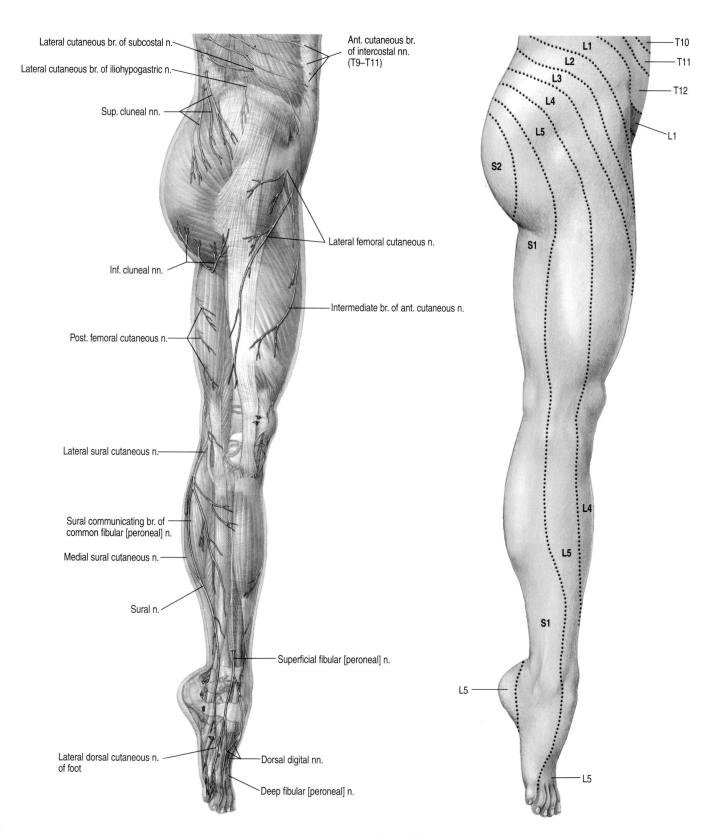

Lateral cutaneous br. of subcostal n.

Lateral cutaneous br. of iliohypogastric n.

Sup. cluneal nn.

Inf. cluneal nn.

Post. femoral cutaneous n.

Lateral sural cutaneous n.

Sural communicating br. of common fibular [peroneal] n.

Medial sural cutaneous n.

Sural n.

Lateral dorsal cutaneous n. of foot

Ant. cutaneous br. of intercostal nn. (T9–T11)

Lateral femoral cutaneous n.

Intermediate br. of ant. cutaneous n.

Superficial fibular [peroneal] n.

Dorsal digital nn.

Deep fibular [peroneal] n.

T10
T11
T12
L1
L1
L2
L3
L4
L5
S2
S1
L4
L5
S1
L5
L5

LATERAL VIEWS

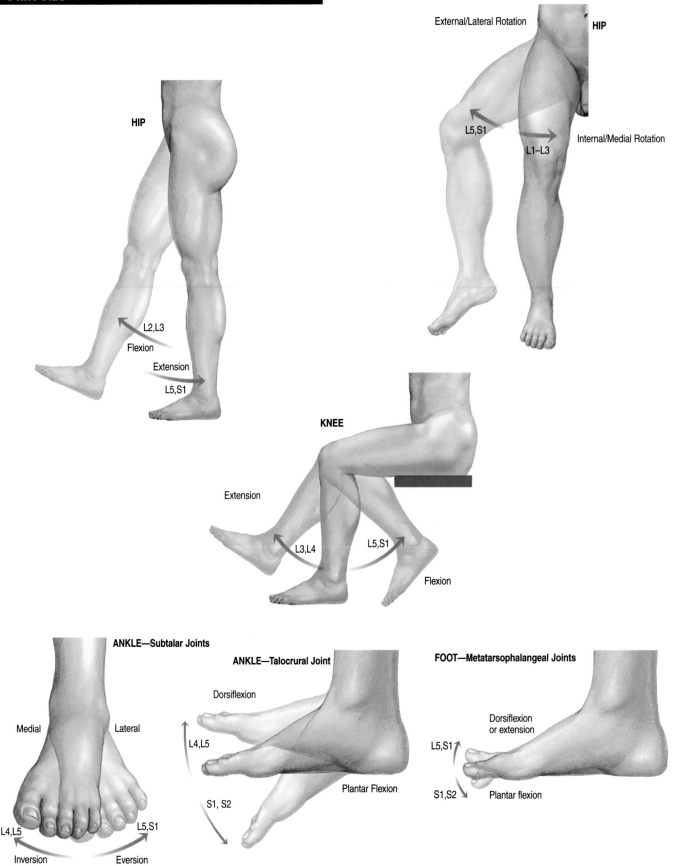

HIP

External/Lateral Rotation

HIP

L5,S1

Internal/Medial Rotation

L1–L3

L2,L3

Flexion

Extension

L5,S1

KNEE

Extension

L3,L4

L5,S1

Flexion

ANKLE—Subtalar Joints

Medial

Lateral

L4,L5

L5,S1

Inversion

Eversion

ANKLE—Talocrural Joint

Dorsiflexion

L4,L5

S1, S2

Plantar Flexion

FOOT—Metatarsophalangeal Joints

Dorsiflexion
or extension

L5,S1

S1,S2

Plantar flexion

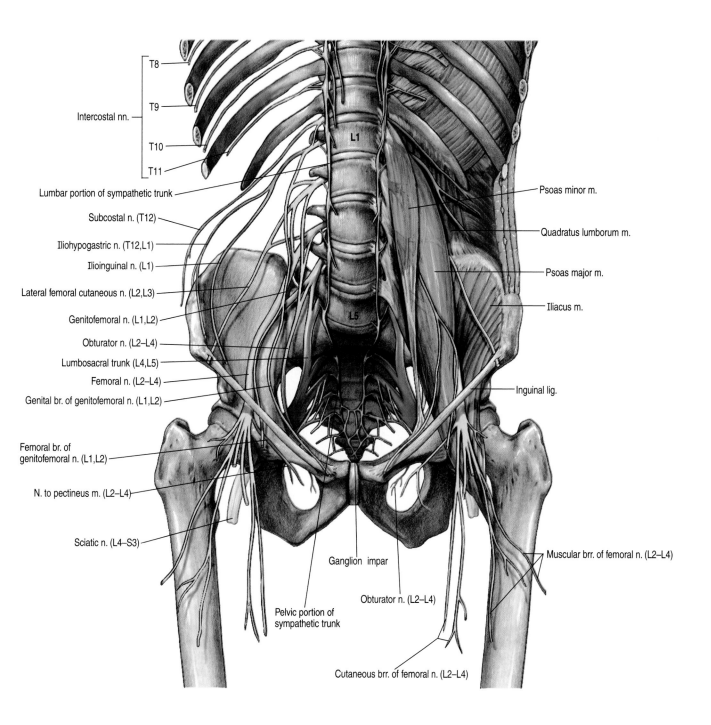

Intercostal nn.

T8

T9

T10

T11

Lumbar portion of sympathetic trunk

Subcostal n. (T12)

Iliohypogastric n. (T12,L1)

Ilioinguinal n. (L1)

Lateral femoral cutaneous n. (L2,L3)

Genitofemoral n. (L1,L2)

Obturator n. (L2–L4)

Lumbosacral trunk (L4,L5)

Femoral n. (L2–L4)

Genital br. of genitofemoral n. (L1,L2)

Femoral br. of genitofemoral n. (L1,L2)

N. to pectineus m. (L2–L4)

Sciatic n. (L4–S3)

L1

L5

Psoas minor m.

Quadratus lumborum m.

Psoas major m.

Iliacus m.

Inguinal lig.

Ganglion impar

Obturator n. (L2–L4)

Pelvic portion of sympathetic trunk

Muscular brr. of femoral n. (L2–L4)

Cutaneous brr. of femoral n. (L2–L4)

ANTERIOR VIEW

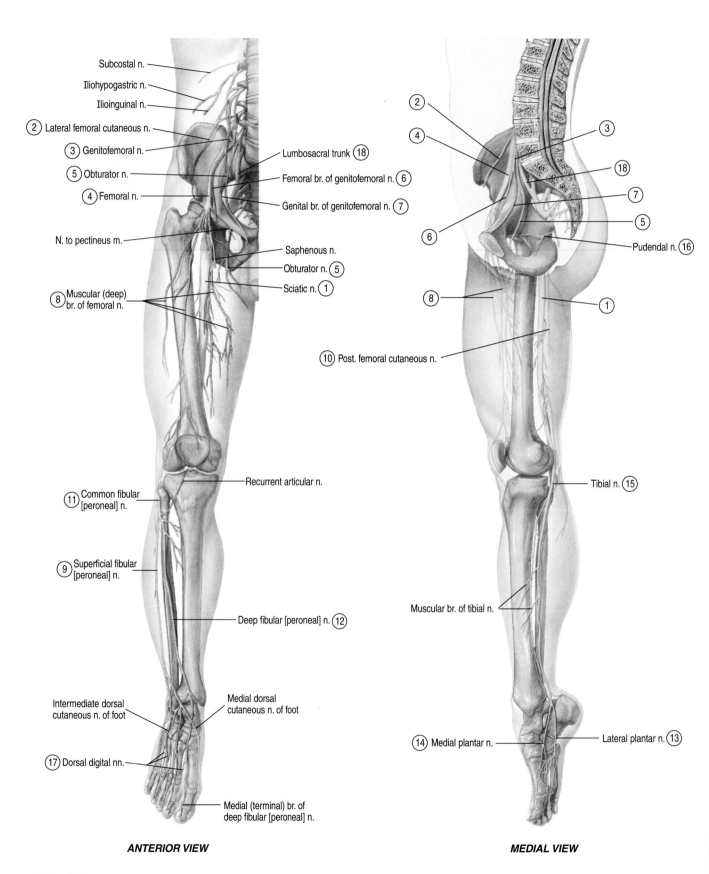

Subcostal n.

Iliohypogastric n.

Ilioinguinal n.

② Lateral femoral cutaneous n.

③ Genitofemoral n.

⑤ Obturator n.

④ Femoral n.

N. to pectineus m.

⑧ Muscular (deep) br. of femoral n.

Lumbosacral trunk ⑱

Femoral br. of genitofemoral n. ⑥

Genital br. of genitofemoral n. ⑦

Saphenous n.

Obturator n. ⑤

Sciatic n. ①

Recurrent articular n.

⑪ Common fibular [peroneal] n.

⑨ Superficial fibular [peroneal] n.

Deep fibular [peroneal] n. ⑫

Intermediate dorsal cutaneous n. of foot

Medial dorsal cutaneous n. of foot

⑰ Dorsal digital nn.

Medial (terminal) br. of deep fibular [peroneal] n.

ANTERIOR VIEW

② ④ ⑥ ⑧

③ ⑱ ⑦ ⑤

Pudendal n. ⑯

①

⑩ Post. femoral cutaneous n.

Tibial n. ⑮

Muscular br. of tibial n.

⑭ Medial plantar n.

Lateral plantar n. ⑬

MEDIAL VIEW

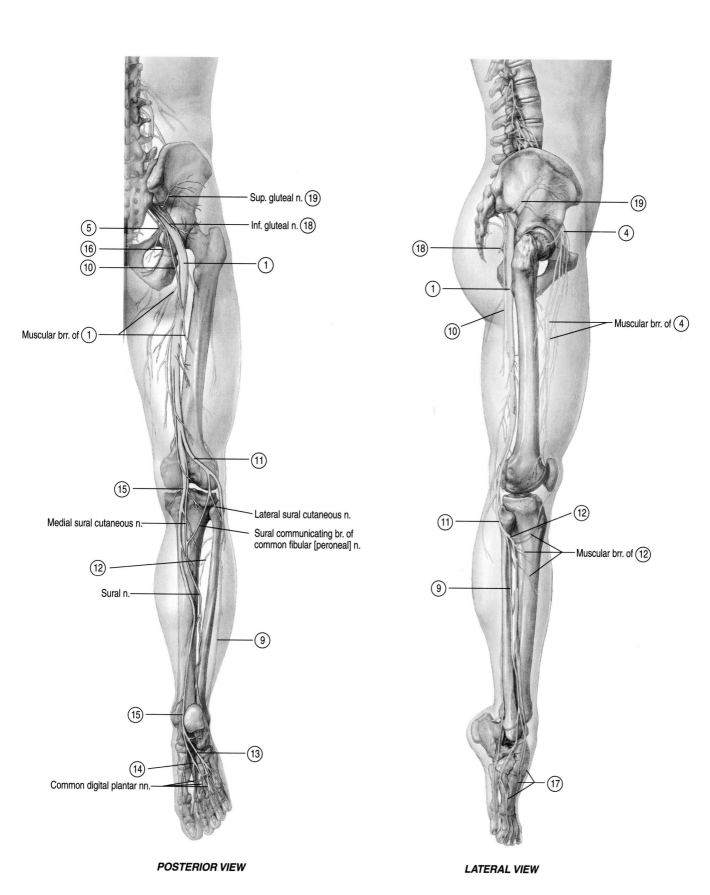

Sup. gluteal n. ⑲

Inf. gluteal n. ⑱

⑤

⑯

⑩

①

Muscular brr. of ①

⑪

⑮

Medial sural cutaneous n.

Lateral sural cutaneous n.

Sural communicating br. of
common fibular [peroneal] n.

⑫

Sural n.

⑨

⑮

⑬

⑭

Common digital plantar nn.

⑲

④

⑱

①

⑩

Muscular brr. of ④

⑪

⑫

Muscular brr. of ⑫

⑨

⑰

POSTERIOR VIEW

LATERAL VIEW

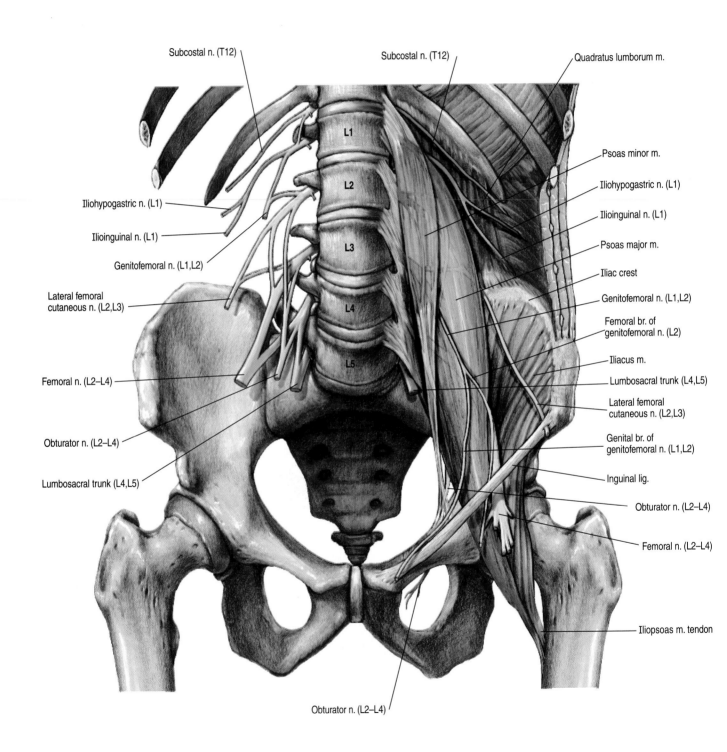

Subcostal n. (T12)

Subcostal n. (T12)

Quadratus lumborum m.

L1

L2

L3

L4

L5

Psoas minor m.

Iliohypogastric n. (L1)

Ilioinguinal n. (L1)

Psoas major m.

Iliac crest

Genitofemoral n. (L1,L2)

Femoral br. of genitofemoral n. (L2)

Iliacus m.

Lumbosacral trunk (L4,L5)

Lateral femoral cutaneous n. (L2,L3)

Genital br. of genitofemoral n. (L1,L2)

Inguinal lig.

Obturator n. (L2–L4)

Femoral n. (L2–L4)

Iliopsoas m. tendon

Iliohypogastric n. (L1)

Ilioinguinal n. (L1)

Genitofemoral n. (L1,L2)

Lateral femoral cutaneous n. (L2,L3)

Femoral n. (L2–L4)

Obturator n. (L2–L4)

Lumbosacral trunk (L4,L5)

Obturator n. (L2–L4)

ANTERIOR VIEW

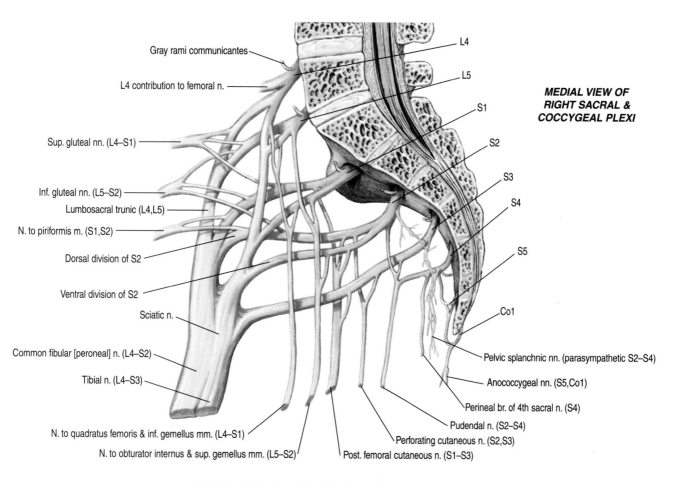

Gray rami communicantes

L4 contribution to femoral n.

L4

L5

S1

S2

S3

S4

S5

**MEDIAL VIEW OF
RIGHT SACRAL &
COCCYGEAL PLEXI**

Sup. gluteal nn. (L4–S1)

Inf. gluteal nn. (L5–S2)

Lumbosacral trunic (L4,L5)

N. to piriformis m. (S1,S2)

Dorsal division of S2

Ventral division of S2

Sciatic n.

Common fibular [peroneal] n. (L4–S2)

Tibial n. (L4–S3)

Co1

Pelvic splanchnic nn. (parasympathetic S2–S4)

Anococcygeal nn. (S5,Co1)

Perineal br. of 4th sacral n. (S4)

Pudendal n. (S2–S4)

Perforating cutaneous n. (S2,S3)

N. to quadratus femoris & inf. gemellus mm. (L4–S1)

N. to obturator internus & sup. gemellus mm. (L5–S2)

Post. femoral cutaneous n. (S1–S3)

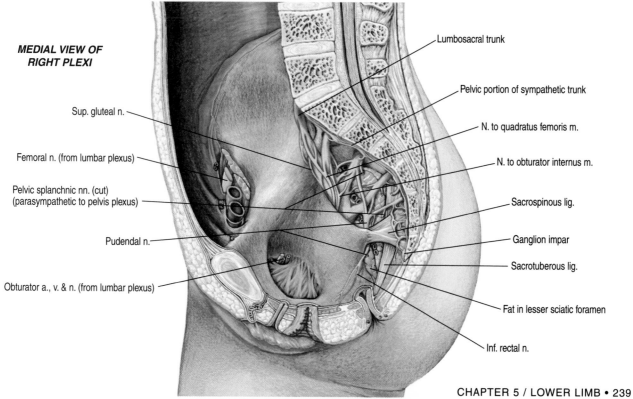

**MEDIAL VIEW OF
RIGHT PLEXI**

Lumbosacral trunk

Pelvic portion of sympathetic trunk

N. to quadratus femoris m.

Sup. gluteal n.

Femoral n. (from lumbar plexus)

Pelvic splanchnic nn. (cut)
(parasympathetic to pelvis plexus)

Pudendal n.

Obturator a., v. & n. (from lumbar plexus)

N. to obturator internus m.

Sacrospinous lig.

Ganglion impar

Sacrotuberous lig.

Fat in lesser sciatic foramen

Inf. rectal n.

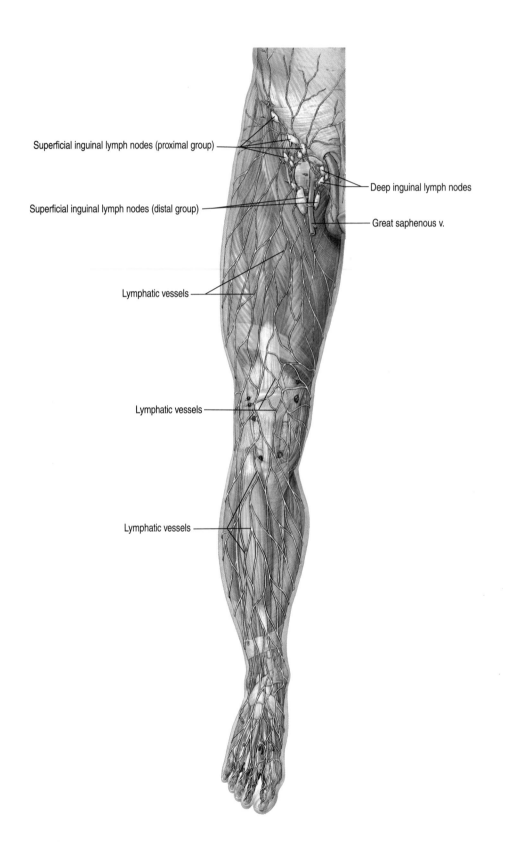

Superficial inguinal lymph nodes (proximal group)

Deep inguinal lymph nodes

Superficial inguinal lymph nodes (distal group)

Great saphenous v.

Lymphatic vessels

Lymphatic vessels

Lymphatic vessels

ANTERIOR VIEW

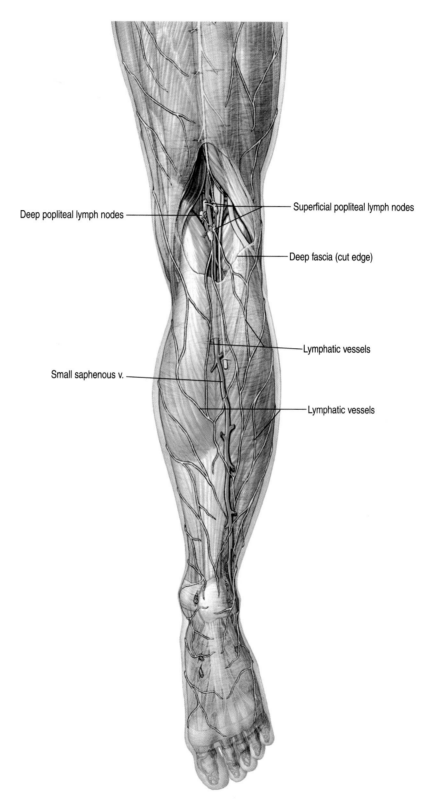

Deep popliteal lymph nodes

Superficial popliteal lymph nodes

Deep fascia (cut edge)

Lymphatic vessels

Small saphenous v.

Lymphatic vessels

POSTERIOR VIEW

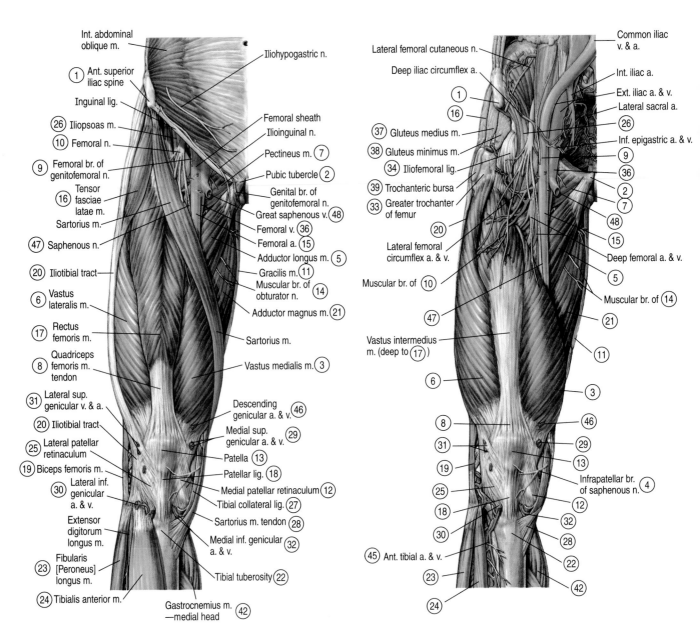

Int. abdominal oblique m.

Iliohypogastric n.

(1) Ant. superior iliac spine

Inguinal lig.

(26) Iliopsoas m.

(10) Femoral n.

(9) Femoral br. of genitofemoral n.

(16) Tensor fasciae latae m.

Sartorius m.

(47) Saphenous n.

(20) Iliotibial tract

(6) Vastus lateralis m.

(17) Rectus femoris m.

(8) Quadriceps femoris m. tendon

(31) Lateral sup. genicular v. & a.

(20) Iliotibial tract

(25) Lateral patellar retinaculum

(19) Biceps femoris m.

(30) Lateral inf. genicular a. & v.

Extensor digitorum longus m.

(23) Fibularis [Peroneus] longus m.

(24) Tibialis anterior m.

Femoral sheath

Ilioinguinal n.

Pectineus m. (7)

Pubic tubercle (2)

Genital br. of genitofemoral n.

Great saphenous v. (48)

Femoral v. (36)

Femoral a. (15)

Adductor longus m. (5)

Gracilis m. (11)

Muscular br. of obturator n. (14)

Adductor magnus m. (21)

Sartorius m.

Vastus medialis m. (3)

Descending genicular a. & v. (46)

Medial sup. genicular a. & v. (29)

Patella (13)

Patellar lig. (18)

Medial patellar retinaculum (12)

Tibial collateral lig. (27)

Sartorius m. tendon (28)

Medial inf. genicular a. & v. (32)

Tibial tuberosity (22)

Gastrocnemius m. —medial head (42)

Lateral femoral cutaneous n.

Deep iliac circumflex a.

(1)

(16)

(37) Gluteus medius m.

(38) Gluteus minimus m.

(34) Iliofemoral lig.

(39) Trochanteric bursa

(33) Greater trochanter of femur

(20)

Lateral femoral circumflex a. & v.

Muscular br. of (10)

(47)

Vastus intermedius m. (deep to (17))

(6)

(8)

(31)

(19)

(25)

(18)

(30)

(45) Ant. tibial a. & v.

(23)

(24)

Common iliac v. & a.

Int. iliac a.

Ext. iliac a. & v.

Lateral sacral a.

(26)

Inf. epigastric a. & v.

(9)

(36)

(2)

(7)

(48)

(15)

Deep femoral a. & v.

(5)

Muscular br. of (14)

(21)

(11)

(3)

(46)

(29)

(13)

Infrapatellar br. of saphenous n. (4)

(12)

(32)

(28)

(22)

(42)

ANTERIOR VIEWS

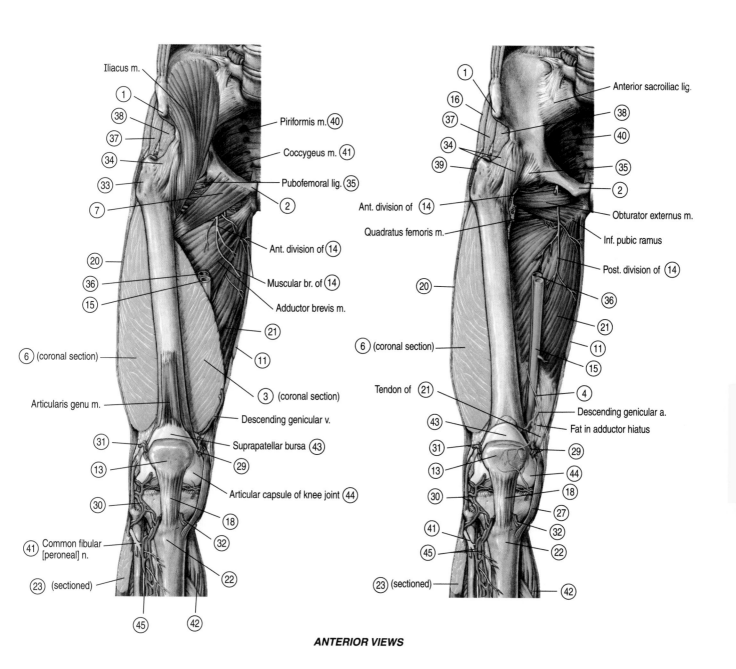

Iliacus m.

①

38

37

34

33

⑦

20

36

15

⑥ (coronal section)

Articularis genu m.

31

13

30

㊶ Common fibular [peroneal] n.

㉓ (sectioned)

45   42

Piriformis m. ④⓪

Coccygeus m. ㊶

Pubofemoral lig. ㉟

②

Ant. division of ⑭

Muscular br. of ⑭

Adductor brevis m.

21

11

③ (coronal section)

Descending genicular v.

Suprapatellar bursa ㊸

29

Articular capsule of knee joint ㊹

18

32

22

①

16

37

34

39

Ant. division of ⑭

Quadratus femoris m.

20

⑥ (coronal section)

Tendon of ㉑

43

31

13

30

㊶

45

㉓ (sectioned)

Anterior sacroiliac lig.

38

40

35

②

Obturator externus m.

Inf. pubic ramus

Post. division of ⑭

36

21

11

15

④

Descending genicular a.

Fat in adductor hiatus

29

44

18

27

32

22

42

ANTERIOR VIEWS

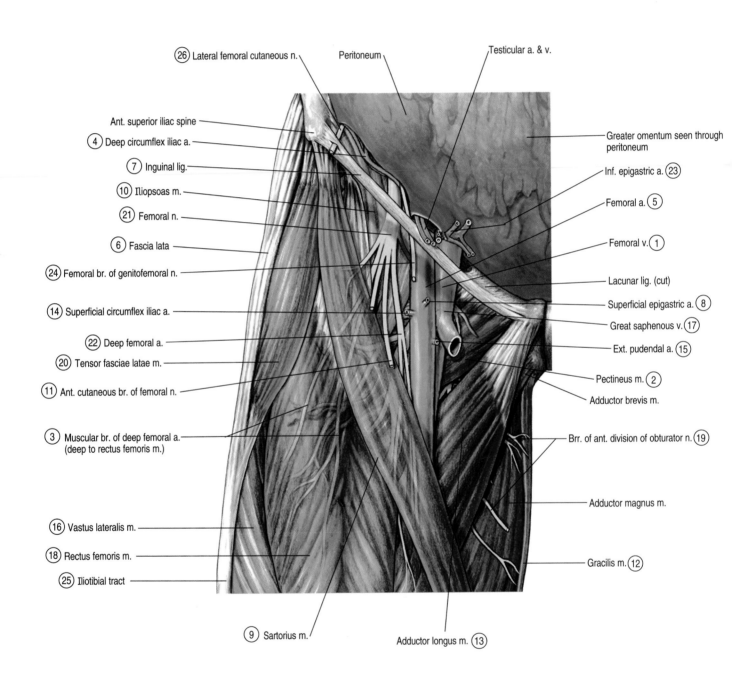

26 Lateral femoral cutaneous n.
Peritoneum
Testicular a. & v.

Ant. superior iliac spine

4 Deep circumflex iliac a.

7 Inguinal lig.

10 Iliopsoas m.

21 Femoral n.

6 Fascia lata

24 Femoral br. of genitofemoral n.

14 Superficial circumflex iliac a.

22 Deep femoral a.

20 Tensor fasciae latae m.

11 Ant. cutaneous br. of femoral n.

3 Muscular br. of deep femoral a.
(deep to rectus femoris m.)

16 Vastus lateralis m.

18 Rectus femoris m.

25 Iliotibial tract

9 Sartorius m.

Adductor longus m. 13

Greater omentum seen through
peritoneum

Inf. epigastric a. 23

Femoral a. 5

Femoral v. 1

Lacunar lig. (cut)

Superficial epigastric a. 8

Great saphenous v. 17

Ext. pudendal a. 15

Pectineus m. 2

Adductor brevis m.

Brr. of ant. division of obturator n. 19

Adductor magnus m.

Gracilis m. 12

ANTERIOR VIEW OF RIGHT PROXIMAL THIGH

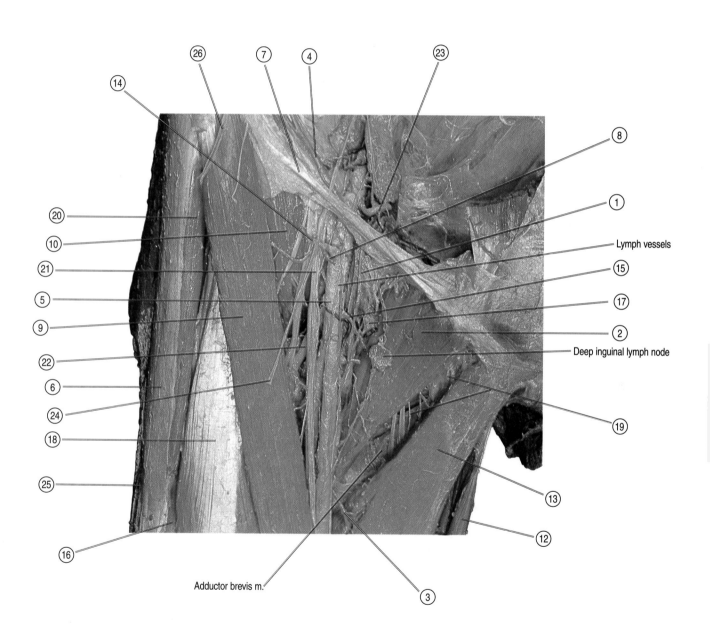

㉖ ⑦ ④ ㉓

⑭

⑧

⑳

①

⑩ Lymph vessels

㉑ ⑮

⑤ ⑰

⑨ ②

㉒ Deep inguinal lymph node

⑥

㉔ ⑲

⑱

㉕ ⑬

⑯ ⑫

Adductor brevis m.

③

ANTERIOR VIEW OF RIGHT PROXIMAL THIGH

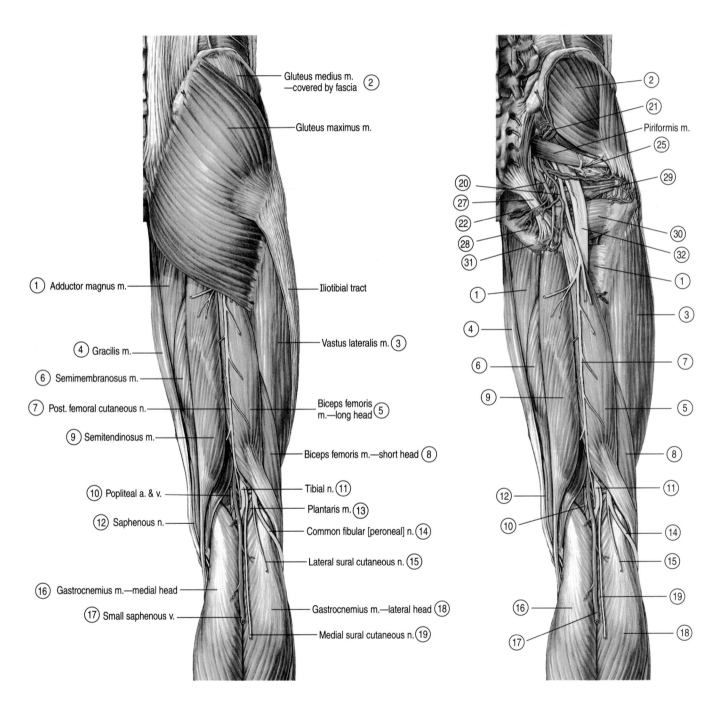

Gluteus medius m. —covered by fascia ②

Gluteus maximus m.

Piriformis m.

② ② ②① ㉕ ㉙

⑳ ㉗ ㉒ ㉘ ㉛

① Adductor magnus m.

Iliotibial tract

① ④ ⑥ ⑨

㉚ ㉜ ① ③ ⑦

④ Gracilis m.

Vastus lateralis m. ③

⑥ Semimembranosus m.

⑦ Post. femoral cutaneous n.

Biceps femoris m.—long head ⑤

⑤

⑨ Semitendinosus m.

Biceps femoris m.—short head ⑧

⑧

⑩ Popliteal a. & v.

Tibial n. ⑪

⑫ ⑩ ⑪

⑫ Saphenous n.

Plantaris m. ⑬

Common fibular [peroneal] n. ⑭

⑭

Lateral sural cutaneous n. ⑮

⑮

⑯ Gastrocnemius m.—medial head

⑯ ⑰ ⑲

⑰ Small saphenous v.

Gastrocnemius m.—lateral head ⑱

⑱

Medial sural cutaneous n. ⑲

POSTERIOR VIEWS

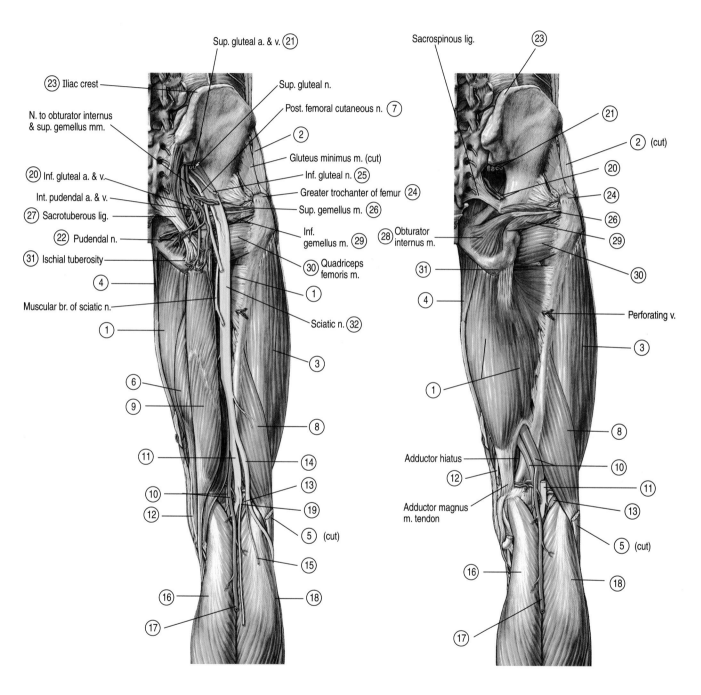

Sup. gluteal a. & v. (21)

Sacrospinous lig. (23)

(23) Iliac crest

Sup. gluteal n.

Post. femoral cutaneous n. (7)

(2)

N. to obturator internus & sup. gemellus mm.

Gluteus minimus m. (cut)

(21)

(20) Inf. gluteal a. & v.

Inf. gluteal n. (25)

(2) (cut)

Int. pudendal a. & v.

Greater trochanter of femur (24)

(20)

(27) Sacrotuberous lig.

Sup. gemellus m. (26)

(24)

(22) Pudendal n.

Inf. gemellus m. (29)

(26)

(28) Obturator internus m.

(29)

(31) Ischial tuberosity

(30) Quadriceps femoris m.

(30)

(4)

(1)

(31)

Muscular br. of sciatic n.

(4)

(1)

Sciatic n. (32)

Perforating v.

(3)

(3)

(6)

(1)

(9)

(8)

(8)

(11)

(14)

Adductor hiatus

(10)

(10)

(13)

(12)

(11)

(12)

(19)

Adductor magnus m. tendon

(13)

(5) (cut)

(5) (cut)

(15)

(16)

(18)

(16)

(18)

(17)

(17)

POSTERIOR VIEWS

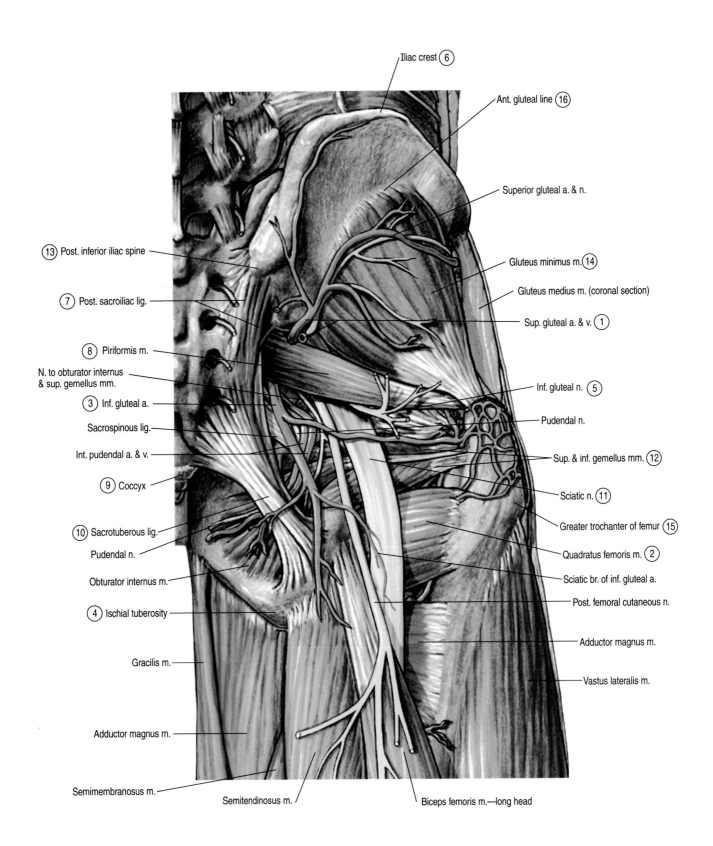

Iliac crest ⑥

Ant. gluteal line ⑯

Superior gluteal a. & n.

Gluteus minimus m.⑭

Gluteus medius m. (coronal section)

Sup. gluteal a. & v. ①

⑬ Post. inferior iliac spine

⑦ Post. sacroiliac lig.

⑧ Piriformis m.

N. to obturator internus
& sup. gemellus mm.

③ Inf. gluteal a.

Sacrospinous lig.

Int. pudendal a. & v.

⑨ Coccyx

⑩ Sacrotuberous lig.

Pudendal n.

Obturator internus m.

④ Ischial tuberosity

Gracilis m.

Adductor magnus m.

Semimembranosus m.

Semitendinosus m.

Inf. gluteal n. ⑤

Pudendal n.

Sup. & inf. gemellus mm. ⑫

Sciatic n. ⑪

Greater trochanter of femur ⑮

Quadratus femoris m. ②

Sciatic br. of inf. gluteal a.

Post. femoral cutaneous n.

Adductor magnus m.

Vastus lateralis m.

Biceps femoris m.—long head

POSTERIOR VIEW

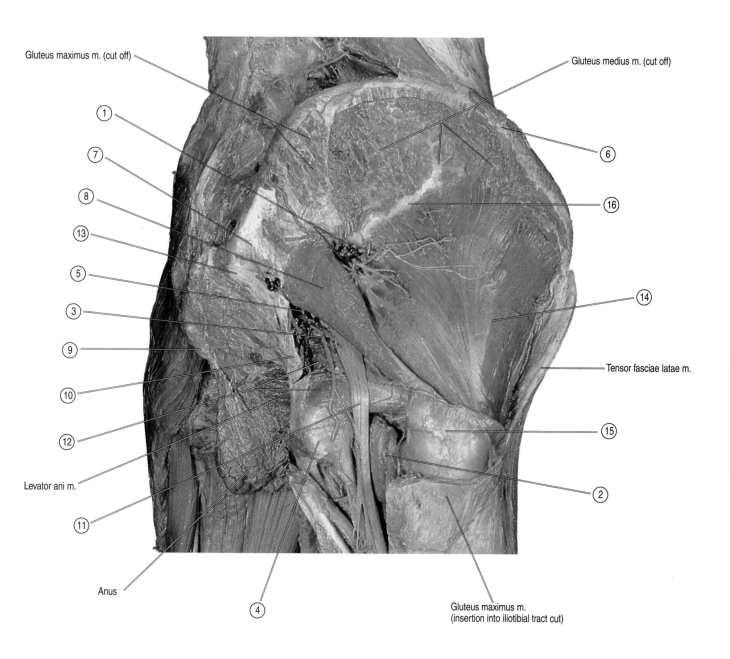

Gluteus maximus m. (cut off)

Gluteus medius m. (cut off)

1

7

8

13

5

3

9

10

12

6

16

14

Tensor fasciae latae m.

15

2

Levator ani m.

11

Anus

4

Gluteus maximus m.
(insertion into iliotibial tract cut)

POSTEROLATERAL VIEW

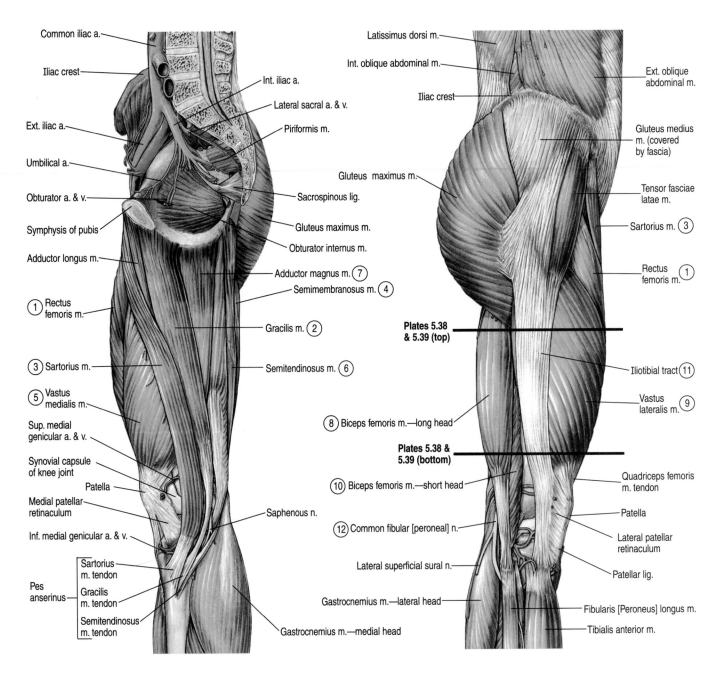

Common iliac a.

Iliac crest

Ext. iliac a.

Umbilical a.

Obturator a. & v.

Symphysis of pubis

Adductor longus m.

(1) Rectus femoris m.

(3) Sartorius m.

(5) Vastus medialis m.

Sup. medial genicular a. & v.

Synovial capsule of knee joint

Patella

Medial patellar retinaculum

Inf. medial genicular a. & v.

Pes anserinus
Sartorius m. tendon
Gracilis m. tendon
Semitendinosus m. tendon

Int. iliac a.

Lateral sacral a. & v.

Piriformis m.

Sacrospinous lig.

Gluteus maximus m.

Obturator internus m.

Adductor magnus m. (7)

Semimembranosus m. (4)

Gracilis m. (2)

Semitendinosus m. (6)

Saphenous n.

Gastrocnemius m.—medial head

MEDIAL VIEW

Latissimus dorsi m.

Int. oblique abdominal m.

Iliac crest

Gluteus maximus m.

Plates 5.38 & 5.39 (top)

(8) Biceps femoris m.—long head

Plates 5.38 & 5.39 (bottom)

(10) Biceps femoris m.—short head

(12) Common fibular [peroneal] n.

Lateral superficial sural n.

Gastrocnemius m.—lateral head

Ext. oblique abdominal m.

Gluteus medius m. (covered by fascia)

Tensor fasciae latae m.

Sartorius m. (3)

Rectus femoris m. (1)

Iliotibial tract (11)

Vastus lateralis m. (9)

Quadriceps femoris m. tendon

Patella

Lateral patellar retinaculum

Patellar lig.

Fibularis [Peroneus] longus m.

Tibialis anterior m.

LATERAL VIEW

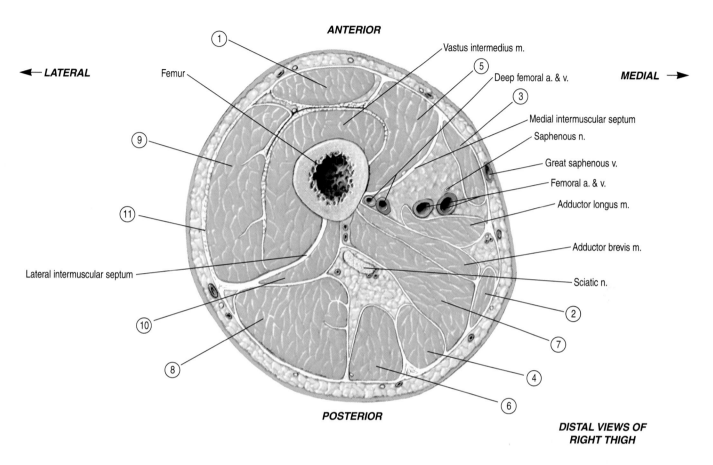

ANTERIOR

① Vastus intermedius m.

LATERAL   ⑤   Deep femoral a. & v.

MEDIAL   ③

Femur   Medial intermuscular septum

⑨   Saphenous n.

Great saphenous v.

Femoral a. & v.

⑪   Adductor longus m.

Adductor brevis m.

Lateral intermuscular septum   Sciatic n.

⑩   ②

⑦

⑧   ④

⑥

POSTERIOR

DISTAL VIEWS OF
RIGHT THIGH

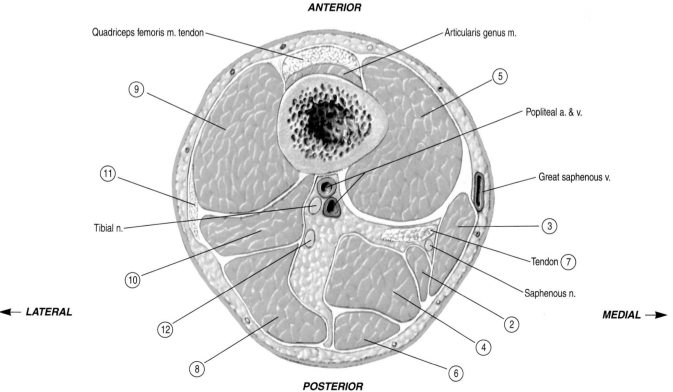

ANTERIOR

Quadriceps femoris m. tendon   Articularis genus m.

⑨   ⑤

Popliteal a. & v.

⑪

Great saphenous v.

③

Tibial n.   Tendon ⑦

⑩   Saphenous n.

②

⑫   ④

⑧   ⑥

LATERAL   MEDIAL

POSTERIOR

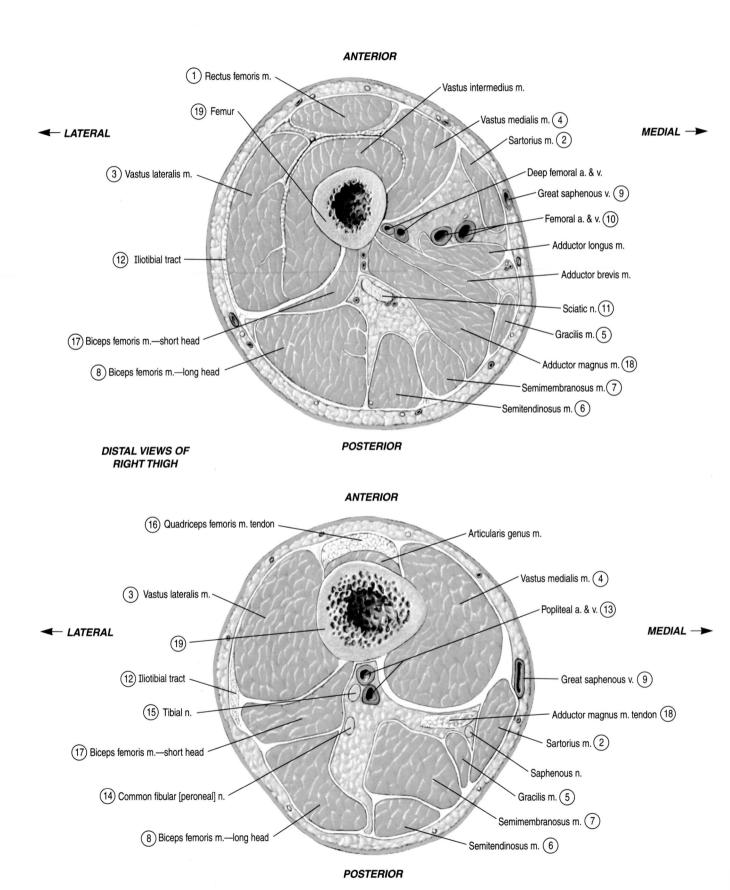

ANTERIOR

① Rectus femoris m.

⑲ Femur

← LATERAL

③ Vastus lateralis m.

⑫ Iliotibial tract

⑰ Biceps femoris m.—short head

⑧ Biceps femoris m.—long head

Vastus intermedius m.

Vastus medialis m. ④

Sartorius m. ②

MEDIAL →

Deep femoral a. & v.

Great saphenous v. ⑨

Femoral a. & v. ⑩

Adductor longus m.

Adductor brevis m.

Sciatic n. ⑪

Gracilis m. ⑤

Adductor magnus m. ⑱

Semimembranosus m. ⑦

Semitendinosus m. ⑥

POSTERIOR

DISTAL VIEWS OF
RIGHT THIGH

ANTERIOR

⑯ Quadriceps femoris m. tendon

③ Vastus lateralis m.

← LATERAL

⑲

⑫ Iliotibial tract

⑮ Tibial n.

⑰ Biceps femoris m.—short head

⑭ Common fibular [peroneal] n.

⑧ Biceps femoris m.—long head

Articularis genus m.

Vastus medialis m. ④

Popliteal a. & v. ⑬

MEDIAL →

Great saphenous v. ⑨

Adductor magnus m. tendon ⑱

Sartorius m. ②

Saphenous n.

Gracilis m. ⑤

Semimembranosus m. ⑦

Semitendinosus m. ⑥

POSTERIOR

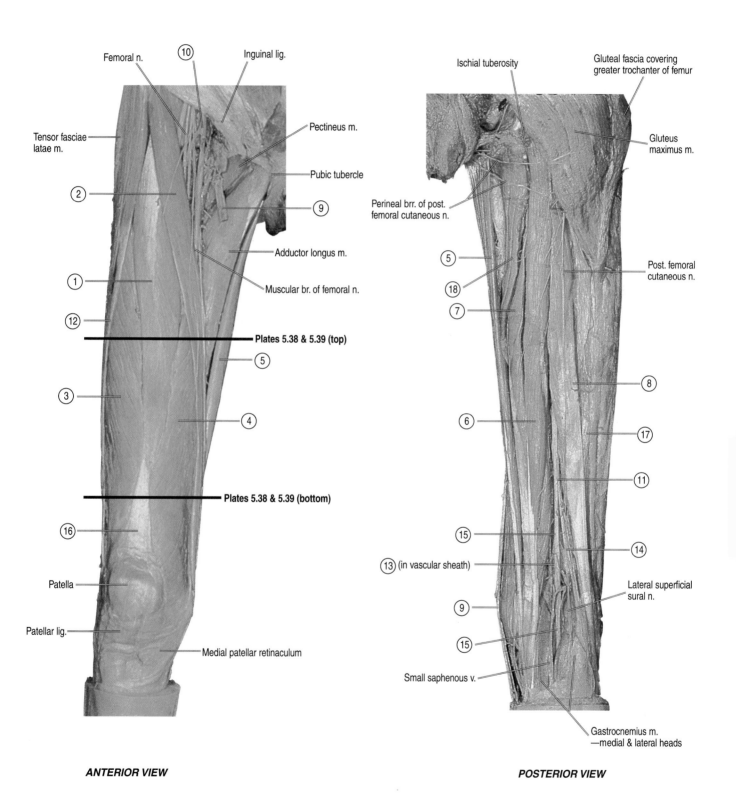

Femoral n.

⑩

Inguinal lig.

Ischial tuberosity

Gluteal fascia covering greater trochanter of femur

Tensor fasciae latae m.

Pectineus m.

Gluteus maximus m.

②

Pubic tubercle

Perineal brr. of post. femoral cutaneous n.

⑨

⑤

⑱

Post. femoral cutaneous n.

Adductor longus m.

①

⑦

Muscular br. of femoral n.

⑫

Plates 5.38 & 5.39 (top)

⑤

⑧

③

⑥

⑰

④

⑪

Plates 5.38 & 5.39 (bottom)

⑯

⑮

⑬ (in vascular sheath)

⑭

Patella

Lateral superficial sural n.

Patellar lig.

⑨

⑮

Medial patellar retinaculum

Small saphenous v.

Gastrocnemius m. —medial & lateral heads

ANTERIOR VIEW

POSTERIOR VIEW

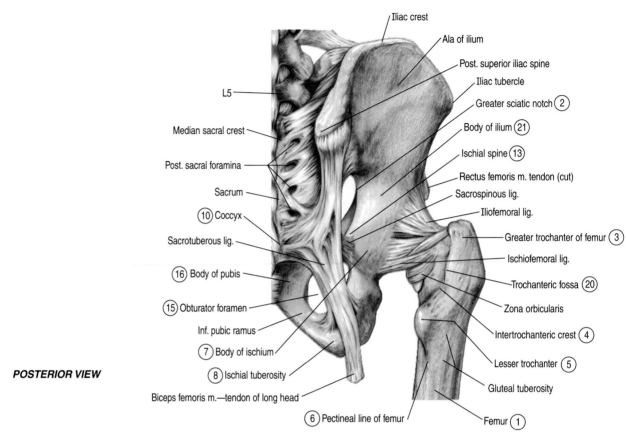

Iliac crest
Ala of ilium
Post. superior iliac spine
Iliac tubercle
Greater sciatic notch (2)
Body of ilium (21)
Ischial spine (13)
Rectus femoris m. tendon (cut)
Sacrospinous lig.
Iliofemoral lig.
Greater trochanter of femur (3)
Ischiofemoral lig.
Trochanteric fossa (20)
Zona orbicularis
Intertrochanteric crest (4)
Lesser trochanter (5)
Gluteal tuberosity
Femur (1)

L5
Median sacral crest
Post. sacral foramina
Sacrum
(10) Coccyx
Sacrotuberous lig.
(16) Body of pubis
(15) Obturator foramen
Inf. pubic ramus
(7) Body of ischium
(8) Ischial tuberosity
Biceps femoris m.—tendon of long head
(6) Pectineal line of femur

POSTERIOR VIEW

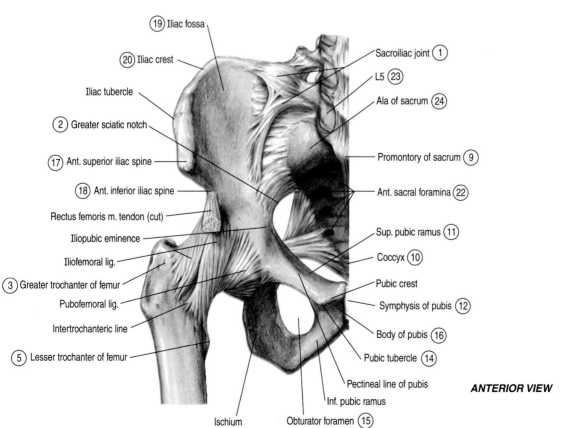

(19) Iliac fossa
(20) Iliac crest
Iliac tubercle
(2) Greater sciatic notch
(17) Ant. superior iliac spine
(18) Ant. inferior iliac spine
Rectus femoris m. tendon (cut)
Iliopubic eminence
Iliofemoral lig.
(3) Greater trochanter of femur
Pubofemoral lig.
Intertrochanteric line
(5) Lesser trochanter of femur

Sacroiliac joint (1)
L5 (23)
Ala of sacrum (24)
Promontory of sacrum (9)
Ant. sacral foramina (22)
Sup. pubic ramus (11)
Coccyx (10)
Pubic crest
Symphysis of pubis (12)
Body of pubis (16)
Pubic tubercle (14)
Pectineal line of pubis
Inf. pubic ramus
Obturator foramen (15)
Ischium

ANTERIOR VIEW

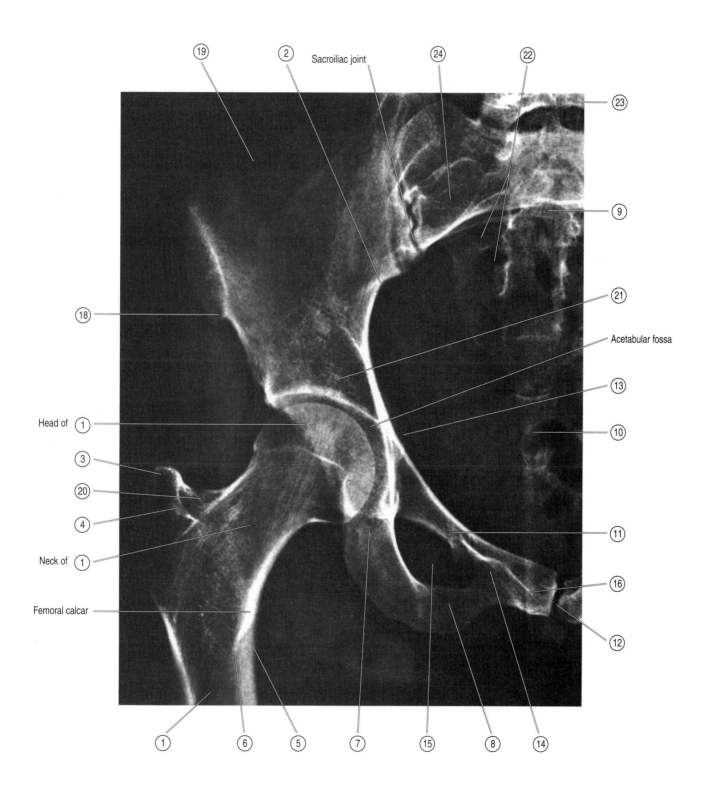

19

2   Sacroiliac joint

24

22

23

9

21

18

Acetabular fossa

13

Head of   1

10

3

20

4

11

Neck of   1

16

Femoral calcar

12

1   6   5   7   15   8   14

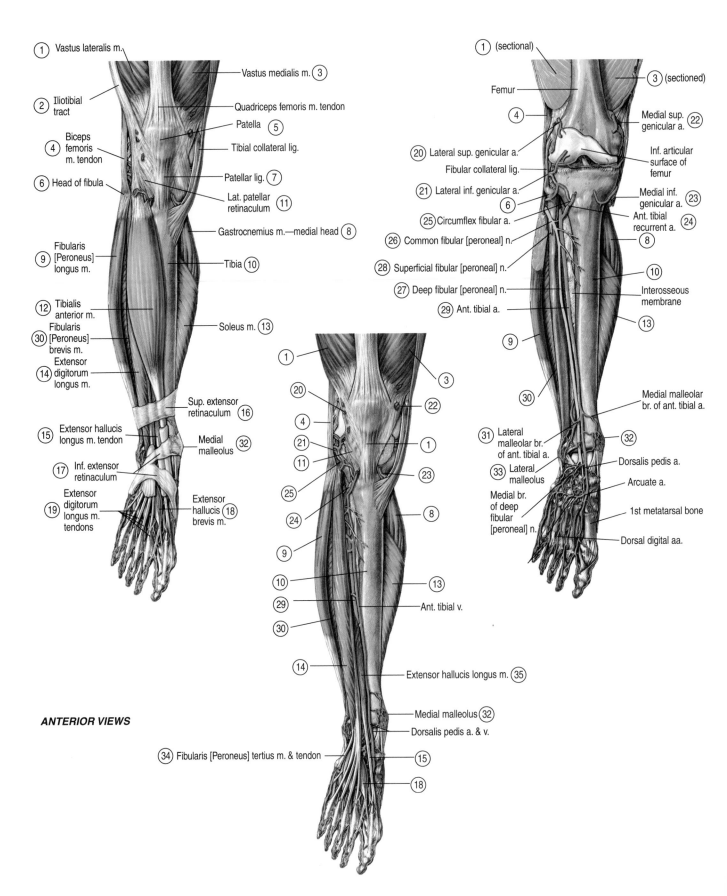

① Vastus lateralis m.

Vastus medialis m. ③

② Iliotibial tract

Quadriceps femoris m. tendon

Patella ⑤

④ Biceps femoris m. tendon

Tibial collateral lig.

⑥ Head of fibula

Patellar lig. ⑦

Lat. patellar retinaculum ⑪

Gastrocnemius m.—medial head ⑧

⑨ Fibularis [Peroneus] longus m.

Tibia ⑩

⑫ Tibialis anterior m.

Soleus m. ⑬

⑳ Fibularis [Peroneus] brevis m.

⑭ Extensor digitorum longus m.

Sup. extensor retinaculum ⑯

⑮ Extensor hallucis longus m. tendon

Medial malleolus ㉜

⑰ Inf. extensor retinaculum

⑲ Extensor digitorum longus m. tendons

Extensor hallucis brevis m. ⑱

ANTERIOR VIEWS

① (sectional)

③ (sectioned)

Femur

④

Medial sup. genicular a. ㉒

⑳ Lateral sup. genicular a.

Inf. articular surface of femur

Fibular collateral lig.

㉑ Lateral inf. genicular a.

⑥

Medial inf. genicular a. ㉓

㉕ Circumflex fibular a.

Ant. tibial recurrent a. ㉔

㉖ Common fibular [peroneal] n.

⑧

㉘ Superficial fibular [peroneal] n.

⑩

㉗ Deep fibular [peroneal] n.

Interosseous membrane

㉙ Ant. tibial a.

⑬

⑨

㉚

Medial malleolar br. of ant. tibial a.

㉛ Lateral malleolar br. of ant. tibial a.

㉜

㉝ Lateral malleolus

Dorsalis pedis a.

Arcuate a.

Medial br. of deep fibular [peroneal] n.

1st metatarsal bone

Dorsal digital aa.

①

③

⑳

㉒

④

⑪

①

㉑

㉕

㉓

㉔

⑨

⑧

⑩

⑬

㉙

Ant. tibial v.

㉚

⑭

Extensor hallucis longus m. ㉟

Medial malleolus ㉜

Dorsalis pedis a. & v.

㉞ Fibularis [Peroneus] tertius m. & tendon

⑮

⑱

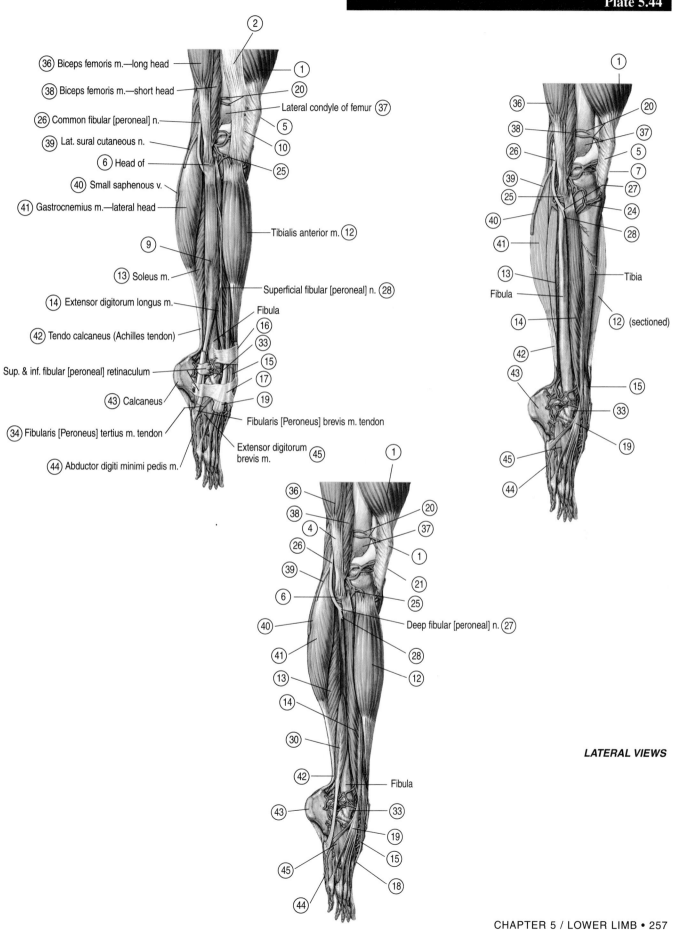

(36) Biceps femoris m.—long head

(38) Biceps femoris m.—short head

(26) Common fibular [peroneal] n.

(39) Lat. sural cutaneous n.

(6) Head of

(40) Small saphenous v.

(41) Gastrocnemius m.—lateral head

(9)

(13) Soleus m.

(14) Extensor digitorum longus m.

(42) Tendo calcaneus (Achilles tendon)

Sup. & inf. fibular [peroneal] retinaculum

(43) Calcaneus

(34) Fibularis [Peroneus] tertius m. tendon

(44) Abductor digiti minimi pedis m.

(2)

(1)

(20)

Lateral condyle of femur (37)

(5)

(10)

(25)

Tibialis anterior m. (12)

Superficial fibular [peroneal] n. (28)

Fibula

(16)

(33)

(15)

(17)

(19)

Fibularis [Peroneus] brevis m. tendon

Extensor digitorum
brevis m. (45)

(1)

(36)

(38)

(26)

(39)

(25)

(40)

(41)

(13)

(14)

(42)

(43)

(45)

(44)

(20)

(37)

(5)

(7)

(27)

(24)

(28)

Tibia

(12) (sectioned)

(15)

(33)

(19)

(1)

(36)

(38)

(4)

(26)

(39)

(6)

(40)

(41)

(13)

(14)

(30)

(42)

(43)

(45)

(44)

(20)

(37)

(1)

(21)

(25)

Deep fibular [peroneal] n. (27)

(28)

(12)

Fibula

(33)

(19)

(15)

(18)

LATERAL VIEWS

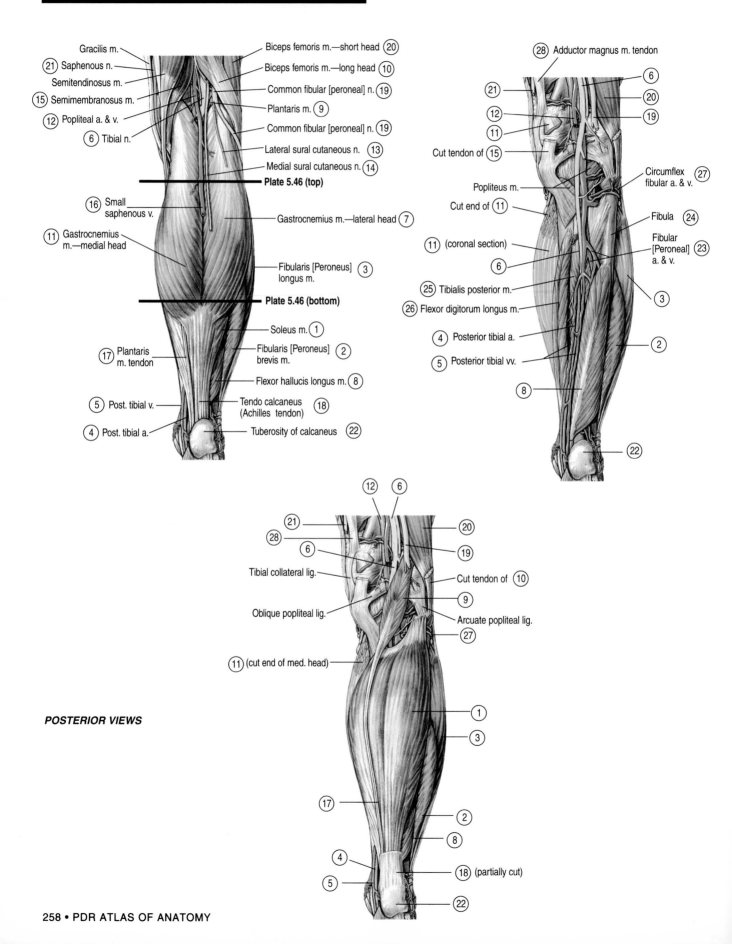

Gracilis m.
21 Saphenous n.
Semitendinosus m.
15 Semimembranosus m.
12 Popliteal a. & v.
6 Tibial n.

Biceps femoris m.—short head 20
Biceps femoris m.—long head 10
Common fibular [peroneal] n. 19
Plantaris m. 9
Common fibular [peroneal] n. 19
Lateral sural cutaneous n. 13
Medial sural cutaneous n. 14
Plate 5.46 (top)

16 Small saphenous v.

Gastrocnemius m.—lateral head 7

11 Gastrocnemius m.—medial head

Fibularis [Peroneus] longus m. 3

Plate 5.46 (bottom)

Soleus m. 1
Fibularis [Peroneus] brevis m. 2

17 Plantaris m. tendon

Flexor hallucis longus m. 8

5 Post. tibial v.

Tendo calcaneus (Achilles tendon) 18

4 Post. tibial a.

Tuberosity of calcaneus 22

28 Adductor magnus m. tendon
21
12
11
Cut tendon of 15
Popliteus m.
Cut end of 11
11 (coronal section)
6
25 Tibialis posterior m.
26 Flexor digitorum longus m.
4 Posterior tibial a.
5 Posterior tibial vv.
8

6
20
19
Circumflex fibular a. & v. 27
Fibula 24
Fibular [Peroneal] a. & v. 23
3
2
22

12 6
21
28
6
Tibial collateral lig.
Oblique popliteal lig.
11 (cut end of med. head)

20
19
Cut tendon of 10
9
Arcuate popliteal lig.
27
1
3

17
2
8
4
5

18 (partially cut)
22

POSTERIOR VIEWS

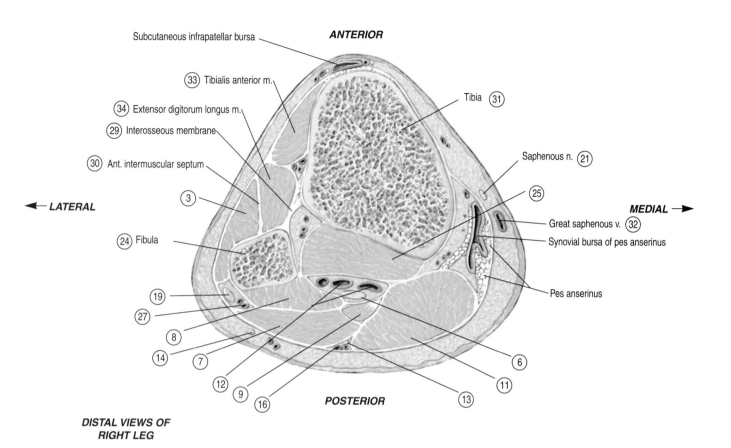

Subcutaneous infrapatellar bursa

ANTERIOR

(33) Tibialis anterior m.

(34) Extensor digitorum longus m.

(29) Interosseous membrane

(30) Ant. intermuscular septum

← LATERAL

(3)

(24) Fibula

(19)

(27)

(8)

(14)

(7)

(12)

(9)

(16)

POSTERIOR

Tibia (31)

Saphenous n. (21)

(25)

MEDIAL →

Great saphenous v. (32)

Synovial bursa of pes anserinus

Pes anserinus

(6)

(11)

(13)

DISTAL VIEWS OF
RIGHT LEG

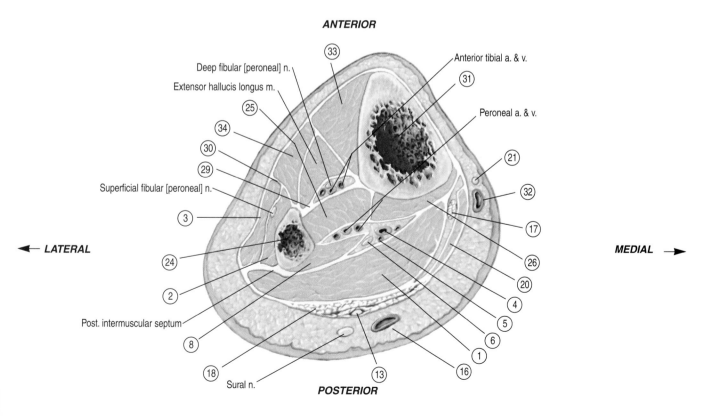

ANTERIOR

(33)

Deep fibular [peroneal] n.

Extensor hallucis longus m.

(25)

(34)

(30)

(29)

Superficial fibular [peroneal] n.

(3)

← LATERAL

(24)

(2)

Post. intermuscular septum

(8)

(18)

Sural n.

Anterior tibial a. & v.

(31)

Peroneal a. & v.

(21)

(32)

(17)

(26)

(20)

(4)

(5)

(6)

(1)

(16)

(13)

MEDIAL →

POSTERIOR

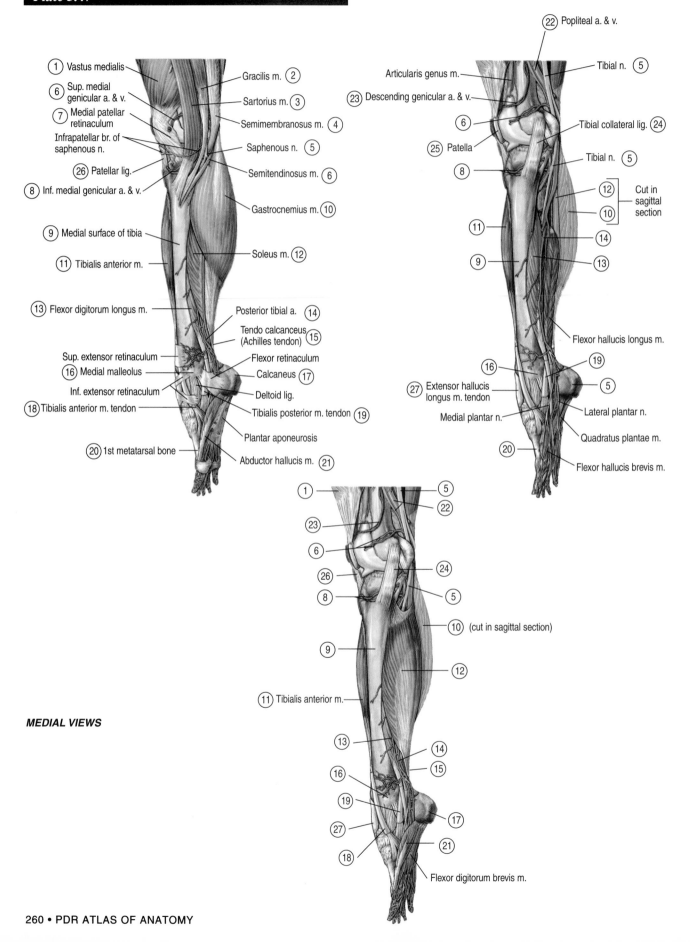

① Vastus medialis
⑥ Sup. medial genicular a. & v.
⑦ Medial patellar retinaculum
Infrapatellar br. of saphenous n.
㉖ Patellar lig.
⑧ Inf. medial genicular a. & v.
⑨ Medial surface of tibia
⑪ Tibialis anterior m.
⑬ Flexor digitorum longus m.
Sup. extensor retinaculum
⑯ Medial malleolus
Inf. extensor retinaculum
⑱ Tibialis anterior m. tendon
⑳ 1st metatarsal bone

Gracilis m. ②
Sartorius m. ③
Semimembranosus m. ④
Saphenous n. ⑤
Semitendinosus m. ⑥
Gastrocnemius m. ⑩
Soleus m. ⑫
Posterior tibial a. ⑭
Tendo calcanceus (Achilles tendon) ⑮
Flexor retinaculum
Calcaneus ⑰
Deltoid lig.
Tibialis posterior m. tendon ⑲
Plantar aponeurosis
Abductor hallucis m. ㉑

㉒ Popliteal a. & v.
Articularis genus m.
㉓ Descending genicular a. & v.
Tibial n. ⑤
⑥
Tibial collateral lig. ㉔
㉕ Patella
⑧
Tibial n. ⑤
⑫
⑪
Cut in sagittal section
⑩
⑭
⑨
⑬
Flexor hallucis longus m.
⑯
⑲
㉗ Extensor hallucis longus m. tendon
⑤
Medial plantar n.
Lateral plantar n.
Quadratus plantae m.
⑳
Flexor hallucis brevis m.

① ⑤
㉒
㉓
⑥
㉔
㉖ ⑤
⑧
⑩ (cut in sagittal section)
⑨
⑫
⑪ Tibialis anterior m.
⑬ ⑭
⑮
⑯
⑲ ⑰
㉗ ㉑
⑱
Flexor digitorum brevis m.

MEDIAL VIEWS

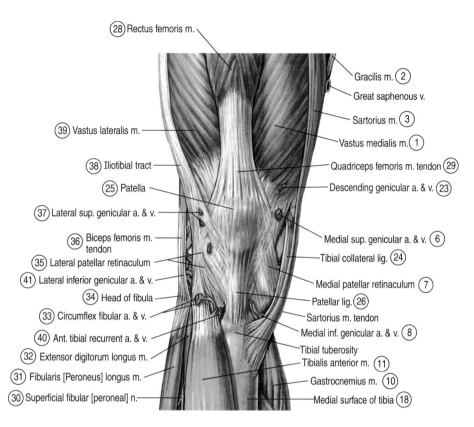

28 Rectus femoris m.

Gracilis m. 2
Great saphenous v.
Sartorius m. 3
Vastus medialis m. 1

39 Vastus lateralis m.

38 Iliotibial tract
25 Patella
37 Lateral sup. genicular a. & v.
36 Biceps femoris m. tendon
35 Lateral patellar retinaculum
41 Lateral inferior genicular a. & v.
34 Head of fibula
33 Circumflex fibular a. & v.
40 Ant. tibial recurrent a. & v.
32 Extensor digitorum longus m.
31 Fibularis [Peroneus] longus m.
30 Superficial fibular [peroneal] n.

Quadriceps femoris m. tendon 29
Descending genicular a. & v. 23

Medial sup. genicular a. & v. 6
Tibial collateral lig. 24
Medial patellar retinaculum 7
Patellar lig. 26
Sartorius m. tendon
Medial inf. genicular a. & v. 8
Tibial tuberosity
Tibialis anterior m. 11
Gastrocnemius m. 10
Medial surface of tibia 18

ANTERIOR VIEW

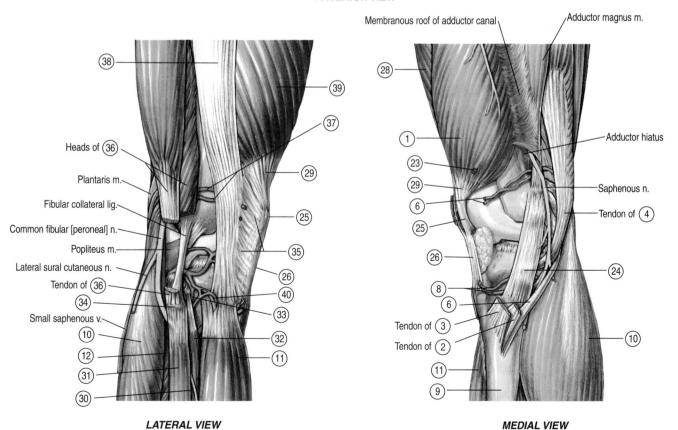

Membranous roof of adductor canal
Adductor magnus m.

38
39
37
Heads of 36
Plantaris m.
Fibular collateral lig.
Common fibular [peroneal] n.
Popliteus m.
Lateral sural cutaneous n.
Tendon of 36
34
Small saphenous v.
10
12
31
30

29
25
35
26
40
33
32
11

28
Adductor hiatus
1
23
29
6
25
Saphenous n.
Tendon of 4
26
24
8
6
Tendon of 3
Tendon of 2
11
9
10

LATERAL VIEW   **MEDIAL VIEW**

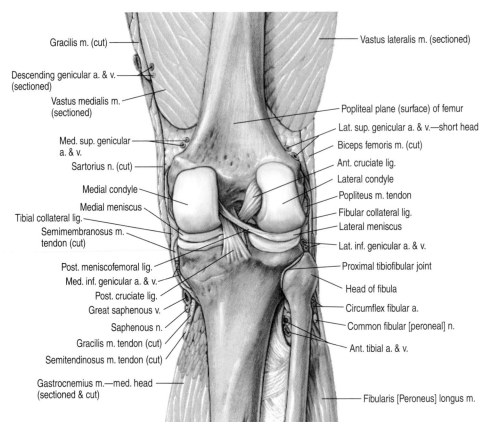

Gracilis m. (cut)

Descending genicular a. & v. (sectioned)

Vastus medialis m. (sectioned)

Med. sup. genicular a. & v.

Sartorius n. (cut)

Medial condyle

Medial meniscus

Tibial collateral lig.

Semimembranosus m. tendon (cut)

Post. meniscofemoral lig.

Med. inf. genicular a. & v.

Post. cruciate lig.

Great saphenous v.

Saphenous n.

Gracilis m. tendon (cut)

Semitendinosus m. tendon (cut)

Gastrocnemius m.—med. head (sectioned & cut)

Vastus lateralis m. (sectioned)

Popliteal plane (surface) of femur

Lat. sup. genicular a. & v.—short head

Biceps femoris m. (cut)

Ant. cruciate lig.

Lateral condyle

Popliteus m. tendon

Fibular collateral lig.

Lateral meniscus

Lat. inf. genicular a. & v.

Proximal tibiofibular joint

Head of fibula

Circumflex fibular a.

Common fibular [peroneal] n.

Ant. tibial a. & v.

Fibularis [Peroneus] longus m.

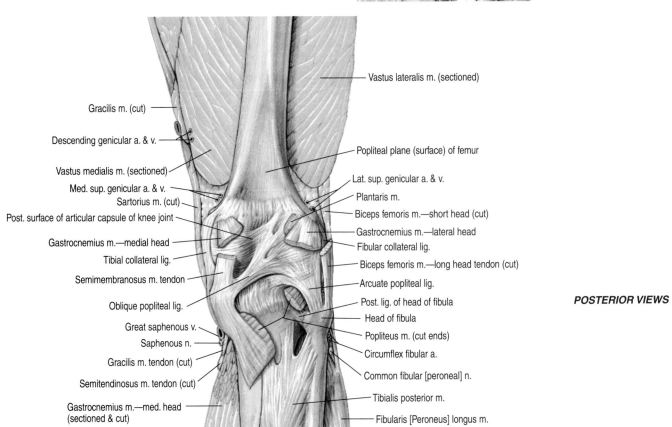

Vastus lateralis m. (sectioned)

Gracilis m. (cut)

Descending genicular a. & v.

Vastus medialis m. (sectioned)

Med. sup. genicular a. & v.

Sartorius m. (cut)

Post. surface of articular capsule of knee joint

Gastrocnemius m.—medial head

Tibial collateral lig.

Semimembranosus m. tendon

Oblique popliteal lig.

Great saphenous v.

Saphenous n.

Gracilis m. tendon (cut)

Semitendinosus m. tendon (cut)

Gastrocnemius m.—med. head (sectioned & cut)

Popliteal plane (surface) of femur

Lat. sup. genicular a. & v.

Plantaris m.

Biceps femoris m.—short head (cut)

Gastrocnemius m.—lateral head

Fibular collateral lig.

Biceps femoris m.—long head tendon (cut)

Arcuate popliteal lig.

Post. lig. of head of fibula

Head of fibula

Popliteus m. (cut ends)

Circumflex fibular a.

Common fibular [peroneal] n.

Tibialis posterior m.

Fibularis [Peroneus] longus m.

POSTERIOR VIEWS

**DISTAL VIEW OF ARTICULAR
SURFACE OF RIGHT FEMUR**

ANTERIOR

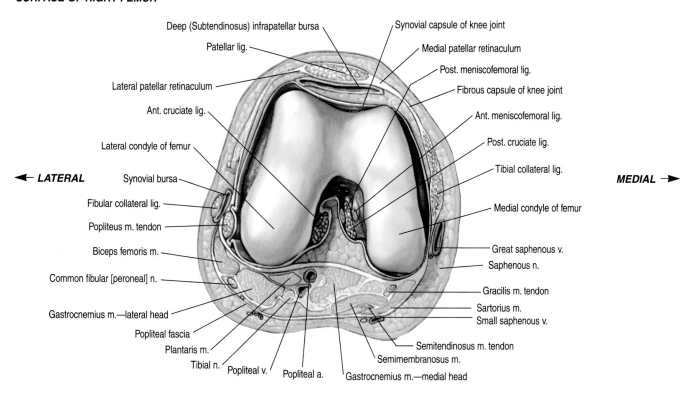

Deep (Subtendinosus) infrapatellar bursa

Patellar lig.

Lateral patellar retinaculum

Ant. cruciate lig.

Lateral condyle of femur

Synovial bursa

Fibular collateral lig.

Popliteus m. tendon

Biceps femoris m.

Common fibular [peroneal] n.

Gastrocnemius m.—lateral head

Popliteal fascia

Plantaris m.

Tibial n.

Popliteal v.

Popliteal a.

Gastrocnemius m.—medial head

Semimembranosus m.

Semitendinosus m. tendon

Synovial capsule of knee joint

Medial patellar retinaculum

Post. meniscofemoral lig.

Fibrous capsule of knee joint

Ant. meniscofemoral lig.

Post. cruciate lig.

Tibial collateral lig.

Medial condyle of femur

Great saphenous v.

Saphenous n.

Gracilis m. tendon

Sartorius m.

Small saphenous v.

LATERAL ←   → MEDIAL

**DISTAL VIEW OF ARTICULAR
SURFACE OF RIGHT TIBIA**

POSTERIOR

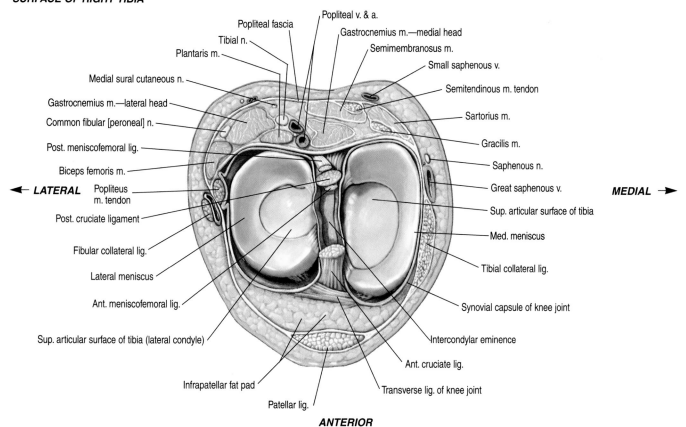

Popliteal fascia

Tibial n.

Plantaris m.

Medial sural cutaneous n.

Gastrocnemius m.—lateral head

Common fibular [peroneal] n.

Post. meniscofemoral lig.

Biceps femoris m.

Popliteus m. tendon

Post. cruciate ligament

Fibular collateral lig.

Lateral meniscus

Ant. meniscofemoral lig.

Sup. articular surface of tibia (lateral condyle)

Infrapatellar fat pad

Patellar lig.

Popliteal v. & a.

Gastrocnemius m.—medial head

Semimembranosus m.

Small saphenous v.

Semitendinous m. tendon

Sartorius m.

Gracilis m.

Saphenous n.

Great saphenous v.

Sup. articular surface of tibia

Med. meniscus

Tibial collateral lig.

Synovial capsule of knee joint

Intercondylar eminence

Ant. cruciate lig.

Transverse lig. of knee joint

LATERAL ←   → MEDIAL

ANTERIOR

Plane of Medial View below

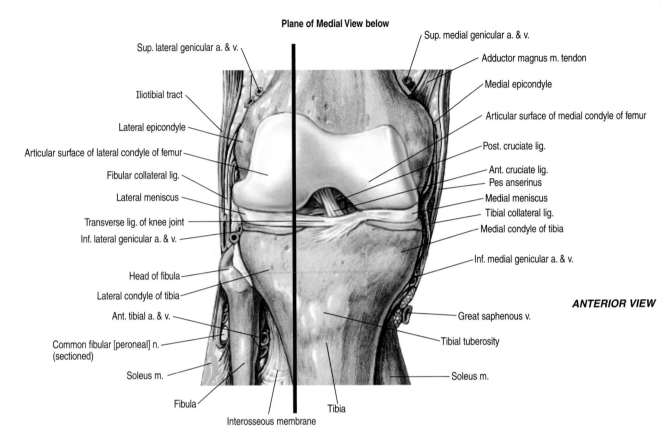

Sup. lateral genicular a. & v.

Sup. medial genicular a. & v.

Adductor magnus m. tendon

Iliotibial tract

Medial epicondyle

Lateral epicondyle

Articular surface of medial condyle of femur

Articular surface of lateral condyle of femur

Post. cruciate lig.

Fibular collateral lig.

Ant. cruciate lig.

Pes anserinus

Lateral meniscus

Medial meniscus

Transverse lig. of knee joint

Tibial collateral lig.

Inf. lateral genicular a. & v.

Medial condyle of tibia

Head of fibula

Inf. medial genicular a. & v.

Lateral condyle of tibia

Ant. tibial a. & v.

Great saphenous v.

Common fibular [peroneal] n.
(sectioned)

Tibial tuberosity

Soleus m.

Soleus m.

Fibula

Interosseous membrane

Tibia

ANTERIOR VIEW

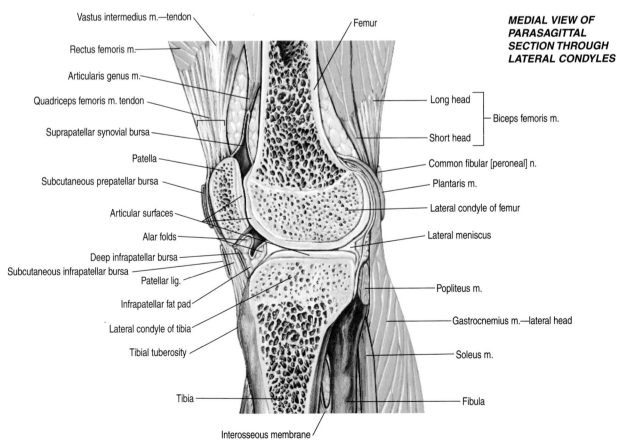

Vastus intermedius m.—tendon

Femur

Rectus femoris m.

Articularis genus m.

Quadriceps femoris m. tendon

Long head

Suprapatellar synovial bursa

Short head

Biceps femoris m.

Patella

Common fibular [peroneal] n.

Subcutaneous prepatellar bursa

Plantaris m.

Articular surfaces

Lateral condyle of femur

Alar folds

Lateral meniscus

Deep infrapatellar bursa

Subcutaneous infrapatellar bursa

Patellar lig.

Popliteus m.

Infrapatellar fat pad

Gastrocnemius m.—lateral head

Lateral condyle of tibia

Tibial tuberosity

Soleus m.

Tibia

Fibula

Interosseous membrane

**MEDIAL VIEW OF
PARASAGITTAL
SECTION THROUGH
LATERAL CONDYLES**

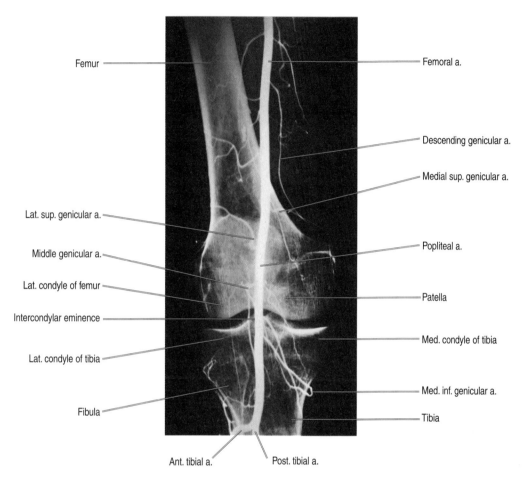

Femur

Femoral a.

Descending genicular a.

Medial sup. genicular a.

Lat. sup. genicular a.

Middle genicular a.

Popliteal a.

Lat. condyle of femur

Patella

Intercondylar eminence

Med. condyle of tibia

Lat. condyle of tibia

Fibula

Med. inf. genicular a.

Tibia

Ant. tibial a.

Post. tibial a.

ANTEROPOSTRIOR VIEW OF RIGHT KNEE ARTERIOGRAM

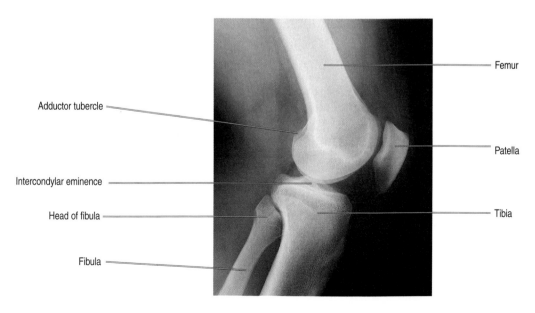

Femur

Adductor tubercle

Patella

Intercondylar eminence

Head of fibula

Tibia

Fibula

LATERAL VIEW OF RIGHT KNEE

Sole of Foot
Plate 5.53

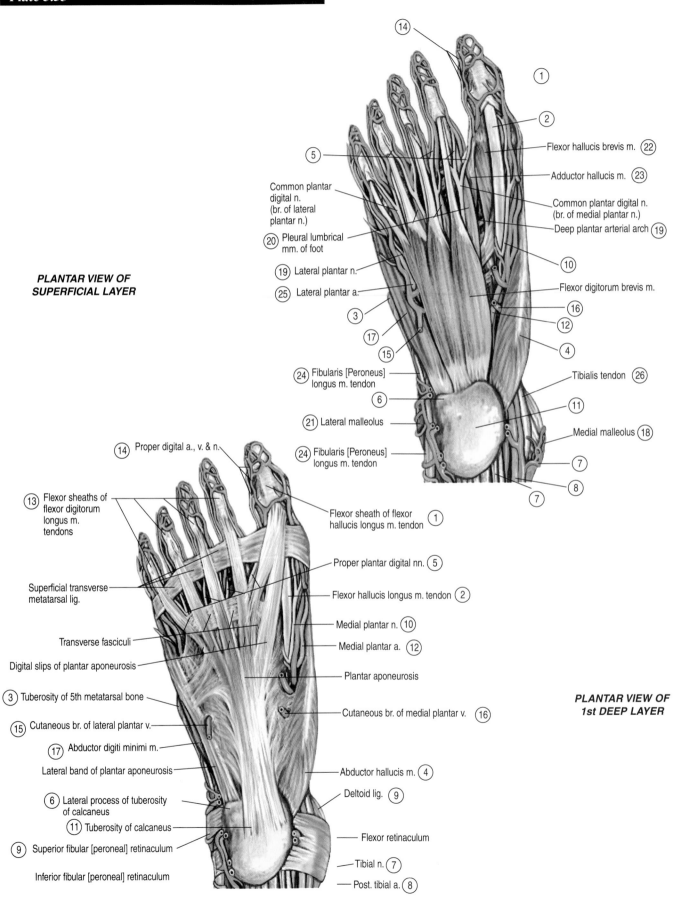

PLANTAR VIEW OF SUPERFICIAL LAYER

(14)

(1)

(2)

Flexor hallucis brevis m. (22)

Adductor hallucis m. (23)

(5)

Common plantar digital n. (br. of lateral plantar n.)

Common plantar digital n. (br. of medial plantar n.)

Deep plantar arterial arch (19)

(20) Pleural lumbrical mm. of foot

(10)

(19) Lateral plantar n.

Flexor digitorum brevis m.

(25) Lateral plantar a.

(16)

(3)

(12)

(17)

(4)

(15)

(24) Fibularis [Peroneus] longus m. tendon

Tibialis tendon (26)

(6)

(11)

(21) Lateral malleolus

Medial malleolus (18)

(24) Fibularis [Peroneus] longus m. tendon

(7)

(8)

(7)

Proper digital a., v. & n. (14)

Flexor sheath of flexor hallucis longus m. tendon (1)

(13) Flexor sheaths of flexor digitorum longus m. tendons

Proper plantar digital nn. (5)

Superficial transverse metatarsal lig.

Flexor hallucis longus m. tendon (2)

Medial plantar n. (10)

Transverse fasciculi

Medial plantar a. (12)

Digital slips of plantar aponeurosis

Plantar aponeurosis

(3) Tuberosity of 5th metatarsal bone

Cutaneous br. of medial plantar v. (16)

(15) Cutaneous br. of lateral plantar v.

(17) Abductor digiti minimi m.

Lateral band of plantar aponeurosis

Abductor hallucis m. (4)

(6) Lateral process of tuberosity of calcaneus

Deltoid lig. (9)

(11) Tuberosity of calcaneus

Flexor retinaculum

(9) Superior fibular [peroneal] retinaculum

Tibial n. (7)

Inferior fibular [peroneal] retinaculum

Post. tibial a. (8)

PLANTAR VIEW OF 1st DEEP LAYER

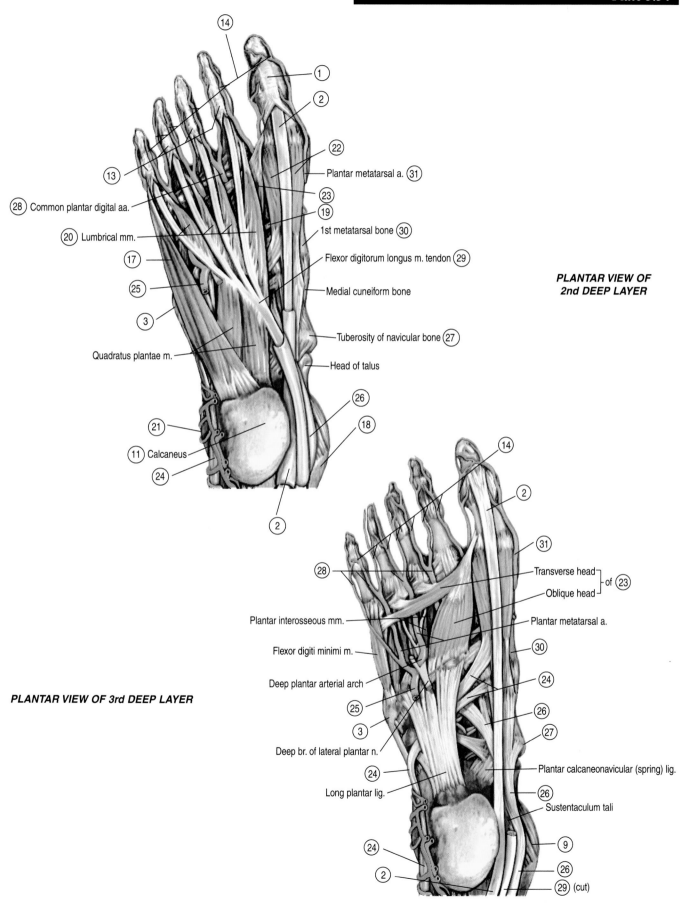

⑭

① 1

② 2

㉒ 22

Plantar metatarsal a. ㉛ 31

㉓ 23

⑲ 19

㉘ 28 Common plantar digital aa.

⑳ 20 Lumbrical mm.

1st metatarsal bone ㉚ 30

⑰ 17

Flexor digitorum longus m. tendon ㉙ 29

⑬ 13

㉕ 25

Medial cuneiform bone

③ 3

PLANTAR VIEW OF
2nd DEEP LAYER

Quadratus plantae m.

Tuberosity of navicular bone ㉗ 27

Head of talus

㉖ 26

⑱ 18

㉑ 21

⑪ 11 Calcaneus

㉔ 24

② 2

⑭ 14

② 2

㉛ 31

㉘ 28

Transverse head⎤
⎬ of ㉓ 23
Oblique head⎦

Plantar interosseous mm.

Plantar metatarsal a.

Flexor digiti minimi m.

㉚ 30

Deep plantar arterial arch

㉔ 24

㉕ 25

㉖ 26

③ 3

㉗ 27

Deep br. of lateral plantar n.

Plantar calcaneonavicular (spring) lig.

PLANTAR VIEW OF 3rd DEEP LAYER

㉔ 24

Long plantar lig.

㉖ 26

Sustentaculum tali

㉔ 24

⑨ 9

② 2

㉖ 26

㉙ 29 (cut)

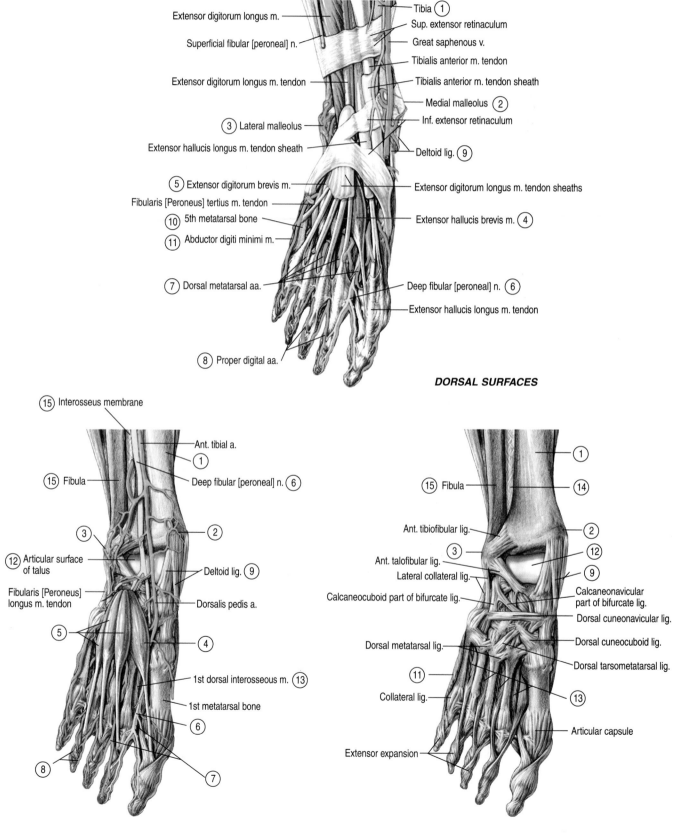

Extensor digitorum longus m.

Superficial fibular [peroneal] n.

Extensor digitorum longus m. tendon

(3) Lateral malleolus

Extensor hallucis longus m. tendon sheath

(5) Extensor digitorum brevis m.

Fibularis [Peroneus] tertius m. tendon

(10) 5th metatarsal bone

(11) Abductor digiti minimi m.

(7) Dorsal metatarsal aa.

(8) Proper digital aa.

Tibia (1)

Sup. extensor retinaculum

Great saphenous v.

Tibialis anterior m. tendon

Tibialis anterior m. tendon sheath

Medial malleolus (2)

Inf. extensor retinaculum

Deltoid lig. (9)

Extensor digitorum longus m. tendon sheaths

Extensor hallucis brevis m. (4)

Deep fibular [peroneal] n. (6)

Extensor hallucis longus m. tendon

DORSAL SURFACES

(15) Interosseus membrane

(15) Fibula

(12) Articular surface of talus

Fibularis [Peroneus] longus m. tendon

(5)

Ant. tibial a.

(1)

Deep fibular [peroneal] n. (6)

(3)

(2)

Deltoid lig. (9)

Dorsalis pedis a.

(4)

1st dorsal interosseous m. (13)

1st metatarsal bone

(6)

(8)

(7)

(15) Fibula

Ant. tibiofibular lig.

Ant. talofibular lig.

Lateral collateral lig.

Calcaneocuboid part of bifurcate lig.

Dorsal metatarsal lig.

(11)

Collateral lig.

Extensor expansion

(1)

(14)

(2)

(12)

(9)

Calcaneonavicular part of bifurcate lig.

Dorsal cuneonavicular lig.

Dorsal cuneocuboid lig.

Dorsal tarsometatarsal lig.

(13)

Articular capsule

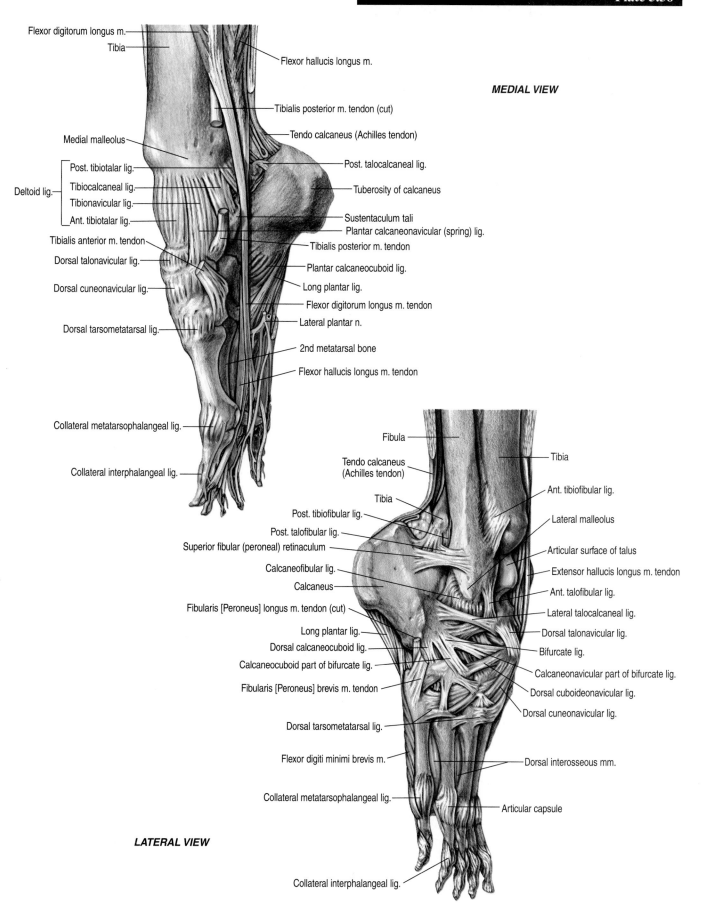

Flexor digitorum longus m.

Tibia

Flexor hallucis longus m.

MEDIAL VIEW

Tibialis posterior m. tendon (cut)

Tendo calcaneus (Achilles tendon)

Medial malleolus

Post. talocalcaneal lig.

Post. tibiotalar lig.

Tibiocalcaneal lig.

Deltoid lig.

Tibionavicular lig.

Ant. tibiotalar lig.

Tuberosity of calcaneus

Sustentaculum tali

Plantar calcaneonavicular (spring) lig.

Tibialis anterior m. tendon

Tibialis posterior m. tendon

Dorsal talonavicular lig.

Plantar calcaneocuboid lig.

Dorsal cuneonavicular lig.

Long plantar lig.

Flexor digitorum longus m. tendon

Dorsal tarsometatarsal lig.

Lateral plantar n.

2nd metatarsal bone

Flexor hallucis longus m. tendon

Collateral metatarsophalangeal lig.

Collateral interphalangeal lig.

Fibula

Tibia

Tendo calcaneus
(Achilles tendon)

Ant. tibiofibular lig.

Tibia

Post. tibiofibular lig.

Lateral malleolus

Post. talofibular lig.

Articular surface of talus

Superior fibular (peroneal) retinaculum

Extensor hallucis longus m. tendon

Calcaneofibular lig.

Ant. talofibular lig.

Calcaneus

Lateral talocalcaneal lig.

Fibularis [Peroneus] longus m. tendon (cut)

Dorsal talonavicular lig.

Long plantar lig.

Bifurcate lig.

Dorsal calcaneocuboid lig.

Calcaneonavicular part of bifurcate lig.

Calcaneocuboid part of bifurcate lig.

Dorsal cuboideonavicular lig.

Fibularis [Peroneus] brevis m. tendon

Dorsal cuneonavicular lig.

Dorsal tarsometatarsal lig.

Flexor digiti minimi brevis m.

Dorsal interosseous mm.

Collateral metatarsophalangeal lig.

Articular capsule

LATERAL VIEW

Collateral interphalangeal lig.

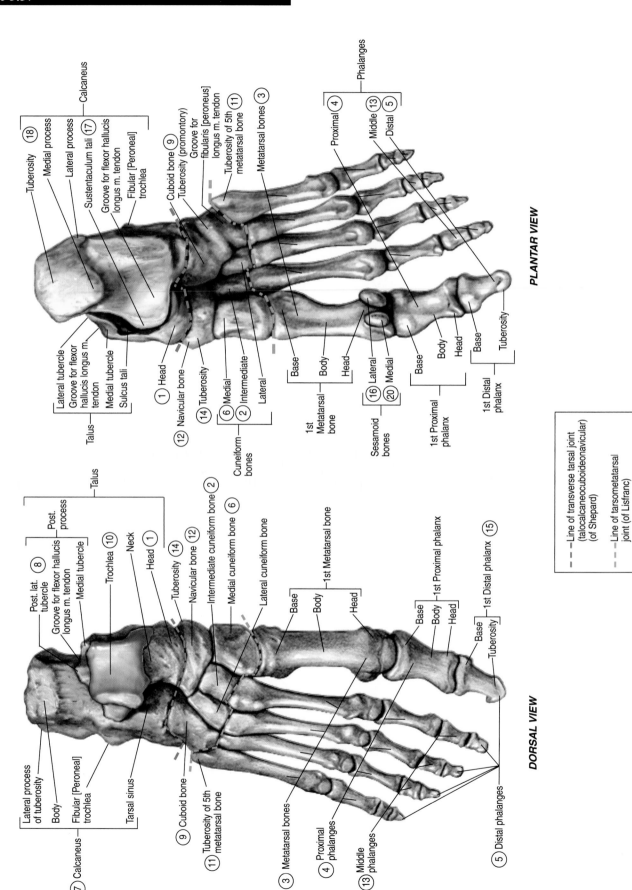

PLANTAR VIEW

Tuberosity ⑱
Medial process
Lateral process
Sustentaculum tali ⑰
Groove for flexor hallucis longus m. tendon
Fibular [Peroneal] trochlea
Calcaneus

Cuboid bone ⑨
Tuberosity (promontory)
Groove for fibularis [peroneus] longus m. tendon
Tuberosity of 5th metatarsal bone ⑪
Metatarsal bones ③

Phalanges
Proximal ④
Middle ⑬
Distal ⑤

Lateral tubercle
Groove for flexor hallucis longus m. tendon
Medial tubercle
Sulcus tali
Talus

① Head
⑫ Navicular bone
⑭ Tuberosity
⑥ Medial
② Intermediate
Lateral
Cuneiform bones

Base
Body
Head
1st Metatarsal bone

⑯ Lateral
⑳ Medial
Sesamoid bones

Base
Body
Head
1st Proximal phalanx

Base
Tuberosity
1st Distal phalanx

DORSAL VIEW

Talus
Post. process
Post. lat. tubercle ⑧
Groove for flexor hallucis longus m. tendon
Medial tubercle
Trochlea ⑩
Neck
Head ①
⑭ Tuberosity
Navicular bone ⑫
Intermediate cuneiform bone ②
Medial cuneiform bone ⑥
Lateral cuneiform bone

Lateral process of tuberosity
Body
Fibular [Peroneal] trochlea
Tarsal sinus
Calcaneus ⑦

⑨ Cuboid bone
Tuberosity of 5th metatarsal bone ⑪

Base
Body
1st Metatarsal bone
Head

Base
Body
Head
1st Proximal phalanx

Base
Tuberosity
1st Distal phalanx ⑮

③ Metatarsal bones
④ Proximal phalanges
⑬ Middle phalanges
⑤ Distal phalanges

- - - Line of transverse tarsal joint (talocalcaneocuboideonavicular) (of Shepard)
- - - Line of tarsometatarsal joint (of Lisfranc)

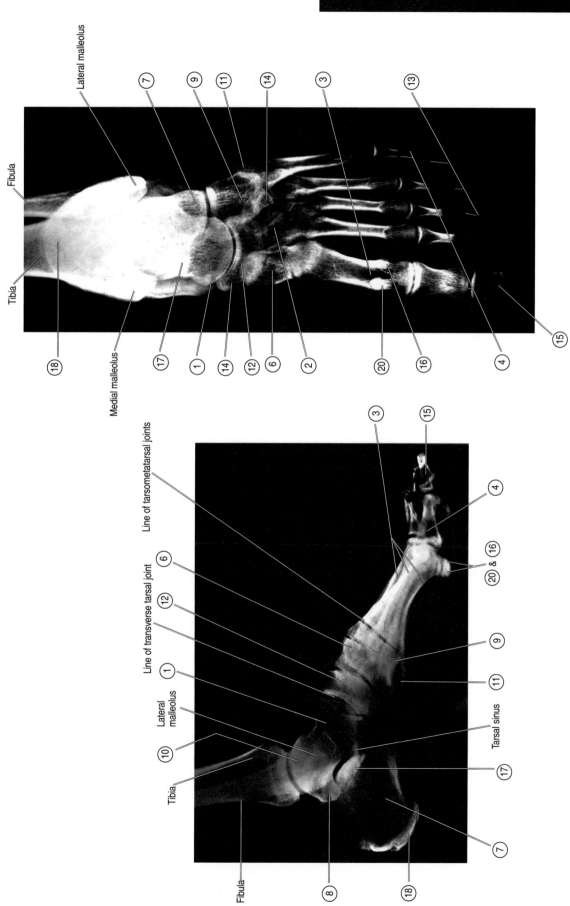

Top figure (ANTEROPOSTERIOR VIEW):

Lateral malleolus — 7, 9, 11, 14, 3, 13

Fibula

Tibia

Medial malleolus — 18

17, 1, 14, 12, 6, 2, 20, 16, 4, 15

Bottom figure (LATERAL VIEW):

Line of tarsometatarsal joints

Line of transverse tarsal joint

3, 15

6, 12, 1

4

20 & 16

9

11

Tarsal sinus

Lateral malleolus — 10

Tibia

17

Fibula — 8, 18, 7

ANTEROPOSTERIOR VIEW

LATERAL VIEW

Upper Limb

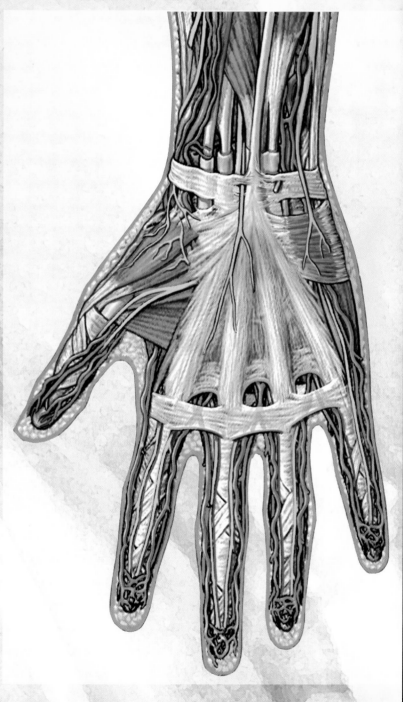

Surface Anatomy
Plate 6.1

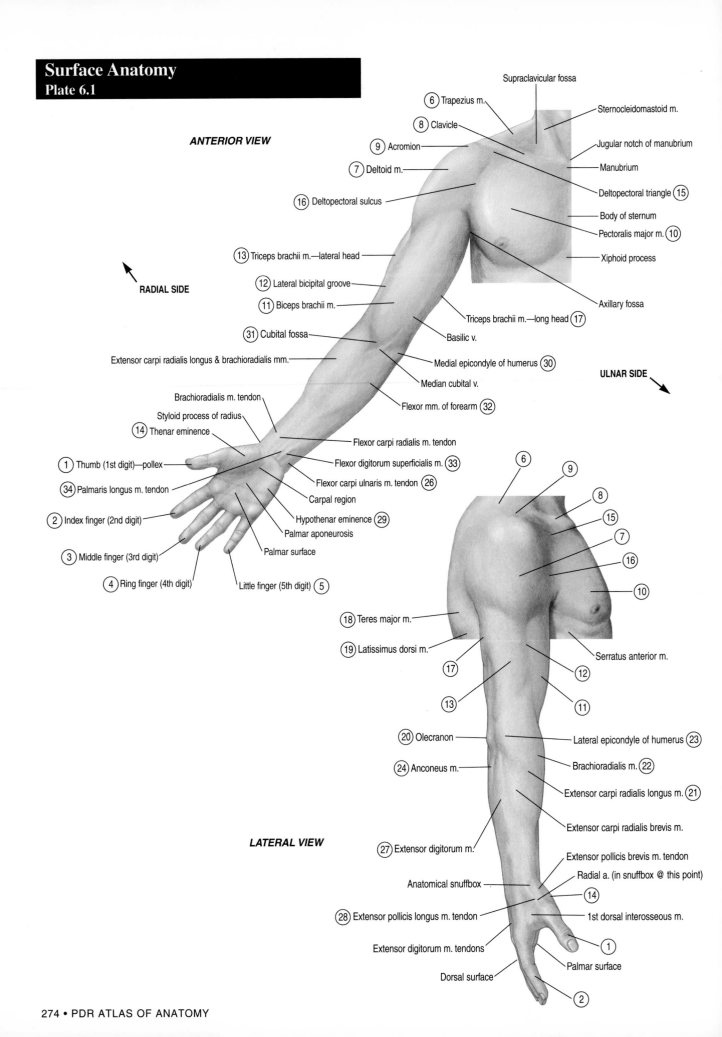

ANTERIOR VIEW

Supraclavicular fossa

⑥ Trapezius m.

⑧ Clavicle

⑨ Acromion

⑦ Deltoid m.

⑯ Deltopectoral sulcus

Sternocleidomastoid m.

Jugular notch of manubrium

Manubrium

Deltopectoral triangle ⑮

Body of sternum

Pectoralis major m. ⑩

Xiphoid process

Axillary fossa

↖ **RADIAL SIDE**

⑬ Triceps brachii m.—lateral head

⑫ Lateral bicipital groove

⑪ Biceps brachii m.

㉛ Cubital fossa

Extensor carpi radialis longus & brachioradialis mm.

Triceps brachii m.—long head ⑰

Basilic v.

Medial epicondyle of humerus ㉚

Median cubital v.

Flexor mm. of forearm ㉜

ULNAR SIDE ↘

Brachioradialis m. tendon

Styloid process of radius

⑭ Thenar eminence

① Thumb (1st digit)—pollex

㉞ Palmaris longus m. tendon

② Index finger (2nd digit)

③ Middle finger (3rd digit)

④ Ring finger (4th digit)

Flexor carpi radialis m. tendon

Flexor digitorum superficialis m. ㉝

Flexor carpi ulnaris m. tendon ㉖

Carpal region

Hypothenar eminence ㉙

Palmar aponeurosis

Palmar surface

Little finger (5th digit) ⑤

⑥ ⑨

⑧

⑮

⑦

⑯

⑩

⑱ Teres major m.

⑲ Latissimus dorsi m.

⑰

⑬

Serratus anterior m.

⑫

⑪

⑳ Olecranon

㉔ Anconeus m.

Lateral epicondyle of humerus ㉓

Brachioradialis m. ㉒

Extensor carpi radialis longus m. ㉑

Extensor carpi radialis brevis m.

LATERAL VIEW

㉗ Extensor digitorum m.

Anatomical snuffbox

㉘ Extensor pollicis longus m. tendon

Extensor digitorum m. tendons

Dorsal surface

Extensor pollicis brevis m. tendon

Radial a. (in snuffbox @ this point)

⑭

1st dorsal interosseous m.

①

Palmar surface

②

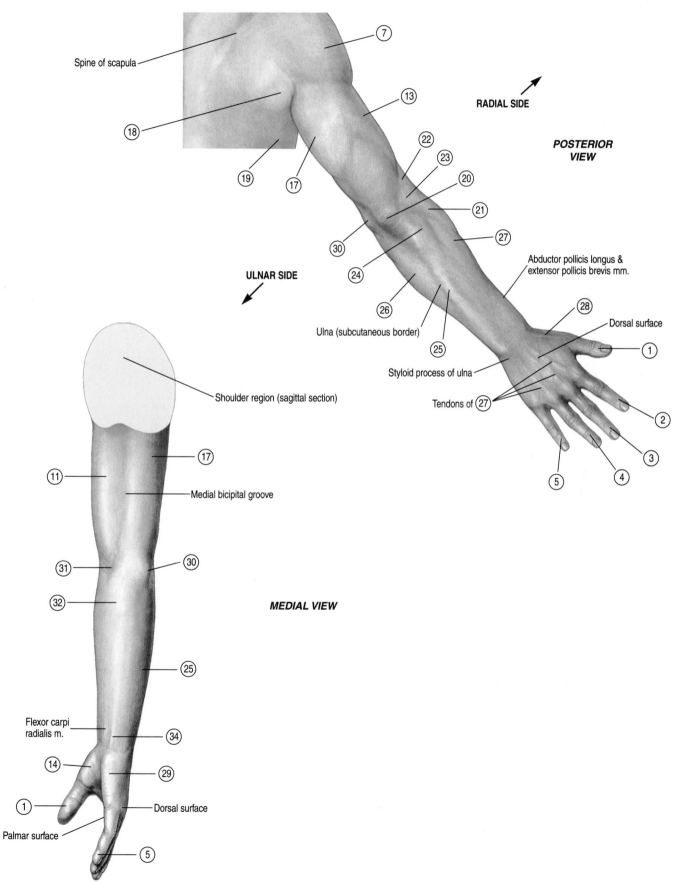

Spine of scapula

⑦

⑬

RADIAL SIDE

⑱

⑲ ⑰

⑲

POSTERIOR VIEW

㉒

㉓

⑳

㉑

㉗

ULNAR SIDE

㉚

㉔

Abductor pollicis longus & extensor pollicis brevis mm.

㉖

㉘

Dorsal surface

Ulna (subcutaneous border)

㉕

①

Styloid process of ulna

Tendons of ㉗

②

③

④

⑤

Shoulder region (sagittal section)

⑰

⑪

Medial bicipital groove

㉛

㉚

⑫

MEDIAL VIEW

㉕

Flexor carpi radialis m.

㉞

⑭

㉙

①

Dorsal surface

Palmar surface

⑤

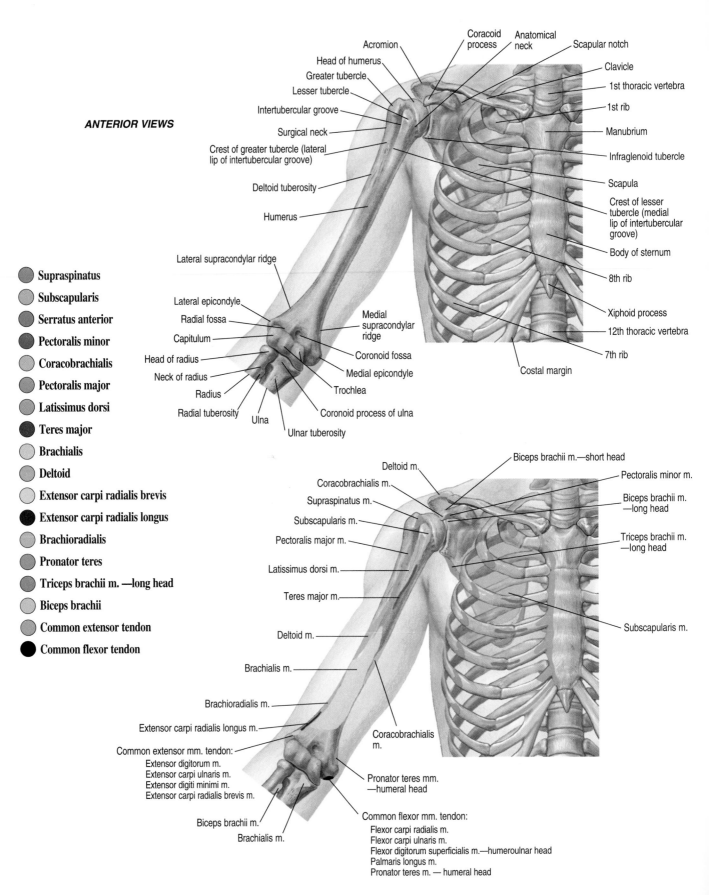

ANTERIOR VIEWS

Coracoid process
Anatomical neck
Acromion
Scapular notch
Head of humerus
Clavicle
Greater tubercle
1st thoracic vertebra
Lesser tubercle
1st rib
Intertubercular groove
Manubrium
Surgical neck
Infraglenoid tubercle
Crest of greater tubercle (lateral lip of intertubercular groove)
Scapula
Deltoid tuberosity
Crest of lesser tubercle (medial lip of intertubercular groove)
Humerus
Body of sternum
8th rib
Lateral supracondylar ridge
Xiphoid process
Lateral epicondyle
12th thoracic vertebra
Radial fossa
Medial supracondylar ridge
Capitulum
7th rib
Head of radius
Coronoid fossa
Neck of radius
Medial epicondyle
Radius
Trochlea
Radial tuberosity
Coronoid process of ulna
Ulna
Costal margin
Ulnar tuberosity

Suprapinatus
Subscapularis
Serratus anterior
Pectoralis minor
Coracobrachialis
Pectoralis major
Latissimus dorsi
Teres major
Brachialis
Deltoid
Extensor carpi radialis brevis
Extensor carpi radialis longus
Brachioradialis
Pronator teres
Triceps brachii m. —long head
Biceps brachii
Common extensor tendon
Common flexor tendon

Biceps brachii m.—short head
Deltoid m.
Pectoralis minor m.
Coracobrachialis m.
Biceps brachii m. —long head
Supraspinatus m.
Subscapularis m.
Triceps brachii m. —long head
Pectoralis major m.
Latissimus dorsi m.
Teres major m.
Subscapularis m.
Deltoid m.
Brachialis m.
Brachioradialis m.
Extensor carpi radialis longus m.
Coracobrachialis m.
Common extensor mm. tendon:
Extensor digitorum m.
Extensor carpi ulnaris m.
Extensor digiti minimi m.
Extensor carpi radialis brevis m.
Pronator teres mm. —humeral head
Common flexor mm. tendon:
Flexor carpi radialis m.
Flexor carpi ulnaris m.
Flexor digitorum superficialis m.—humeroulnar head
Palmaris longus m.
Pronator teres m. — humeral head
Biceps brachii m.
Brachialis m.

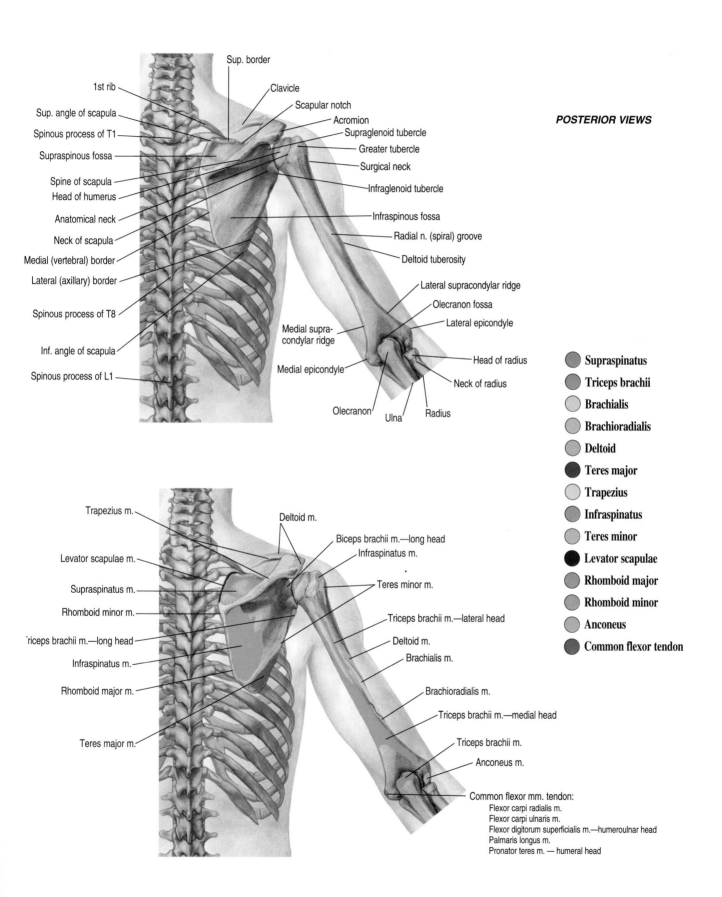

Sup. border

1st rib

Clavicle

Sup. angle of scapula

Scapular notch

Spinous process of T1

Acromion

Supraspinous fossa

Supraglenoid tubercle

Greater tubercle

Spine of scapula

Surgical neck

Head of humerus

Infraglenoid tubercle

Anatomical neck

Infraspinous fossa

Neck of scapula

Radial n. (spiral) groove

Medial (vertebral) border

Deltoid tuberosity

Lateral (axillary) border

Lateral supracondylar ridge

Spinous process of T8

Olecranon fossa

Lateral epicondyle

Medial supra-
condylar ridge

Head of radius

Inf. angle of scapula

Medial epicondyle

Spinous process of L1

Neck of radius

Olecranon

Ulna

Radius

POSTERIOR VIEWS

Trapezius m.

Deltoid m.

Biceps brachii m.—long head

Levator scapulae m.

Infraspinatus m.

Supraspinatus m.

Teres minor m.

Rhomboid minor m.

Triceps brachii m.—lateral head

Triceps brachii m.—long head

Deltoid m.

Infraspinatus m.

Brachialis m.

Rhomboid major m.

Brachioradialis m.

Triceps brachii m.—medial head

Teres major m.

Triceps brachii m.

Anconeus m.

Common flexor mm. tendon:
Flexor carpi radialis m.
Flexor carpi ulnaris m.
Flexor digitorum superficialis m.—humeroulnar head
Palmaris longus m.
Pronator teres m. — humeral head

🔵 **Supraspinatus**
🔵 **Triceps brachii**
🔵 **Brachialis**
🔵 **Brachioradialis**
🔵 **Deltoid**
⚫ **Teres major**
⚪ **Trapezius**
🔵 **Infraspinatus**
🔵 **Teres minor**
⚫ **Levator scapulae**
🔵 **Rhomboid major**
🔵 **Rhomboid minor**
⚪ **Anconeus**
🔵 **Common flexor tendon**

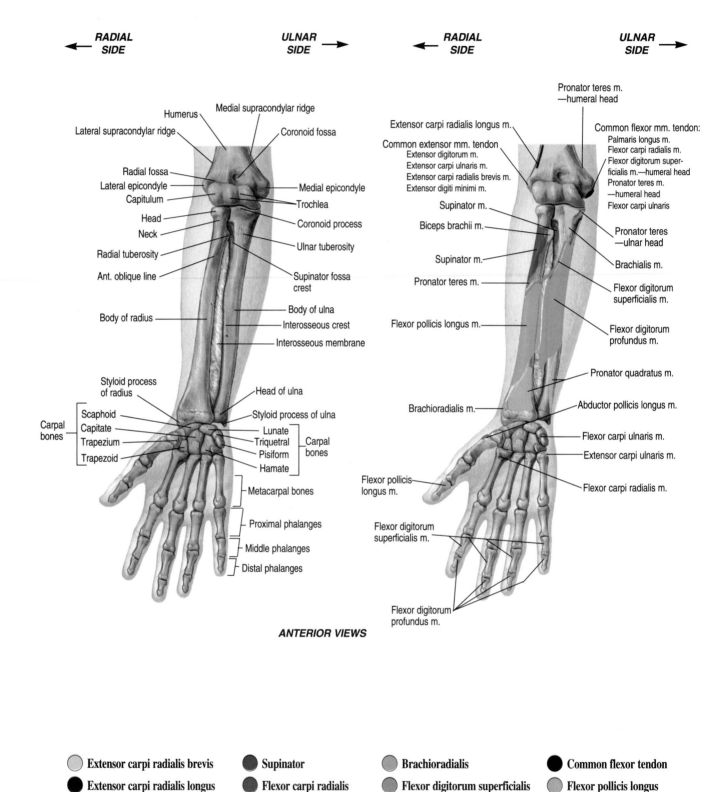

ANTERIOR VIEWS

RADIAL SIDE ← | ULNAR SIDE → | RADIAL SIDE ← | ULNAR SIDE →

Humerus
Medial supracondylar ridge
Lateral supracondylar ridge
Coronoid fossa
Radial fossa
Lateral epicondyle
Medial epicondyle
Capitulum
Trochlea
Head
Coronoid process
Neck
Ulnar tuberosity
Radial tuberosity
Ant. oblique line
Supinator fossa crest
Body of radius
Body of ulna
Interosseous crest
Interosseous membrane
Styloid process of radius
Head of ulna
Scaphoid
Styloid process of ulna
Carpal bones
Capitate
Lunate
Trapezium
Triquetral
Trapezoid
Pisiform
Hamate
Carpal bones
Metacarpal bones
Proximal phalanges
Middle phalanges
Distal phalanges

Pronator teres m. —humeral head
Extensor carpi radialis longus m.
Common flexor mm. tendon:
Palmaris longus m.
Common extensor mm. tendon
Flexor carpi radialis m.
Extensor digitorum m.
Flexor digitorum superficialis m.—humeral head
Extensor carpi ulnaris m.
Pronator teres m.—humeral head
Extensor carpi radialis brevis m.
Flexor carpi ulnaris
Extensor digiti minimi m.
Supinator m.
Pronator teres —ulnar head
Biceps brachii m.
Supinator m.
Brachialis m.
Pronator teres m.
Flexor digitorum superficialis m.
Flexor pollicis longus m.
Flexor digitorum profundus m.
Pronator quadratus m.
Abductor pollicis longus m.
Brachioradialis m.
Flexor carpi ulnaris m.
Extensor carpi ulnaris m.
Flexor pollicis longus m.
Flexor carpi radialis m.
Flexor digitorum superficialis m.
Flexor digitorum profundus m.

Legend:
- Extensor carpi radialis brevis
- Extensor carpi radialis longus
- Brachialis
- Pronator teres
- Supinator
- Flexor carpi radialis
- Abductor pollicis longus
- Biceps brachii
- Brachioradialis
- Flexor digitorum superficialis
- Flexor digitorum profundus
- Pronator quadratus
- Common flexor tendon
- Flexor pollicis longus
- Flexor carpi ulnaris
- Extensor carpi ulnaris

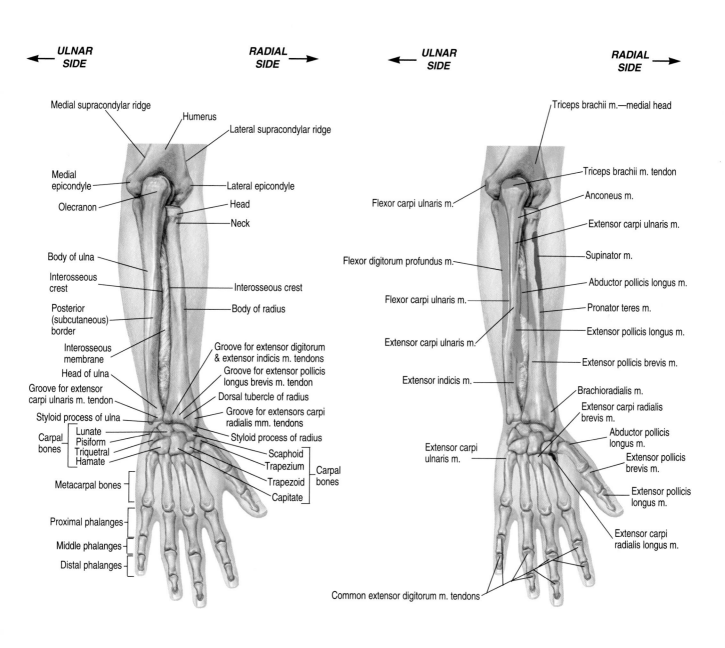

← **ULNAR SIDE** **RADIAL SIDE** →

Medial supracondylar ridge

Humerus

Lateral supracondylar ridge

Medial epicondyle

Lateral epicondyle

Olecranon

Head

Neck

Body of ulna

Interosseous crest

Interosseous crest

Posterior (subcutaneous) border

Body of radius

Interosseous membrane

Groove for extensor digitorum & extensor indicis m. tendons

Head of ulna

Groove for extensor pollicis longus brevis m. tendon

Groove for extensor carpi ulnaris m. tendon

Dorsal tubercle of radius

Styloid process of ulna

Groove for extensors carpi radialis mm. tendons

Styloid process of radius

Carpal bones { Lunate
Pisiform
Triquetral
Hamate

Scaphoid
Trapezium
Trapezoid
Capitate } Carpal bones

Metacarpal bones

Proximal phalanges

Middle phalanges

Distal phalanges

← **ULNAR SIDE** **RADIAL SIDE** →

Triceps brachii m.—medial head

Triceps brachii m. tendon

Flexor carpi ulnaris m.

Anconeus m.

Extensor carpi ulnaris m.

Supinator m.

Flexor digitorum profundus m.

Abductor pollicis longus m.

Flexor carpi ulnaris m.

Pronator teres m.

Extensor pollicis longus m.

Extensor carpi ulnaris m.

Extensor pollicis brevis m.

Extensor indicis m.

Brachioradialis m.

Extensor carpi radialis brevis m.

Extensor carpi ulnaris m.

Abductor pollicis longus m.

Extensor pollicis brevis m.

Extensor pollicis longus m.

Extensor carpi radialis longus m.

Common extensor digitorum m. tendons

POSTERIOR VIEWS

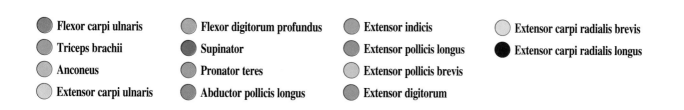

● **Flexor carpi ulnaris**   ● **Flexor digitorum profundus**   ● **Extensor indicis**   ● **Extensor carpi radialis brevis**

● **Triceps brachii**   ● **Supinator**   ● **Extensor pollicis longus**   ● **Extensor carpi radialis longus**

● **Anconeus**   ● **Pronator teres**   ● **Extensor pollicis brevis**

● **Extensor carpi ulnaris**   ● **Abductor pollicis longus**   ● **Extensor digitorum**

Pectoral & Scapular Muscles
Table 6.1

Muscles in Pectoral Region

Muscle	Proximal Attachment	Distal Attachment	Innervation[a]	Main Actions
Pectoralis major	*Clavicular head:* ant. surface of the medial half of clavicle *Sternocostal head:* ant. surface of sternum, sup. six costal cartilages & aponeurosis of ext. abdominal oblique muscle	Lateral lip of intertubercular groove of humerus	Lateral & medial pectoral n.: clavicular head (C5 & **C6**) Sternocostal head (**C7, C8,** & T1)	Adducts & medially rotates humerus Draws shoulder joint anteriorly & inferiorly *Acting alone:* Clavicular head flexes humerus & sternoclavicular head extends it
Pectoralis minor	Ribs 3–5 near their costal cartilages	Medial border & sup. surface of coracoid process of scapula	Medial pectoral n. (C8 & T1)	Stabilizes scapula by drawing it inferiorly & anteriorly against thoracic wall
Subclavius	Junction of rib 1 & its costal cartilage	Inf. surface of middle third of clavicle	N. to subclavius (**C5** & C6)	(Draws clavicle medially?)
Serratus anterior	Ext. surfaces of lateral parts of ribs 1–8/9	Ant. surface of medial border of scapula	Long thoracic n. (C5, **C6,** & **C7**)	Protracts scapula & holds it against thoracic wall; rotates scapula superiorly

Muscles Connecting Upper Limb to Vertebral Column

Muscle	Medial Attachment	Lateral Attachment	Innervation[a]	Main Actions
Trapezius	Medial third of sup. nuchal line; ext. occipital protuberance, ligamentum nuchae & spinous processes of C7–T12 vertebrae	Lateral thrid of clavicle, acromion & spine of scapula	Spinal root of accessory n. (CN XI) & cervical nn. (C3 & C4)	Elevates, retracts & rotates scapula; *sup. fibers* elevate, *middle fibers* retract, *inf. fibers* depress scapula; sup. & inf. fibers act together in sup. rotation of scapula
Latissimus dorsi	Spinous processes of the inf. six thoracic vertebrae, thoracolumbar fascia, iliac crest & inf. 3 or 4 ribs	Floor of intertubercular groove & crest of lesser tubercle of humerus	Thoracodorsal n. (**C6, C7,** & C8)	Extends, adducts & medially rotates humerus; raises body toward arms during climbing
Levator scapulae	Post. tubercles of transverse processes of C1–C4 vertebrae	Sup. part of medial border of scapula	Dorsal scapular (C5) & cervical (C3 & C4) nn.	Elevates scapula & tilts its glenoid cavity inferiorly by rotating scapula
Rhomboid minor & major	*Minor:* Ligamentum nuchae & spinous processes of C7 & T1 vertebrae *Major:* Spinous processes of T2–T5 vertebrae	Medial border of scapula from level of spine to inf. angle	Dorsal scapular n. (C4 & **C5**) rotate	Retracts scapula & rotates it to depress glenoid cavity; fixes scapula to thoracic wall

[a]In this and subsequent tables, the numbers indicate the spinal cord segmental innervation of the nerves (*e.g.,* C5 and C6 indicate that the nerves supplying the clavicular head of the pectoralis major muscle are derived from the 5th and 6th cervical segments of the spinal cord). **Boldface** indicates the main segmental innervation. Damage to these segments of the spinal cord, or to the motor nerve roots arising from them, results in paralysis of the muscles concerned.

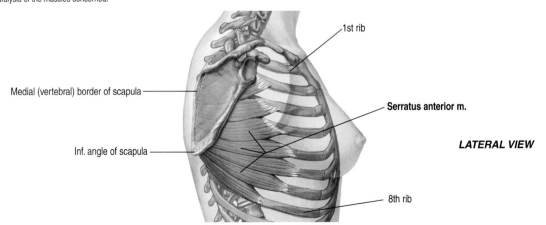

1st rib

Medial (vertebral) border of scapula

Serratus anterior m.

Inf. angle of scapula

LATERAL VIEW

8th rib

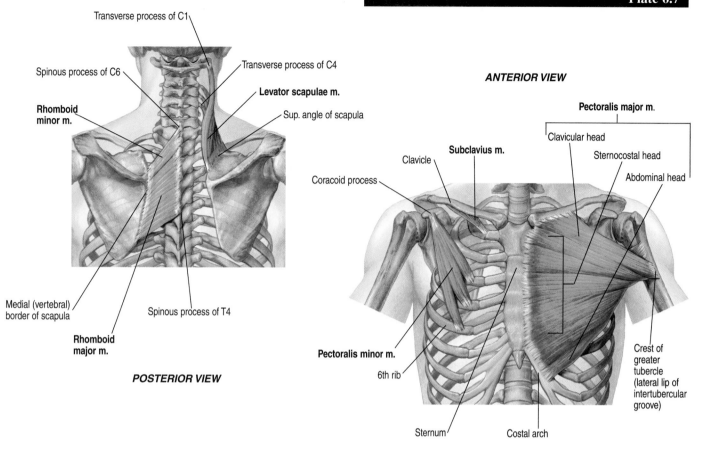

Transverse process of C1

Spinous process of C6

Rhomboid minor m.

Transverse process of C4

Levator scapulae m.

Sup. angle of scapula

Medial (vertebral) border of scapula

Spinous process of T4

Rhomboid major m.

POSTERIOR VIEW

ANTERIOR VIEW

Pectoralis major m.

Clavicular head

Sternocostal head

Abdominal head

Clavicle

Subclavius m.

Coracoid process

Pectoralis minor m.

6th rib

Sternum

Costal arch

Crest of greater tubercle (lateral lip of intertubercular groove)

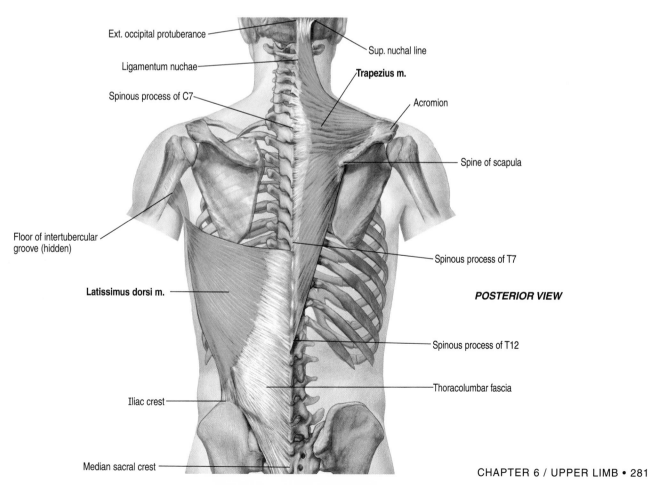

Ext. occipital protuberance

Ligamentum nuchae

Spinous process of C7

Sup. nuchal line

Trapezius m.

Acromion

Spine of scapula

Floor of intertubercular groove (hidden)

Latissimus dorsi m.

Spinous process of T7

POSTERIOR VIEW

Spinous process of T12

Thoracolumbar fascia

Iliac crest

Median sacral crest

Scapular & Posterior Arm Muscles
Table 6.2

Scapular Muscles

Muscle	Proximal/Medial Attachment	Distal/Lateral Attachment	Innervation[a]	Main Actions
Deltoid	Lateral third of clavicle, acromion & spine of scapula	Deltoid tuberosity of humerus	Axillary n. (**C5** & **C6**)	*Anterior part:* flexes & medially rotates arm *Middle part:* abducts arm *Posterior part:* extends & laterally rotates arm
Supraspinatus[a]	Supraspinous fossa of scapula	Sup. facet on greater tubercle of humerus	Suprascapular n. (C4, **C5** & C6)	Helps deltoid to abduct arm & acts with rotator cuff muscles[a]
Infraspinatus[a]	Infraspinous fossa of scapula	Middle facet on greater tubercle of humerus	Suprascapular n. (C4, **C5** & C6)	Laterally rotate arm; help to hold humeral head in glenoid cavity of scapula
Teres minor[a]	Sup. part of lateral border of scapula	Inf. facet on greater tubercle of humerus	Axillary n. (**C5** & C6)	
Teres major	Dorsal surface of inf. angle of scapula	Medial lip of intertubular groove of humerus	Lower subscapular n. (**C6** & C7)	Adducts & medially rotates arm
Subscapularis[a]	Subscapular fossa	Lesser tubercle of humerus	Upper & lower subscapular nn. (C5, **C6** & C7)	Medially rotates arm & adducts it; helps to hold humeral head in glenoid cavity

[a]Collectively, the supraspinatus, infraspinatus, teres minor, and subscapularis muscles are referred to as the **rotator cuff muscles**. Their prime function during all movements of the shoulder joint is to hold the head of the humerus in the glenoid cavity of the scapula.

Posterior Arm Muscles

Muscle	Proximal Attachment	Distal Attachment	Innervation	Main Actions
Triceps brachii	*Long head:* infraglenoid tubercle of scapula *Lateral head:* post. surface of humerus, sup. to radial n. groove *Medial head:* post. surface of humerus, inf. to radial n. groove	Proximal end of olecranon ulna & fascia of forearm	Radial n. (**C6**, **C7**, & C8)	Extends the forearm; it is *chief extensor of forearm*, long head steadies head of abducted humerus
Anconeus	Lateral epicondyle of humerus	Lateral surface of olecranon & sup. part of post. surface of ulna	Radial n. (C7, C8 & T1)	Assists triceps in extending forearm; stabilizes elbow joint; abducts ulna during pronation

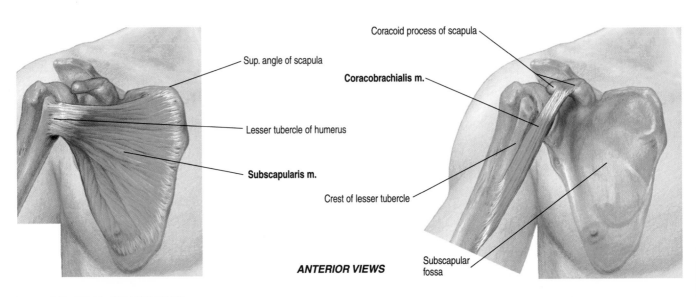

Sup. angle of scapula

Lesser tubercle of humerus

Subscapularis m.

Coracoid process of scapula

Coracobrachialis m.

Crest of lesser tubercle

Subscapular fossa

ANTERIOR VIEWS

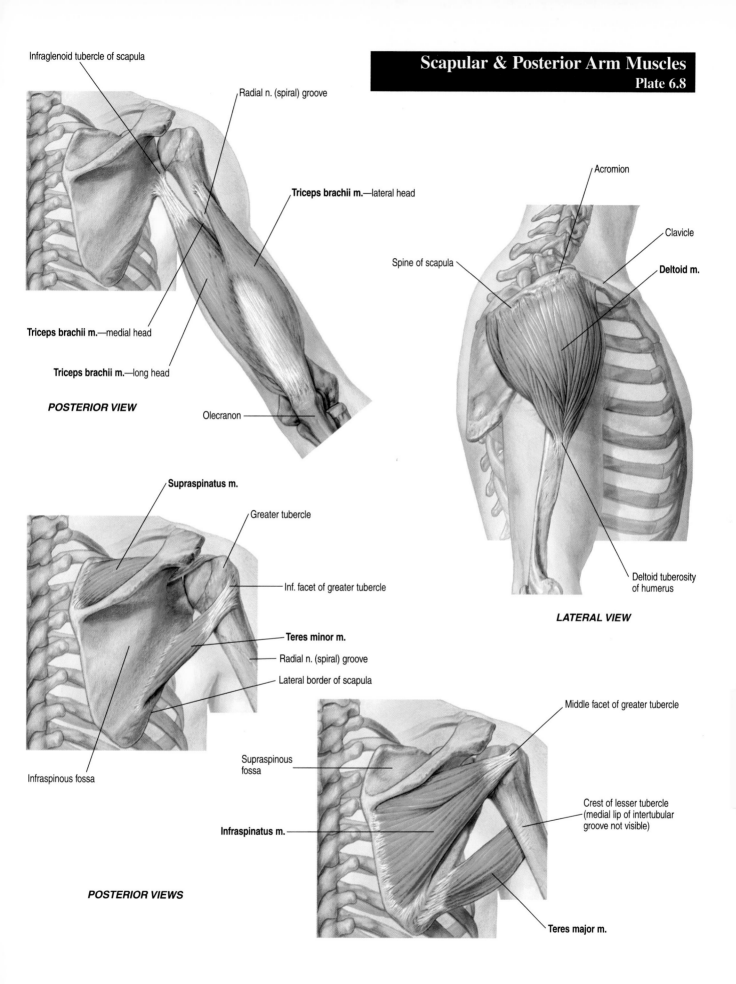

Infraglenoid tubercle of scapula

Radial n. (spiral) groove

Triceps brachii m.—lateral head

Triceps brachii m.—medial head

Triceps brachii m.—long head

POSTERIOR VIEW

Olecranon

Acromion

Clavicle

Deltoid m.

Spine of scapula

Deltoid tuberosity
of humerus

LATERAL VIEW

Supraspinatus m.

Greater tubercle

Inf. facet of greater tubercle

Teres minor m.

Radial n. (spiral) groove

Lateral border of scapula

Infraspinous fossa

Middle facet of greater tubercle

Supraspinous
fossa

Crest of lesser tubercle
(medial lip of intertubular
groove not visible)

Infraspinatus m.

Teres major m.

POSTERIOR VIEWS

Anterior Arm & Forearm Muscles
Table 6.3

Muscles of Anterior Arm

Muscle	Proximal Attachment	Distal Attachment	Innervation[a]	Main Actions
Biceps brachii	*Short head:* Tip of coracoid process of scapula *Long head:* Supraglenoid tubercle of scapula	Tuberosity of radius & fascia of forearm via bicipital aponeurosis	Musculocutaneous n. (C5 & **C6**)	Supinates forearm and, when it is supine, flexes forearm
Brachialis	Distal half of ant. surface of humerus	Coronoid process & tuberosity of ulna		Flexes forearm in all positions
Coracobrachialis	Tip of coracoid process of scapula	Middle third of medial surface of humerus	Musculocutaneous n. (C5, **C6** & C7)	Helps to flex & adduct arm

Superficial and Intermediate Layers of Muscles on Anterior Surface of Forearm[a]

Muscle	Proximal Attachment	Distal Attachment	Innervation[b]	Main Actions
Pronator teres	Medial epicondyle of humerus & coronoid process of ulna	Middle of lateral surface of radius	Median n. (C6 & **C7**)	Pronates forearm & flexes it
Flexor carpi radialis	Medial epicondyle of humerus	Base of 2nd metacarpal bone		Flexes hand & abducts it radially
Palmaris longus	Medial epicondyle of humerus	Distal half of flexor retinanculum & palmar aponeurosis	Median n. (C7 & C8)	Flexes hand & tightens palmar aponeurosis
Flexor carpi ulnaris[b]	*Humeral head:* medial epicondyle of humerus *Ulnar head:* olecranon & post. border of ulna	Pisiform bone (hook of hamate bone & 5th metacarpal bone)	Ulnar n. (C7 & **C8**)	Flexes hand & adducts it ulnarly
Flexor digitorum superficialis[c]	*Humeroulnar head:* medial epicondyle of humerus, ulnar collateral lig. & coronoid process of ulna *Radial head:* sup. half of ant. border of radius	Bodies of the middle phalanges of medial four digits	Median n. (C7, **C8** & T1)	Flexes middle phalanges of medial four digits: acting more strongly, it flexes proximal phalanges & hand

[a]The superficial muscles of the *flexor-pronator group* are attached, in whole or in part, to the anterior surface of the medial epicondyle by a *common flexor tendon.*
[b]In contrast to the other superficial flexor muscles, the flexor carpi ulnaris is supplied by the ulnar nerve.
[c]This muscle comprises the *intermediate muscle layer* in the anterior part of the forearm. In some clinical texts, this muscle is referred to by its old name, "flexor digitorum sublimis."

Deep Layer of Muscles on Anterior Surface of Forearm

Muscle	Proximal Attachment	Distal Attachment	Innervation	Main Actions
Pronator quadratus	Distal fourth of ant. surface of ulna	Distal fourth of ant. surface of radius	Ant. interosseous n. from median (**C8** & T1)	Pronates forearm; deep fibers bind radius & ulna together

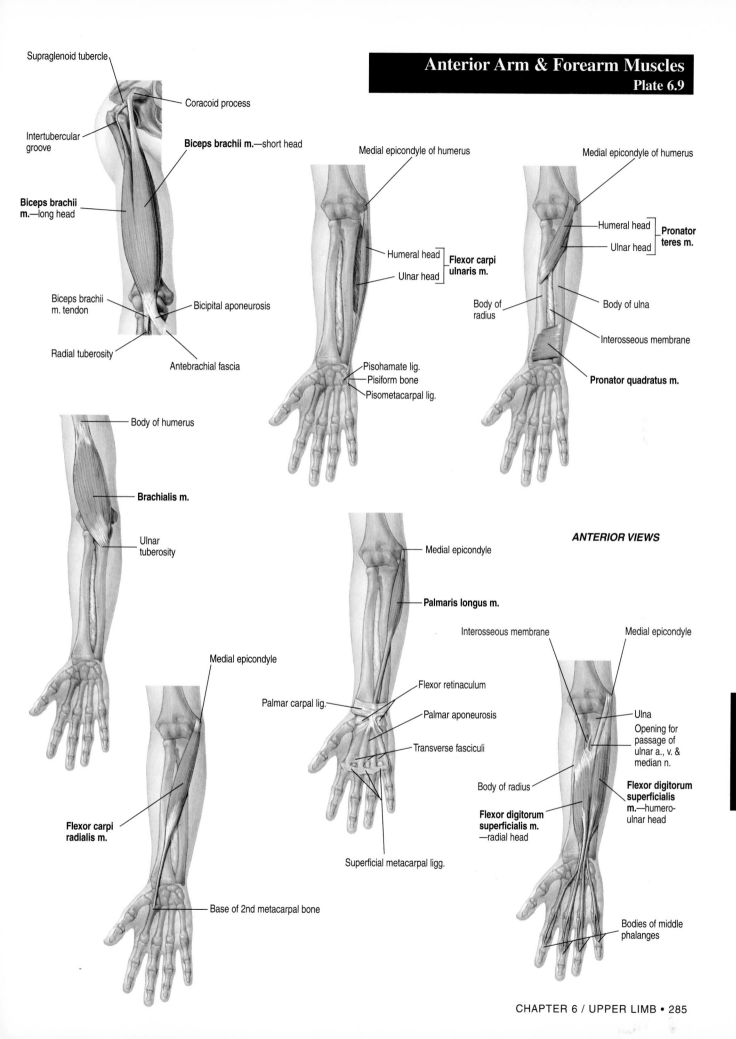

Supraglenoid tubercle

Coracoid process

Intertubercular groove

Biceps brachii m.—short head

Biceps brachii m.—long head

Biceps brachii m. tendon

Bicipital aponeurosis

Radial tuberosity

Antebrachial fascia

Medial epicondyle of humerus

Humeral head **Flexor carpi ulnaris m.**
Ulnar head

Pisohamate lig.
Pisiform bone
Pisometacarpal lig.

Medial epicondyle of humerus

Humeral head **Pronator teres m.**
Ulnar head

Body of radius

Body of ulna

Interosseous membrane

Pronator quadratus m.

Body of humerus

Brachialis m.

Ulnar tuberosity

ANTERIOR VIEWS

Medial epicondyle

Palmaris longus m.

Interosseous membrane

Medial epicondyle

Palmar carpal lig.

Flexor retinaculum

Palmar aponeurosis

Transverse fasciculi

Ulna

Opening for passage of ulnar a., v. & median n.

Medial epicondyle

Body of radius

Flexor digitorum superficialis m.—humero-ulnar head

Medial epicondyle

Flexor carpi radialis m.

Flexor digitorum superficialis m. —radial head

Base of 2nd metacarpal bone

Superficial metacarpal ligg.

Bodies of middle phalanges

Forearm Muscles
Table 6.4

Deep Layer of Muscles on Anterior Surface of Forearm

Muscle	Proximal Attachment	Distal Attachment	Innervation	Main Actions
Flexor digitorum profundus	Proximal three-fourths of medial & ant. surfaces of ulna & interosseous membrane	Bases of distal phalanges of medial four digits	*Medial part:* Ulnar n. (**C8** & T1) *Lateral part:* Median n. (**C8** & T1)	Flexes distal phalanges of medial four digits (fingers)
Flexor pollicis longus	Ant. surface of the distal radius & adjacent interosseous membrane	Base of distal phalanx of thumb	Ant. interosseous n. from median (**C8** & T1)	Flexes phalanges of first digit (thumb)

Superficial Muscles on Posterior or Extensor Surface of Forearm

Muscle	Proximal Attachment	Distal Attachment	Innervation	Main Actions
Brachioradialis	Proximal two-thirds of lateral supracondylar ridge of humerus, lat. intermuscular septum	Lateral surface of distal end of radius	Radial n. (C5, **C6** & C7)	Flexes forearm
Extensor carpi radialis longus	Lateral supracondylar ridge of humerus, lat. intermuscular septum	Base of 2nd metacarpal bone	Radial n. (C6 & C7)	Extend & abduct hand at wrist joint
Extensor carpi radialis brevis	Lateral epicondyle of humerus	Base of 3rd metacarpal bone	Deep br. of radial n. (**C7** & C8)	Extend & abduct hand at wrist joint
Extensor digitorum	Lateral epicondyle of humerus	Extensor expansions of medial four digits	Post. interosseous n. (**C7** & C8), a br. of the radial n.	Extends medial four digits at metacarpophalangeal joints; extends hand at wrist joint
Extensor carpi ulnaris	Lateral epicondyle of humerus & post. border of ulna	Base of 5th metacarpal bone	Post. interosseous n. (**C7** & C8), a br. of the radial n.	Extends & adducts hand at wrist joint

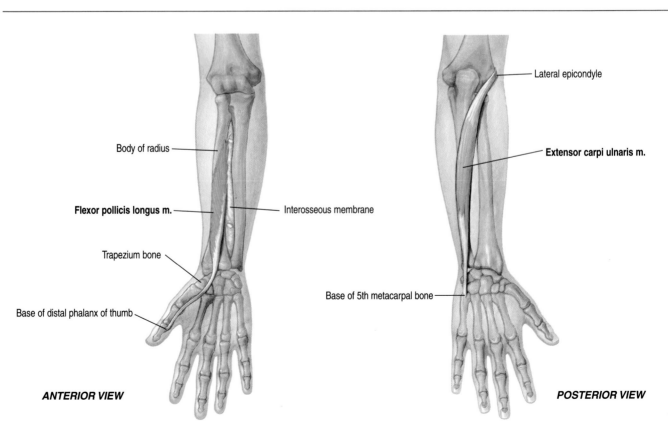

ANTERIOR VIEW

- Body of radius
- Flexor pollicis longus m.
- Trapezium bone
- Base of distal phalanx of thumb
- Interosseous membrane

POSTERIOR VIEW

- Lateral epicondyle
- **Extensor carpi ulnaris m.**
- Base of 5th metacarpal bone

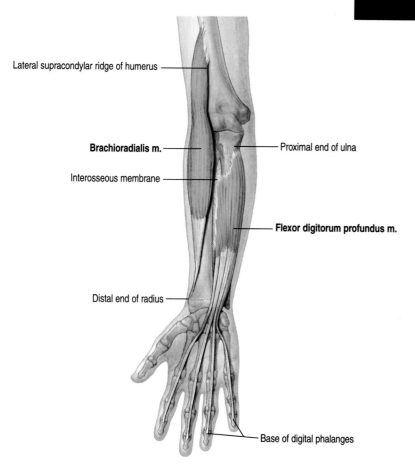

Lateral supracondylar ridge of humerus

Brachioradialis m.

Interosseous membrane

Proximal end of ulna

Flexor digitorum profundus m.

Distal end of radius

Base of digital phalanges

ANTERIOR VIEW

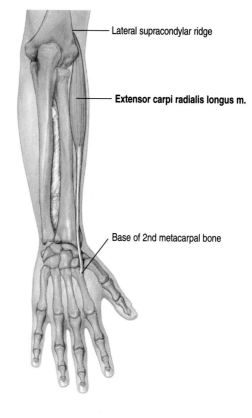

Lateral supracondylar ridge

Extensor carpi radialis longus m.

Base of 2nd metacarpal bone

POSTERIOR VIEW

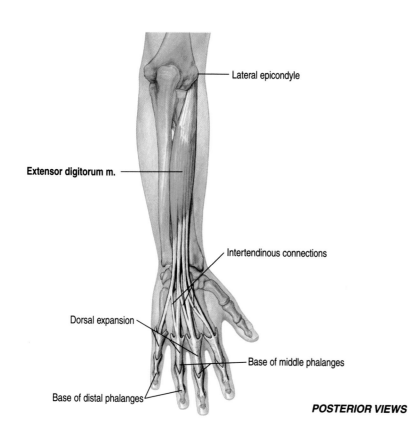

Lateral epicondyle

Extensor digitorum m.

Intertendinous connections

Dorsal expansion

Base of middle phalanges

Base of distal phalanges

POSTERIOR VIEWS

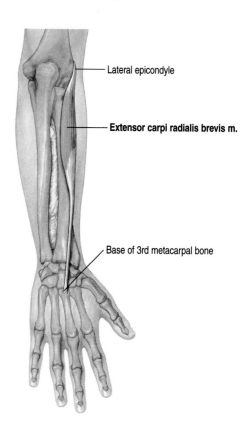

Lateral epicondyle

Extensor carpi radialis brevis m.

Base of 3rd metacarpal bone

Posterior Forearm Muscles
Table 6.5

Deep Muscles on Posterior or Extensor Surface of Forearm

Muscle	Proximal Attachment	Distal Attachment	Innervation	Main Actions
Supinator	Lateral epicondyle of humerus, radial collateral & anular ligaments, supinator fossa & crest of ulna	Lateral, post. & ant. surfaces of proximal third of radius	Deep br. of radial n. (C5 & **C6**)	Supinates forearm, *i.e.,* rotates radius to turn palm anteriorly
Abductor pollicis longus	Post. surfaces of ulna & radius & interosseous membrane	Base of 1st metacarpal bone	Post. interosseous n. (C7 & **C8**)	Abducts thumb & extends it at carpometacarpal joint
Extensor pollicis brevis	Post. surface of radius & interosseous membrane	Base of proximal phalanx of thumb		Extends proximal phalanx of thumb at carpometacarpal joint
Extensor pollicis longus	Post. surface of middle third of ulnar & interosseous membrane	Base of distal phalanx of thumb		Extends distal phalanx of thumb at metacarpophalangeal & interphalangeal joints
Extensor indicis	Post. surface of ulna & interosseous membrane	Extensor expansion of second digit (index finger)		Extends digit 2 & helps to extend wrist
Extensor digiti minimi	Lateral epicondyle of humerus	Extensor expansion of 5th digit	Post. interosseous n. (**C7** & C8), a br. of the radial n.	Extends digit 5 at metacarpophalangeal & interphalangeal joints

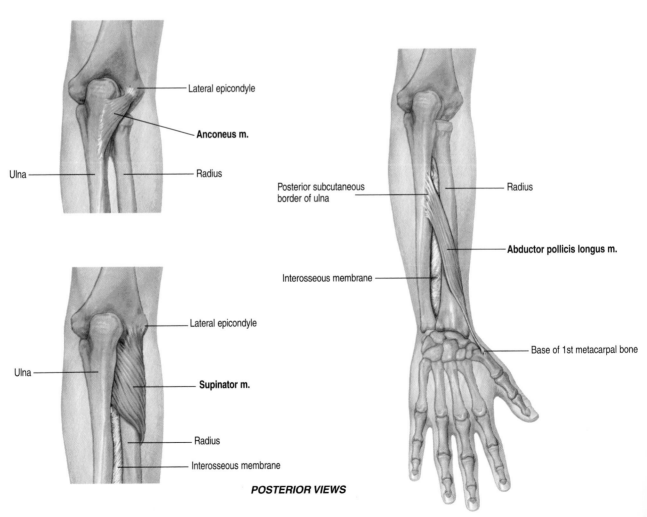

Lateral epicondyle

Anconeus m.

Ulna

Radius

Lateral epicondyle

Supinator m.

Ulna

Radius

Interosseous membrane

Posterior subcutaneous border of ulna

Radius

Interosseous membrane

Abductor pollicis longus m.

Base of 1st metacarpal bone

POSTERIOR VIEWS

Posterior Forearm Muscles
Plate 6.11

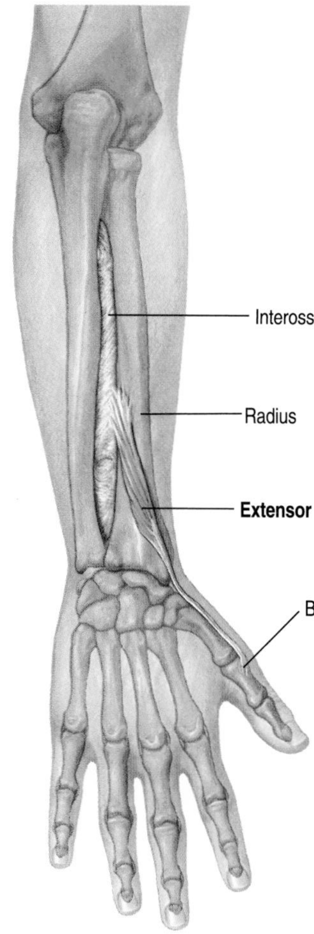
Interosseous membrane
Radius
Extensor pollicis brevis m.
Base of 1st proximal phalanx

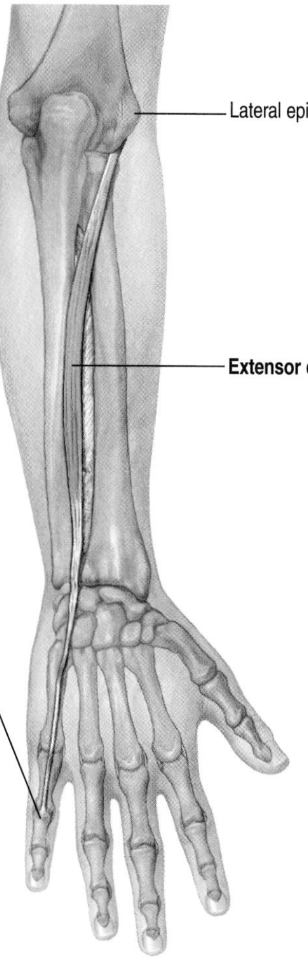
Lateral epicondyle
Extensor digiti minimi m.
Extensor expansion over base of 5th middle phalanx

POSTERIOR VIEWS

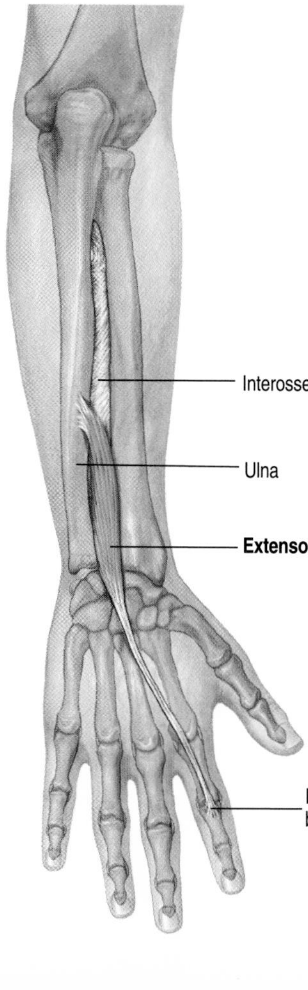
Interosseous membrane
Ulna
Extensor indicis m.
Extensor expansion over base of 2nd middle phalanx

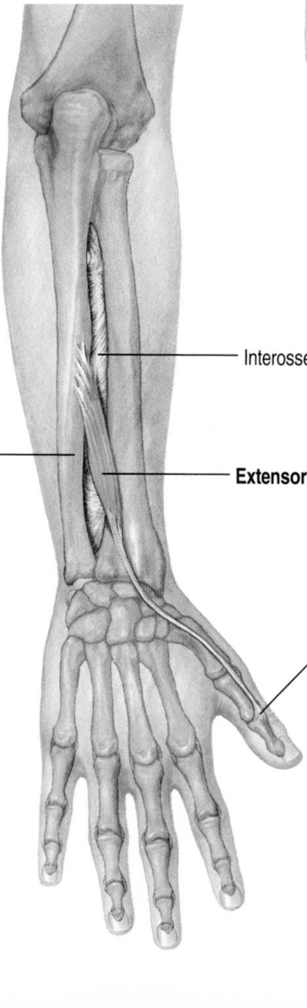
Interosseous membrane
Ulna
Extensor pollicis longus m.
Extensor (dorsal) expansion over base of 1st distal phalanx

Short Muscles of Hand

Muscle	Proximal Attachment	Distal Attachment	Innervation	Main Actions
Lumbricalis 1 & 2	Lateral two tendons of flexor digitorum profundus	Lateral sides of extensor expansions of digits 2 to 5	*Lumbricals 1 & 2,* median n. (C8 & **T1**)	Flex digits at metacarpophalangeal joints & extend interphalangeal joints
Lumbricalis 3 & 4	Medial three tendons of flexor digitorum profundus		*Lumbricals 3 & 4,* deep br. of ulnar n. (C8 & **T1**)	
Dorsal interossei 1–4	Adjacent sides of two metacarpal bones	Extensor expansions & bases of proximal phalanges of digits 2–4	Deep br. of ulnar n. (C8 & **T1**)	Abduct digits 2–4
Palmar interossei 1–3	Palmar surfaces of 1st, 2nd, 4th & 5th metacarpal bones	Extensor expansions of digits and bases of proximal phalanges of digits 1, 2, 4 & 5		Adduct digits 2–4
Abductor digiti minimi	Pisiform bone	Medial side of base of proximal phalanx of digit 5 (little finger)	Deep br. of ulnar n. (C8 & **T1**)	Abducts digit 5 (little finger)
Flexor digiti minimi brevis	Hook of hamate bone & flexor retinaculum			Flexes proximal phalanx of digit 5
Opponens digiti minimi		Medial border of 5th metacarpal bone		Draws 5th metacarpal bone anteriorly & rotates it, bringing digit 5 into opposition with thumb
Abductor pollicis brevis	Flexor retinaculum & tubercles of scaphoid & trapezium bones	Lateral side of base of proximal phalanx of thumb	Recurrent br. of median n. (**C8** & T1)	Abducts thumb & helps oppose it
Flexor pollicis brevis	Flexor retinaculum & tubercle of trapezium bone			Flexes thumb
Opponens pollicis		Lateral side of 1st metacarpal bone		Opposes thumb toward center of palm & rotates it medially
Adductor pollicis	*Oblique head:* Bases of 2nd & 3rd metacarpals, captate & adjacent carpal bones *Transverse head:* Ant. surface of body of 3rd metacarpal bone	Medial side of base of proximal phalanx of thumb	Deep br. of ulnar n. (C8 & **T1**)	Adducts thumb toward middle digit

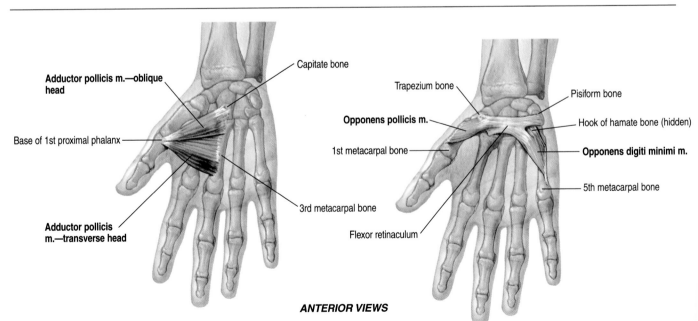

Adductor pollicis m.—oblique head

Capitate bone

Base of 1st proximal phalanx

Adductor pollicis m.—transverse head

3rd metacarpal bone

Trapezium bone

Pisiform bone

Opponens pollicis m.

Hook of hamate bone (hidden)

1st metacarpal bone

Opponens digiti minimi m.

5th metacarpal bone

Flexor retinaculum

ANTERIOR VIEWS

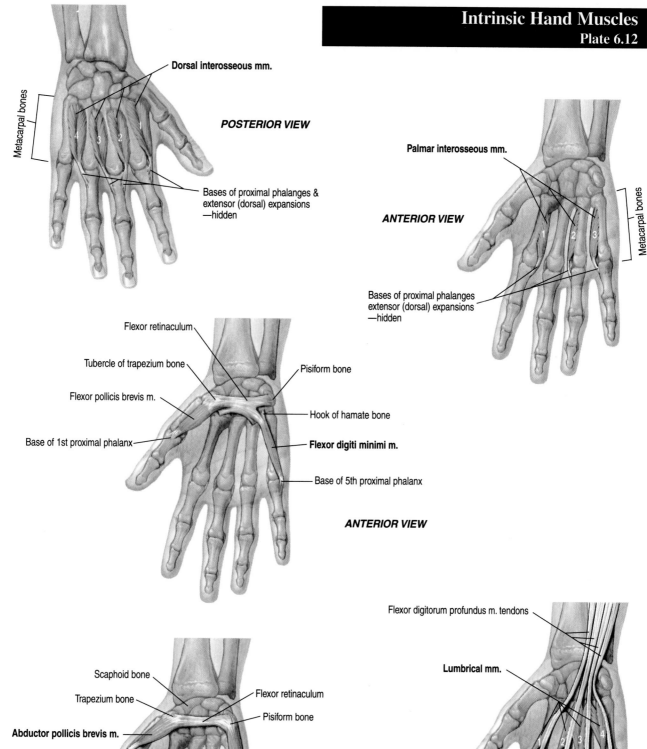

Dorsal interosseous mm.

Metacarpal bones

POSTERIOR VIEW

Bases of proximal phalanges &
extensor (dorsal) expansions
—hidden

Palmar interosseous mm.

ANTERIOR VIEW

Metacarpal bones

Bases of proximal phalanges
extensor (dorsal) expansions
—hidden

Flexor retinaculum

Tubercle of trapezium bone

Flexor pollicis brevis m.

Base of 1st proximal phalanx

Pisiform bone

Hook of hamate bone

Flexor digiti minimi m.

Base of 5th proximal phalanx

ANTERIOR VIEW

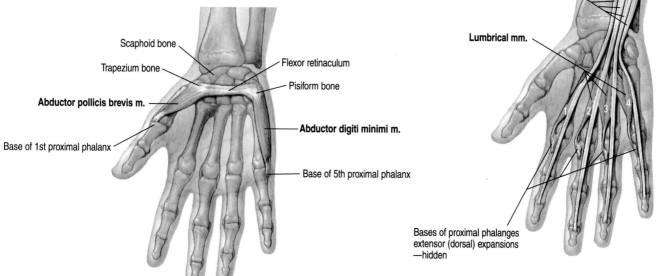

Scaphoid bone

Trapezium bone

Abductor pollicis brevis m.

Base of 1st proximal phalanx

Flexor retinaculum

Pisiform bone

Abductor digiti minimi m.

Base of 5th proximal phalanx

Flexor digitorum profundus m. tendons

Lumbrical mm.

Bases of proximal phalanges
extensor (dorsal) expansions
—hidden

ANTERIOR VIEWS

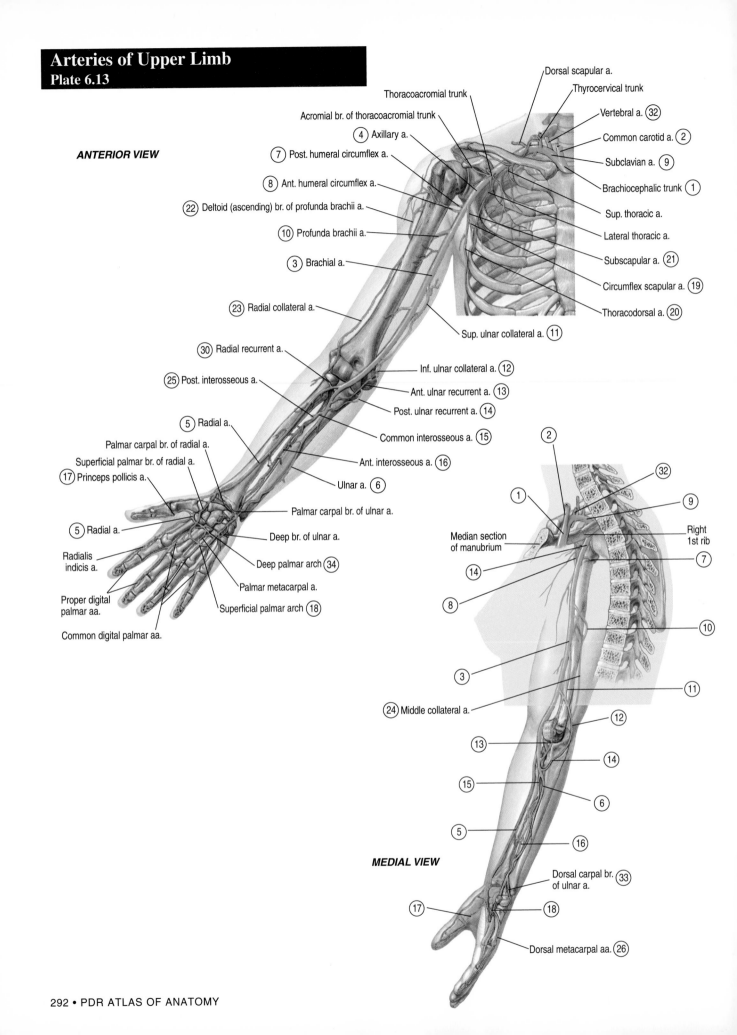

ANTERIOR VIEW

Dorsal scapular a.

Thoracoacromial trunk

Thyrocervical trunk

Acromial br. of thoracoacromial trunk

Vertebral a. (32)

(4) Axillary a.

Common carotid a. (2)

(7) Post. humeral circumflex a.

Subclavian a. (9)

(8) Ant. humeral circumflex a.

Brachiocephalic trunk (1)

(22) Deltoid (ascending) br. of profunda brachii a.

Sup. thoracic a.

(10) Profunda brachii a.

Lateral thoracic a.

(3) Brachial a.

Subscapular a. (21)

(23) Radial collateral a.

Circumflex scapular a. (19)

Thoracodorsal a. (20)

Sup. ulnar collateral a. (11)

(30) Radial recurrent a.

Inf. ulnar collateral a. (12)

(25) Post. interosseous a.

Ant. ulnar recurrent a. (13)

Post. ulnar recurrent a. (14)

(5) Radial a.

Common interosseous a. (15)

Palmar carpal br. of radial a.

Ant. interosseous a. (16)

Superficial palmar br. of radial a.

Ulnar a. (6)

(17) Princeps pollicis a.

Palmar carpal br. of ulnar a.

(5) Radial a.

Deep br. of ulnar a.

Radialis indicis a.

Deep palmar arch (34)

Proper digital palmar aa.

Palmar metacarpal a.

Superficial palmar arch (18)

Common digital palmar aa.

Median section of manubrium

Right 1st rib

(24) Middle collateral a.

MEDIAL VIEW

Dorsal carpal br. (33) of ulnar a.

Dorsal metacarpal aa. (26)

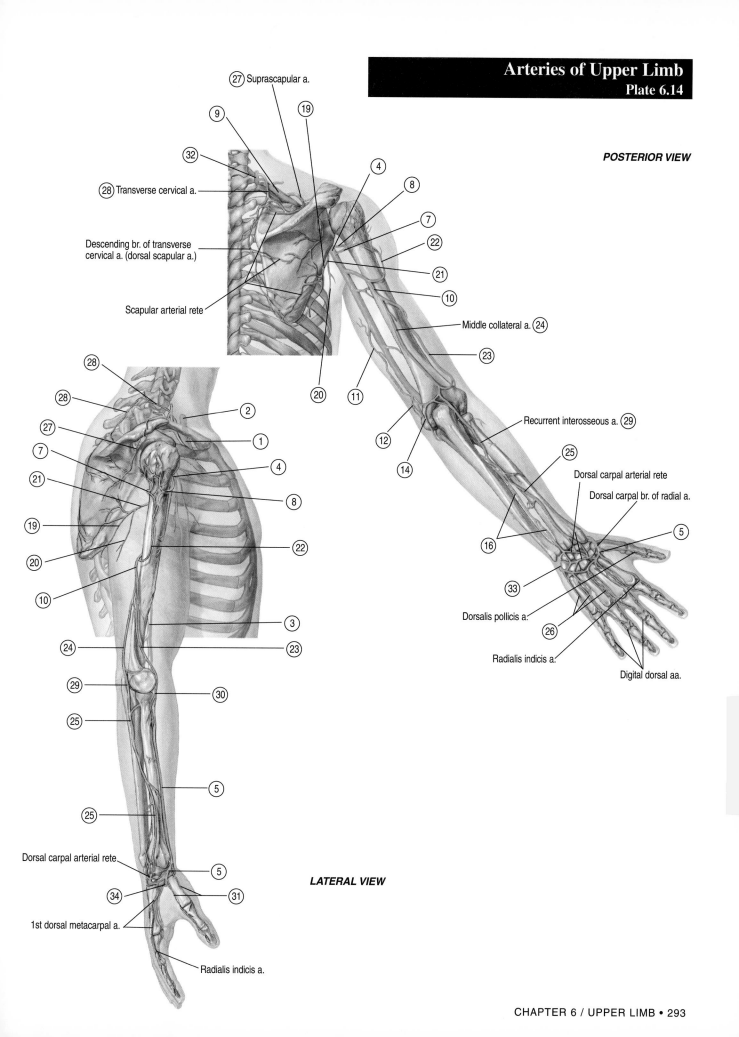

㉗ Suprascapular a.

⑨

⑲

㉜

㉘ Transverse cervical a.

POSTERIOR VIEW

④

⑧

⑦

㉒

㉑

⑩

Descending br. of transverse
cervical a. (dorsal scapular a.)

Middle collateral a. ㉔

㉓

Scapular arterial rete

⑳

⑪

Recurrent interosseous a. ㉙

⑫

⑭

㉕

⑯

Dorsal carpal arterial rete

Dorsal carpal br. of radial a.

⑤

⑬

Dorsalis pollicis a.

㉖

Radialis indicis a.

Digital dorsal aa.

㉘

㉘

㉗

⑦

㉑

⑲

⑳

⑩

②

①

④

⑧

㉒

③

㉔

㉓

㉙

㉚

㉕

⑤

㉕

Dorsal carpal arterial rete

⑤

LATERAL VIEW

㉞

㉛

1st dorsal metacarpal a.

Radialis indicis a.

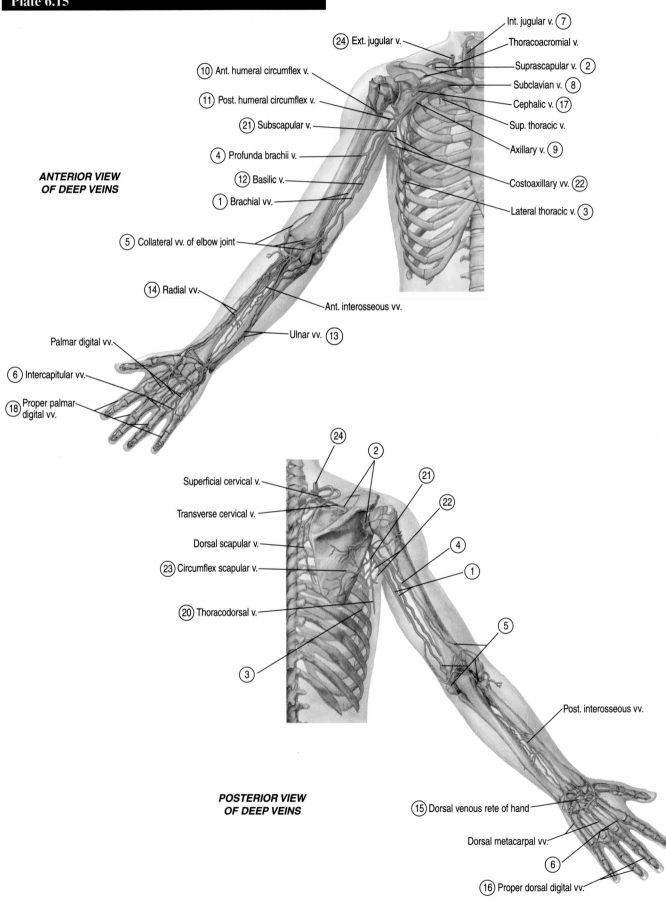

ANTERIOR VIEW OF DEEP VEINS

- ⑦ Int. jugular v.
- ㉔ Ext. jugular v.
- Thoracoacromial v.
- ⑩ Ant. humeral circumflex v.
- Suprascapular v. ②
- ⑪ Post. humeral circumflex v.
- Subclavian v. ⑧
- ㉑ Subscapular v.
- Cephalic v. ⑰
- ④ Profunda brachii v.
- Sup. thoracic v.
- Axillary v. ⑨
- ⑫ Basilic v.
- ① Brachial vv.
- Costoaxillary vv. ㉒
- Lateral thoracic v. ③
- ⑤ Collateral vv. of elbow joint
- ⑭ Radial vv.
- Ant. interosseous vv.
- Palmar digital vv.
- Ulnar vv. ⑬
- ⑥ Intercapitular vv.
- ⑱ Proper palmar digital vv.

POSTERIOR VIEW OF DEEP VEINS

- Superficial cervical v.
- Transverse cervical v.
- Dorsal scapular v.
- ㉓ Circumflex scapular v.
- ⑳ Thoracodorsal v.
- Post. interosseous vv.
- ⑮ Dorsal venous rete of hand
- Dorsal metacarpal vv.
- ⑥
- ⑯ Proper dorsal digital vv.

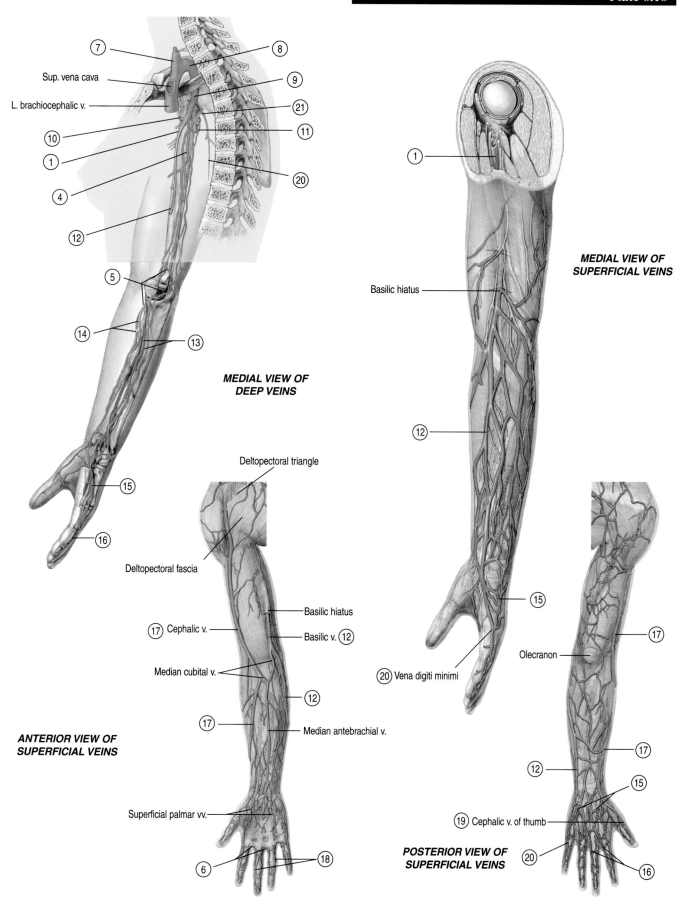

Sup. vena cava

L. brachiocephalic v.

*MEDIAL VIEW OF
SUPERFICIAL VEINS*

Basilic hiatus

*MEDIAL VIEW OF
DEEP VEINS*

Deltopectoral triangle

Deltopectoral fascia

Basilic hiatus

⑰ Cephalic v.

Basilic v. ⑫

Median cubital v.

⑫

⑰

Median antebrachial v.

*ANTERIOR VIEW OF
SUPERFICIAL VEINS*

Superficial palmar vv.

⑥

⑱

⑳ Vena digiti minimi

Olecranon

⑰

⑰

⑫

⑮

⑲ Cephalic v. of thumb

⑳

⑯

*POSTERIOR VIEW OF
SUPERFICIAL VEINS*

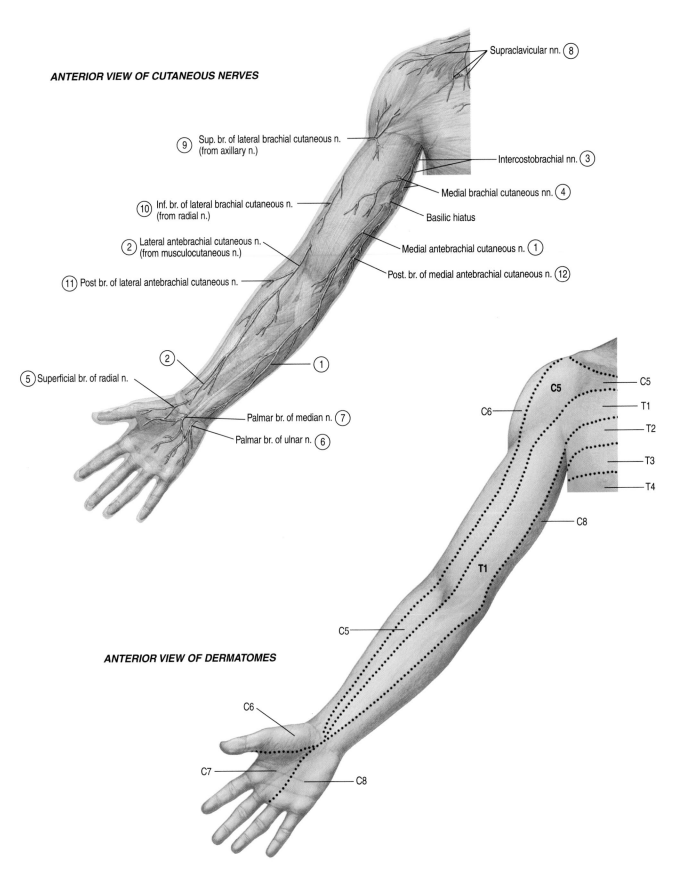

ANTERIOR VIEW OF CUTANEOUS NERVES

Supraclavicular nn. (8)

(9) Sup. br. of lateral brachial cutaneous n. (from axillary n.)

Intercostobrachial nn. (3)

Medial brachial cutaneous nn. (4)

(10) Inf. br. of lateral brachial cutaneous n. (from radial n.)

Basilic hiatus

(2) Lateral antebrachial cutaneous n. (from musculocutaneous n.)

Medial antebrachial cutaneous n. (1)

(11) Post br. of lateral antebrachial cutaneous n.

Post. br. of medial antebrachial cutaneous n. (12)

(2)   (1)

(5) Superficial br. of radial n.

Palmar br. of median n. (7)

Palmar br. of ulnar n. (6)

C5

C6

C5

T1

T2

T3

T4

C8

T1

C5

C6

C7

C8

ANTERIOR VIEW OF DERMATOMES

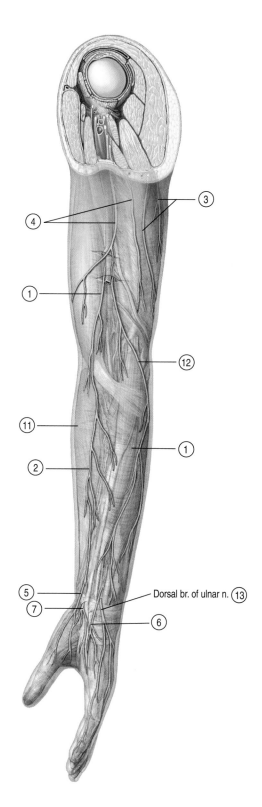

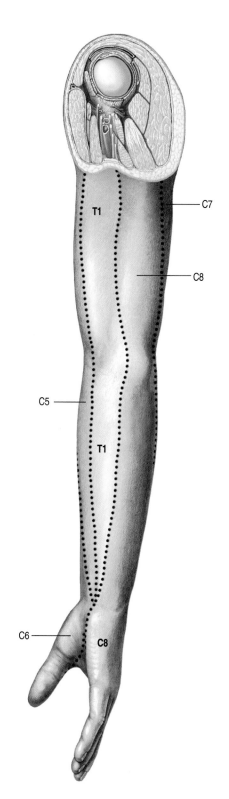

MEDIAL VIEW OF CUTANEOUS NERVES

MEDIAL VIEW OF DERMATOMES

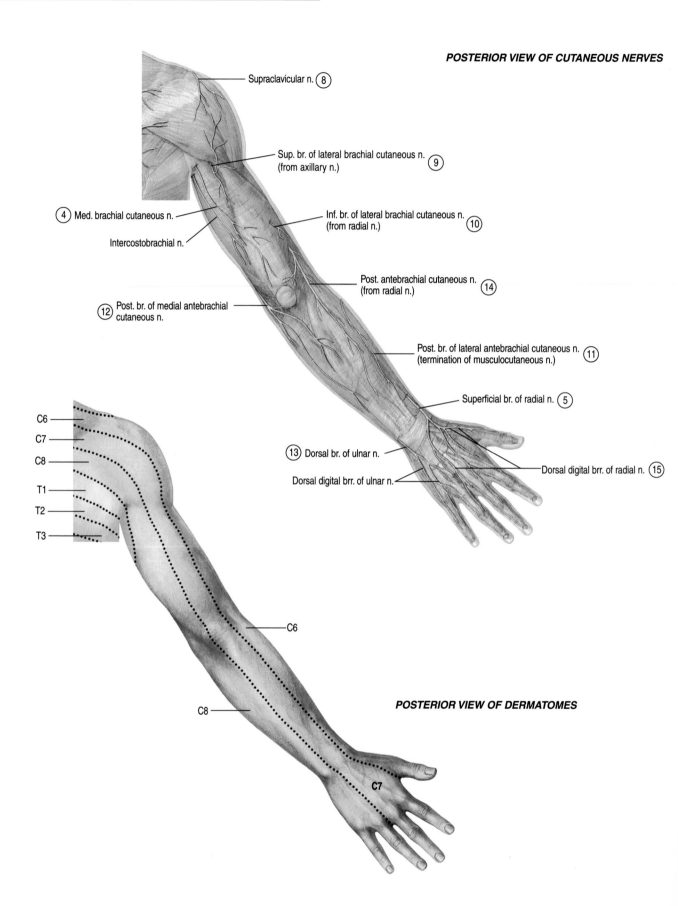

POSTERIOR VIEW OF CUTANEOUS NERVES

Supraclavicular n. (8)

Sup. br. of lateral brachial cutaneous n. (9)
(from axillary n.)

(4) Med. brachial cutaneous n.

Intercostobrachial n.

Inf. br. of lateral brachial cutaneous n. (10)
(from radial n.)

Post. antebrachial cutaneous n. (14)
(from radial n.)

(12) Post. br. of medial antebrachial cutaneous n.

Post. br. of lateral antebrachial cutaneous n. (11)
(termination of musculocutaneous n.)

Superficial br. of radial n. (5)

(13) Dorsal br. of ulnar n.

Dorsal digital brr. of ulnar n.

Dorsal digital brr. of radial n. (15)

C6
C7
C8
T1
T2
T3

C6

C8

C7

POSTERIOR VIEW OF DERMATOMES

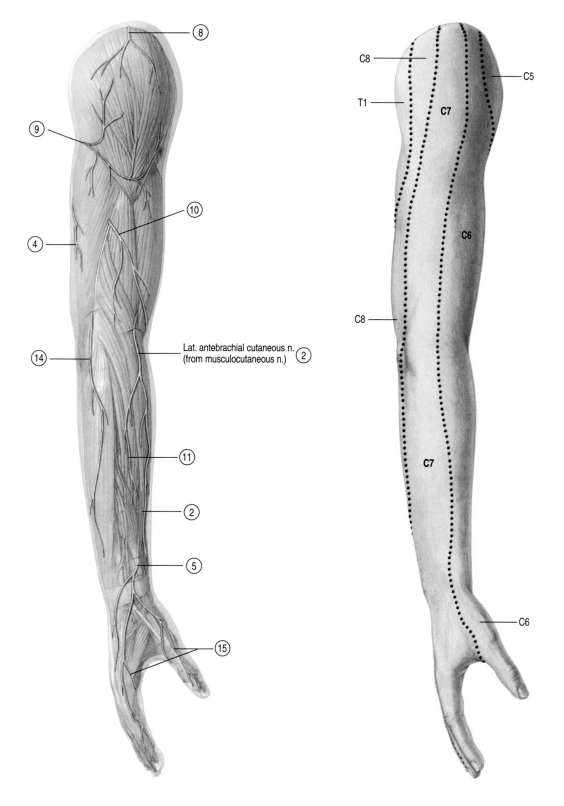

Lat. antebrachial cutaneous n. ② (from musculocutaneous n.)

LATERAL VIEW OF CUTANEOUS NERVES

LATERAL VIEW OF DERMATOMES

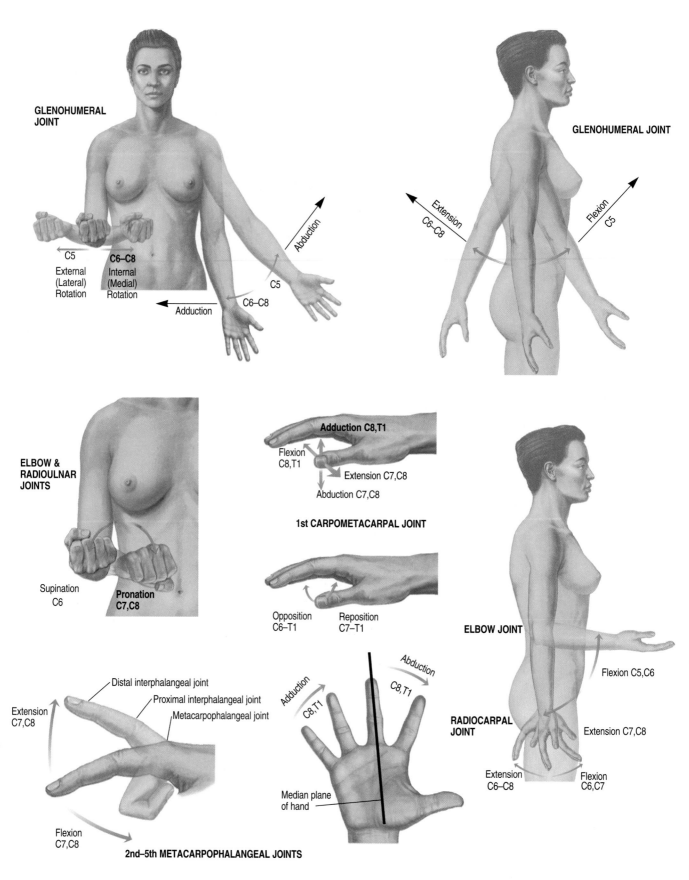

GLENOHUMERAL JOINT

C5

C6–C8

External (Lateral) Rotation

Internal (Medial) Rotation

Abduction

C5

C6–C8

Adduction

GLENOHUMERAL JOINT

Extension C6–C8

Flexion C5

ELBOW & RADIOULNAR JOINTS

Supination C6

Pronation C7,C8

Adduction C8,T1

Flexion C8,T1

Extension C7,C8

Abduction C7,C8

1st CARPOMETACARPAL JOINT

Opposition C6–T1

Reposition C7–T1

ELBOW JOINT

Flexion C5,C6

RADIOCARPAL JOINT

Extension C7,C8

Extension C6–C8

Flexion C6,C7

Distal interphalangeal joint

Proximal interphalangeal joint

Metacarpophalangeal joint

Extension C7,C8

Flexion C7,C8

Adduction C8,T1

Abduction C8,T1

Median plane of hand

2nd–5th METACARPOPHALANGEAL JOINTS

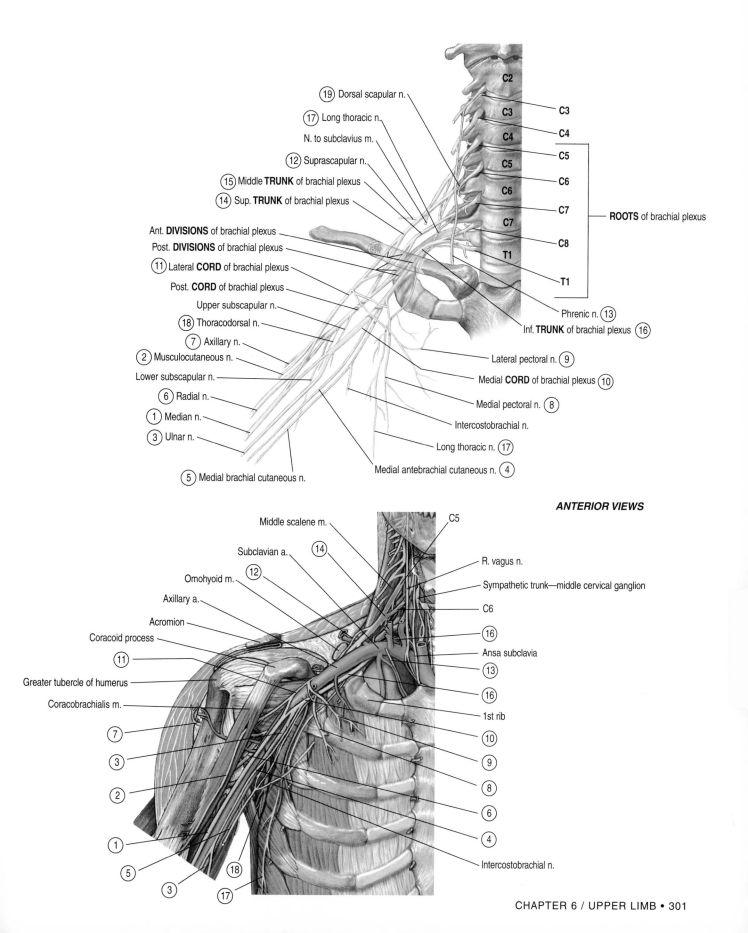

⑲ Dorsal scapular n.

⑰ Long thoracic n.

N. to subclavius m.

⑫ Suprascapular n.

⑮ Middle **TRUNK** of brachial plexus

⑭ Sup. **TRUNK** of brachial plexus

Ant. **DIVISIONS** of brachial plexus

Post. **DIVISIONS** of brachial plexus

⑪ Lateral **CORD** of brachial plexus

Post. **CORD** of brachial plexus

Upper subscapular n.

⑱ Thoracodorsal n.

⑦ Axillary n.

② Musculocutaneous n.

Lower subscapular n.

⑥ Radial n.

① Median n.

③ Ulnar n.

⑤ Medial brachial cutaneous n.

C2

C3

C4

C5

C6

C7

T1

C3

C4

C5

C6

C7

C8

T1

} **ROOTS** of brachial plexus

Phrenic n. ⑬

Inf. **TRUNK** of brachial plexus ⑯

Lateral pectoral n. ⑨

Medial **CORD** of brachial plexus ⑩

Medial pectoral n. ⑧

Intercostobrachial n.

Long thoracic n. ⑰

Medial antebrachial cutaneous n. ④

ANTERIOR VIEWS

Middle scalene m.

Subclavian a.

⑭

⑫

Omohyoid m.

Axillary a.

Acromion

Coracoid process

⑪

Greater tubercle of humerus

Coracobrachialis m.

⑦

③

②

①

⑤

⑱

③

⑰

C5

R. vagus n.

Sympathetic trunk—middle cervical ganglion

C6

⑯

Ansa subclavia

⑬

⑯

1st rib

⑩

⑨

⑧

⑥

④

Intercostobrachial n.

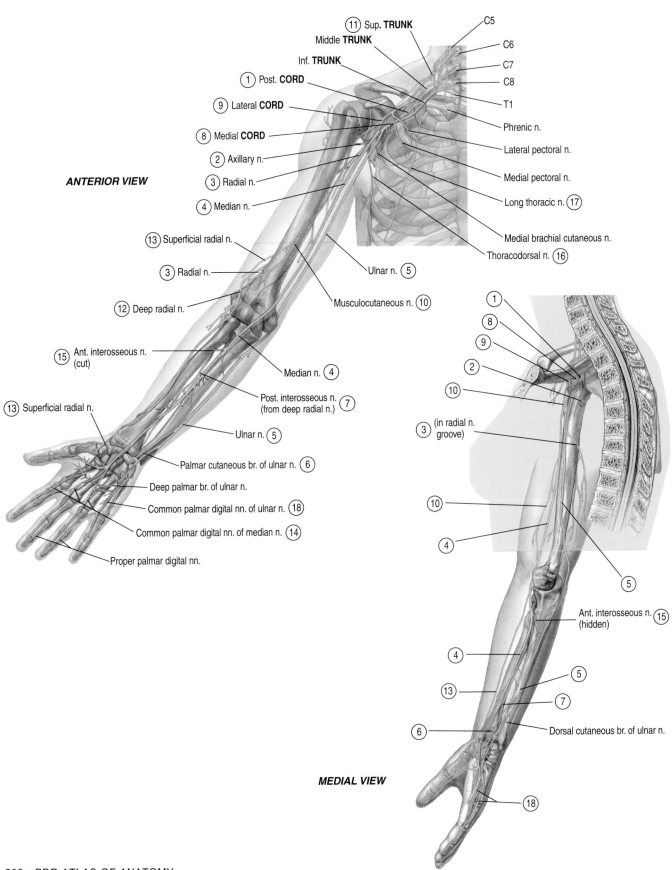

ANTERIOR VIEW

(11) Sup. **TRUNK**
Middle **TRUNK**
Inf. **TRUNK**
(1) Post. **CORD**
(9) Lateral **CORD**
(8) Medial **CORD**
(2) Axillary n.
(3) Radial n.
(4) Median n.

C5
C6
C7
C8
T1
Phrenic n.
Lateral pectoral n.
Medial pectoral n.
Long thoracic n. (17)
Medial brachial cutaneous n.
Thoracodorsal n. (16)

(13) Superficial radial n.
(3) Radial n.
(12) Deep radial n.

Ulnar n. (5)
Musculocutaneous n. (10)

(15) Ant. interosseous n. (cut)

Median n. (4)
Post. interosseous n. (7)
(from deep radial n.)

(13) Superficial radial n.

Ulnar n. (5)
Palmar cutaneous br. of ulnar n. (6)
Deep palmar br. of ulnar n.
Common palmar digital nn. of ulnar n. (18)
Common palmar digital nn. of median n. (14)
Proper palmar digital nn.

(1)
(8)
(9)
(2)
(10)

(3) (in radial n. groove)

(10)
(4)

(5)

Ant. interosseous n. (15)
(hidden)

(4)
(5)
(13)
(7)
(6)
Dorsal cutaneous br. of ulnar n.

(18)

MEDIAL VIEW

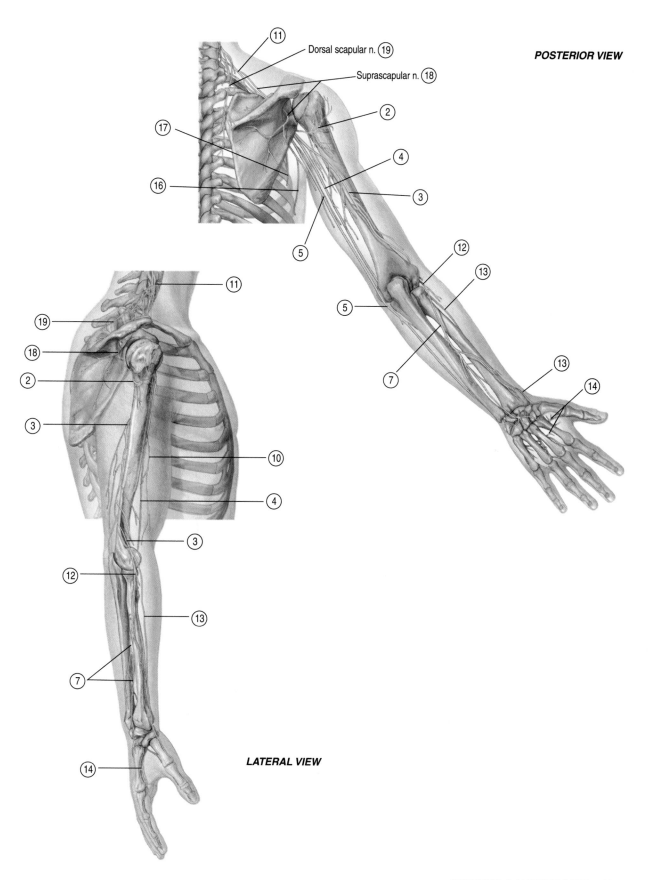

POSTERIOR VIEW

Dorsal scapular n. ⑲

Suprascapular n. ⑱

LATERAL VIEW

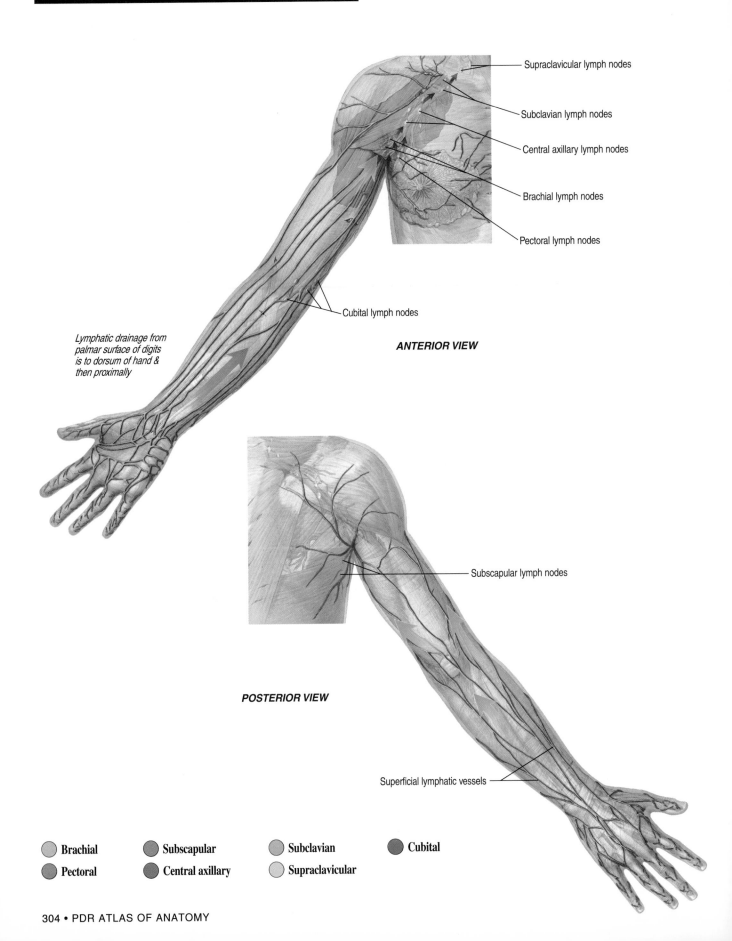

Supraclavicular lymph nodes

Subclavian lymph nodes

Central axillary lymph nodes

Brachial lymph nodes

Pectoral lymph nodes

Cubital lymph nodes

Lymphatic drainage from palmar surface of digits is to dorsum of hand & then proximally

ANTERIOR VIEW

Subscapular lymph nodes

POSTERIOR VIEW

Superficial lymphatic vessels

⬤ **Brachial**   ⬤ **Subscapular**   ⬤ **Subclavian**   ⬤ **Cubital**

⬤ **Pectoral**   ⬤ **Central axillary**   ⬤ **Supraclavicular**

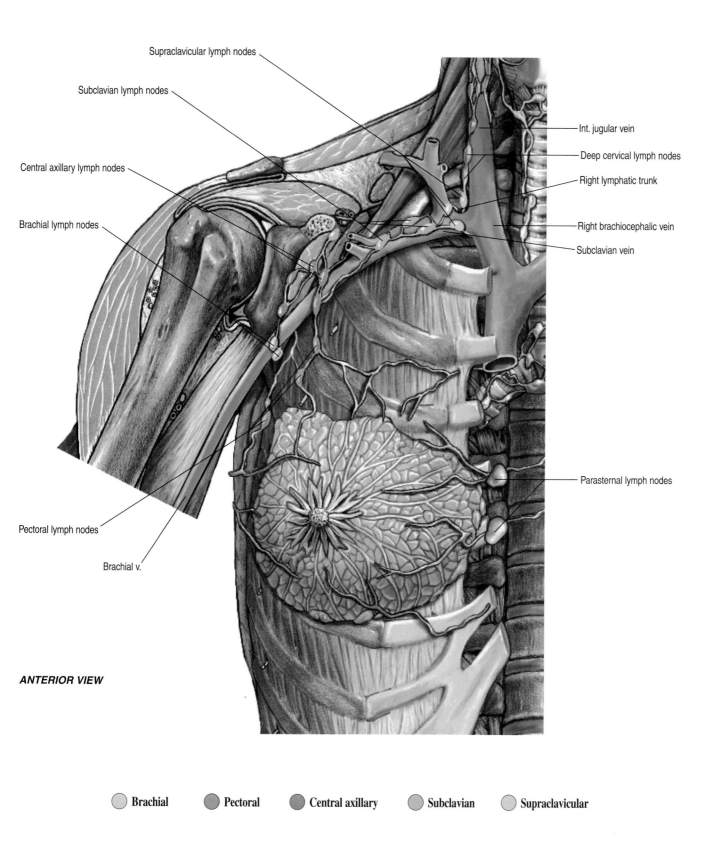

Supraclavicular lymph nodes

Subclavian lymph nodes

Central axillary lymph nodes

Brachial lymph nodes

Pectoral lymph nodes

Brachial v.

Int. jugular vein

Deep cervical lymph nodes

Right lymphatic trunk

Right brachiocephalic vein

Subclavian vein

Parasternal lymph nodes

ANTERIOR VIEW

Brachial ○ Pectoral ● Central axillary ● Subclavian ○ Supraclavicular ○

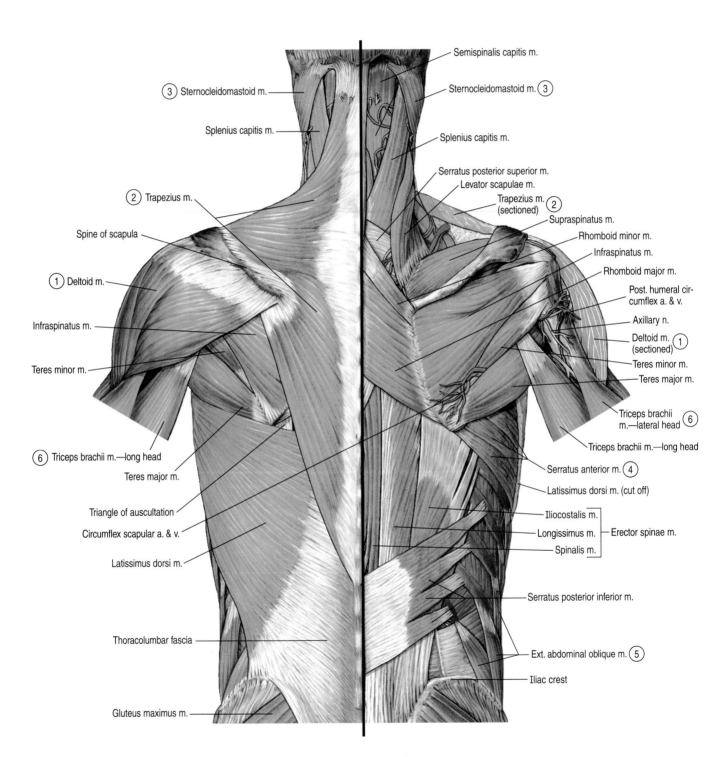

Semispinalis capitis m.

③ Sternocleidomastoid m.

Sternocleidomastoid m. ③

Splenius capitis m.

Splenius capitis m.

Serratus posterior superior m.

Levator scapulae m.

② Trapezius m.

Trapezius m. (sectioned) ②

Supraspinatus m.

Spine of scapula

Rhomboid minor m.

Infraspinatus m.

① Deltoid m.

Rhomboid major m.

Post. humeral circumflex a. & v.

Infraspinatus m.

Axillary n.

Deltoid m. (sectioned) ①

Teres minor m.

Teres minor m.

Teres major m.

Triceps brachii m.—lateral head ⑥

⑥ Triceps brachii m.—long head

Triceps brachii m.—long head

Teres major m.

Serratus anterior m. ④

Triangle of auscultation

Latissimus dorsi m. (cut off)

Circumflex scapular a. & v.

Iliocostalis m.

Longissimus m. — Erector spinae m.

Spinalis m.

Latissimus dorsi m.

Serratus posterior inferior m.

Thoracolumbar fascia

Ext. abdominal oblique m. ⑤

Iliac crest

Gluteus maximus m.

POSTERIOR VIEW

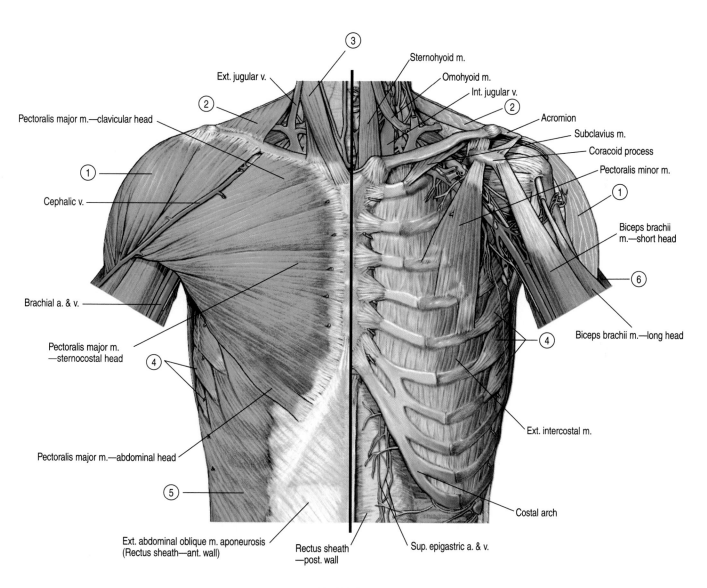

③

Sternohyoid m.

Ext. jugular v.

Omohyoid m.

② Int. jugular v.

②

Pectoralis major m.—clavicular head

Acromion

Subclavius m.

Coracoid process

① Pectoralis minor m.

Cephalic v.

①

Biceps brachii
m.—short head

⑥

Brachial a. & v.

Biceps brachii m.—long head

Pectoralis major m.
—sternocostal head

④

④

Ext. intercostal m.

Pectoralis major m.—abdominal head

⑤

Costal arch

Ext. abdominal oblique m. aponeurosis
(Rectus sheath—ant. wall)

Rectus sheath
—post. wall

Sup. epigastric a. & v.

ANTERIOR VIEW

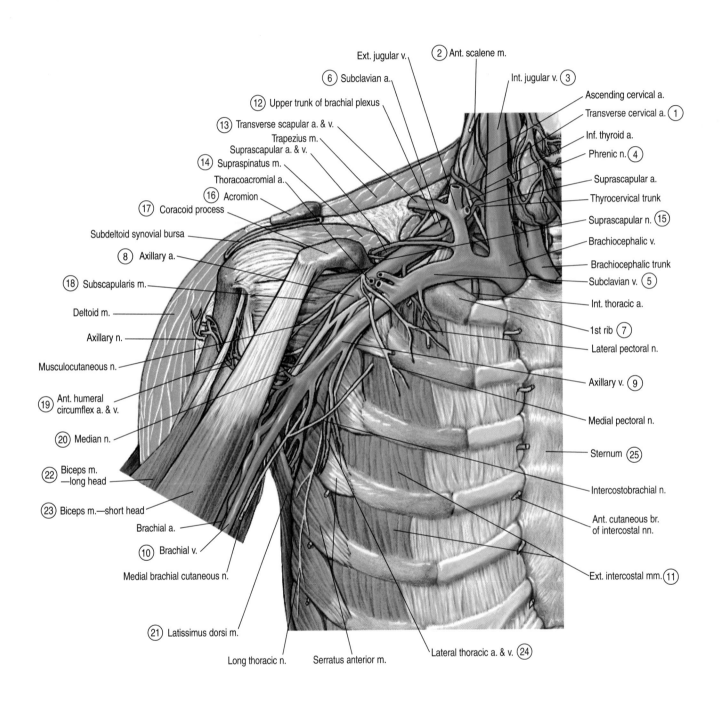

Ext. jugular v.

② Ant. scalene m.

⑥ Subclavian a.

Int. jugular v. ③

⑫ Upper trunk of brachial plexus

Ascending cervical a.

⑬ Transverse scapular a. & v.

Transverse cervical a. ①

Trapezius m.

Inf. thyroid a.

Suprascapular a. & v.

Phrenic n. ④

⑭ Supraspinatus m.

Suprascapular a.

Thoracoacromial a.

Thyrocervical trunk

⑯ Acromion

Suprascapular n. ⑮

⑰ Coracoid process

Brachiocephalic v.

Subdeltoid synovial bursa

Brachiocephalic trunk

⑧ Axillary a.

Subclavian v. ⑤

⑱ Subscapularis m.

Int. thoracic a.

Deltoid m.

1st rib ⑦

Axillary n.

Lateral pectoral n.

Musculocutaneous n.

Axillary v. ⑨

⑲ Ant. humeral circumflex a. & v.

Medial pectoral n.

⑳ Median n.

Sternum ㉕

㉒ Biceps m. —long head

Intercostobrachial n.

㉓ Biceps m.—short head

Ant. cutaneous br. of intercostal nn.

Brachial a.

⑩ Brachial v.

Ext. intercostal mm. ⑪

Medial brachial cutaneous n.

㉑ Latissimus dorsi m.

Lateral thoracic a. & v. ㉔

Long thoracic n.

Serratus anterior m.

ANTERIOR VIEW

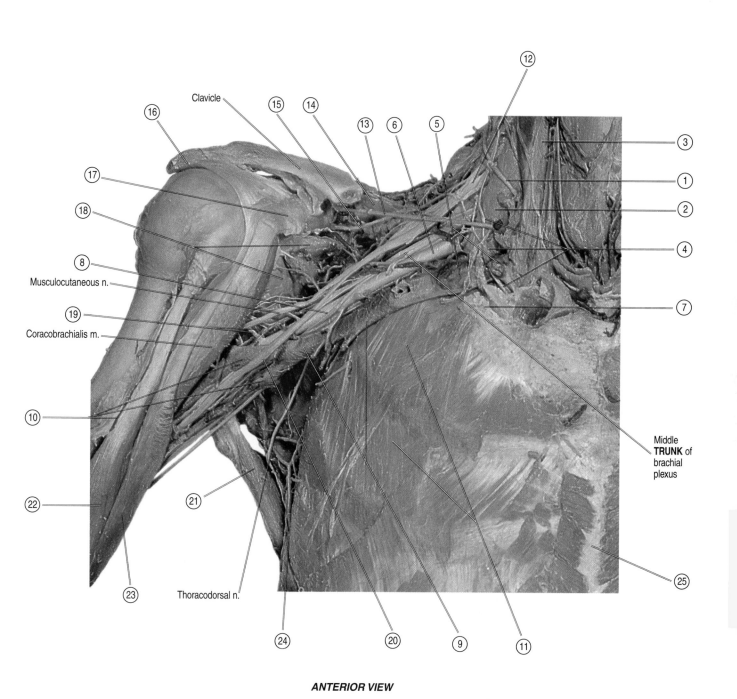

Clavicle

Musculocutaneous n.

Coracobrachialis m.

Thoracodorsal n.

Middle
TRUNK of
brachial
plexus

ANTERIOR VIEW

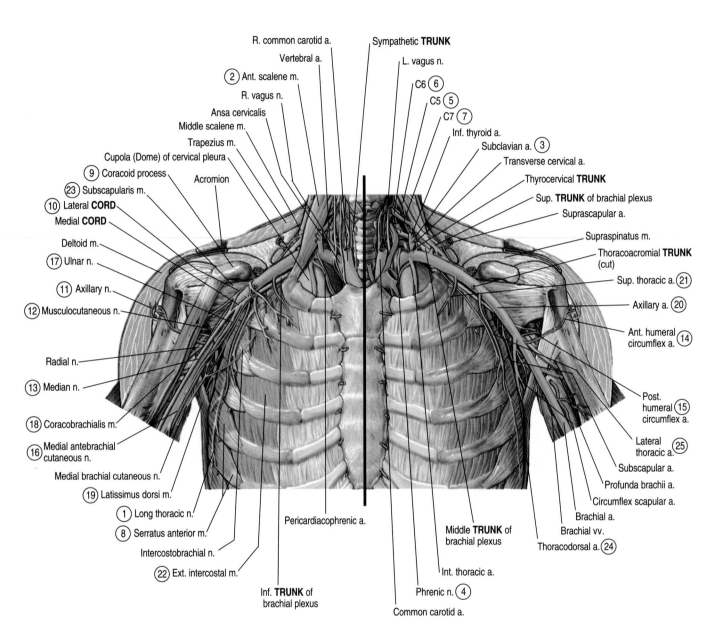

R. common carotid a.

Sympathetic **TRUNK**

Vertebral a.

L. vagus n.

② Ant. scalene m.

C6 ⑥

C5 ⑤

R. vagus n.

C7 ⑦

Ansa cervicalis

Inf. thyroid a.

Middle scalene m.

Subclavian a. ③

Trapezius m.

Transverse cervical a.

Cupola (Dome) of cervical pleura

Thyrocervical **TRUNK**

⑨ Coracoid process

Acromion

Sup. **TRUNK** of brachial plexus

㉓ Subscapularis m.

Suprascapular a.

⑩ Lateral **CORD**

Supraspinatus m.

Medial **CORD**

Thoracoacromial **TRUNK** (cut)

Deltoid m.

⑰ Ulnar n.

Sup. thoracic a. ㉑

⑪ Axillary n.

Axillary a. ⑳

⑫ Musculocutaneous n.

Ant. humeral circumflex a. ⑭

Radial n.

⑬ Median n.

Post. humeral ⑮ circumflex a.

⑱ Coracobrachialis m.

Lateral ㉕ thoracic a.

⑯ Medial antebrachial cutaneous n.

Subscapular a.

Medial brachial cutaneous n.

Profunda brachii a.

⑲ Latissimus dorsi m.

Circumflex scapular a.

① Long thoracic n.

Brachial a.

⑧ Serratus anterior m.

Brachial vv.

Pericardiacophrenic a.

Middle **TRUNK** of brachial plexus

Thoracodorsal a. ㉔

Intercostobrachial n.

㉒ Ext. intercostal m.

Int. thoracic a.

Inf. **TRUNK** of brachial plexus

Phrenic n. ④

Common carotid a.

ANTERIOR VIEW

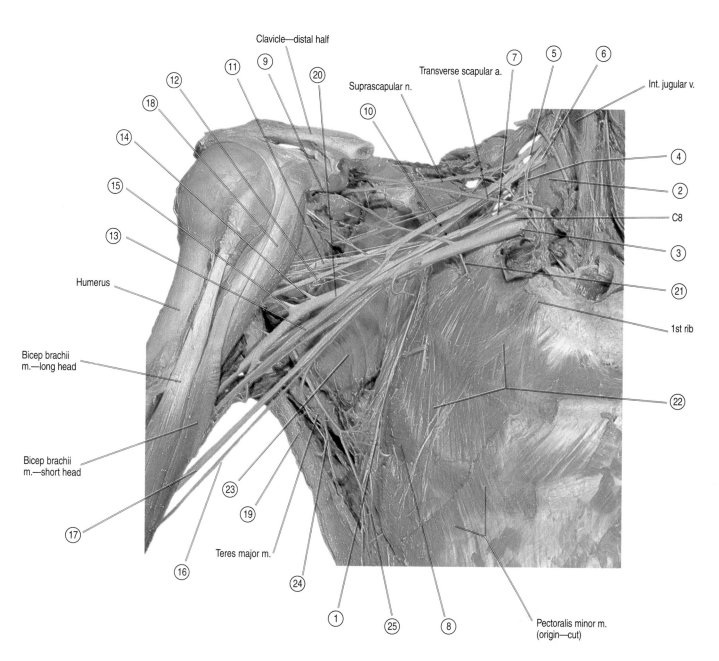

Clavicle—distal half

Transverse scapular a.

Suprascapular n.

Int. jugular v.

Humerus

Bicep brachii
m.—long head

Bicep brachii
m.—short head

Teres major m.

Pectoralis minor m.
(origin—cut)

C8

1st rib

ANTERIOR VIEW

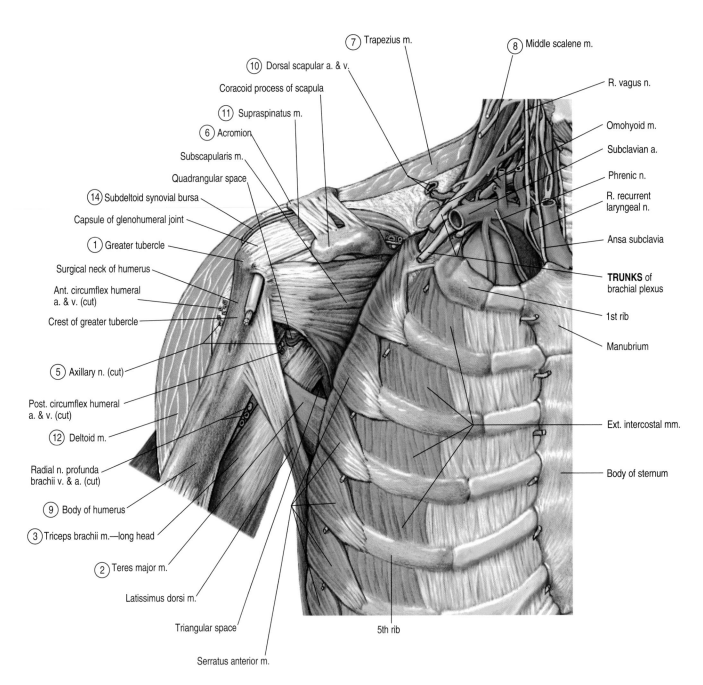

(7) Trapezius m.

(8) Middle scalene m.

(10) Dorsal scapular a. & v.

Coracoid process of scapula

R. vagus n.

(11) Supraspinatus m.

Omohyoid m.

(6) Acromion

Subclavian a.

Subscapularis m.

Phrenic n.

Quadrangular space

R. recurrent laryngeal n.

(14) Subdeltoid synovial bursa

Ansa subclavia

Capsule of glenohumeral joint

TRUNKS of brachial plexus

(1) Greater tubercle

1st rib

Surgical neck of humerus

Manubrium

Ant. circumflex humeral a. & v. (cut)

Crest of greater tubercle

(5) Axillary n. (cut)

Post. circumflex humeral a. & v. (cut)

Ext. intercostal mm.

(12) Deltoid m.

Radial n. profunda brachii v. & a. (cut)

Body of sternum

(9) Body of humerus

(3) Triceps brachii m.—long head

(2) Teres major m.

Latissimus dorsi m.

Triangular space

5th rib

Serratus anterior m.

ANTERIOR VIEW

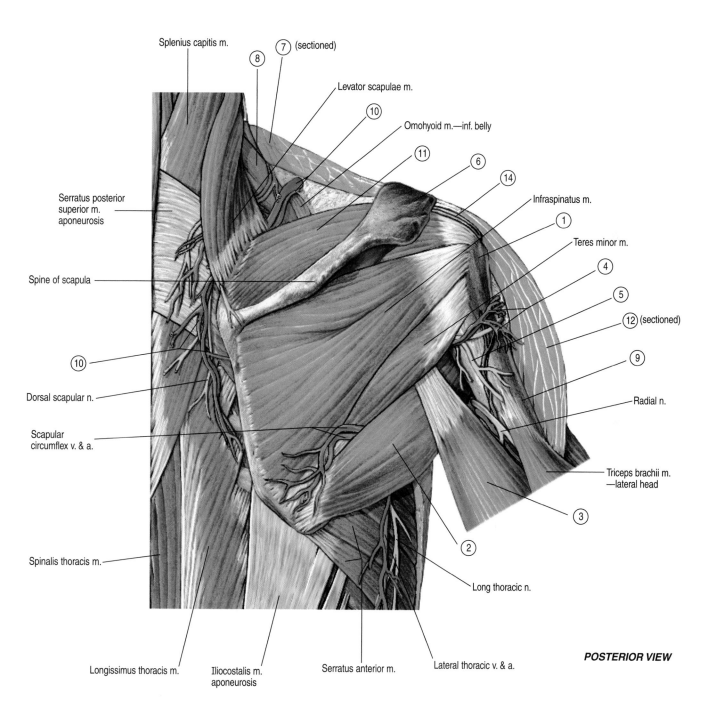

Splenius capitis m.

⑦ (sectioned)

⑧

Levator scapulae m.

⑩

Omohyoid m.—inf. belly

⑪

⑥

⑭

Infraspinatus m.

①

Teres minor m.

④

⑤

⑫ (sectioned)

⑨

Radial n.

Triceps brachii m.
—lateral head

③

②

Long thoracic n.

Serratus posterior
superior m.
aponeurosis

Spine of scapula

⑩

Dorsal scapular n.

Scapular
circumflex v. & a.

Spinalis thoracis m.

Longissimus thoracis m.

Iliocostalis m.
aponeurosis

Serratus anterior m.

Lateral thoracic v. & a.

POSTERIOR VIEW

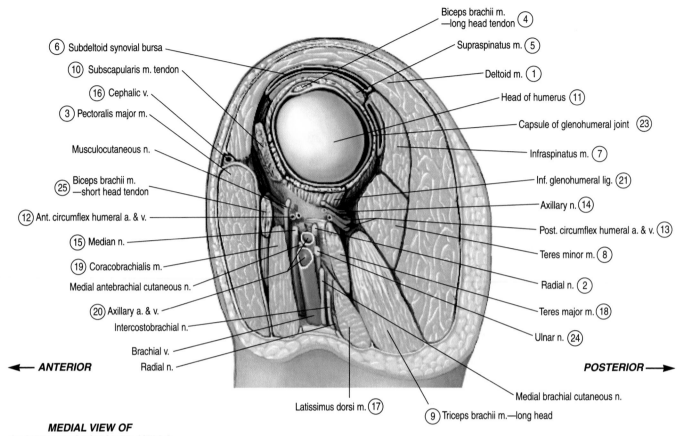

Biceps brachii m. —long head tendon (4)

(6) Subdeltoid synovial bursa

(10) Subscapularis m. tendon

(16) Cephalic v.

(3) Pectoralis major m.

Musculocutaneous n.

(25) Biceps brachii m. —short head tendon

(12) Ant. circumflex humeral a. & v.

(15) Median n.

(19) Coracobrachialis m.

Medial antebrachial cutaneous n.

(20) Axillary a. & v.

Intercostobrachial n.

Brachial v.

Radial n.

← **ANTERIOR**

Supraspinatus m. (5)

Deltoid m. (1)

Head of humerus (11)

Capsule of glenohumeral joint (23)

Infraspinatus m. (7)

Inf. glenohumeral lig. (21)

Axillary n. (14)

Post. circumflex humeral a. & v. (13)

Teres minor m. (8)

Radial n. (2)

Teres major m. (18)

Ulnar n. (24)

POSTERIOR →

Medial brachial cutaneous n.

Latissimus dorsi m. (17)

(9) Triceps brachii m.—long head

**MEDIAL VIEW OF
SAGITTALLY SECTIONED AXILLA**

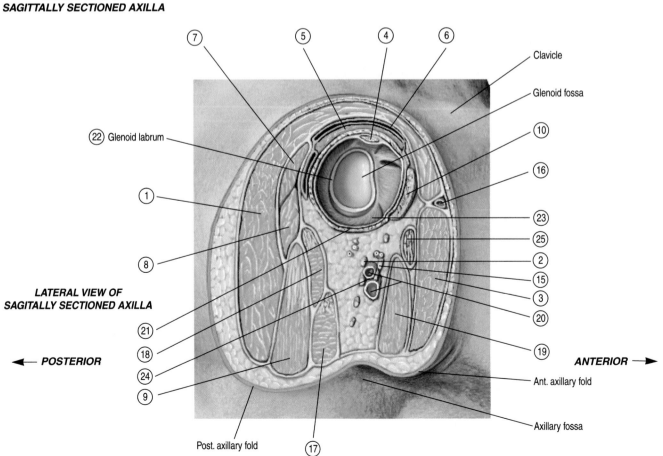

(7) (5) (4) (6)

Clavicle

Glenoid fossa

(22) Glenoid labrum

(10)

(16)

(1)

(23)

(25)

(8)

(2)

(15)

(3)

**LATERAL VIEW OF
SAGITALLY SECTIONED AXILLA**

(21)

(20)

(19)

(18)

(24)

Ant. axillary fold

(9)

Axillary fossa

← **POSTERIOR**

ANTERIOR →

Post. axillary fold

(17)

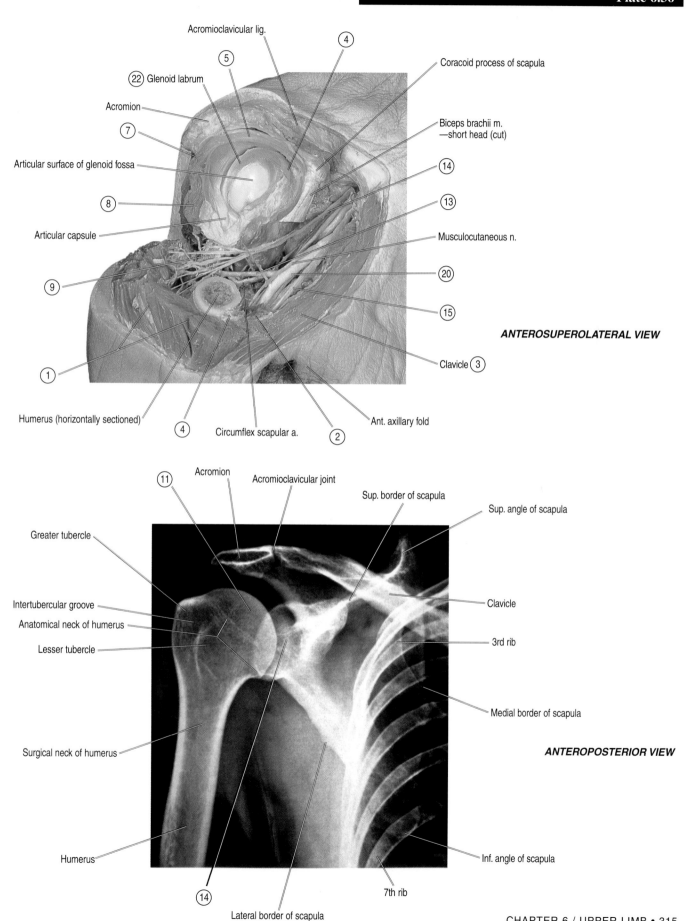

Acromioclavicular lig.

⑤

④

(22) Glenoid labrum

Acromion

⑦

Articular surface of glenoid fossa

⑧

Articular capsule

⑨

①

Humerus (horizontally sectioned)

④

Circumflex scapular a.

②

Coracoid process of scapula

Biceps brachii m.
—short head (cut)

⑭

⑬

Musculocutaneous n.

⑳

⑮

Clavicle ③

Ant. axillary fold

ANTEROSUPEROLATERAL VIEW

⑪

Acromion

Acromioclavicular joint

Sup. border of scapula

Sup. angle of scapula

Greater tubercle

Intertubercular groove

Anatomical neck of humerus

Lesser tubercle

Surgical neck of humerus

Humerus

⑭

Lateral border of scapula

7th rib

Clavicle

3rd rib

Medial border of scapula

ANTEROPOSTERIOR VIEW

Inf. angle of scapula

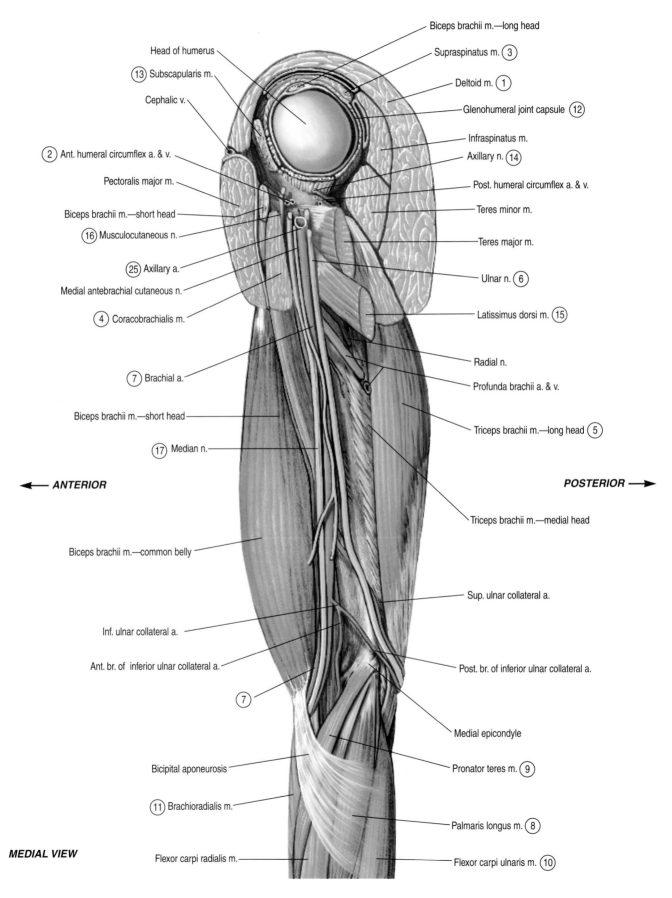

Head of humerus

(13) Subscapularis m.

Cephalic v.

(2) Ant. humeral circumflex a. & v.

Pectoralis major m.

Biceps brachii m.—short head

(16) Musculocutaneous n.

(25) Axillary a.

Medial antebrachial cutaneous n.

(4) Coracobrachialis m.

(7) Brachial a.

Biceps brachii m.—short head

(17) Median n.

Biceps brachii m.—long head

Supraspinatus m. (3)

Deltoid m. (1)

Glenohumeral joint capsule (12)

Infraspinatus m.

Axillary n. (14)

Post. humeral circumflex a. & v.

Teres minor m.

Teres major m.

Ulnar n. (6)

Latissimus dorsi m. (15)

Radial n.

Profunda brachii a. & v.

Triceps brachii m.—long head (5)

Triceps brachii m.—medial head

◄— **ANTERIOR**

POSTERIOR —►

Biceps brachii m.—common belly

Sup. ulnar collateral a.

Inf. ulnar collateral a.

Ant. br. of inferior ulnar collateral a.

(7)

Post. br. of inferior ulnar collateral a.

Medial epicondyle

Bicipital aponeurosis

Pronator teres m. (9)

(11) Brachioradialis m.

Palmaris longus m. (8)

MEDIAL VIEW

Flexor carpi radialis m.

Flexor carpi ulnaris m. (10)

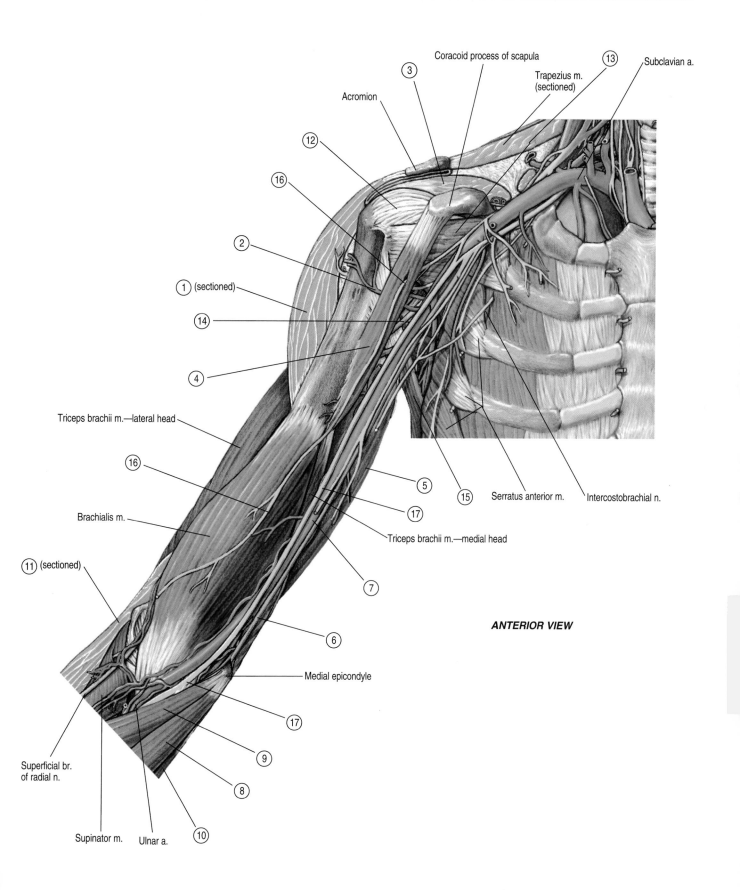

Coracoid process of scapula

③

⑬

Subclavian a.

Trapezius m.
(sectioned)

Acromion

⑫

⑯

②

① (sectioned)

⑭

④

Triceps brachii m.—lateral head

⑯

Brachialis m.

⑪ (sectioned)

⑤

⑰

⑮   Serratus anterior m.   Intercostobrachial n.

Triceps brachii m.—medial head

⑦

⑥

ANTERIOR VIEW

Medial epicondyle

⑰

⑨

⑧

Superficial br.
of radial n.

⑩

Supinator m.   Ulnar a.

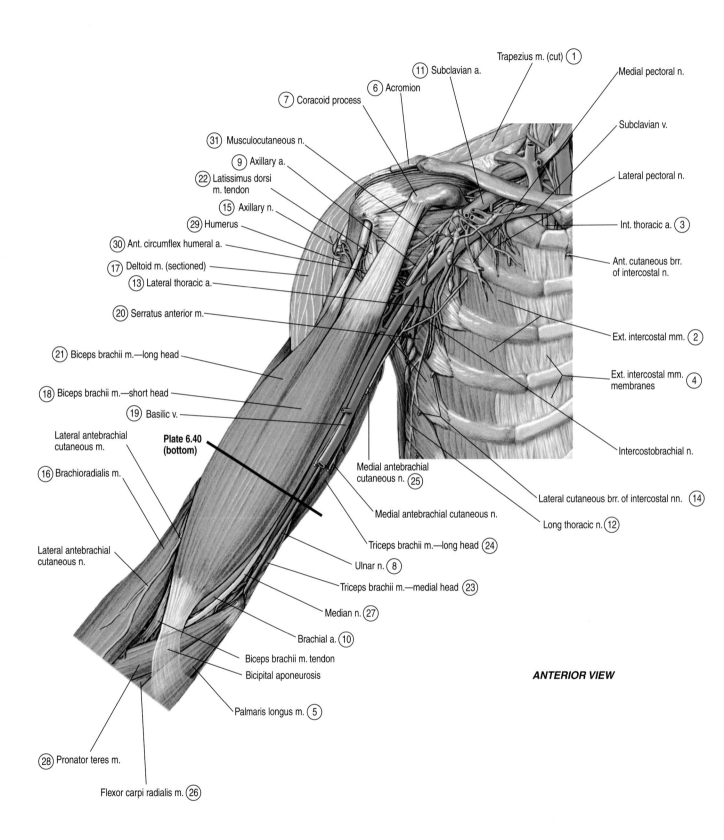

11 Subclavian a.

Trapezius m. (cut) 1

Medial pectoral n.

6 Acromion

7 Coracoid process

Subclavian v.

31 Musculocutaneous n.

Lateral pectoral n.

9 Axillary a.

22 Latissimus dorsi
m. tendon

Int. thoracic a. 3

15 Axillary n.

29 Humerus

Ant. cutaneous brr.
of intercostal n.

30 Ant. circumflex humeral a.

17 Deltoid m. (sectioned)

13 Lateral thoracic a.

20 Serratus anterior m.

Ext. intercostal mm. 2

21 Biceps brachii m.—long head

18 Biceps brachii m.—short head

Ext. intercostal mm. 4
membranes

19 Basilic v.

Lateral antebrachial
cutaneous m.

**Plate 6.40
(bottom)**

16 Brachioradialis m.

Medial antebrachial
cutaneous n. 25

Intercostobrachial n.

Lateral antebrachial
cutaneous n.

Medial antebrachial cutaneous n.

Lateral cutaneous brr. of intercostal nn. 14

Triceps brachii m.—long head 24

Long thoracic n. 12

Ulnar n. 8

Triceps brachii m.—medial head 23

Median n. 27

Brachial a. 10

Biceps brachii m. tendon

Bicipital aponeurosis

ANTERIOR VIEW

Palmaris longus m. 5

28 Pronator teres m.

Flexor carpi radialis m. 26

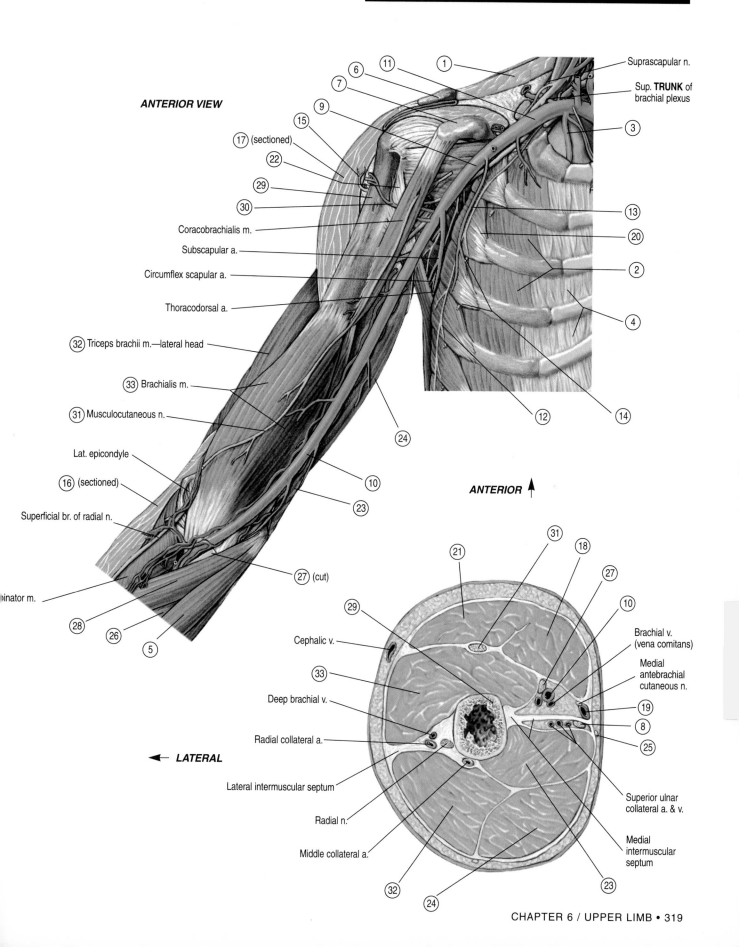

ANTERIOR VIEW

Suprascapular n.

Sup. **TRUNK** of
brachial plexus

⑰ (sectioned)

Coracobrachialis m.

Subscapular a.

Circumflex scapular a.

Thoracodorsal a.

㉜ Triceps brachii m.—lateral head

㉝ Brachialis m.

㉛ Musculocutaneous n.

Lat. epicondyle

⑯ (sectioned)

Superficial br. of radial n.

...pinator m.

㉗ (cut)

ANTERIOR

LATERAL

Cephalic v.

Deep brachial v.

Radial collateral a.

Lateral intermuscular septum

Radial n.

Middle collateral a.

Brachial v.
(vena comitans)

Medial
antebrachial
cutaneous n.

Superior ulnar
collateral a. & v.

Medial
intermuscular
septum

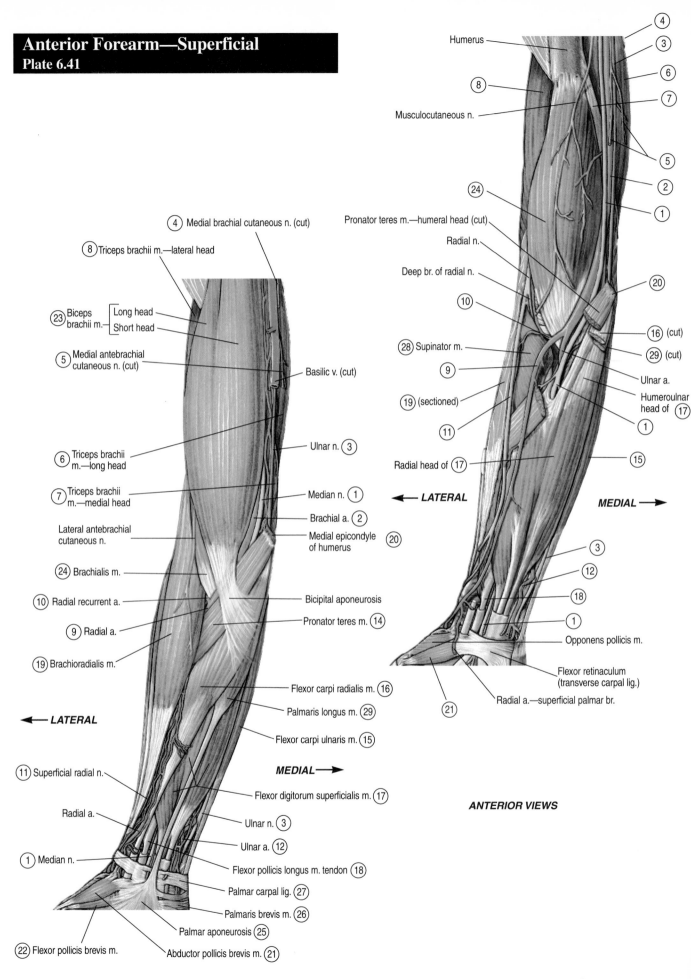

Humerus

④

③

⑥

⑦

⑧

Musculocutaneous n.

⑤

②

①

㉔

Pronator teres m.—humeral head (cut)

Radial n.

Deep br. of radial n.

⑳

⑩

⑯ (cut)

㉘ Supinator m.

㉙ (cut)

⑨

Ulnar a.

⑲ (sectioned)

Humeroulnar head of ⑰

⑪

①

Radial head of ⑰

⑮

← LATERAL

MEDIAL →

③

⑫

⑱

①

Opponens pollicis m.

Flexor retinaculum (transverse carpal lig.)

㉑

Radial a.—superficial palmar br.

ANTERIOR VIEWS

④ Medial brachial cutaneous n. (cut)

⑧ Triceps brachii m.—lateral head

㉓ Biceps brachii m.— { Long head / Short head }

⑤ Medial antebrachial cutaneous n. (cut)

Basilic v. (cut)

⑥ Triceps brachii m.—long head

⑦ Triceps brachii m.—medial head

Ulnar n. ③

Lateral antebrachial cutaneous n.

Median n. ①

Brachial a. ②

Medial epicondyle of humerus ⑳

㉔ Brachialis m.

⑩ Radial recurrent a.

Bicipital aponeurosis

Pronator teres m. ⑭

⑨ Radial a.

⑲ Brachioradialis m.

Flexor carpi radialis m. ⑯

Palmaris longus m. ㉙

← LATERAL

Flexor carpi ulnaris m. ⑮

MEDIAL →

⑪ Superficial radial n.

Radial a.

Flexor digitorum superficialis m. ⑰

Ulnar n. ③

Ulnar a. ⑫

① Median n.

Flexor pollicis longus m. tendon ⑱

Palmar carpal lig. ㉗

Palmaris brevis m. ㉖

Palmar aponeurosis ㉕

㉒ Flexor pollicis brevis m.

Abductor pollicis brevis m. ㉑

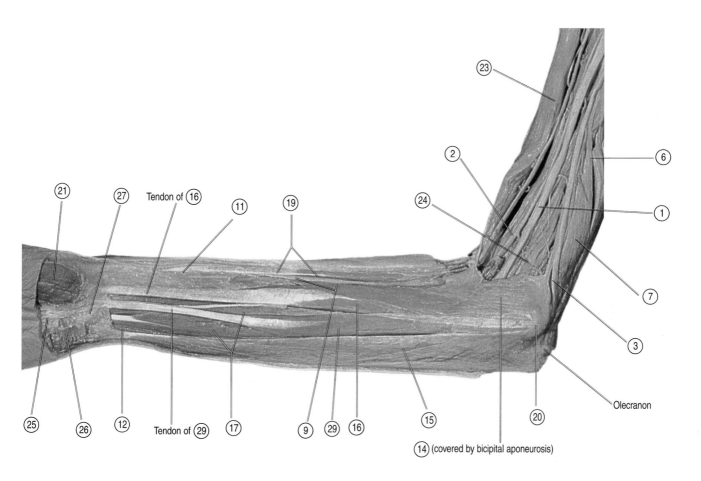

MEDIAL ARM & ANTERIOR FOREARM & WRIST

- ㉓
- ②
- ⑥
- ㉑
- ㉗
- Tendon of ⑯
- ⑪
- ⑲
- ㉔
- ①
- ⑦
- ③
- ㉕
- ㉖
- ⑫
- Tendon of ㉙
- ⑰
- ⑨
- ㉙
- ⑯
- ⑮
- ⑳
- Olecranon
- ⑭ (covered by bicipital aponeurosis)

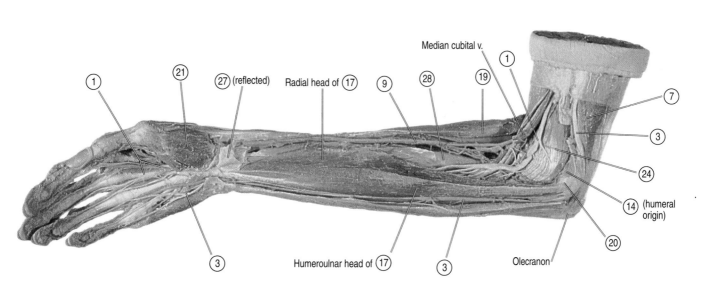

MEDIAL ELBOW & ANTERIOR FOREARM & HAND

- ①
- ㉑
- ㉗ (reflected)
- Radial head of ⑰
- ⑨
- ㉘
- ⑲
- Median cubital v.
- ①
- ⑦
- ③
- ㉔
- ⑭ (humeral origin)
- ⑳
- Olecranon
- ③
- Humeroulnar head of ⑰
- ③

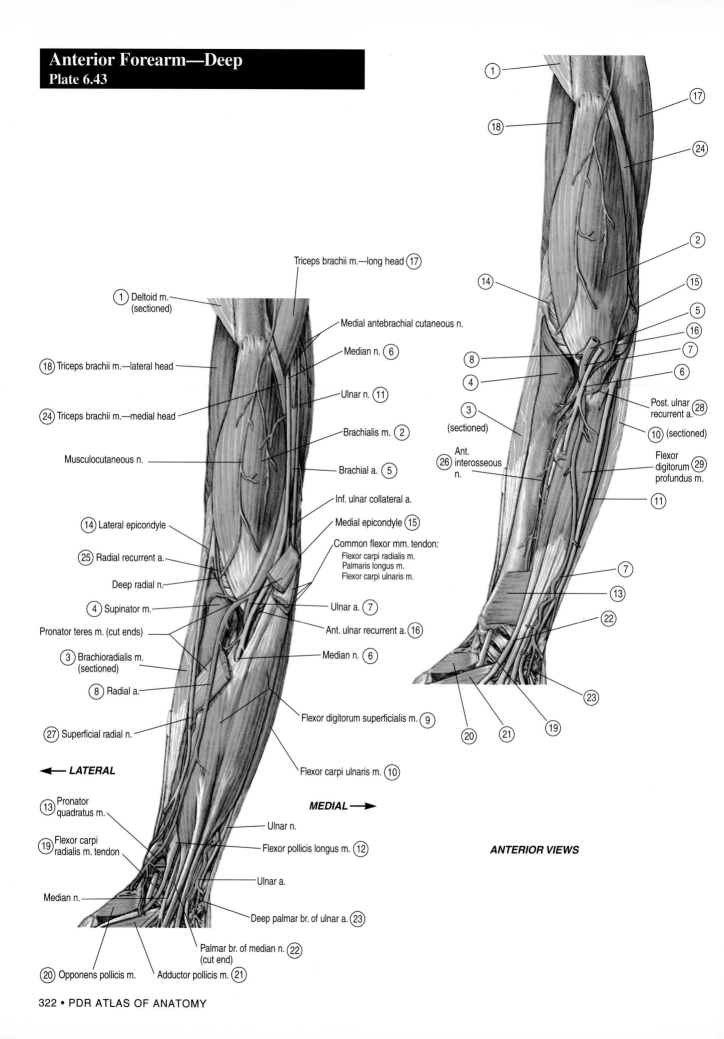

Triceps brachii m.—long head (17)

(1) Deltoid m. (sectioned)

Medial antebrachial cutaneous n.

Median n. (6)

(18) Triceps brachii m.—lateral head

Ulnar n. (11)

(24) Triceps brachii m.—medial head

Brachialis m. (2)

Musculocutaneous n.

Brachial a. (5)

Inf. ulnar collateral a.

(14) Lateral epicondyle

Medial epicondyle (15)

(25) Radial recurrent a.

Common flexor mm. tendon:
Flexor carpi radialis m.
Palmaris longus m.
Flexor carpi ulnaris m.

Deep radial n.

(4) Supinator m.

Ulnar a. (7)

Pronator teres m. (cut ends)

Ant. ulnar recurrent a. (16)

(3) Brachioradialis m. (sectioned)

Median n. (6)

(8) Radial a.

(27) Superficial radial n.

Flexor digitorum superficialis m. (9)

← LATERAL

Flexor carpi ulnaris m. (10)

MEDIAL →

(13) Pronator quadratus m.

Ulnar n.

(19) Flexor carpi radialis m. tendon

Flexor pollicis longus m. (12)

Median n.

Ulnar a.

Deep palmar br. of ulnar a. (23)

Palmar br. of median n. (22) (cut end)

(20) Opponens pollicis m.   Adductor pollicis m. (21)

(1)

(17)

(18)

(24)

(14)

(2)

(15)

(5)

(16)

(8)

(7)

(4)

(6)

(3) (sectioned)

Post. ulnar recurrent a. (28)

(10) (sectioned)

Ant. (26) interosseous n.

Flexor digitorum profundus m. (29)

(11)

(7)

(13)

(22)

(20)

(21)

(19)

(23)

ANTERIOR VIEWS

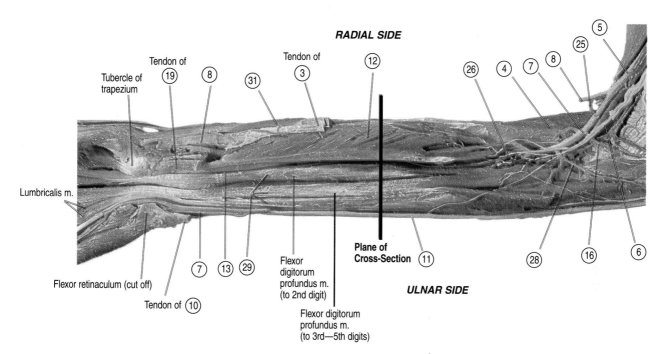

RADIAL SIDE

Tubercle of trapezium

Tendon of ⑲ ⑧

③① Tendon of ③

⑫

㉖ ④ ⑦ ⑧ ㉕ ⑤

Lumbricalis m.

Flexor retinaculum (cut off)

Tendon of ⑩

⑦ ⑬ ㉙

Flexor digitorum profundus m. (to 2nd digit)

Plane of Cross-Section

⑪

⑧ ㉘ ⑯ ⑥

ULNAR SIDE

Flexor digitorum profundus m. (to 3rd—5th digits)

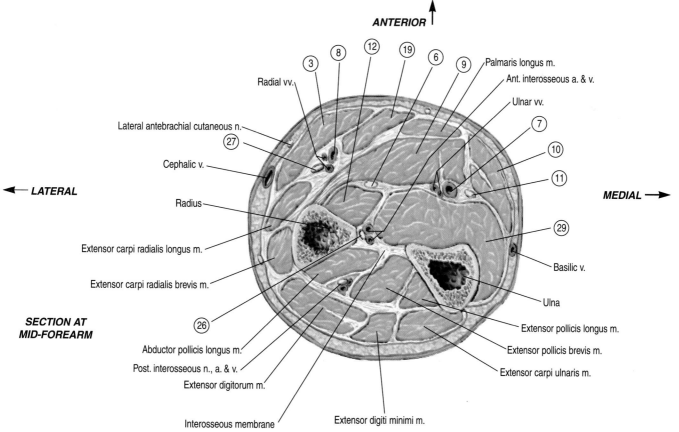

ANTERIOR ↑

③ ⑧ ⑫ ⑲ ⑥ ⑨ Palmaris longus m.

Radial vv.

Ant. interosseous a. & v.

Ulnar vv.

Lateral antebrachial cutaneous n.

㉗

Cephalic v.

⑦

⑩

⑪

◄— LATERAL

MEDIAL —►

Radius

Extensor carpi radialis longus m.

㉙

Basilic v.

Extensor carpi radialis brevis m.

Ulna

SECTION AT MID-FOREARM

㉖

Extensor pollicis longus m.

Abductor pollicis longus m.

Extensor pollicis brevis m.

Post. interosseous n., a. & v.

Extensor carpi ulnaris m.

Extensor digitorum m.

Interosseous membrane

Extensor digiti minimi m.

Elbow & Wrist Joints
Plate 6.45

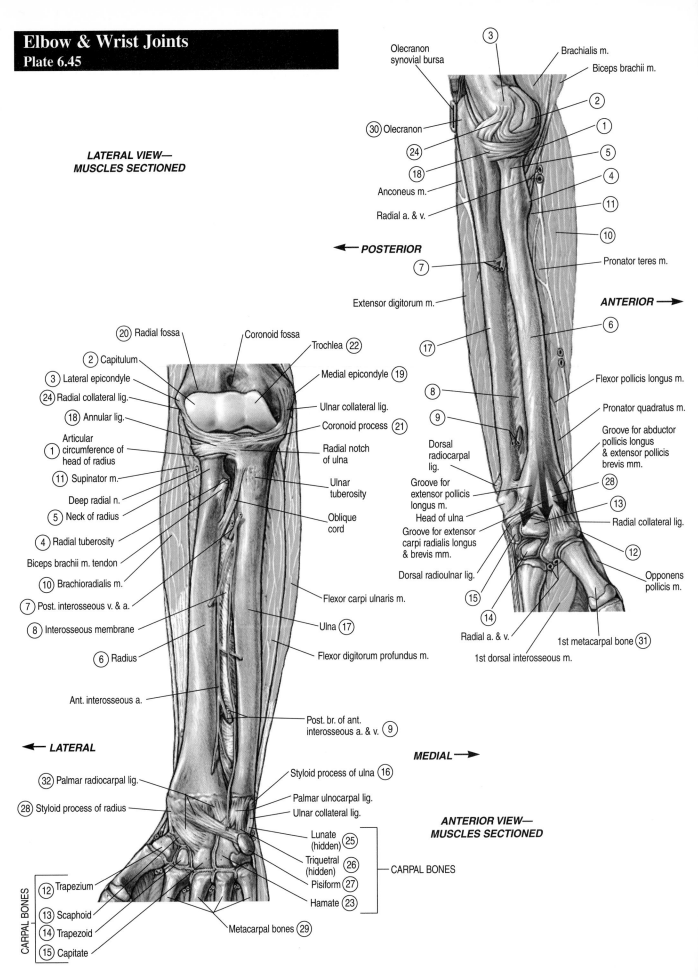

LATERAL VIEW— MUSCLES SECTIONED

Olecranon synovial bursa

Brachialis m.

Biceps brachii m.

③

(30) Olecranon

②

①

(24)

⑤

(18)

④

Anconeus m.

(11)

Radial a. & v.

(10)

Pronator teres m.

◄ **POSTERIOR**

Extensor digitorum m.

⑦

ANTERIOR ►

⑥

(17)

Flexor pollicis longus m.

⑧

Pronator quadratus m.

⑨

Groove for abductor pollicis longus & extensor pollicis brevis mm.

Dorsal radiocarpal lig.

(28)

Groove for extensor pollicis longus m.

(13)

Head of ulna

Radial collateral lig.

Groove for extensor carpi radialis longus & brevis mm.

(12)

Dorsal radioulnar lig.

Opponens pollicis m.

(15)

(14)

Radial a. & v.

1st metacarpal bone (31)

1st dorsal interosseous m.

(20) Radial fossa

Coronoid fossa

Trochlea (22)

② Capitulum

Medial epicondyle (19)

③ Lateral epicondyle

(24) Radial collateral lig.

Ulnar collateral lig.

(18) Annular lig.

Coronoid process (21)

① Articular circumference of head of radius

Radial notch of ulna

(11) Supinator m.

Ulnar tuberosity

Deep radial n.

⑤ Neck of radius

Oblique cord

④ Radial tuberosity

Biceps brachii m. tendon

(10) Brachioradialis m.

Flexor carpi ulnaris m.

⑦ Post. interosseous v. & a.

Ulna (17)

⑧ Interosseous membrane

Flexor digitorum profundus m.

⑥ Radius

Ant. interosseous a.

Post. br. of ant. interosseous a. & v. ⑨

◄ **LATERAL**

MEDIAL ►

Styloid process of ulna (16)

(32) Palmar radiocarpal lig.

Palmar ulnocarpal lig.

(28) Styloid process of radius

Ulnar collateral lig.

ANTERIOR VIEW— MUSCLES SECTIONED

Lunate (hidden) (25)

Triquetral (hidden) (26)

CARPAL BONES

(12) Trapezium

Pisiform (27)

Hamate (23)

(13) Scaphoid

(14) Trapezoid

Metacarpal bones (29)

(15) Capitate

CARPAL BONES

LATERAL VIEW

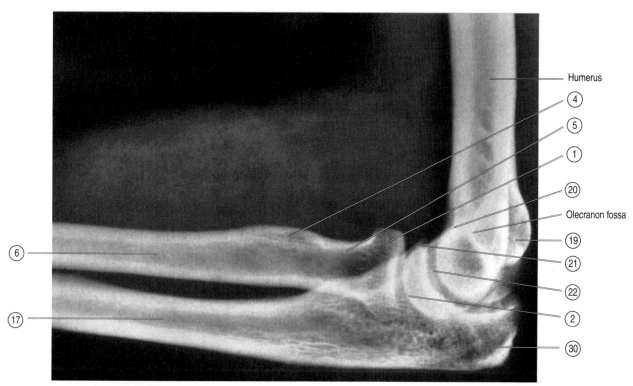

Humerus

④
⑤
①
⑳
Olecranon fossa
⑲
㉑
㉒
②
㉚
⑥
⑰

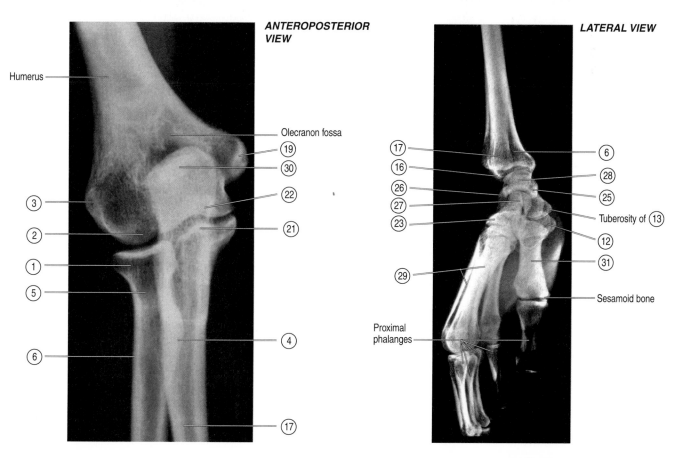

ANTEROPOSTERIOR VIEW

Humerus

Olecranon fossa
⑲
㉚
㉒
㉑
③
②
①
⑤
⑥
④
⑰

LATERAL VIEW

⑰
⑯
㉖
㉗
㉓
㉙
⑥
㉘
㉕
Tuberosity of ⑬
⑫
㉛
Sesamoid bone

Proximal phalanges

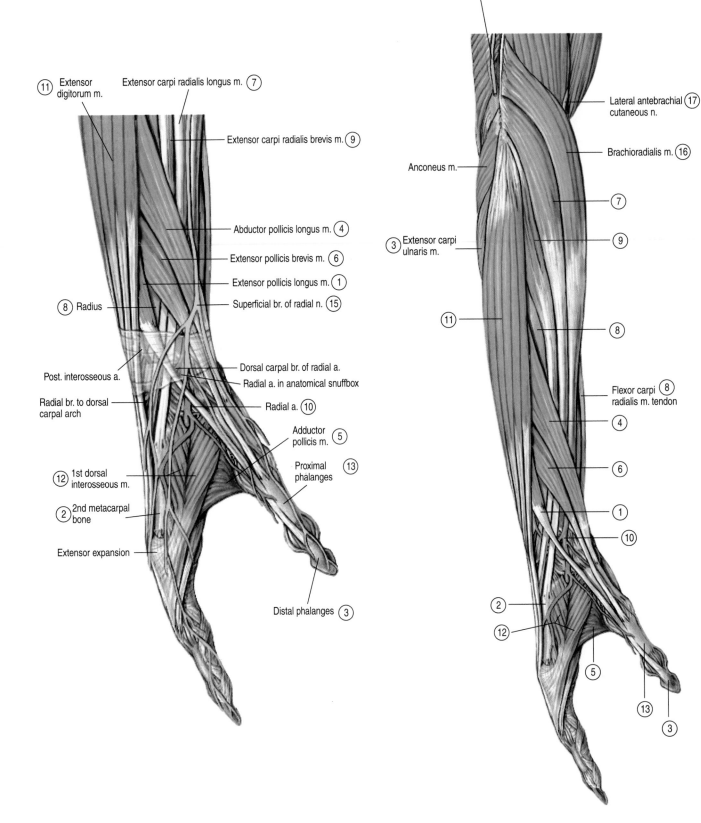

(18) Post. antebrachial cutaneous n.

(11) Extensor digitorum m.

Extensor carpi radialis longus m. (7)

Extensor carpi radialis brevis m. (9)

Abductor pollicis longus m. (4)

Extensor pollicis brevis m. (6)

Extensor pollicis longus m. (1)

(8) Radius

Superficial br. of radial n. (15)

Post. interosseous a.

Dorsal carpal br. of radial a.

Radial a. in anatomical snuffbox

Radial br. to dorsal carpal arch

Radial a. (10)

Adductor pollicis m. (5)

(12) 1st dorsal interosseous m.

Proximal phalanges (13)

(2) 2nd metacarpal bone

Extensor expansion

Distal phalanges (3)

Lateral antebrachial (17) cutaneous n.

Brachioradialis m. (16)

Anconeus m.

(7)

(3) Extensor carpi ulnaris m.

(9)

(11)

(8)

Flexor carpi (8) radialis m. tendon

(4)

(6)

(1)

(10)

(2)

(12)

(5)

(13)

(3)

LATERAL VIEWS

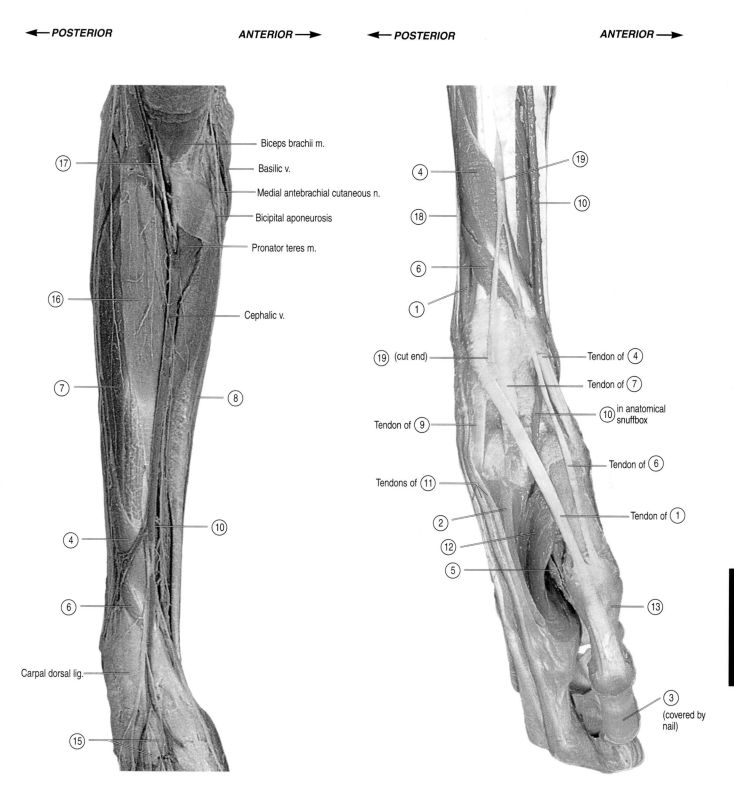

← POSTERIOR   ANTERIOR →   ← POSTERIOR   ANTERIOR →

17

16

7

4

6

Carpal dorsal lig.

15

Biceps brachii m.

Basilic v.

Medial antebrachial cutaneous n.

Bicipital aponeurosis

Pronator teres m.

Cephalic v.

8

10

4

18

6

1

19 (cut end)

Tendon of 9

Tendons of 11

2

12

5

19

10

Tendon of 4

Tendon of 7

10 in anatomical snuffbox

Tendon of 6

Tendon of 1

13

3 (covered by nail)

LATERAL VIEWS

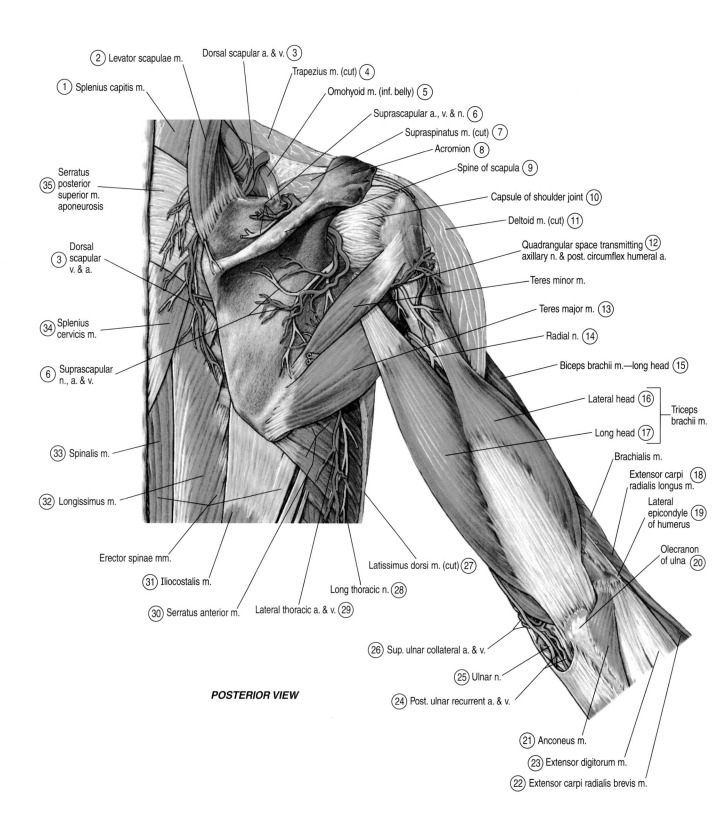

② Levator scapulae m.

① Splenius capitis m.

Dorsal scapular a. & v. ③

Trapezius m. (cut) ④

Omohyoid m. (inf. belly) ⑤

Suprascapular a., v. & n. ⑥

Supraspinatus m. (cut) ⑦

Acromion ⑧

Spine of scapula ⑨

Capsule of shoulder joint ⑩

Deltoid m. (cut) ⑪

Quadrangular space transmitting ⑫ axillary n. & post. circumflex humeral a.

Teres minor m.

Teres major m. ⑬

Radial n. ⑭

Biceps brachii m.—long head ⑮

Lateral head ⑯ ⎱ Triceps
Long head ⑰ ⎰ brachii m.

Brachialis m.

Extensor carpi ⑱ radialis longus m.

Lateral epicondyle ⑲ of humerus

Olecranon of ulna ⑳

㉟ Serratus posterior superior m. aponeurosis

③ Dorsal scapular v. & a.

㉞ Splenius cervicis m.

⑥ Suprascapular n., a. & v.

㉝ Spinalis m.

㉜ Longissimus m.

Erector spinae mm.

㉛ Iliocostalis m.

㉚ Serratus anterior m.

Lateral thoracic a. & v. ㉙

Latissimus dorsi m. (cut) ㉗

Long thoracic n. ㉘

POSTERIOR VIEW

㉖ Sup. ulnar collateral a. & v.

㉕ Ulnar n.

㉔ Post. ulnar recurrent a. & v.

㉑ Anconeus m.

㉓ Extensor digitorum m.

㉒ Extensor carpi radialis brevis m.

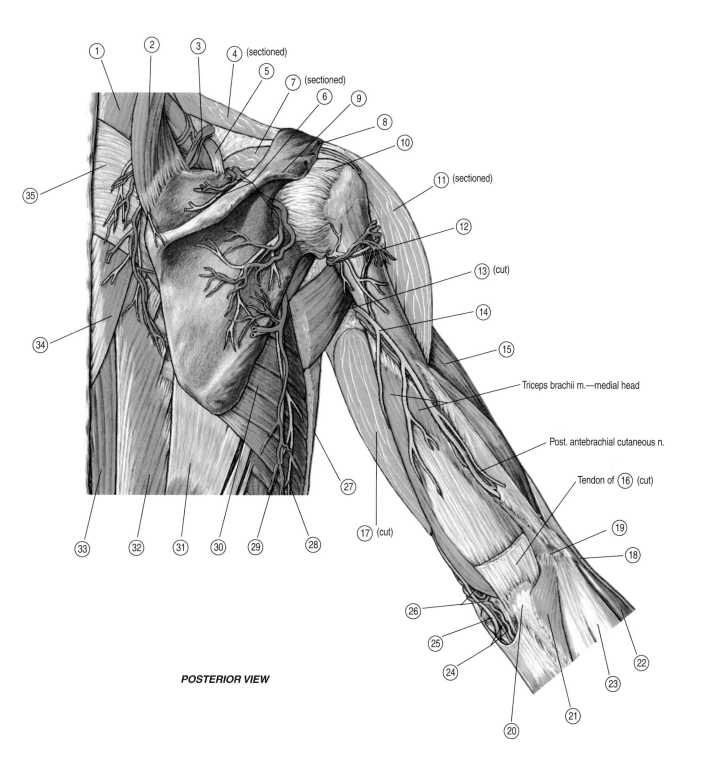

① ② ③ ④ (sectioned)
⑤
⑦ (sectioned)
⑥
⑨
⑧
⑩
⑪ (sectioned)
⑫
⑬ (cut)
⑭
⑮

Triceps brachii m.—medial head

Post. antebrachial cutaneous n.

Tendon of ⑯ (cut)
⑲
⑱

㉟
㉞
㉗
㉖
㉕
㉔
⑰ (cut)
㉓
㉒
⑳
㉑

㉝ ㉜ ㉛ ㉚ ㉙ ㉘

POSTERIOR VIEW

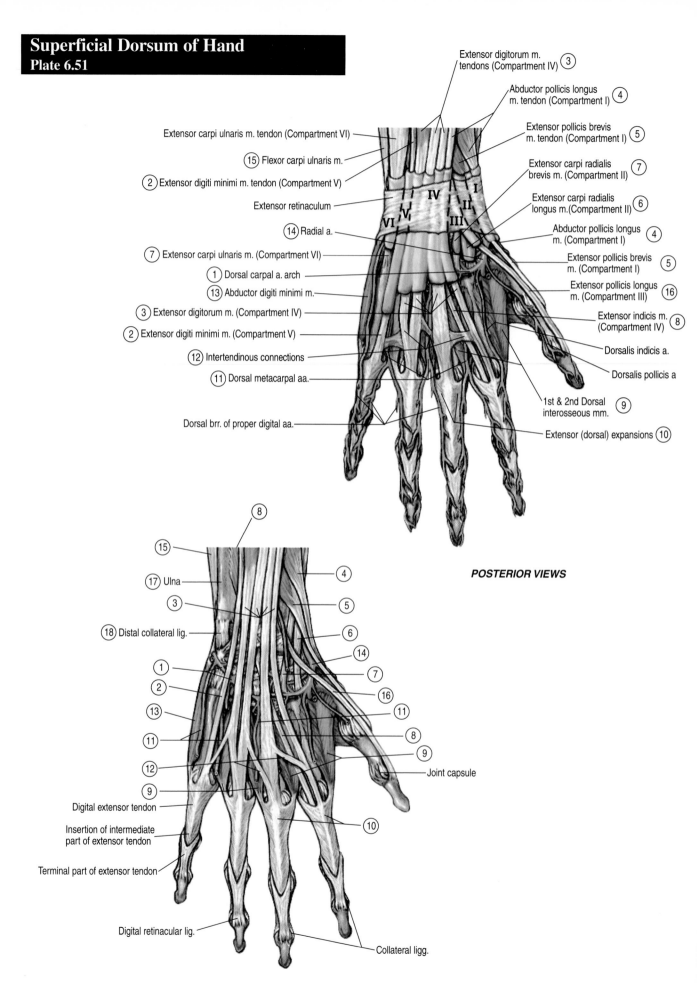

Extensor digitorum m. tendons (Compartment IV) ③

Abductor pollicis longus m. tendon (Compartment I) ④

Extensor pollicis brevis m. tendon (Compartment I) ⑤

Extensor carpi radialis brevis m. (Compartment II) ⑦

Extensor carpi radialis longus m.(Compartment II) ⑥

Abductor pollicis longus m. (Compartment I) ④

Extensor pollicis brevis m. (Compartment I) ⑤

Extensor pollicis longus m. (Compartment III) ⑯

Extensor indicis m. (Compartment IV) ⑧

Dorsalis indicis a.

Dorsalis pollicis a

1st & 2nd Dorsal interosseous mm. ⑨

Extensor (dorsal) expansions ⑩

Extensor carpi ulnaris m. tendon (Compartment VI)

⑮ Flexor carpi ulnaris m.

② Extensor digiti minimi m. tendon (Compartment V)

Extensor retinaculum

⑭ Radial a.

⑦ Extensor carpi ulnaris m. (Compartment VI)

① Dorsal carpal a. arch

⑬ Abductor digiti minimi m.

③ Extensor digitorum m. (Compartment IV)

② Extensor digiti minimi m. (Compartment V)

⑫ Intertendinous connections

⑪ Dorsal metacarpal aa.

Dorsal brr. of proper digital aa.

POSTERIOR VIEWS

⑧

⑮

⑰ Ulna

③

⑱ Distal collateral lig.

①

②

⑬

⑪

⑫

⑨

Digital extensor tendon

Insertion of intermediate part of extensor tendon

Terminal part of extensor tendon

Digital retinacular lig.

④

⑤

⑥

⑭

⑦

⑯

⑪

⑧

⑨

Joint capsule

⑩

Collateral ligg.

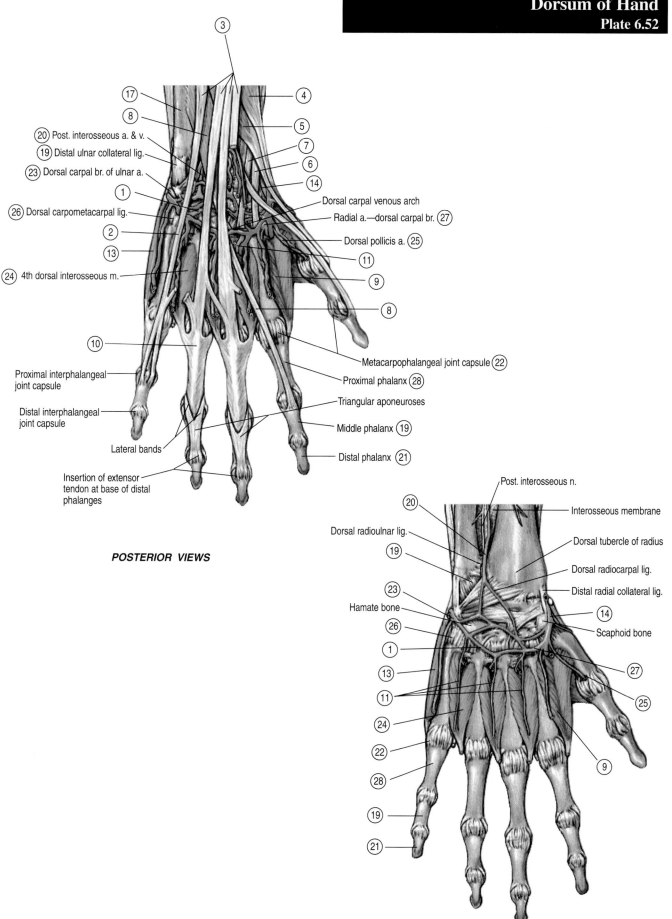

20 Post. interosseous a. & v.

19 Distal ulnar collateral lig.

23 Dorsal carpal br. of ulnar a.

1

26 Dorsal carpometacarpal lig.

2

13

24 4th dorsal interosseous m.

10

Proximal interphalangeal joint capsule

Distal interphalangeal joint capsule

Lateral bands

Insertion of extensor tendon at base of distal phalanges

Dorsal carpal venous arch

Radial a.—dorsal carpal br. 27

Dorsal pollicis a. 25

11

9

8

Metacarpophalangeal joint capsule 22

Proximal phalanx 28

Triangular aponeuroses

Middle phalanx 19

Distal phalanx 21

POSTERIOR VIEWS

Post. interosseous n.

20

Dorsal radioulnar lig.

19

23

Hamate bone

26

1

13

11

24

22

28

19

21

Interosseous membrane

Dorsal tubercle of radius

Dorsal radiocarpal lig.

Distal radial collateral lig.

14

Scaphoid bone

27

25

9

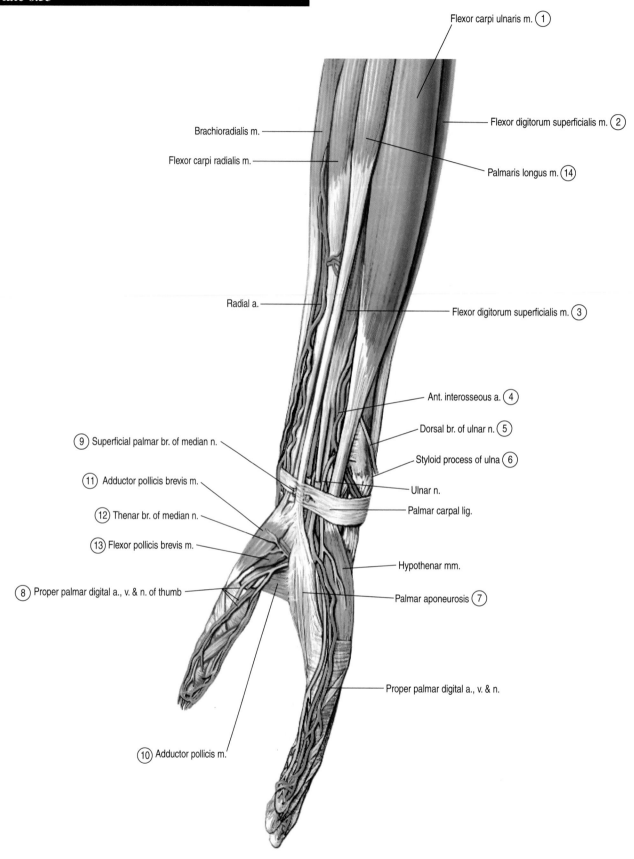

Flexor carpi ulnaris m. (1)

Flexor digitorum superficialis m. (2)

Brachioradialis m.

Flexor carpi radialis m.

Palmaris longus m. (14)

Radial a.

Flexor digitorum superficialis m. (3)

Ant. interosseous a. (4)

Dorsal br. of ulnar n. (5)

(9) Superficial palmar br. of median n.

Styloid process of ulna (6)

(11) Adductor pollicis brevis m.

Ulnar n.

Palmar carpal lig.

(12) Thenar br. of median n.

(13) Flexor pollicis brevis m.

Hypothenar mm.

(8) Proper palmar digital a., v. & n. of thumb

Palmar aponeurosis (7)

Proper palmar digital a., v. & n.

(10) Adductor pollicis m.

MEDIAL VIEW

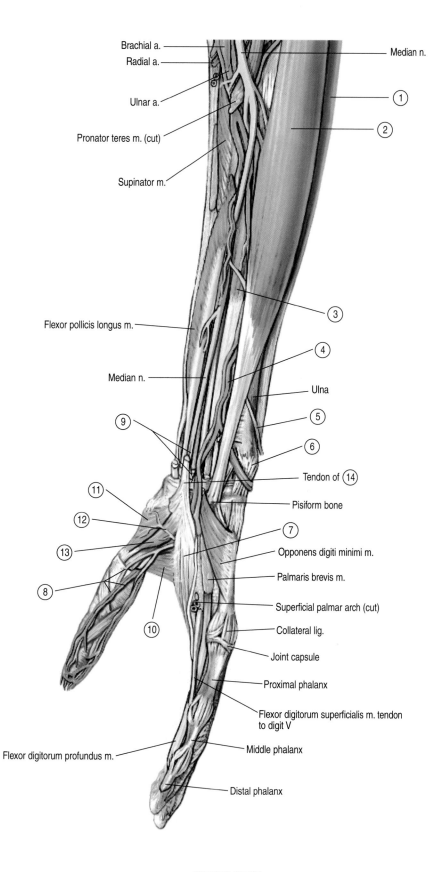

Brachial a.

Radial a.

Ulnar a.

Pronator teres m. (cut)

Supinator m.

Median n.

①

②

③

Flexor pollicis longus m.

④

Median n.

Ulna

⑤

⑨

⑥

Tendon of ⑭

Pisiform bone

⑪

⑫

⑬

⑦

Opponens digiti minimi m.

Palmaris brevis m.

⑧

Superficial palmar arch (cut)

⑩

Collateral lig.

Joint capsule

Proximal phalanx

Flexor digitorum superficialis m. tendon
to digit V

Flexor digitorum profundus m.

Middle phalanx

Distal phalanx

MEDIAL VIEW

Superficial Palm of Hand
Plate 6.55

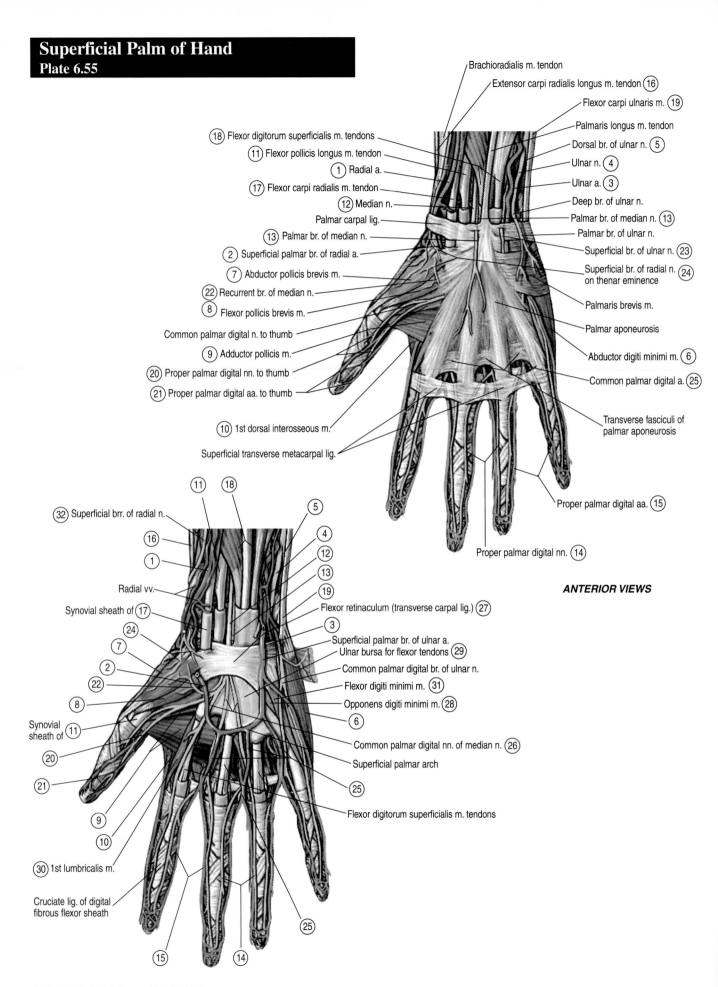

Brachioradialis m. tendon

Extensor carpi radialis longus m. tendon (16)

Flexor carpi ulnaris m. (19)

(18) Flexor digitorum superficialis m. tendons

(11) Flexor pollicis longus m. tendon

Palmaris longus m. tendon

(1) Radial a.

Dorsal br. of ulnar n. (5)

(17) Flexor carpi radialis m. tendon

Ulnar n. (4)

(12) Median n.

Ulnar a. (3)

Palmar carpal lig.

Deep br. of ulnar n.

(13) Palmar br. of median n.

Palmar br. of median n. (13)

(2) Superficial palmar br. of radial a.

Palmar br. of ulnar n.

(7) Abductor pollicis brevis m.

Superficial br. of ulnar n. (23)

(22) Recurrent br. of median n.

Superficial br. of radial n. (24) on thenar eminence

(8) Flexor pollicis brevis m.

Palmaris brevis m.

Common palmar digital n. to thumb

Palmar aponeurosis

(9) Adductor pollicis m.

Abductor digiti minimi m. (6)

(20) Proper palmar digital nn. to thumb

Common palmar digital a. (25)

(21) Proper palmar digital aa. to thumb

Transverse fasciculi of palmar aponeurosis

(10) 1st dorsal interosseous m.

Superficial transverse metacarpal lig.

Proper palmar digital aa. (15)

Proper palmar digital nn. (14)

ANTERIOR VIEWS

(11) (18)

(32) Superficial brr. of radial n.

(5)

(16)

(4)

(1)

(12)

Radial vv.

(13)

Synovial sheath of (17)

(19)

(24)

Flexor retinaculum (transverse carpal lig.) (27)

(7)

(3)

(2)

Superficial palmar br. of ulnar a.

Ulnar bursa for flexor tendons (29)

(22)

Common palmar digital br. of ulnar n.

(8)

Flexor digiti minimi m. (31)

Synovial sheath of (11)

Opponens digiti minimi m. (28)

(20)

(6)

(21)

Common palmar digital nn. of median n. (26)

(9)

Superficial palmar arch

(10)

(25)

(30) 1st lumbricalis m.

Flexor digitorum superficialis m. tendons

Cruciate lig. of digital fibrous flexor sheath

(15) (14)

(25)

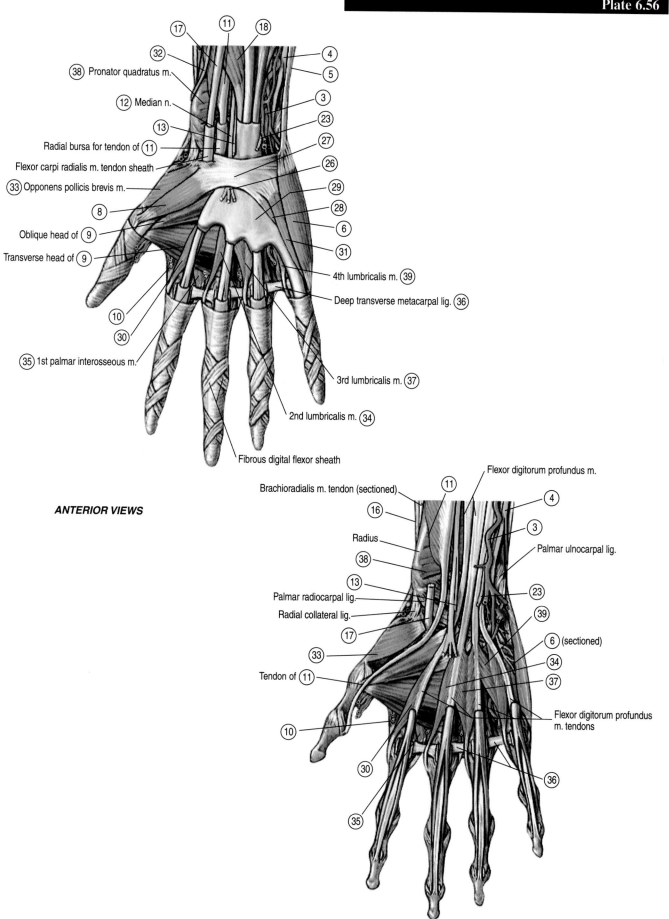

(17) (11) (18)

(32)

(38) Pronator quadratus m.

(4)
(5)

(12) Median n.

(3)

(13)

(23)

(27)

Radial bursa for tendon of (11)

Flexor carpi radialis m. tendon sheath

(26)

(33) Opponens pollicis brevis m.

(29)

(8)

(28)

Oblique head of (9)

(6)

Transverse head of (9)

(31)

4th lumbricalis m. (39)

Deep transverse metacarpal lig. (36)

(10)

(30)

(35) 1st palmar interosseous m.

3rd lumbricalis m. (37)

2nd lumbricalis m. (34)

Fibrous digital flexor sheath

ANTERIOR VIEWS

Brachioradialis m. tendon (sectioned)

Flexor digitorum profundus m.

(11)

(16)

(4)

Radius

(3)

(38)

Palmar ulnocarpal lig.

(13)

Palmar radiocarpal lig.

(23)

Radial collateral lig.

(39)

(17)

(6) (sectioned)

(33)

(34)

Tendon of (11)

(37)

Flexor digitorum profundus m. tendons

(10)

(30)

(36)

(35)

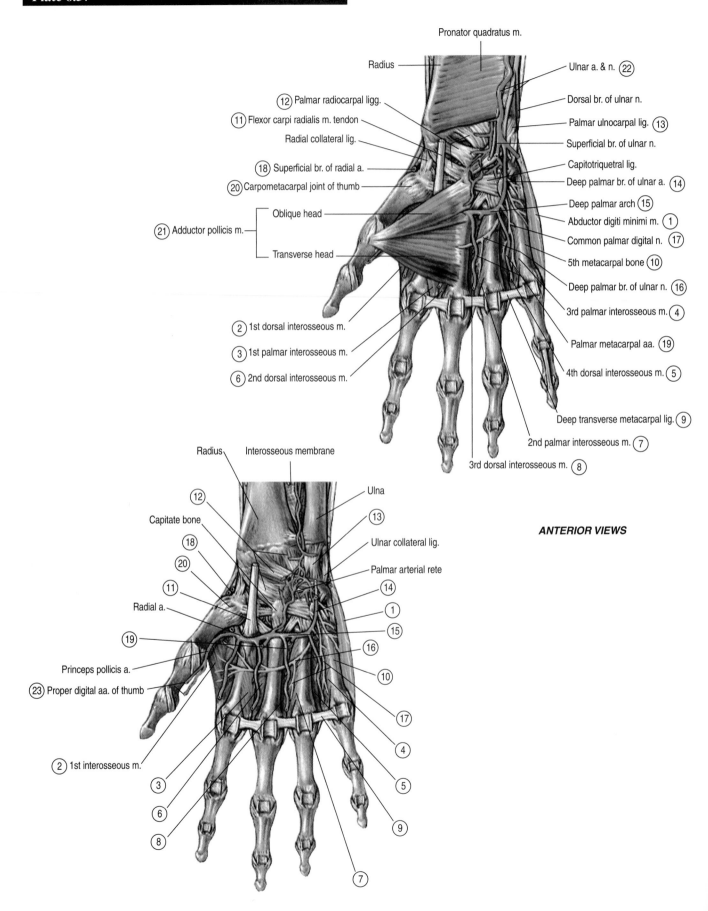

Pronator quadratus m.

Radius

Ulnar a. & n. (22)

Dorsal br. of ulnar n.

(12) Palmar radiocarpal ligg.

(11) Flexor carpi radialis m. tendon

Palmar ulnocarpal lig. (13)

Radial collateral lig.

Superficial br. of ulnar n.

(18) Superficial br. of radial a.

Capitotriquetral lig.

(20) Carpometacarpal joint of thumb

Deep palmar br. of ulnar a. (14)

Deep palmar arch (15)

Oblique head

Abductor digiti minimi m. (1)

(21) Adductor pollicis m.

Common palmar digital n. (17)

Transverse head

5th metacarpal bone (10)

Deep palmar br. of ulnar n. (16)

3rd palmar interosseous m. (4)

(2) 1st dorsal interosseous m.

Palmar metacarpal aa. (19)

(3) 1st palmar interosseous m.

4th dorsal interosseous m. (5)

(6) 2nd dorsal interosseous m.

Deep transverse metacarpal lig. (9)

2nd palmar interosseous m. (7)

3rd dorsal interosseous m. (8)

Radius   Interosseous membrane

(12)

Ulna

Capitate bone

(13)

(18)

Ulnar collateral lig.

(20)

Palmar arterial rete

(11)

(14)

Radial a.

(1)

(19)

(15)

(16)

Princeps pollicis a.

(10)

(23) Proper digital aa. of thumb

(17)

(4)

(2) 1st interosseous m.

(5)

(3)

(6)

(9)

(8)

(7)

ANTERIOR VIEWS

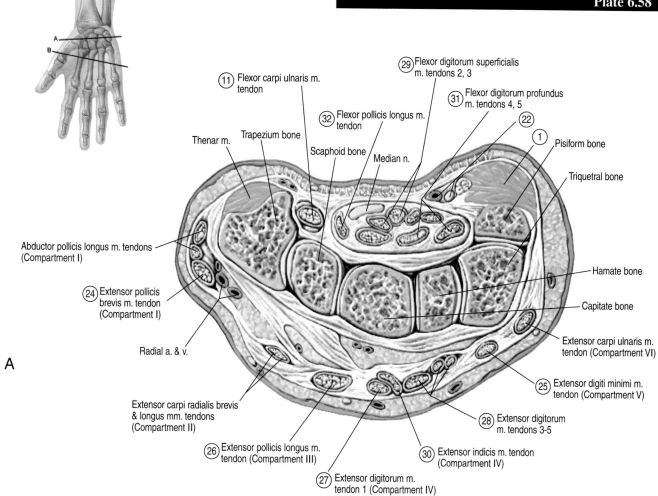

(11) Flexor carpi ulnaris m. tendon

(29) Flexor digitorum superficialis m. tendons 2, 3

(31) Flexor digitorum profundus m. tendons 4, 5

(32) Flexor pollicis longus m. tendon

(22)

(1)

Pisiform bone

Triquetral bone

Thenar m.

Trapezium bone

Scaphoid bone

Median n.

Abductor pollicis longus m. tendons (Compartment I)

Hamate bone

Capitate bone

(24) Extensor pollicis brevis m. tendon (Compartment I)

Extensor carpi ulnaris m. tendon (Compartment VI)

Radial a. & v.

(25) Extensor digiti minimi m. tendon (Compartment V)

Extensor carpi radialis brevis & longus mm. tendons (Compartment II)

(28) Extensor digitorum m. tendons 3-5

(26) Extensor pollicis longus m. tendon (Compartment III)

(30) Extensor indicis m. tendon (Compartment IV)

(27) Extensor digitorum m. tendon 1 (Compartment IV)

A

← RADIAL SIDE

DISTAL VIEWS OF SECTIONS THROUGH RIGHT WRIST (TOP) & HAND (BOTTOM)

ULNAR SIDE →

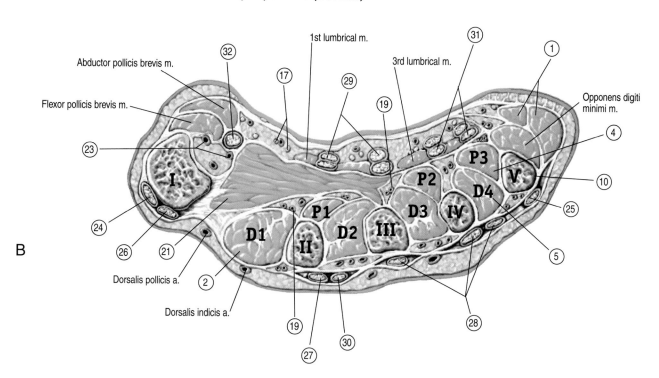

1st lumbrical m.

(31)

(1)

Abductor pollicis brevis m.

3rd lumbrical m.

(32)

(17)

(29)

(19)

Opponens digiti minimi m.

Flexor pollicis brevis m.

(23)

(4)

P3

P2

V

(10)

D4

(25)

I

D3

IV

(24)

P1

D2

III

(5)

(26)

(21)

D1

II

Dorsalis pollicis a.

(2)

Dorsalis indicis a.

(19)

(28)

(27)

(30)

B

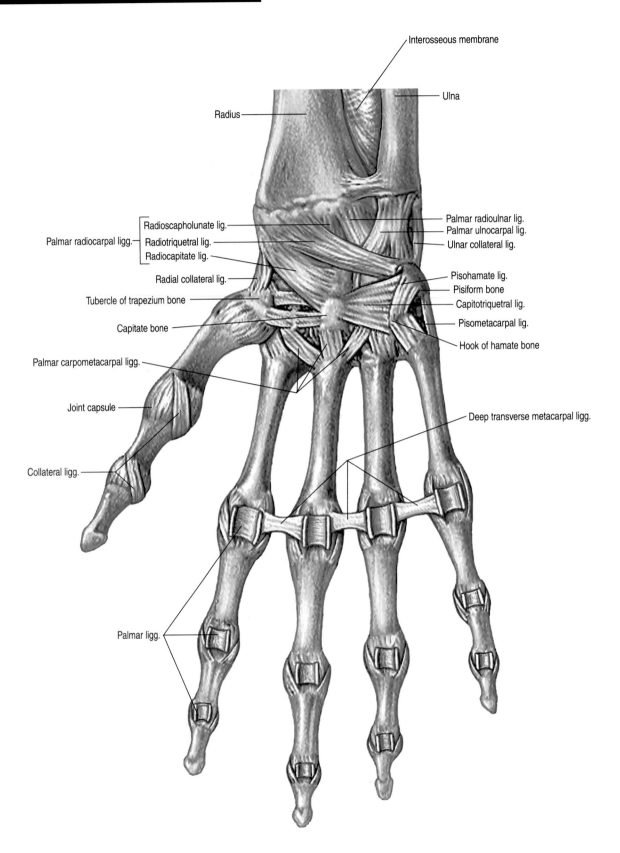

Interosseous membrane

Ulna

Radius

Palmar radiocarpal ligg. {
  Radioscapholunate lig.
  Radiotriquetral lig.
  Radiocapitate lig.

Radial collateral lig.

Tubercle of trapezium bone

Capitate bone

Palmar carpometacarpal ligg.

Joint capsule

Collateral ligg.

Palmar ligg.

Palmar radioulnar lig.
Palmar ulnocarpal lig.
Ulnar collateral lig.

Pisohamate lig.
Pisiform bone
Capitotriquetral lig.
Pisometacarpal lig.

Hook of hamate bone

Deep transverse metacarpal ligg.

ANTERIOR VIEW OF PALMAR SURFACE

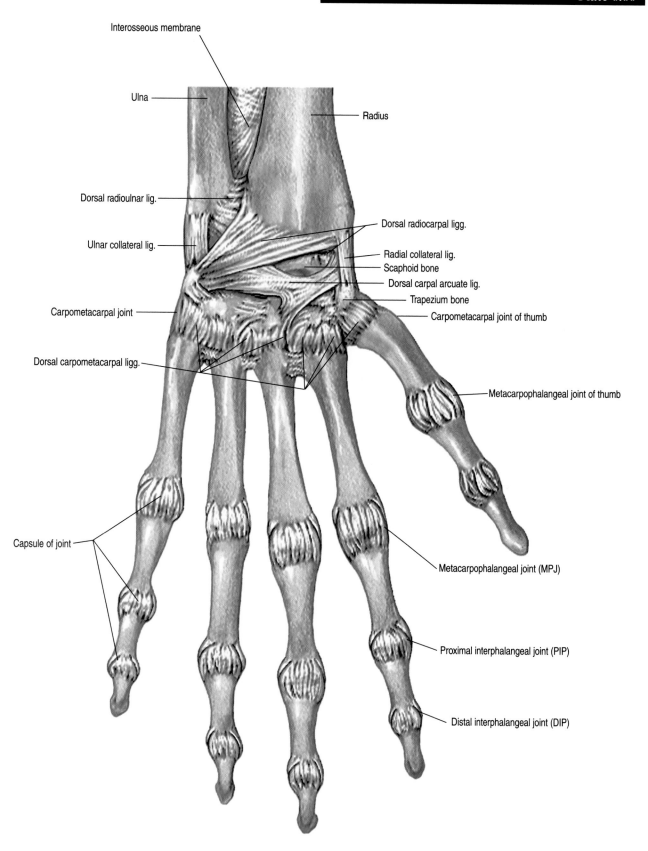

Interosseous membrane

Ulna

Radius

Dorsal radioulnar lig.

Dorsal radiocarpal ligg.

Ulnar collateral lig.

Radial collateral lig.

Scaphoid bone

Dorsal carpal arcuate lig.

Trapezium bone

Carpometacarpal joint

Carpometacarpal joint of thumb

Dorsal carpometacarpal ligg.

Metacarpophalangeal joint of thumb

Capsule of joint

Metacarpophalangeal joint (MPJ)

Proximal interphalangeal joint (PIP)

Distal interphalangeal joint (DIP)

POSTERIOR VIEW OF DORSAL SURFACE

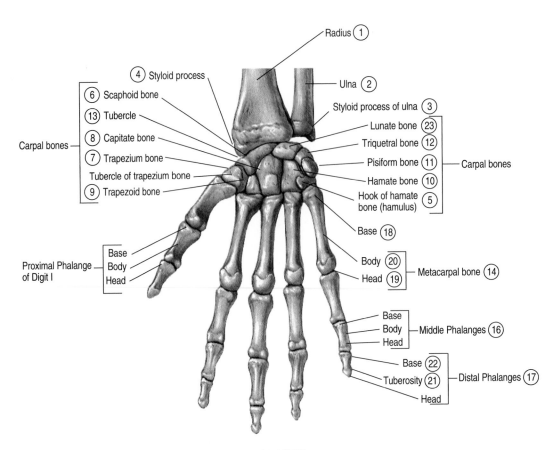

Radius ①
Styloid process ④
Scaphoid bone ⑥
Tubercle ⑬
Capitate bone ⑧
Carpal bones
Trapezium bone ⑦
Tubercle of trapezium bone
Trapezoid bone ⑨
Ulna ②
Styloid process of ulna ③
Lunate bone ㉓
Triquetral bone ⑫
Pisiform bone ⑪
Hamate bone ⑩
Hook of hamate bone (hamulus) ⑤
Carpal bones
Base ⑱
Body ⑳
Head ⑲
Metacarpal bone ⑭
Proximal Phalange of Digit I
Base
Body
Head
Base
Body
Head
Middle Phalanges ⑯
Base ㉒
Tuberosity ㉑
Head
Distal Phalanges ⑰

ANTERIOR VIEW

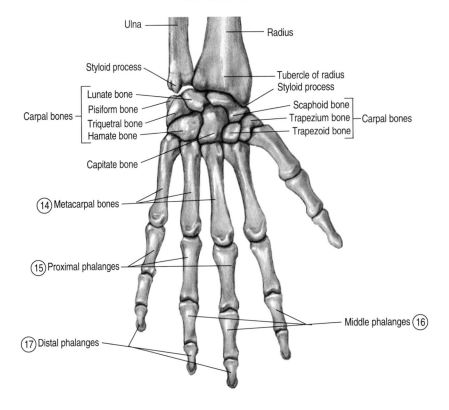

Ulna
Radius
Styloid process
Tubercle of radius
Styloid process
Lunate bone
Pisiform bone
Triquetral bone
Hamate bone
Carpal bones
Scaphoid bone
Trapezium bone
Trapezoid bone
Carpal bones
Capitate bone
⑭ Metacarpal bones
⑮ Proximal phalanges
Middle phalanges ⑯
⑰ Distal phalanges

POSTERIOR VIEW

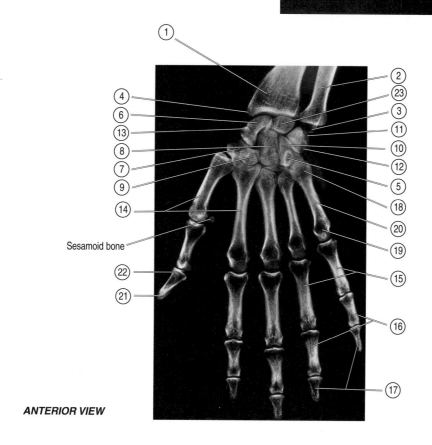

ANTERIOR VIEW

Sesamoid bone

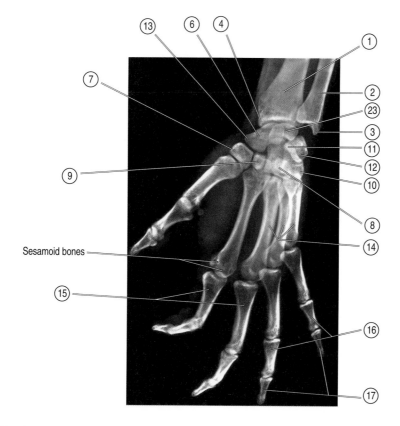

Sesamoid bones

OBLIQUE VIEW

Head and Neck

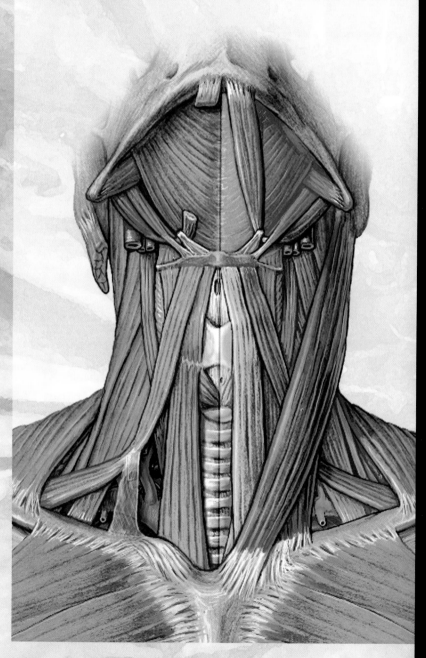

Chapter 7

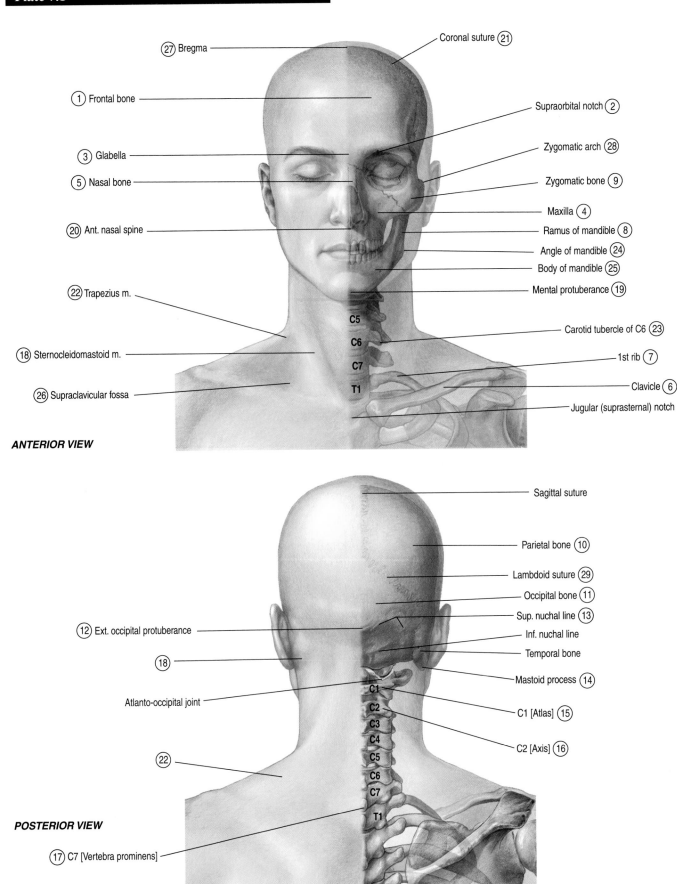

27 Bregma — Coronal suture 21

1 Frontal bone — Supraorbital notch 2

3 Glabella — Zygomatic arch 28

5 Nasal bone — Zygomatic bone 9

20 Ant. nasal spine — Maxilla 4

— Ramus of mandible 8

— Angle of mandible 24

— Body of mandible 25

22 Trapezius m. — Mental protuberance 19

C5 — Carotid tubercle of C6 23

C6

18 Sternocleidomastoid m. — C7 — 1st rib 7

T1 — Clavicle 6

26 Supraclavicular fossa — Jugular (suprasternal) notch

ANTERIOR VIEW

— Sagittal suture

— Parietal bone 10

— Lambdoid suture 29

— Occipital bone 11

— Sup. nuchal line 13

12 Ext. occipital protuberance — Inf. nuchal line

— Temporal bone

18 — Mastoid process 14

Atlanto-occipital joint — C1

C2 — C1 [Atlas] 15

C3

C4 — C2 [Axis] 16

22 — C5

C6

C7

T1

POSTERIOR VIEW

17 C7 [Vertebra prominens]

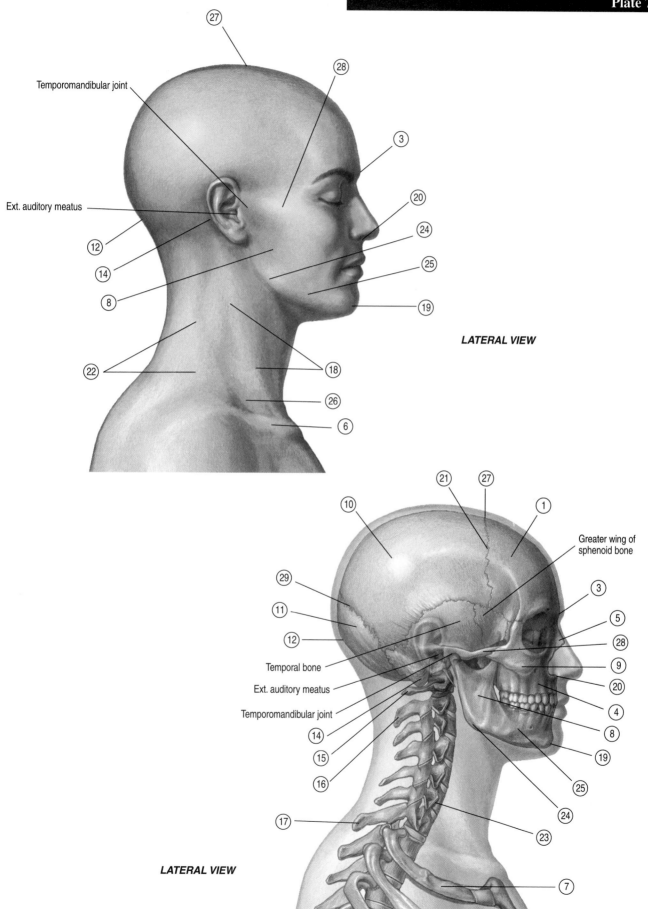

Temporomandibular joint

Ext. auditory meatus

㉗

㉘

③

⑫

⑭

⑧

㉒

⑳

㉔

㉕

⑲

LATERAL VIEW

⑱

㉖

⑥

㉑ ㉗ ①

⑩

Greater wing of
sphenoid bone

㉙

③

⑪

⑤

⑫

㉘

⑨

Temporal bone

⑳

Ext. auditory meatus

④

Temporomandibular joint

⑧

⑭

⑲

⑮

㉕

⑯

㉔

⑰

㉓

LATERAL VIEW

⑦

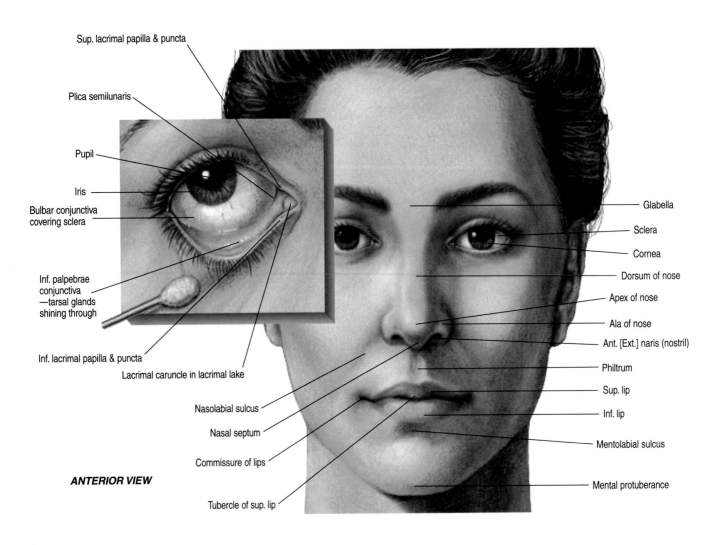

Sup. lacrimal papilla & puncta

Plica semilunaris

Pupil

Iris

Bulbar conjunctiva
covering sclera

Inf. palpebrae
conjunctiva
—tarsal glands
shining through

Inf. lacrimal papilla & puncta

Lacrimal caruncle in lacrimal lake

Nasolabial sulcus

Nasal septum

Commissure of lips

ANTERIOR VIEW

Tubercle of sup. lip

Glabella

Sclera

Cornea

Dorsum of nose

Apex of nose

Ala of nose

Ant. [Ext.] naris (nostril)

Philtrum

Sup. lip

Inf. lip

Mentolabial sulcus

Mental protuberance

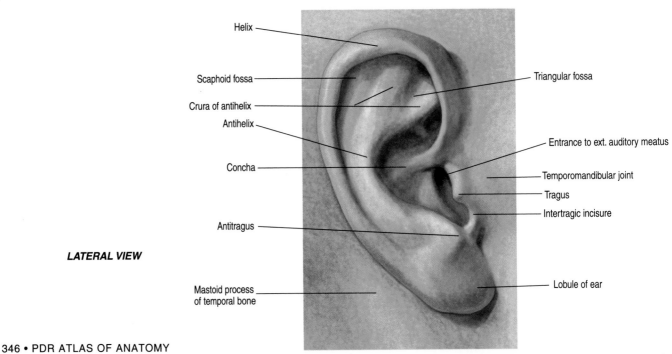

Helix

Scaphoid fossa

Crura of antihelix

Antihelix

Concha

Antitragus

LATERAL VIEW

Mastoid process
of temporal bone

Triangular fossa

Entrance to ext. auditory meatus

Temporomandibular joint

Tragus

Intertragic incisure

Lobule of ear

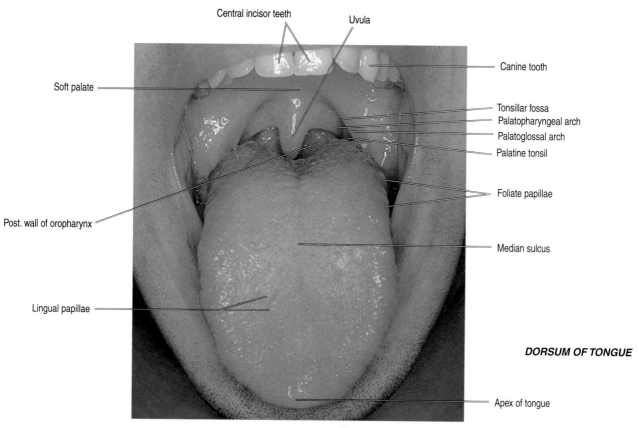

Central incisor teeth

Uvula

Canine tooth

Soft palate

Tonsillar fossa

Palatopharyngeal arch

Palatoglossal arch

Palatine tonsil

Foliate papillae

Post. wall of oropharynx

Median sulcus

Lingual papillae

DORSUM OF TONGUE

Apex of tongue

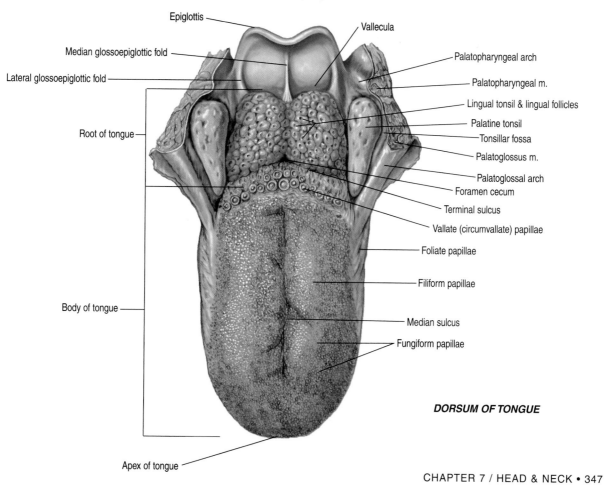

Epiglottis

Vallecula

Median glossoepiglottic fold

Palatopharyngeal arch

Lateral glossoepiglottic fold

Palatopharyngeal m.

Lingual tonsil & lingual follicles

Root of tongue

Palatine tonsil

Tonsillar fossa

Palatoglossus m.

Palatoglossal arch

Foramen cecum

Terminal sulcus

Vallate (circumvallate) papillae

Foliate papillae

Filiform papillae

Body of tongue

Median sulcus

Fungiform papillae

DORSUM OF TONGUE

Apex of tongue

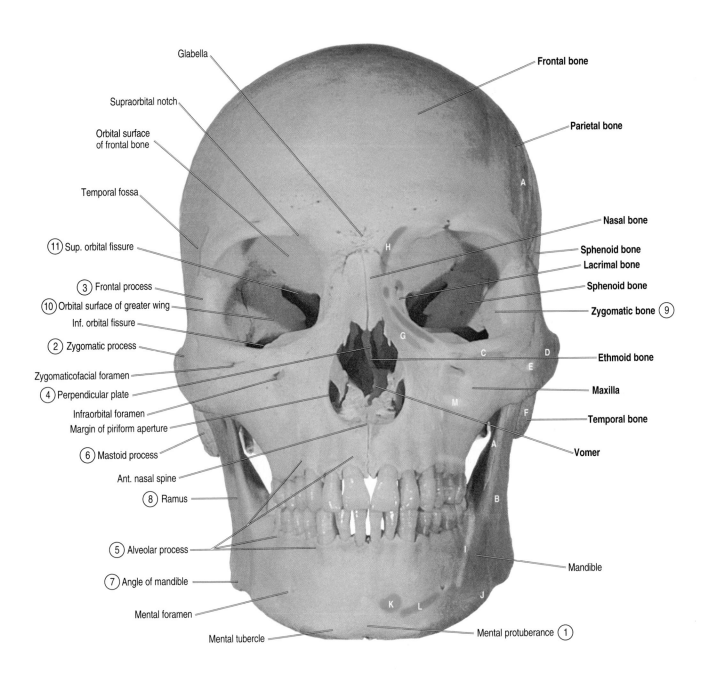

Glabella

Frontal bone

Supraorbital notch

Parietal bone

Orbital surface
of frontal bone

Temporal fossa

Nasal bone

(11) Sup. orbital fissure

Sphenoid bone

Lacrimal bone

(3) Frontal process

Sphenoid bone

(10) Orbital surface of greater wing

Zygomatic bone (9)

Inf. orbital fissure

(2) Zygomatic process

Zygomaticofacial foramen

Ethmoid bone

(4) Perpendicular plate

Maxilla

Infraorbital foramen

Temporal bone

Margin of piriform aperture

(6) Mastoid process

Vomer

Ant. nasal spine

(8) Ramus

(5) Alveolar process

Mandible

(7) Angle of mandible

Mental foramen

Mental tubercle

Mental protuberance (1)

ANTERIOR VIEW

- **(A) Temporalis**
- **(B) Masseter**
- **(C) Levator labii superioris**
- **(D) Zygomaticus major**
- **(E) Zygomaticus minor**
- **(F) Sternocleidomastoid**
- **(G) Levator labii superioris alaeque nasi**
- **(H) Orbicularis oculi**
- **(I) Buccinator**
- **(J) Platysma**
- **(K) Mentalis**
- **(L) Depressor labii inferioris & Depressor anguli oris**
- **(M) Levator anguli oris**

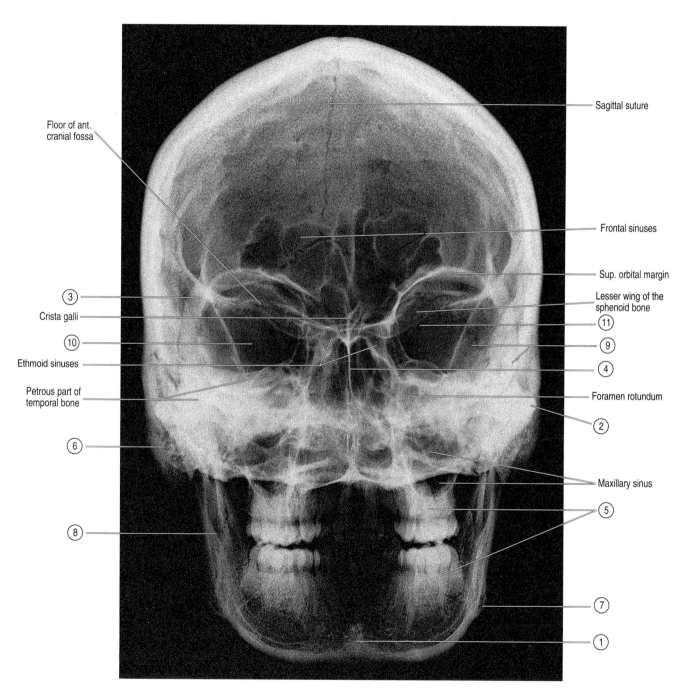

Sagittal suture

Floor of ant. cranial fossa

Frontal sinuses

Sup. orbital margin

③

Lesser wing of the sphenoid bone

Crista galli

⑪

⑩

⑨

Ethmoid sinuses

④

Foramen rotundum

Petrous part of temporal bone

②

⑥

Maxillary sinus

⑤

⑧

⑦

①

ANTEROPOSTERIOR VIEW OF SKULL

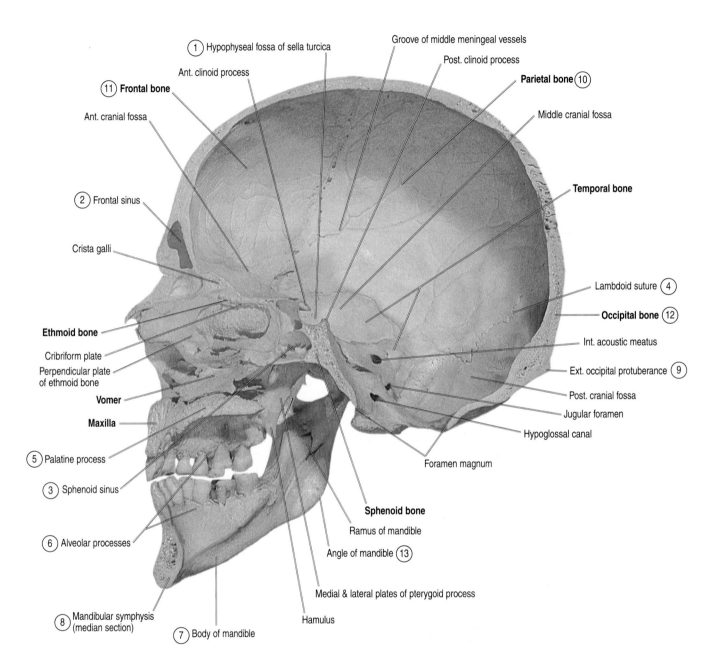

① Hypophyseal fossa of sella turcica

Groove of middle meningeal vessels

Ant. clinoid process

Post. clinoid process

⑪ **Frontal bone**

Parietal bone ⑩

Ant. cranial fossa

Middle cranial fossa

② Frontal sinus

Crista galli

Temporal bone

Lambdoid suture ④

Ethmoid bone

Occipital bone ⑫

Cribriform plate

Int. acoustic meatus

Perpendicular plate
of ethmoid bone

Ext. occipital protuberance ⑨

Vomer

Post. cranial fossa

Maxilla

Jugular foramen

⑤ Palatine process

Hypoglossal canal

③ Sphenoid sinus

Foramen magnum

⑥ Alveolar processes

Sphenoid bone

Ramus of mandible

Angle of mandible ⑬

⑧ Mandibular symphysis
(median section)

Medial & lateral plates of pterygoid process

Hamulus

⑦ Body of mandible

LEFT LATERAL VIEW OF SKULL SECTIONED IN MEDIAN PLANE

● **Mylohyoid**   ● **Lateral pterygoid**   ● **Genioglossus**

● **Superior pharyngeal constrictor**   ● **Medial pterygoid**   ● **Temporalis**

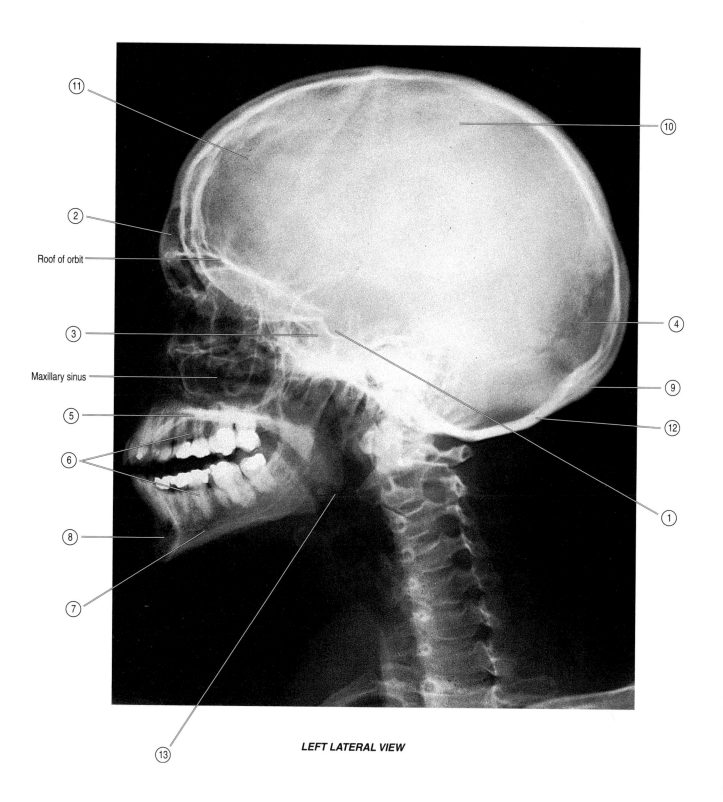

Roof of orbit

Maxillary sinus

LEFT LATERAL VIEW

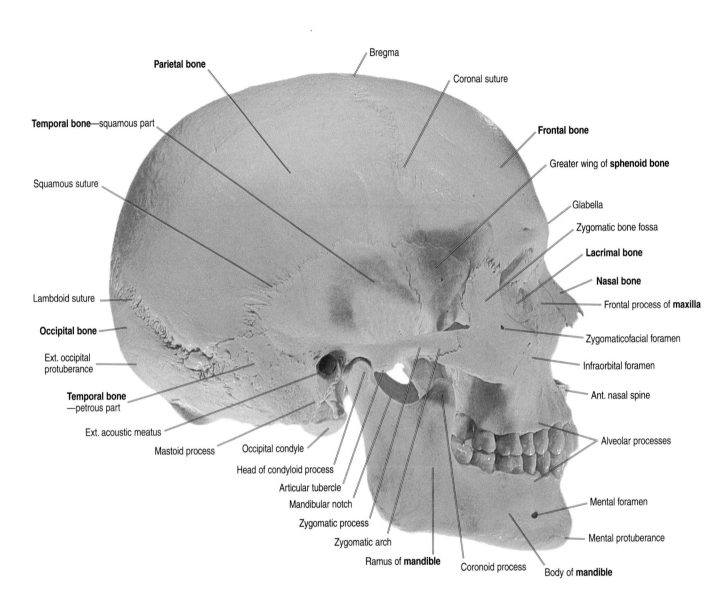

Bregma

Parietal bone

Coronal suture

Temporal bone—squamous part

Frontal bone

Greater wing of sphenoid bone

Squamous suture

Glabella

Zygomatic bone fossa

Lacrimal bone

Nasal bone

Frontal process of maxilla

Lambdoid suture

Zygomaticofacial foramen

Occipital bone

Infraorbital foramen

Ext. occipital protuberance

Ant. nasal spine

Temporal bone —petrous part

Ext. acoustic meatus

Alveolar processes

Mastoid process

Occipital condyle

Head of condyloid process

Articular tubercle

Mandibular notch

Mental foramen

Zygomatic process

Mental protuberance

Zygomatic arch

Ramus of mandible

Coronoid process

Body of mandible

LATERAL VIEW

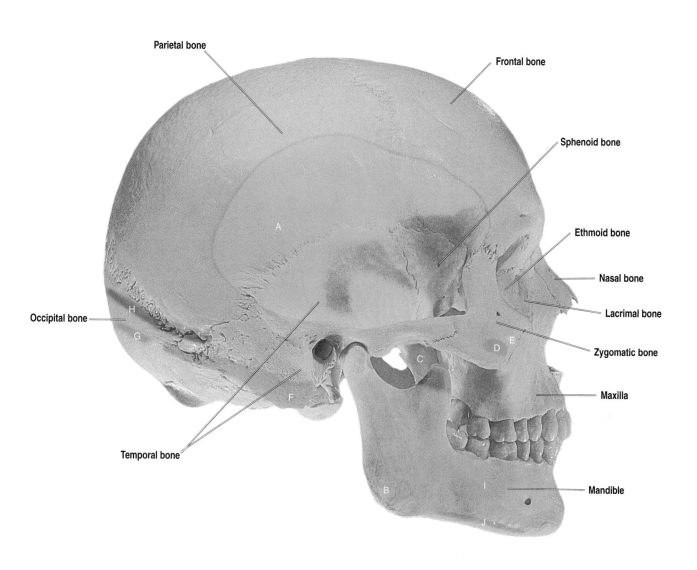

Parietal bone

Frontal bone

Sphenoid bone

Ethmoid bone

Nasal bone

Lacrimal bone

Zygomatic bone

Occipital bone

Maxilla

Temporal bone

Mandible

A Temporalis
B Masseter
C Lateral pterygoid
D Zygomaticus major
E Zygomaticus minor
F Sternocleidomastoid
G Trapezius
H Epicranius-occipital belly
I Buccinator
J Platysma

Cranial Foramina, Fissures & Canals
Table 7.1

Foramina/Openings	Contents
FACE	
Supraorbital notch/foramen	CN V^1 - supraorbital n. & vessels
Infraorbital notch/foramen	CN V^2 - infraorbital n. & vessels
Mental foramen	CN V^3 - mental n. & vessels
Zygomaticofacial foramen	CN V^2 - zygomaticofacial n. & vessels
ORBIT	
Superior orbital fissure	Passage between middle cranial fossa & orbit for CN III, V, VI, IV^1 — lacrimal n., IV^1 — frontal n., IV^1—nasociliary n., postganglionic sympathetic n. fibers, & ophthalmic v.
Optic canal	CN II, & ophthalmic a.
Inferior orbital fissure	Passage between pterygopalatine fossa & orbit for CN V^2 — infraorbital n. & vessels, & nerves from pterygopalatine ganglion
Anterior ethmoidal foramen	CN V^1— ant. ethmoidal br. of nasociliary n. & vessels
Posterior ethmoidal foramen	CN V^1— post. ethmoidal br. of nasociliary n. & vessels
Nasolacrimal canal	Nasolacrimal duct
NASAL CAVITY	
Piriform aperture (anterior nasal aperture)	Anterior opening into nasal cavity
Incisive canals	CN V^1— nasopalatine n. & greater palatine vessels
Foramina in cribriform plates	CN I — Sensory axons from olfactory epithelium that collectively constitute olfactory nn.
Sphenoethmoidal recess	Duct from sphenoid sinuses
Superior meatus	Duct from post. ethmoid sinuses
Middle meatus	Ducts from frontal sinus, ant. & middle ethmoidl sinuses, & duct from maxillary sinus through semilunar hiatus
Anterior meatus	Nasolacrimal duct
Sphenopalatine foramen	CN V^2 — nasopalatine n. & sphenopalatine vessels
Choana (posterior nasal aperture)	Opening between nasal cavity & nasopharynx
LATERAL CRANIAL SURFACE	
Zygomaticofacial foramen	CN V^2 — zygomaticofacial n. & vessels
Pterygomaxillary fissure	Passage between infratemporal & pterygopalatine fossae for CN V^2 — post. sup. alveolar nn. & vessels, & 3rd part of maxillary a.
External acoustic meatus—bony part	Opening in temporal bone leading to tympanic membrane
Mastoid foramen	Mastoid br. of occipital a. & mastoid emissary v. to sigmoid sinus & diploic vv.
CRANIAL BASE	
Incisive fossa & canals	CN V^2 — nasopalatine n., & greater palatine vessels
Greater palatine foramen/canal	Passage between oral cavity & pterygopalatine fossa for CN V^2 — greater palatine n. & vessels
Lesser palatine foramina	Passages between greater palatine canal & oral cavity for CN V^2 — lesser palatine n. & vessels
Mandibular canal	CN V^3 — inf. alveolar n. & vessels
Foramen lacerum	Closed inferoexternally by fibrocartilage plug
Auditory tube - bony portion	Passage between nasopharynx & middle ear, tensor tympani m., & sup. tympanic a.
Pterygoid (vidian) canal	Passage through base of median pterygoid process between foramen lacerum & pterygopalatine fossa for CN VII — n. & vessels of pterygoid (vidian) canal
Foramen ovale	CN V^3 — mandibular n., CH IX — lesser petrosal n. & accessory meningeal a.
Foramen spinosum	CN V^3 — meningeal br. & middle meningeal vessels
Carotid canal	Internal carotid a. & sympathetic n. plexus
Stylomastoid foramen	CN VII — facial n., & stylomastoid vessels
Petrotympanic fissure	CN VII — chorda tympani n., & ant. tympanic a.
Mastoid canaliculus	CN IX — auricular br.
Tympanic canaliculus	CN IX — tympanic br., & inf. tympanic a.
Jugular fossa & foramen	CN IX, X & XI, sup. bulb of internal jugular v., inferior petrosal & sigmoid sinuses, & meningeal brr. of ascending pharyngeal & occipital aa.
Condylar fossa & canal	*Inconsistent* passage for condylar emissary v. between sigmoid sinus & vertebral venous plexi
Hypoglossal canal	CN XII — hypoglossal n., meningeal br. of ascending pharyngeal a.
Foramen magnum	Medulla & meninges of spinal cord, CN XI — spinal roots, vertebral aa., ant. & post. spinal aa., & brr. ofinternal vertebral venous plexus

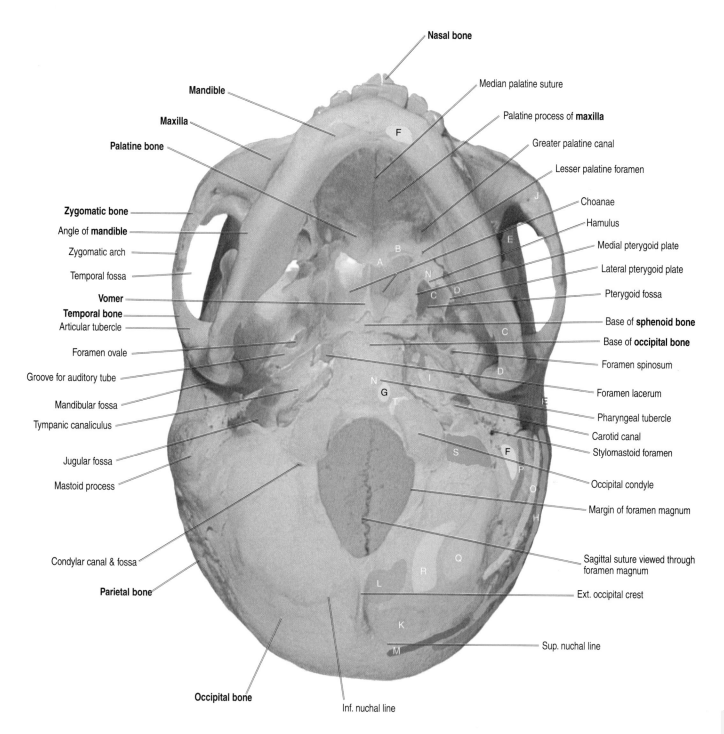

Nasal bone

Mandible

Maxilla

Palatine bone

Median palatine suture

Palatine process of **maxilla**

Greater palatine canal

Lesser palatine foramen

Choanae

Hamulus

Medial pterygoid plate

Lateral pterygoid plate

Pterygoid fossa

Base of **sphenoid bone**

Base of **occipital bone**

Foramen spinosum

Foramen lacerum

Pharyngeal tubercle

Carotid canal

Stylomastoid foramen

Occipital condyle

Margin of foramen magnum

Sagittal suture viewed through foramen magnum

Ext. occipital crest

Sup. nuchal line

Zygomatic bone

Angle of **mandible**

Zygomatic arch

Temporal fossa

Vomer

Temporal bone

Articular tubercle

Foramen ovale

Groove for auditory tube

Mandibular fossa

Tympanic canaliculus

Jugular fossa

Mastoid process

Condylar canal & fossa

Parietal bone

Occipital bone

Inf. nuchal line

INFERIOR VIEW OF CRANIAL BASE

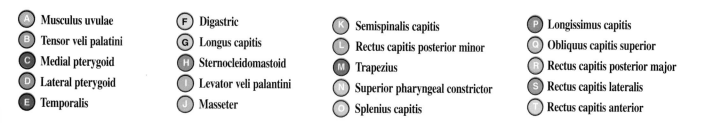

- (A) Musculus uvulae
- (B) Tensor veli palatini
- (C) Medial pterygoid
- (D) Lateral pterygoid
- (E) Temporalis
- (F) Digastric
- (G) Longus capitis
- (H) Sternocleidomastoid
- (I) Levator veli palantini
- (J) Masseter
- (K) Semispinalis capitis
- (L) Rectus capitis posterior minor
- (M) Trapezius
- (N) Superior pharyngeal constrictor
- (O) Splenius capitis
- (P) Longissimus capitis
- (Q) Obliquus capitis superior
- (R) Rectus capitis posterior major
- (S) Rectus capitis lateralis
- (T) Rectus capitis anterior

Foramina/Openings	Contents

ANTERIOR CRANIAL FOSSA

Foramen cecum	Inconsistent passage for nasal emissary vv. tributaries of superior sagittal sinus
Foramina in cribriform plates	CN I — Sensory axons from olfactory epithelium that collectively constitute the olfactory nn.
Anterior ethmoidal foramen	CN V^1 — anterior ethmoidal br. of nasociliary n. & vessels
Posterior ethmoidal foramen	CN V^1 — posterior ethmoidal br. of nasociliary n. & vessels

MIDDLE CRANIAL FOSSA

Optic canal	CN II, & ophthalmic a.
Superior orbital fissure	Passage between middle cranial fossa & orbit for CN III, IV, VI, V1 — lacrimal n., V1 — frontal n., V^1 — nasociliary n., postganglionic sympathetic n. fibers, & ophthalmic v.
Foramen rotundum	CN V^2 — maxillary n.
Foramen ovale	CN V^3 — mandibular n., CH IX - lesser petrosal n. & accessory meningeal a.
Foramen spinosum	CN V^3 — meningeal br. & middle meningeal vessels
Foramen lacerum	Internal carotid a., sympathetic nn. & venous plexi from carotid canal, & CN VII — greater petrosal n.. Closed inferoexternally by fibrocartilage plug
Hiatus for greater petrosal n. (Facial hiatus)	CN VII — greater petrosal n., & petrosal br. of middle meningeal a.
Hiatus for lesser petrosal n.	CN IX — lesser petrosal n.

POSTERIOR CRANIAL FOSSA

Internal acoustic meatus	CN VII & VIII, labyrinthine a.
Jugular fossa & foramen	CN IX, X & XI, superior bulb of internal jugular v., inferior petrosal & sigmoid sinuses, & meningeal brr. of ascendingpharyngeal & occipital aa.
Condylar fossa & canal	*Inconsistent* passage for condylar emissary v. between sigmoid sinus & vertebral venous plexi
Mastoid foramen	Mastoid br. of occipital a. & mastoid emissary v. to sigmoid sinus & diploic vv.
Hypoglossal canal	CN XII — hypoglossal n.
Foramen magnum	Medulla & meninges of spinal cord, CN XI— spinal roots, vertebral aa., ant. & post. spinal aa., & brr. of internal vertebral venous plexus

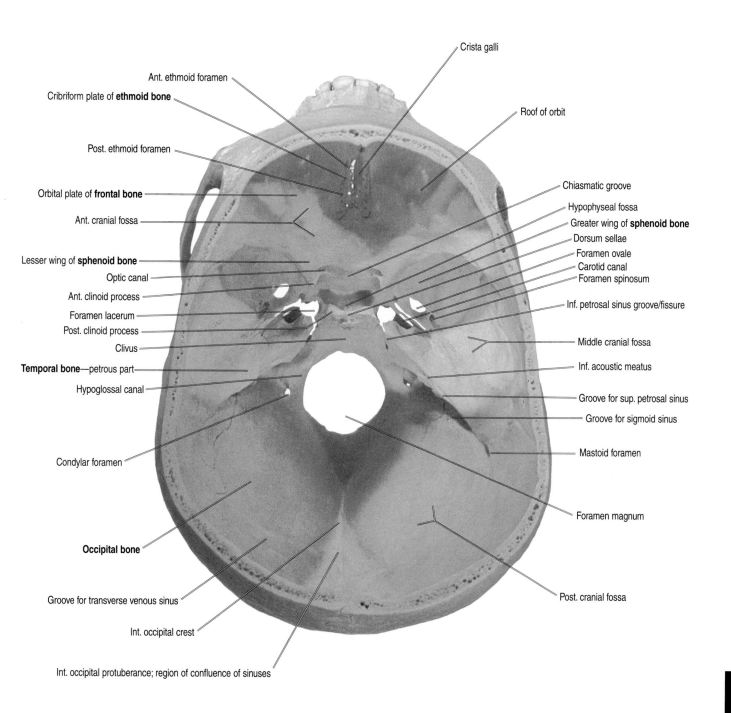

Crista galli

Ant. ethmoid foramen

Cribriform plate of **ethmoid bone**

Roof of orbit

Post. ethmoid foramen

Orbital plate of **frontal bone**

Chiasmatic groove

Ant. cranial fossa

Hypophyseal fossa

Greater wing of **sphenoid bone**

Dorsum sellae

Lesser wing of **sphenoid bone**

Foramen ovale

Optic canal

Carotid canal

Foramen spinosum

Ant. clinoid process

Foramen lacerum

Inf. petrosal sinus groove/fissure

Post. clinoid process

Clivus

Middle cranial fossa

Temporal bone—petrous part

Inf. acoustic meatus

Hypoglossal canal

Groove for sup. petrosal sinus

Groove for sigmoid sinus

Condylar foramen

Mastoid foramen

Foramen magnum

Occipital bone

Groove for transverse venous sinus

Int. occipital crest

Post. cranial fossa

Int. occipital protuberance; region of confluence of sinuses

SUPERIOR VIEW WITH CALVARIA REMOVED

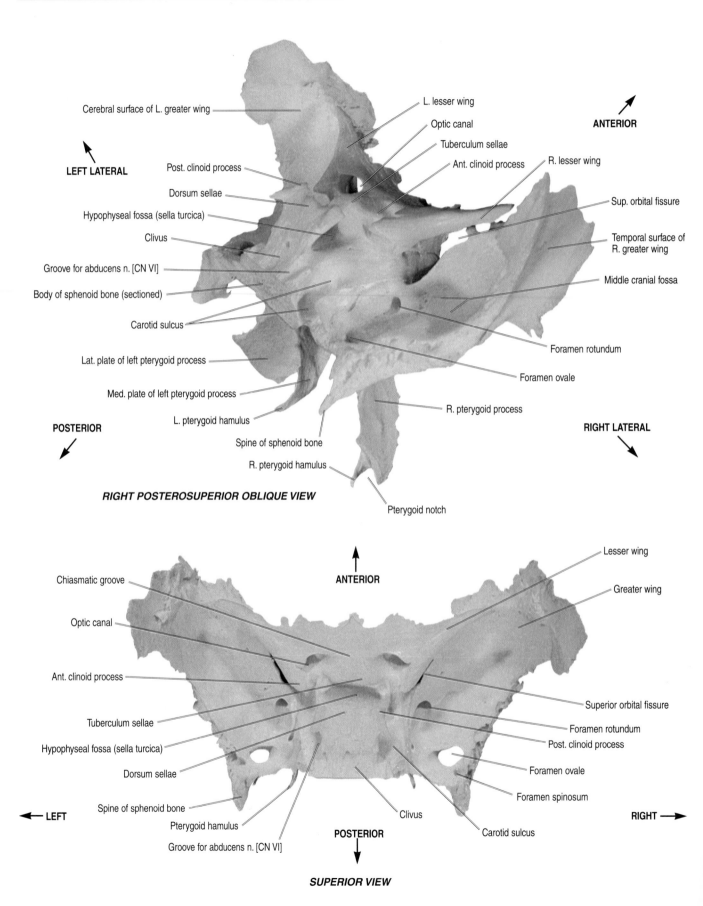

Cerebral surface of L. greater wing

L. lesser wing

Optic canal

Tuberculum sellae

Ant. clinoid process

R. lesser wing

ANTERIOR

LEFT LATERAL

Post. clinoid process

Dorsum sellae

Sup. orbital fissure

Hypophyseal fossa (sella turcica)

Temporal surface of R. greater wing

Clivus

Groove for abducens n. [CN VI]

Middle cranial fossa

Body of sphenoid bone (sectioned)

Carotid sulcus

Foramen rotundum

Lat. plate of left pterygoid process

Foramen ovale

Med. plate of left pterygoid process

R. pterygoid process

L. pterygoid hamulus

POSTERIOR

RIGHT LATERAL

Spine of sphenoid bone

R. pterygoid hamulus

RIGHT POSTEROSUPERIOR OBLIQUE VIEW

Pterygoid notch

Chiasmatic groove

Lesser wing

ANTERIOR

Greater wing

Optic canal

Ant. clinoid process

Tuberculum sellae

Superior orbital fissure

Hypophyseal fossa (sella turcica)

Foramen rotundum

Post. clinoid process

Dorsum sellae

Foramen ovale

Spine of sphenoid bone

Foramen spinosum

Pterygoid hamulus

LEFT

Clivus

Carotid sulcus

RIGHT

Groove for abducens n. [CN VI]

POSTERIOR

SUPERIOR VIEW

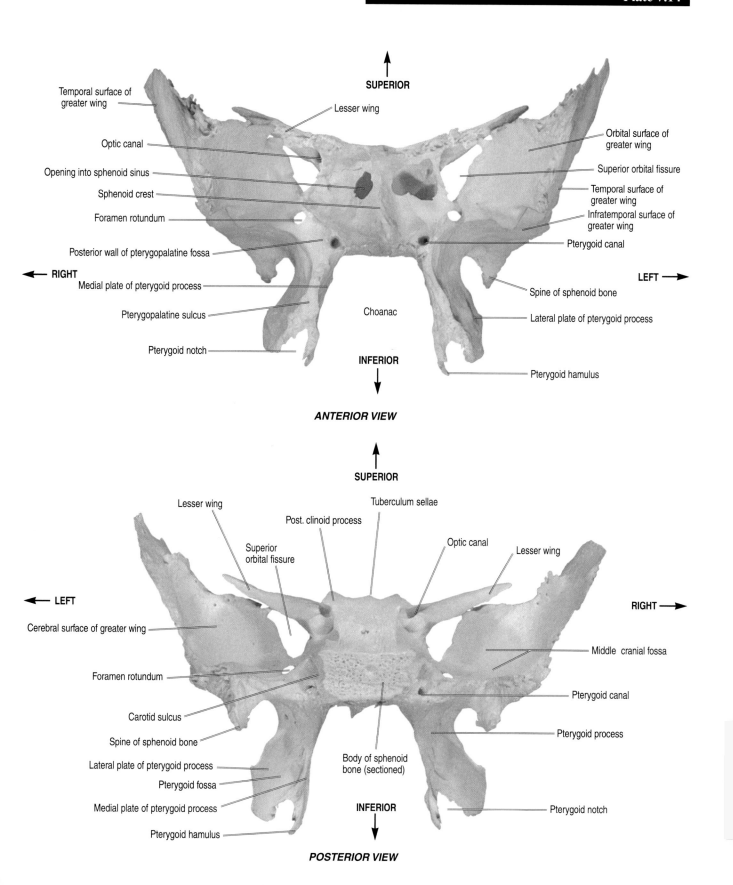

SUPERIOR

Temporal surface of greater wing

Lesser wing

Optic canal

Orbital surface of greater wing

Opening into sphenoid sinus

Superior orbital fissure

Sphenoid crest

Temporal surface of greater wing

Foramen rotundum

Infratemporal surface of greater wing

Posterior wall of pterygopalatine fossa

Pterygoid canal

RIGHT

LEFT

Medial plate of pterygoid process

Spine of sphenoid bone

Pterygopalatine sulcus

Choanac

Lateral plate of pterygoid process

Pterygoid notch

INFERIOR

Pterygoid hamulus

ANTERIOR VIEW

SUPERIOR

Lesser wing

Tuberculum sellae

Post. clinoid process

Optic canal

Superior orbital fissure

Lesser wing

LEFT

RIGHT

Cerebral surface of greater wing

Middle cranial fossa

Foramen rotundum

Carotid sulcus

Pterygoid canal

Spine of sphenoid bone

Pterygoid process

Lateral plate of pterygoid process

Pterygoid fossa

Body of sphenoid bone (sectioned)

Medial plate of pterygoid process

Pterygoid notch

Pterygoid hamulus

INFERIOR

POSTERIOR VIEW

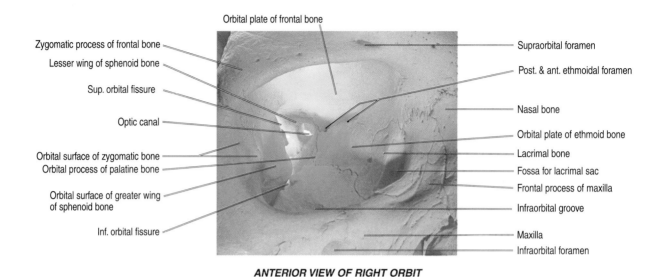

Orbital plate of frontal bone

Zygomatic process of frontal bone

Lesser wing of sphenoid bone

Sup. orbital fissure

Optic canal

Orbital surface of zygomatic bone

Orbital process of palatine bone

Orbital surface of greater wing of sphenoid bone

Inf. orbital fissure

Supraorbital foramen

Post. & ant. ethmoidal foramen

Nasal bone

Orbital plate of ethmoid bone

Lacrimal bone

Fossa for lacrimal sac

Frontal process of maxilla

Infraorbital groove

Maxilla

Infraorbital foramen

ANTERIOR VIEW OF RIGHT ORBIT

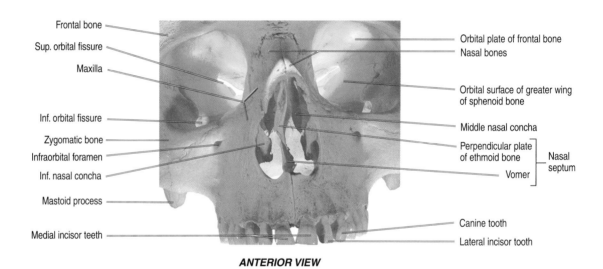

Frontal bone

Sup. orbital fissure

Maxilla

Inf. orbital fissure

Zygomatic bone

Infraorbital foramen

Inf. nasal concha

Mastoid process

Medial incisor teeth

Orbital plate of frontal bone

Nasal bones

Orbital surface of greater wing of sphenoid bone

Middle nasal concha

Perpendicular plate of ethmoid bone

Vomer

Nasal septum

Canine tooth

Lateral incisor tooth

ANTERIOR VIEW

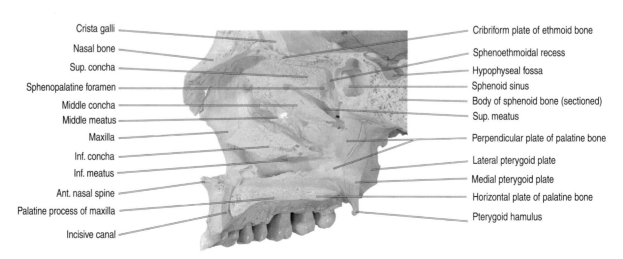

Crista galli

Nasal bone

Sup. concha

Sphenopalatine foramen

Middle concha

Middle meatus

Maxilla

Inf. concha

Inf. meatus

Ant. nasal spine

Palatine process of maxilla

Incisive canal

Cribriform plate of ethmoid bone

Sphenoethmoidal recess

Hypophyseal fossa

Sphenoid sinus

Body of sphenoid bone (sectioned)

Sup. meatus

Perpendicular plate of palatine bone

Lateral pterygoid plate

Medial pterygoid plate

Horizontal plate of palatine bone

Pterygoid hamulus

MEDIAL VIEW OF RIGHT NASAL CAVITY

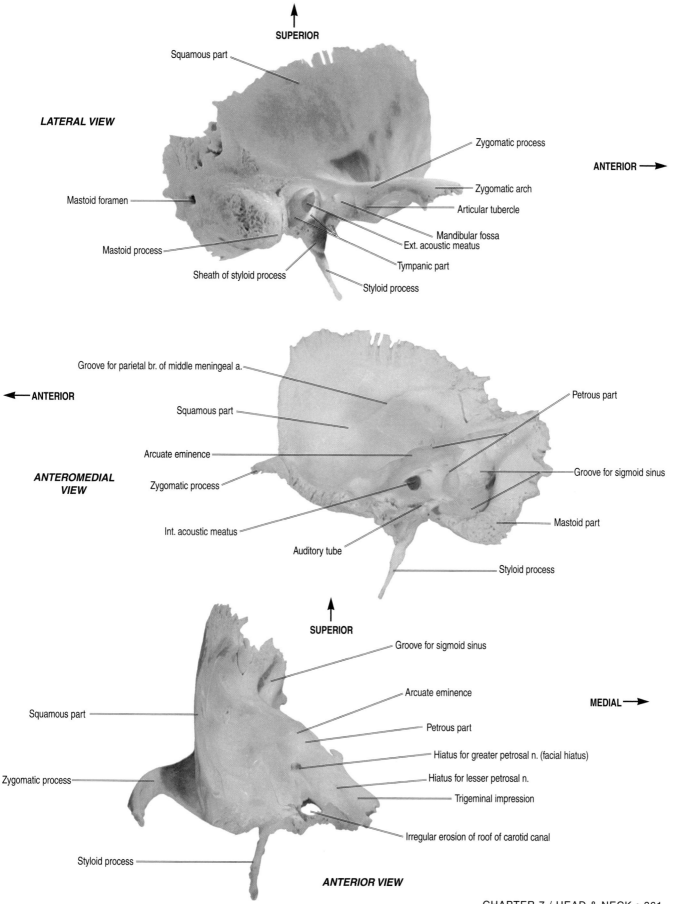

LATERAL VIEW

SUPERIOR

Squamous part

Zygomatic process

ANTERIOR →

Zygomatic arch

Mastoid foramen

Articular tubercle

Mandibular fossa

Ext. acoustic meatus

Mastoid process

Tympanic part

Sheath of styloid process

Styloid process

ANTEROMEDIAL VIEW

Groove for parietal br. of middle meningeal a.

← ANTERIOR

Petrous part

Squamous part

Arcuate eminence

Groove for sigmoid sinus

Zygomatic process

Int. acoustic meatus

Mastoid part

Auditory tube

Styloid process

SUPERIOR

Groove for sigmoid sinus

Arcuate eminence

MEDIAL →

Squamous part

Petrous part

Hiatus for greater petrosal n. (facial hiatus)

Zygomatic process

Hiatus for lesser petrosal n.

Trigeminal impression

Irregular erosion of roof of carotid canal

Styloid process

ANTERIOR VIEW

← RIGHT   ↑ ANTERIOR   LEFT →

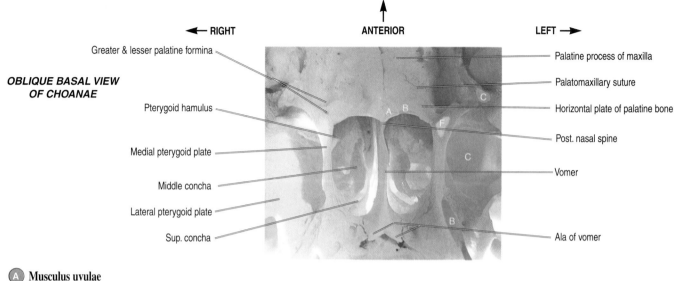

OBLIQUE BASAL VIEW OF CHOANAE

Greater & lesser palatine formina

Pterygoid hamulus

Medial pterygoid plate

Middle concha

Lateral pterygoid plate

Sup. concha

Palatine process of maxilla

Palatomaxillary suture

Horizontal plate of palatine bone

Post. nasal spine

Vomer

Ala of vomer

(A) **Musculus uvulae**

(B) **Tensor veli palatini**

(C) **Medial pterygoid**

(D) **Lateral pterygoid**

(E) **Temporalis**

(F) **Superior pharyngeal constrictor**

(G) **Tensor tympani**

(H) **Levator veli palatini**

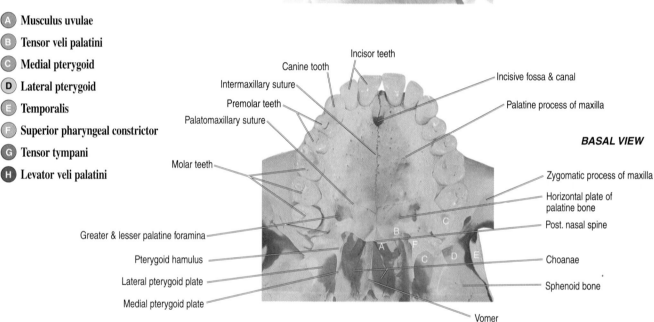

Incisor teeth

Canine tooth

Intermaxillary suture

Premolar teeth

Palatomaxillary suture

Molar teeth

Greater & lesser palatine foramina

Pterygoid hamulus

Lateral pterygoid plate

Medial pterygoid plate

Incisive fossa & canal

Palatine process of maxilla

BASAL VIEW

Zygomatic process of maxilla

Horizontal plate of palatine bone

Post. nasal spine

Choanae

Sphenoid bone

Vomer

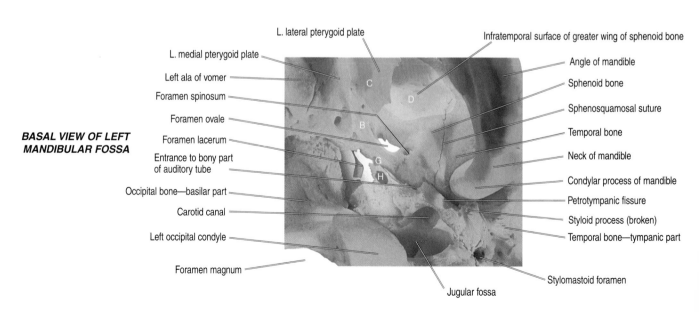

BASAL VIEW OF LEFT MANDIBULAR FOSSA

L. lateral pterygoid plate

L. medial pterygoid plate

Left ala of vomer

Foramen spinosum

Foramen ovale

Foramen lacerum

Entrance to bony part of auditory tube

Occipital bone—basilar part

Carotid canal

Left occipital condyle

Foramen magnum

Infratemporal surface of greater wing of sphenoid bone

Angle of mandible

Sphenoid bone

Sphenosquamosal suture

Temporal bone

Neck of mandible

Condylar process of mandible

Petrotympanic fissure

Styloid process (broken)

Temporal bone—tympanic part

Stylomastoid foramen

Jugular fossa

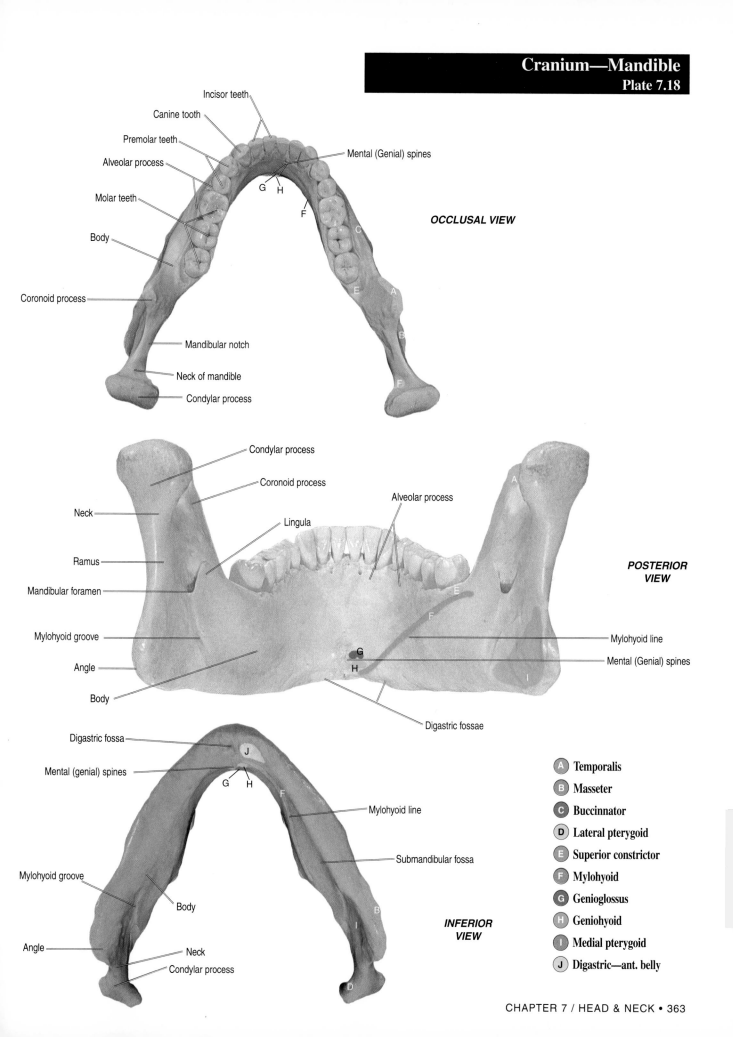

Incisor teeth

Canine tooth

Premolar teeth

Alveolar process

Molar teeth

Body

Coronoid process

Mandibular notch

Neck of mandible

Condylar process

Mental (Genial) spines

G H

F

C

E A

B

F

OCCLUSAL VIEW

Condylar process

Coronoid process

Alveolar process

Neck

Lingula

Ramus

Mandibular foramen

Mylohyoid groove

Angle

Body

A

E

F

Mylohyoid line

Mental (Genial) spines

G

H

I

Digastric fossae

**POSTERIOR
VIEW**

Digastric fossa

Mental (genial) spines

G H

J

F

Mylohyoid line

Submandibular fossa

Mylohyoid groove

Body

B

I

Angle

Neck

Condylar process

D

**INFERIOR
VIEW**

- Ⓐ **Temporalis**
- Ⓑ **Masseter**
- Ⓒ **Buccinnator**
- Ⓓ **Lateral pterygoid**
- Ⓔ **Superior constrictor**
- Ⓕ **Mylohyoid**
- Ⓖ **Genioglossus**
- Ⓗ **Geniohyoid**
- Ⓘ **Medial pterygoid**
- Ⓙ **Digastric—ant. belly**

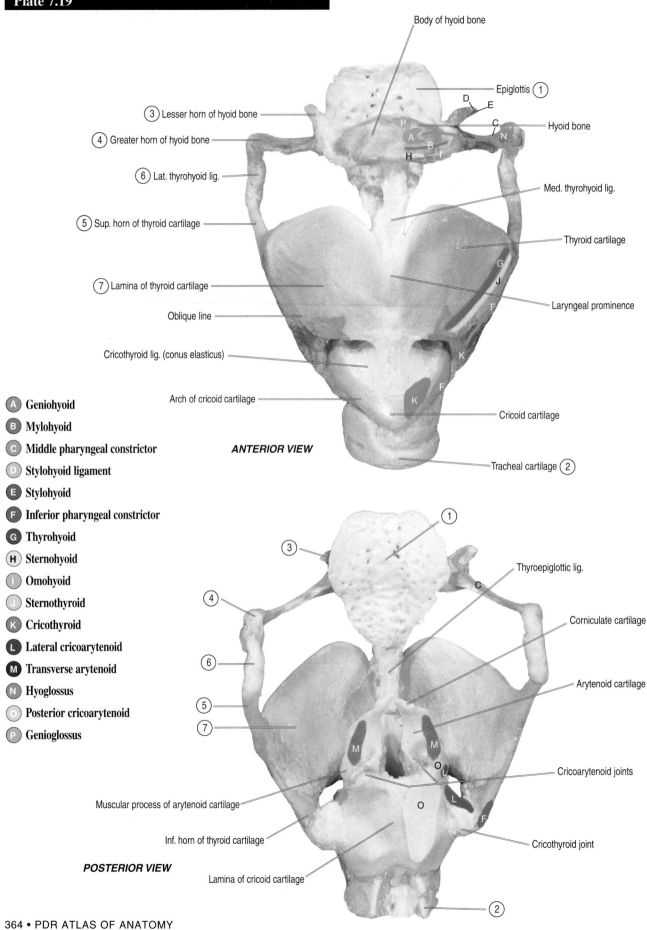

Body of hyoid bone

Epiglottis ①

D

E

③ Lesser horn of hyoid bone

P

C

Hyoid bone

④ Greater horn of hyoid bone

A

B

N

H

I

⑥ Lat. thyrohyoid lig.

Med. thyrohyoid lig.

⑤ Sup. horn of thyroid cartilage

Thyroid cartilage

G

J

⑦ Lamina of thyroid cartilage

Laryngeal prominence

F

Oblique line

Cricothyroid lig. (conus elasticus)

K

F

Arch of cricoid cartilage

K

Cricoid cartilage

ANTERIOR VIEW

Tracheal cartilage ②

Ⓐ **Geniohyoid**

Ⓑ **Mylohyoid**

Ⓒ **Middle pharyngeal constrictor**

Ⓓ **Stylohyoid ligament**

Ⓔ **Stylohyoid**

Ⓕ **Inferior pharyngeal constrictor**

Ⓖ **Thyrohyoid**

Ⓗ **Sternohyoid**

Ⓘ **Omohyoid**

Ⓙ **Sternothyroid**

Ⓚ **Cricothyroid**

Ⓛ **Lateral cricoarytenoid**

Ⓜ **Transverse arytenoid**

Ⓝ **Hyoglossus**

Ⓞ **Posterior cricoarytenoid**

Ⓟ **Genioglossus**

①

③

Thyroepiglottic lig.

C

④

Corniculate cartilage

⑥

⑤

Arytenoid cartilage

⑦

M

M

Muscular process of arytenoid cartilage

O

L

Cricoarytenoid joints

L

Inf. horn of thyroid cartilage

O

F

Cricothyroid joint

POSTERIOR VIEW

Lamina of cricoid cartilage

②

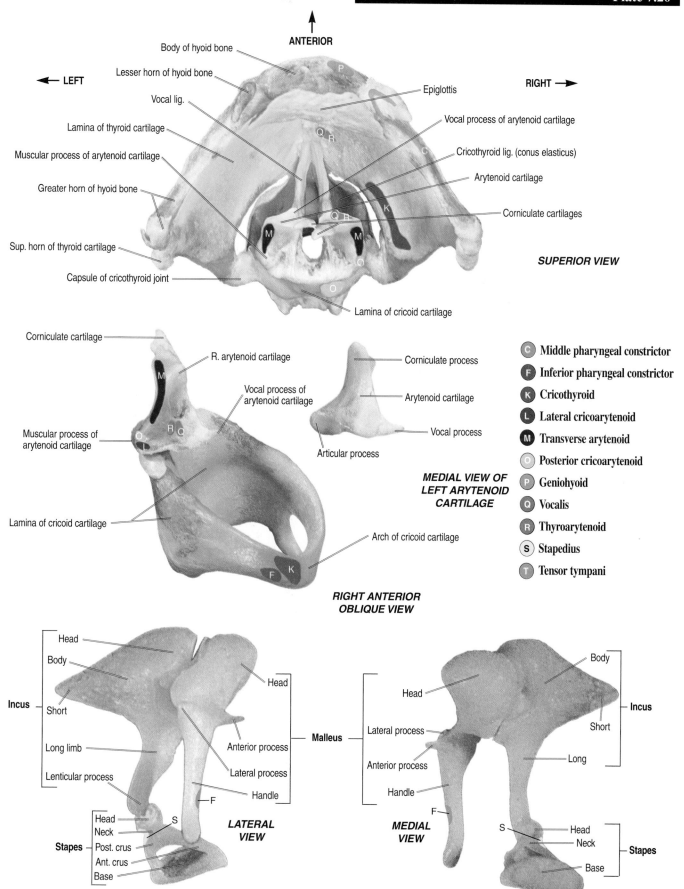

ANTERIOR

← **LEFT**

RIGHT →

Body of hyoid bone

Lesser horn of hyoid bone

Vocal lig.

Lamina of thyroid cartilage

Muscular process of arytenoid cartilage

Greater horn of hyoid bone

Sup. horn of thyroid cartilage

Capsule of cricothyroid joint

Epiglottis

Vocal process of arytenoid cartilage

Cricothyroid lig. (conus elasticus)

Arytenoid cartilage

Corniculate cartilages

SUPERIOR VIEW

Lamina of cricoid cartilage

Corniculate cartilage

R. arytenoid cartilage

Corniculate process

Arytenoid cartilage

Vocal process of arytenoid cartilage

Vocal process

Muscular process of arytenoid cartilage

Articular process

MEDIAL VIEW OF LEFT ARYTENOID CARTILAGE

Lamina of cricoid cartilage

Arch of cricoid cartilage

RIGHT ANTERIOR OBLIQUE VIEW

C Middle pharyngeal constrictor

F Inferior pharyngeal constrictor

K Cricothyroid

L Lateral cricoarytenoid

M Transverse arytenoid

O Posterior cricoarytenoid

P Geniohyoid

Q Vocalis

R Thyroarytenoid

S Stapedius

T Tensor tympani

Head

Body

Incus

Short

Long limb

Lenticular process

Head

Neck

Stapes — Post. crus

Ant. crus

Base

Head

Anterior process

Lateral process

Handle

LATERAL VIEW

Malleus

Body

Head

Incus

Short

Lateral process

Long

Anterior process

Handle

MEDIAL VIEW

Head

Neck

Stapes

Base

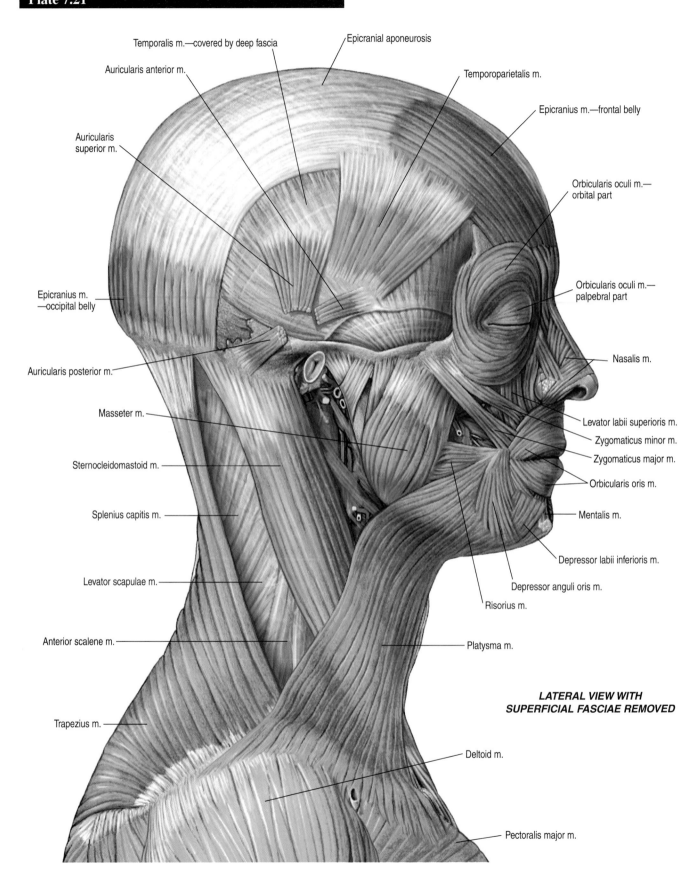

Temporalis m.—covered by deep fascia

Epicranial aponeurosis

Auricularis anterior m.

Temporoparietalis m.

Epicranius m.—frontal belly

Auricularis superior m.

Orbicularis oculi m.—orbital part

Epicranius m.—occipital belly

Orbicularis oculi m.—palpebral part

Auricularis posterior m.

Nasalis m.

Masseter m.

Levator labii superioris m.

Zygomaticus minor m.

Sternocleidomastoid m.

Zygomaticus major m.

Orbicularis oris m.

Splenius capitis m.

Mentalis m.

Levator scapulae m.

Depressor labii inferioris m.

Anterior scalene m.

Depressor anguli oris m.

Risorius m.

Platysma m.

**LATERAL VIEW WITH
SUPERFICIAL FASCIAE REMOVED**

Trapezius m.

Deltoid m.

Pectoralis major m.

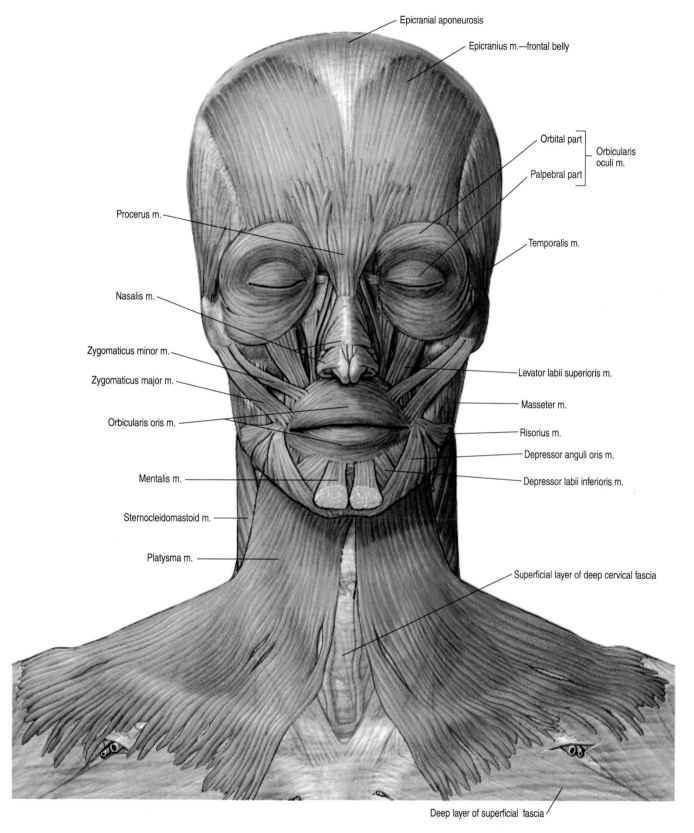

Epicranial aponeurosis

Epicranius m.—frontal belly

Orbital part

Palpebral part

Orbicularis oculi m.

Procerus m.

Temporalis m.

Nasalis m.

Zygomaticus minor m.

Zygomaticus major m.

Levator labii superioris m.

Orbicularis oris m.

Masseter m.

Risorius m.

Mentalis m.

Depressor anguli oris m.

Depressor labii inferioris m.

Sternocleidomastoid m.

Platysma m.

Superficial layer of deep cervical fascia

Deep layer of superficial fascia

ANTERIOR VIEW

Muscles Acting on the Temporomandibular Joint

Muscle	Stable Attachment	Mobile Attachment	Innervation	Main Actions
Temporalis	Floor of temporal fossa & deep surface of temporal fascia	Tip & medial surface of coronoid process & ant. border of ramus of mandible	Deep temporal br. of mandibular n. (CN V^3)	Elevates mandible, closing jaws; its posterior fibers retrude mandible after protrusion
Masseter	Inf. border & medial surface of zygomatic arch	Lateral surface of ramus of mandible & its coronoid process	Mandibular n. (CN V^3) via masseteric nerve that enters its deep surface	Elevates & protrudes mandible, thus closing jaws;
Lateral pterygoid	*Superior head:* Infratemporal surface & infratemporal crest of greater wing of sphenoid bone	Articular disc & capsule of temporomandibular joint	Mandibular n. (CN V^3) via lateral pterygoid n. from ant. trunk, which enters it unilaterally deep surface	*Acting bilaterally,* they protrude mandible & depress chin *Acting unilaterally* & alternately, they produce side-to-side movements of mandible
	Inferior head: Lateral surface of lateral pterygoid plate	Neck of mandible		
Medial pterygoid	*Deep head:* Medial surface of lateral pterygoid plate & pyramidal process of palatine bone	Medial surface of ramus of mandible, inf. to mandibular foramen	Mandibular n. (CN V^3) via medial pterygoid n.	Helps to elevate mandible, closing jaws *Acting bilaterally,* they help to protrude mandible *Acting unilaterally,* it protrudes side of jaw *Acting alternately,* they produce a grinding motion
	Superficial head: Tuberosity of maxilla			

Actions and Nerve Supply of the Ocular Muscles

Muscle	Action(s) on the Eyeball	Nerve Supply
Medial rectus[a]	Adducts	CN III
Lateral rectus[a]	Abducts	CN VI[b]
Superior rectus	Elevates, adducts & rotate medially	CN III
Inferior rectus	Depresses, adducts & rotates laterally	CN III
Superior oblique[c]	Abducts, depresses & rotates eye medially (intorsion), depresses adducted eye	CN IV[b]
Inferior oblique[c]	Abducts, elevates & rotates eye laterally (extorsion), elevates adducted eye	CN III

[a]The medial and lateral rectus muscles move the eyeball in one axis only, whereas each of the other four muscles moves it in all three axes.
[b]CN IV and VI each supply one muscle, whereas CN III supplies the other four muscles.
[c]The superior and inferior oblique muscles are used with the medial rectus muscle in adducting both eyes medially for near vision. This movement, accompanied by pupillary construction, is known as accommodation.

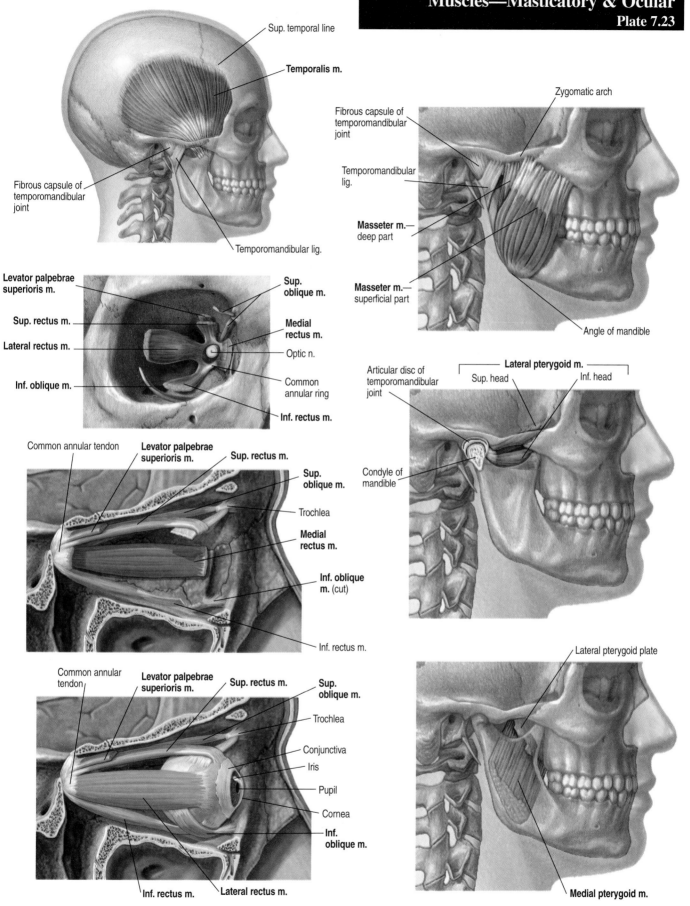

Sup. temporal line

Temporalis m.

Fibrous capsule of
temporomandibular
joint

Temporomandibular lig.

Zygomatic arch

Fibrous capsule of
temporomandibular
joint

Temporomandibular
lig.

Masseter m.—
deep part

Masseter m.—
superficial part

Angle of mandible

**Levator palpebrae
superioris m.**

Sup. rectus m.

Lateral rectus m.

Inf. oblique m.

**Sup.
oblique m.**

**Medial
rectus m.**

Optic n.

Common
annular ring

Inf. rectus m.

Common annular tendon

**Levator palpebrae
superioris m.**

Sup. rectus m.

**Sup.
oblique m.**

Trochlea

**Medial
rectus m.**

**Inf. oblique
m. (cut)**

Inf. rectus m.

Articular disc of
temporomandibular
joint

Condyle of
mandible

Lateral pterygoid m.
Sup. head   Inf. head

Common annular
tendon

**Levator palpebrae
superioris m.**

Sup. rectus m.

**Sup.
oblique m.**

Trochlea

Conjunctiva

Iris

Pupil

Cornea

**Inf.
oblique m.**

Inf. rectus m.   Lateral rectus m.

Lateral pterygoid plate

Medial pterygoid m.

Muscles of the Soft Palate

Muscle	Superior Attachment	Inferior Attachment	Innervation	Main Actions
Levator veli palatini	Cartilage of auditory tube & petrous part of temporal bone	Palatine aponeurosis	Pharyngeal br. of vagus n. via pharyngeal plexus (CN X)	Elevates soft palate during swallowing & yawning
Tensor veli palatini	Scaphoid fossa of medial pterygoid plate, spine of sphenoid bone & cartilage of auditory tube		Medial pterygoid n. (a br. of the mandibular n.) via otic ganglion (CN V^3)	Tenses soft palate & opens cartilagenous part of auditory tube during swallowing & yawning
Palatoglossus	Palatine aponeurosis	Side of tongue	Cranial part of CN XI through pharyngeal br. of vagus n. (CN X) via pharyngeal plexus	Elevates posterior part of tongue & draws soft palate onto tongue
Palatopharyngeus	Hard palate & palatine aponeurosis	Lateral wall of pharynx		Tenses soft palate & pulls walls of pharynx superiorly, anteriorly, and medially during swallowing
Musculus uvulae	Posterior nasal spine & palatine aponeurosis	Mucosa of uvula		Shortens uvula & pulls it superiorly

Extrinsic Muscles of the Tongue

Muscle	Stable Attachment	Mobile Attachment	Innervation	Actions
Genioglossus	Sup. part of mental spine of mandible	Dorsum of tongue & body of hyoid bone	Hypoglossal n. CN XII	Protrudes, retracts & depresses tongue; its post. part protrudes tongue
Hyoglossus	Body & greater horn of hyoid bone	Side of tongue		Depresses & retracts tongue
Styloglossus	Styloid process & stylohyoid lig.	Side & inf. aspect of tongue		Retracts tongue & draws it up to create a trough for swallowing
Palatoglossus	Palatine aponeurosis of soft palate	Side of tongue	Cranial root of CN XI via pharyngeal br. CN X & pharyngeal plexus	Elevates post. part of tongue

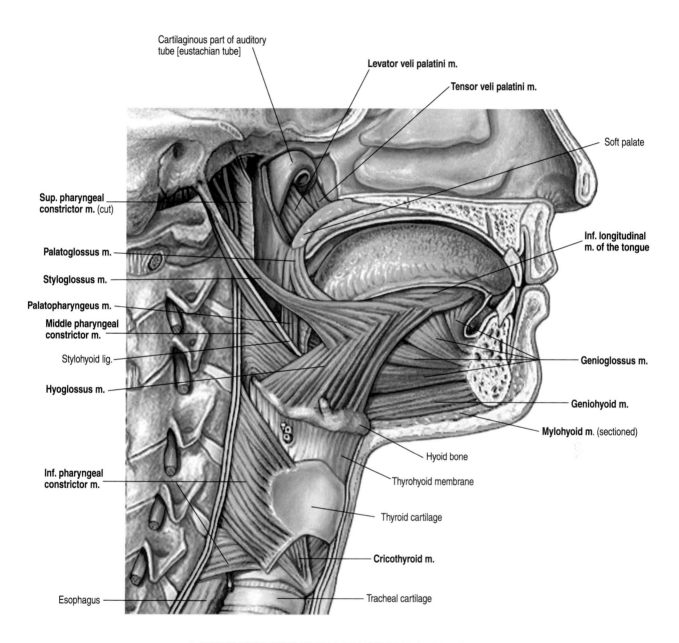

Cartilaginous part of auditory tube [eustachian tube]

Levator veli palatini m.

Tensor veli palatini m.

Soft palate

Sup. pharyngeal constrictor m. (cut)

Inf. longitudinal m. of the tongue

Palatoglossus m.

Styloglossus m.

Palatopharyngeus m.

Middle pharyngeal constrictor m.

Stylohyoid lig.

Hyoglossus m.

Genioglossus m.

Geniohyoid m.

Mylohyoid m. (sectioned)

Inf. pharyngeal constrictor m.

Hyoid bone

Thyrohyoid membrane

Thyroid cartilage

Cricothyroid m.

Esophagus

Tracheal cartilage

LATERAL VIEW OF TONGUE & PHARYNGEAL MUSCLES

Muscles—Hyoid
Table 7.5

Suprahyoid Muscles[a]

Muscle	Superior Attachment	Inferior Attachment	Innervation	Main Actions
Mylohyoid	Mylohyoid line of mandible	Oral raphe & body of hyoid bone	Mylohyoid n., a br. of inf. alveolar n. (CN V^3)	Elevates hyoid bone, floor of mouth & tongue during swallowing & speaking
Geniohyoid	Inf. mental spine of mandible	Body of hyoid bone	C1 via the hypoglossal n. (CN XII)	Pulls hyoid bone anterosuperiorly, shortens floor of mouth & widens pharynx
Stylohyoid	Styloid process of temporal bone	Body of hyoid bone	Cervical br. of facial n. (CN VII)	Elevates & retracts hyoid bone, thereby elongating floor of mouth
Digastric	*Anterior belly:* Digastric fossa of mandible *Posterior belly:* Mastoid notch of temporal bone	Intermediate tendon to body & greater horn of hyoid bone	*Anterior belly:* Mylohyoid n., a br. of inf. alveolar n. (CN V^3) *Posterior belly:* Facial n. (CN VII)	Depresses mandible, raises hyoid bone & steadies it during swallowing & speaking

[a]These muscles connect the hyoid bone to the skull.

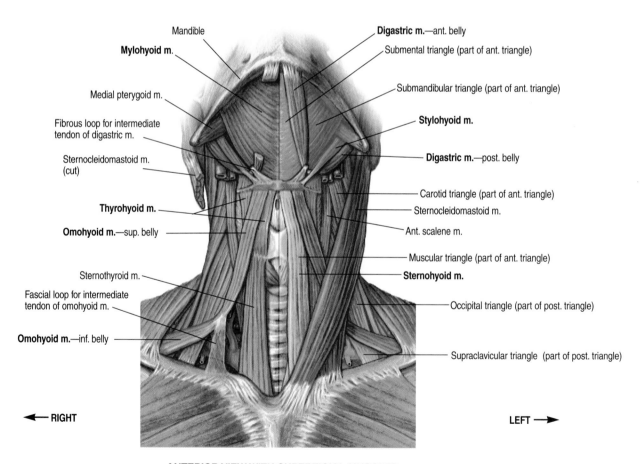

ANTERIOR VIEW WITH SUPERFICIAL MUSCLES ON LEFT & DEEPER MUSCLES ON RIGHT

Infrahyoid Muscles[a]

Muscle	Origin	Insertion	Innervation	Actions
Sternohyoid	Manubrium of sternum & medial end of clavicle	Body of hyoid bone	C1, C2 & C3 from ansa cervicalis	Depresses hyoid bone after it has been elevated during swallowing
Sternothyroid	Post. surface of manubrium of sternum	Oblique line of thyroid cartilage	C2 & C3 by a br. of ansa cervicalis	Depresses hyoid bone & larynx
Thyrohyoid	Oblique line of thyroid cartilage	Inf. border of body & greater horn of hyoid bone	C1 via hypoglossal n. (CN XII)	Depresses hyoid bone & elevates larynx
Omohyoid	Sup. border of scapula near suprascapular notch	Inf. border of hyoid bone	C1, C2 & C3 by a br. of ansa cervicalis	Depresses, retracts & steadies hyoid bone

[a]These four step-like muscles anchor the hyoid bone (*i.e.,* they fix and steady it). They are concerned with the suprahyoid muscles in movements of the tongue, hyoid bone, and larynx in both swallowing and speaking.

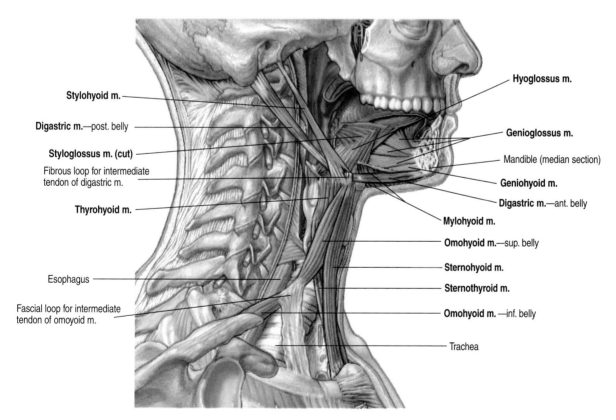

Stylohyoid m.

Digastric m.—post. belly

Styloglossus m. (cut)

Fibrous loop for intermediate tendon of digastric m.

Thyrohyoid m.

Esophagus

Fascial loop for intermediate tendon of omoyoid m.

Hyoglossus m.

Genioglossus m.

Mandible (median section)

Geniohyoid m.

Digastric m.—ant. belly

Mylohyoid m.

Omohyoid m.—sup. belly

Sternohyoid m.

Sternothyroid m.

Omohyoid m. —inf. belly

Trachea

LATERAL VIEW WITH RIGHT HALF OF MANDIBLE REMOVED

Muscle	Lateral Attachments	Medial Attachments	Innervation	Main Actions
CIRCULAR PHARYNGEAL MUSCLES				
Superior constrictor	Pterygoid hamulus, ptergomandibular raphe, post. end of mylohyoid line of mandible & side of tongue	Median raphe of pharynx & pharyngeal tubercle	Pharyngeal & sup. laryngeal brr. of vagus n. [CN X] through pharyngeal plexus	Constrict wall of pharynx during swallowing
Middle constrictor	Stylohyoid lig. and greater & lesser horns of hyoid bone	Median raphe of pharynx		
Inferior constrictor	Oblique line of thyroid cartilage & side of cricoid cartilage			
LONGITUDINAL PHARYNGEAL MUSCLES				
Palatopharyngeus	Hard palate & palatine aponeurosis	Post. border of lamina of thyroid cartilage & side of pharynx & esophagus		Elevate pharynx & larynx during swallowing & speaking[a]
Salpingopharynegeus	Cartilaginous part of auditory tube	Blends with palatopharynegeus		
Stylopharyngeus	Styloid process of temporal bone	Post. & sup. borders of thyroid cartilage with palatopharynegus m.	Glossopharyngeal n.[CN IX]	

[a]The salpingopharyngeus muscle also opens the auditory tube.

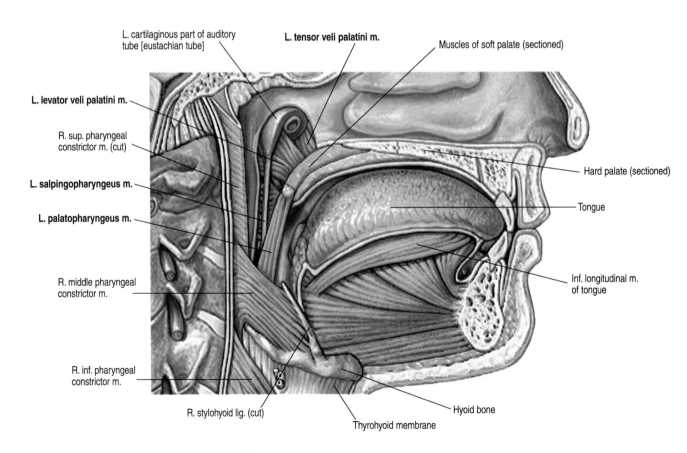

L. cartilaginous part of auditory tube [eustachian tube]

L. tensor veli palatini m.

Muscles of soft palate (sectioned)

L. levator veli palatini m.

R. sup. pharyngeal constrictor m. (cut)

L. salpingopharyngeus m.

L. palatopharyngeus m.

Hard palate (sectioned)

Tongue

R. middle pharyngeal constrictor m.

Inf. longitudinal m. of tongue

R. inf. pharyngeal constrictor m.

R. stylohyoid lig. (cut)

Thyrohyoid membrane

Hyoid bone

LATERAL VIEW OF NECK & MEDIAN SECTIONED SKULL

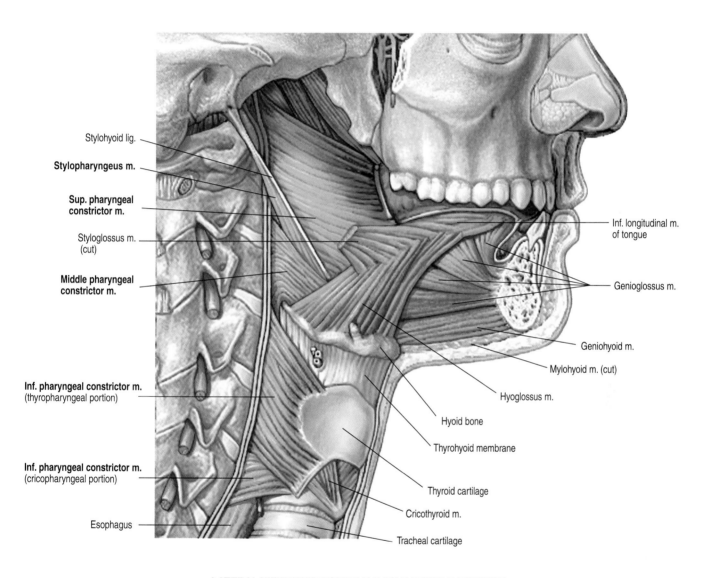

Stylohyoid lig.

Stylopharyngeus m.

**Sup. pharyngeal
constrictor m.**

Styloglossus m.
(cut)

**Middle pharyngeal
constrictor m.**

Inf. longitudinal m.
of tongue

Genioglossus m.

Geniohyoid m.

Mylohyoid m. (cut)

Hyoglossus m.

Inf. pharyngeal constrictor m.
(thyropharyngeal portion)

Hyoid bone

Thyrohyoid membrane

Inf. pharyngeal constrictor m.
(cricopharyngeal portion)

Thyroid cartilage

Cricothyroid m.

Esophagus

Tracheal cartilage

LATERAL VIEW WITH RIGHT HALF OF MANDIBLE REMOVED

Muscles of the Larynx

Muscle	Origin	Insertion	Innervation	Main Actions
Cricothyroid	Anterolateral part of cricoid cartilage	Inf. margin & inf. horn of thyroid cartilage	Ext. laryngeal n. (CN X)	Stretches & tenses the vocal fold
Posterior cricoarytenoid	Post. surface of laminae of cricoid cartilage	Muscular process of arytenoid cartilage		Abducts vocal fold
Lateral cricoarytenoid	Arch of cricoid cartilage			Adducts vocal fold
Thyroarytenoid[a]	Post. surface of thyroid cartilage	Muscular process of arytenoid process	Recurrent laryngeal n. (CN X)	Relaxes vocal fold
Transverse & oblique arytenoids	One arytenoid cartilage	Opposition arytenoid cartilage		Close laryngeal aditus by approximating arytenoid cartilages
Vocalis[b]	Angle between laminae of thyroid cartilage	Vocal process of arytenoid cartilage		Alters vocal fold during phonation

[a]The superior fibers of the thyroarytenoid muscle pass into the aryepiglottic fold, and some of them reach the epiglottic cartilage. These fibers constitute the *thyroepiglottic muscle,* which widens the inlet of the larynx.
[b]These short fine muscular slips are derived from the most medial fibers of the thyroarytenoid muscle.

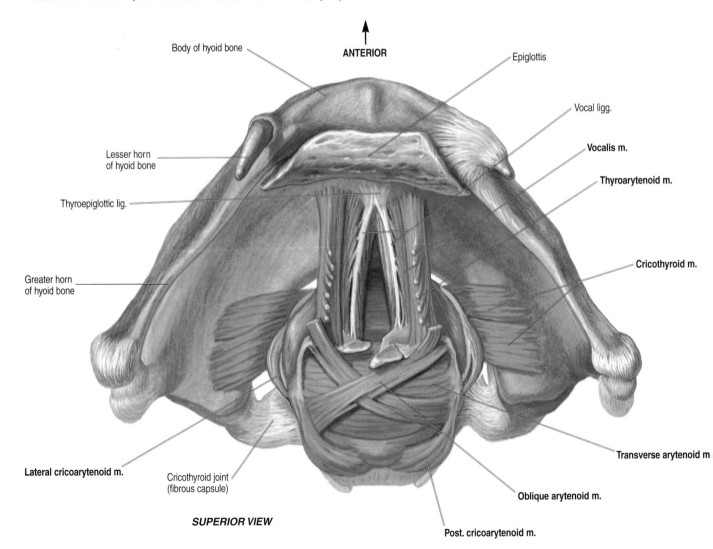

SUPERIOR VIEW

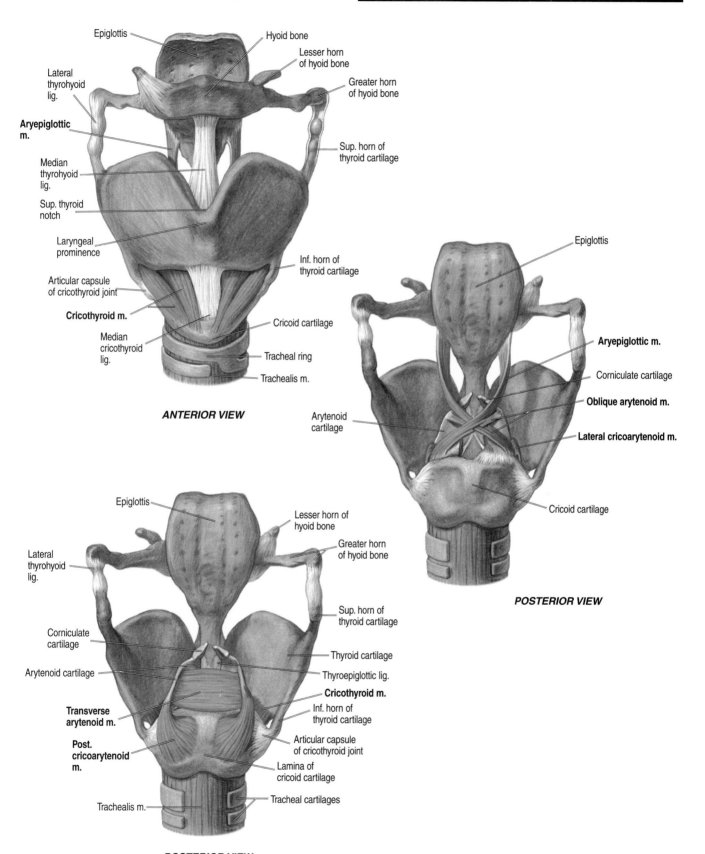

Epiglottis

Hyoid bone

Lesser horn of hyoid bone

Greater horn of hyoid bone

Lateral thyrohyoid lig.

Aryepiglottic m.

Sup. horn of thyroid cartilage

Median thyrohyoid lig.

Sup. thyroid notch

Laryngeal prominence

Inf. horn of thyroid cartilage

Articular capsule of cricothyroid joint

Cricothyroid m.

Cricoid cartilage

Median cricothyroid lig.

Tracheal ring

Trachealis m.

ANTERIOR VIEW

Epiglottis

Aryepiglottic m.

Corniculate cartilage

Oblique arytenoid m.

Lateral cricoarytenoid m.

Arytenoid cartilage

Cricoid cartilage

POSTERIOR VIEW

Epiglottis

Lesser horn of hyoid bone

Greater horn of hyoid bone

Lateral thyrohyoid lig.

Sup. horn of thyroid cartilage

Corniculate cartilage

Arytenoid cartilage

Thyroid cartilage

Thyroepiglottic lig.

Cricothyroid m.

Inf. horn of thyroid cartilage

Transverse arytenoid m.

Articular capsule of cricothyroid joint

Post. cricoarytenoid m.

Lamina of cricoid cartilage

Trachealis m.

Tracheal cartilages

POSTERIOR VIEW

Muscle	Inferior Attachment	Superior Attachment	Innervation	Main Actions
Sternocleidomastoid				
Sternal head	Ventral surface of the manubrium sterni	Lateral surface of mastoid process; sup. nuchal line of occipital bone	Spinal accessory n. (motor); sensory fibers of C2 n.	Various: both sides together support head, move chin upward, and pull back of head down. One side alone turns chin upward and to opposite side.
Clavicular head	Cranial surface of medial third of clavicle			
Splenius capitis	Inf. half of ligamentum nuchae & spinous process of sup. six thoracic vertebrae	Lateral aspect of mastoid process & lateral third of sup. nuchal line	Dorsal rami of middle cervical spinal nn.	Laterally flexes & rotates head & neck to same side; acting bilaterally, they extend head & neck
Splenius cervicis	Spines of 3rd (or 4th) to 6th thoracic vertebrae	Posterior tubercles of the transverse process of the upper three cervical vertebrae	Dorsal rami of nerves C2-C5, lateral brr. (same as splenius capitis m.)	
Posterior scalene	Post. tubercles of transverse processes of C4-C6	Ext. border of second rib	Ventral rami of cervical spinal nn. (C7 & C8)	Flexes neck laterally; elevates second rib during forced inspiration
Middle scalene	Posterior tubercles of transverse processes of C2 & C7	Sup. surface of first rib, posterior to groove for subclavian a.	Ventral rami of cervical spinal nn. (C3-C8)	Flexes neck laterally; elevates first rib during forced inspiration
Anterior scalene	Ant. tubercles of transverse processes of C3-C6	Scalene tubercle of 1st rib	Long thoracic n. (C5-C7)	
Longus colli				
Vertical portion	Body of first three thoracic & last three cervical vertebrae	Bodies of C2-C4	Ventral rami of C2-C6	Bilaterally acting to flex neck and head anteriorly, unilaterally to flex head and neck laterally and to rotate the head toward the same side
Superior oblique	Ant. tubercles of transverse process of C3-C5	Tubercle on ant. arch of the atlas & body axis	Ventral rami of C1 to C4	
Inferior oblique	Ant. surface of bodies of first two or three thoracic vertebrae	Ant. tubercles of the transverse processes of C5 & C6		
Longus capitis	Ant. tubercle of transverse processes of C3-C6	Inf. border of basilar part of occipital		

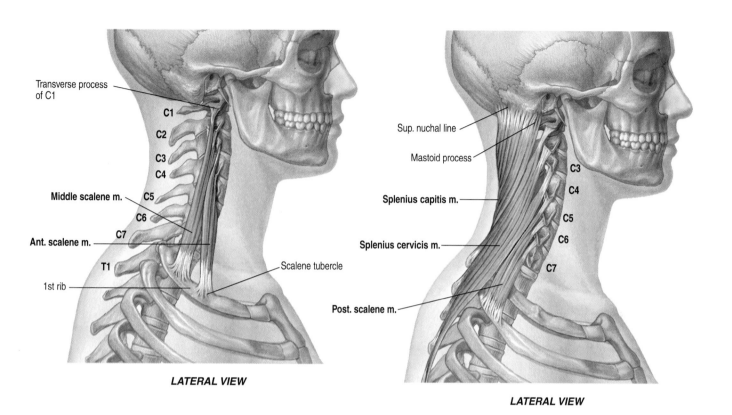

Transverse process
of C1

C1
C2
C3
C4

Middle scalene m.   C5

C6

Ant. scalene m.   C7

T1

1st rib

Scalene tubercle

LATERAL VIEW

Sup. nuchal line

Mastoid process

Splenius capitis m.   C3

C4

C5

Splenius cervicis m.   C6

C7

Post. scalene m.

LATERAL VIEW

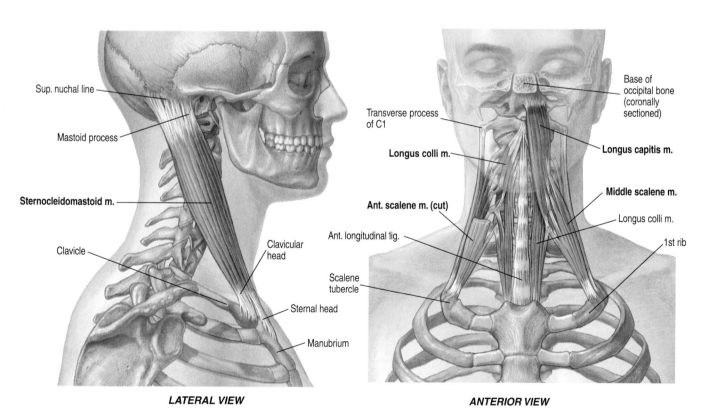

Sup. nuchal line

Mastoid process

Sternocleidomastoid m.

Clavicle

Clavicular
head

Sternal head

Manubrium

LATERAL VIEW

Transverse process
of C1

Longus colli m.

Ant. scalene m. (cut)

Ant. longitudinal lig.

Scalene
tubercle

Base of
occipital bone
(coronally
sectioned)

Longus capitis m.

Middle scalene m.

Longus colli m.

1st rib

ANTERIOR VIEW

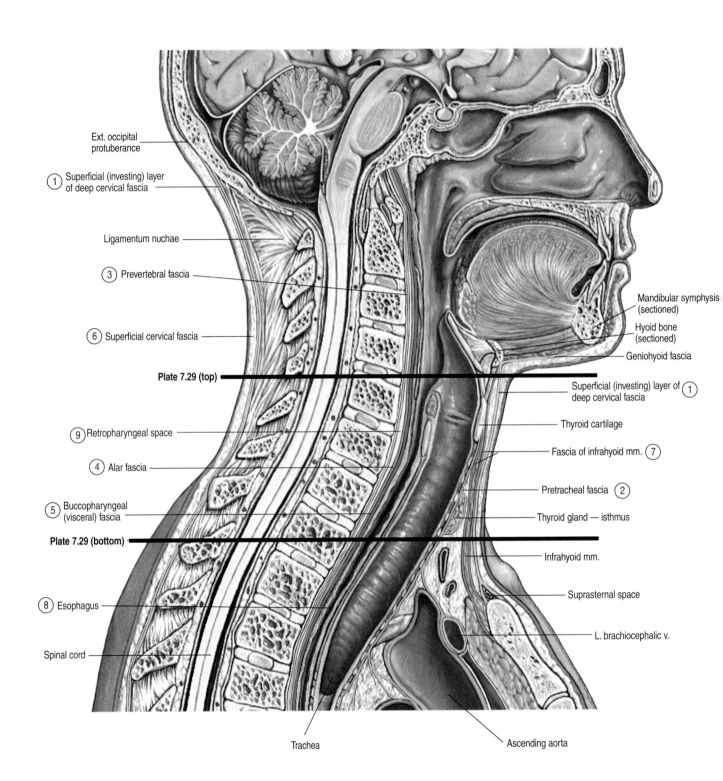

Ext. occipital protuberance

(1) Superficial (investing) layer of deep cervical fascia

Ligamentum nuchae

(3) Prevertebral fascia

(6) Superficial cervical fascia

Plate 7.29 (top)

(9) Retropharyngeal space

(4) Alar fascia

(5) Buccopharyngeal (visceral) fascia

Plate 7.29 (bottom)

(8) Esophagus

Spinal cord

Mandibular symphysis (sectioned)

Hyoid bone (sectioned)

Geniohyoid fascia

Superficial (investing) layer of (1) deep cervical fascia

Thyroid cartilage

Fascia of infrahyoid mm. (7)

Pretracheal fascia (2)

Thyroid gland — isthmus

Infrahyoid mm.

Suprasternal space

L. brachiocephalic v.

Trachea

Ascending aorta

LATERAL VIEW OF MEDIAN SECTION

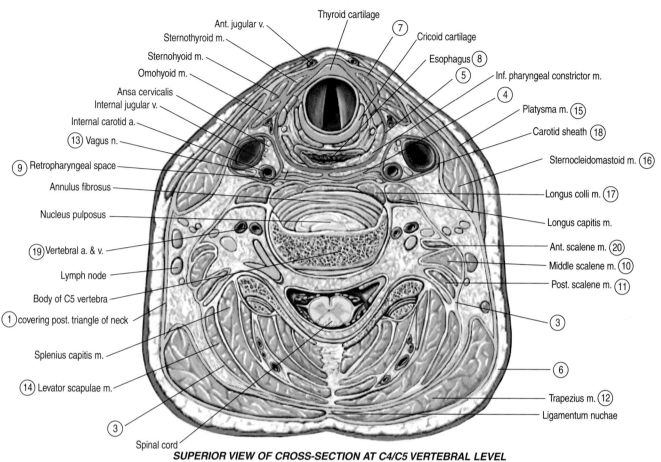

Ant. jugular v.
Sternothyroid m.
Sternohyoid m.
Omohyoid m.
Ansa cervicalis
Internal jugular v.
Internal carotid a.
(13) Vagus n.
(9) Retropharyngeal space
Annulus fibrosus
Nucleus pulposus
(19) Vertebral a. & v.
Lymph node
Body of C5 vertebra
(1) covering post. triangle of neck
Splenius capitis m.
(14) Levator scapulae m.
(3)
Spinal cord

Thyroid cartilage
(7)
Cricoid cartilage
Esophagus (8)
(5)
Inf. pharyngeal constrictor m.
(4)
Platysma m. (15)
Carotid sheath (18)
Sternocleidomastoid m. (16)
Longus colli m. (17)
Longus capitis m.
Ant. scalene m. (20)
Middle scalene m. (10)
Post. scalene m. (11)
(3)
(6)
Trapezius m. (12)
Ligamentum nuchae

SUPERIOR VIEW OF CROSS-SECTION AT C4/C5 VERTEBRAL LEVEL

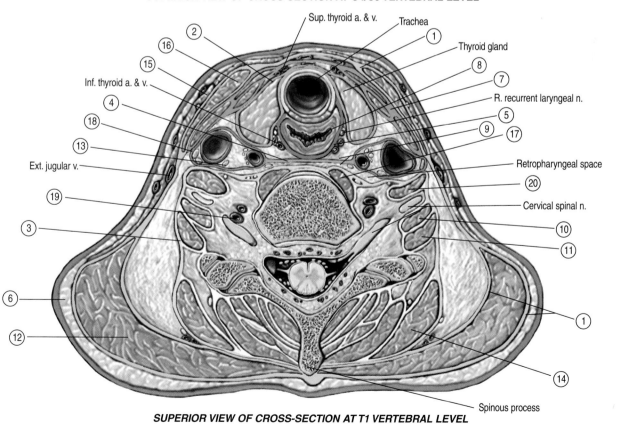

(2)
(16)
(15)
Inf. thyroid a. & v.
(4)
(18)
(13)
Ext. jugular v.
(19)
(3)
(6)
(12)

Sup. thyroid a. & v.
Trachea
(1)
Thyroid gland
(8)
(7)
R. recurrent laryngeal n.
(5)
(9) (17)
Retropharyngeal space
(20)
Cervical spinal n.
(10)
(11)
(1)
(14)
Spinous process

SUPERIOR VIEW OF CROSS-SECTION AT T1 VERTEBRAL LEVEL

LATERAL VIEW

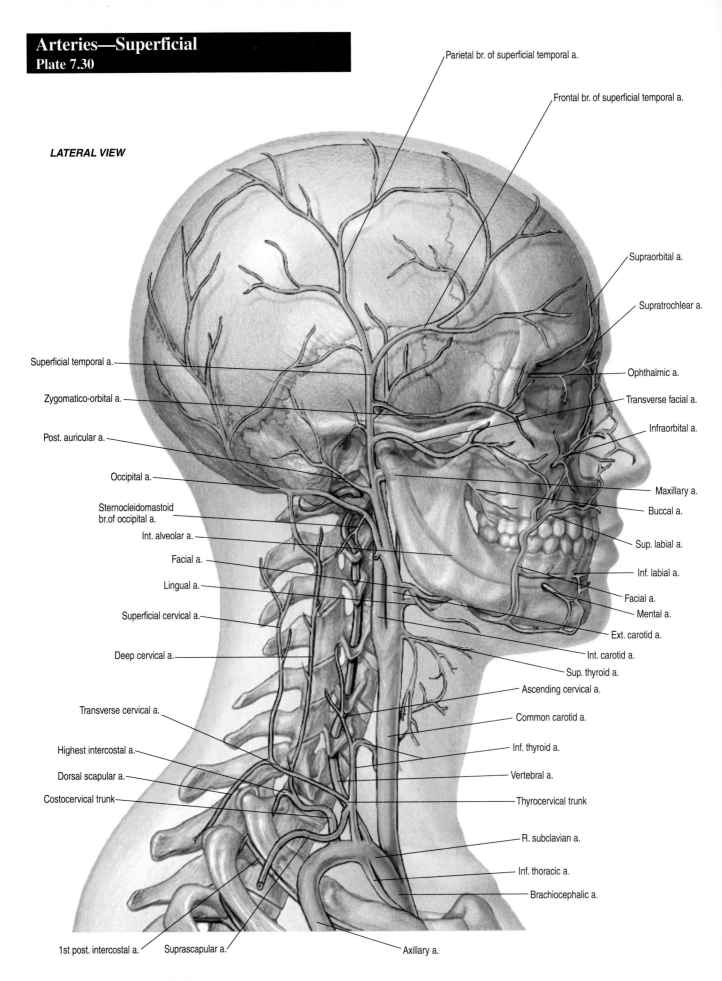

Parietal br. of superficial temporal a.

Frontal br. of superficial temporal a.

Supraorbital a.

Supratrochlear a.

Superficial temporal a.

Zygomatico-orbital a.

Ophthalmic a.

Transverse facial a.

Infraorbital a.

Post. auricular a.

Occipital a.

Maxillary a.

Buccal a.

Sternocleidomastoid br. of occipital a.

Int. alveolar a.

Sup. labial a.

Facial a.

Inf. labial a.

Lingual a.

Facial a.

Mental a.

Superficial cervical a.

Ext. carotid a.

Deep cervical a.

Int. carotid a.

Sup. thyroid a.

Ascending cervical a.

Transverse cervical a.

Common carotid a.

Highest intercostal a.

Inf. thyroid a.

Dorsal scapular a.

Vertebral a.

Costocervical trunk

Thyrocervical trunk

R. subclavian a.

Inf. thoracic a.

Brachiocephalic a.

1st post. intercostal a.

Suprascapular a.

Axillary a.

LATERAL VIEW

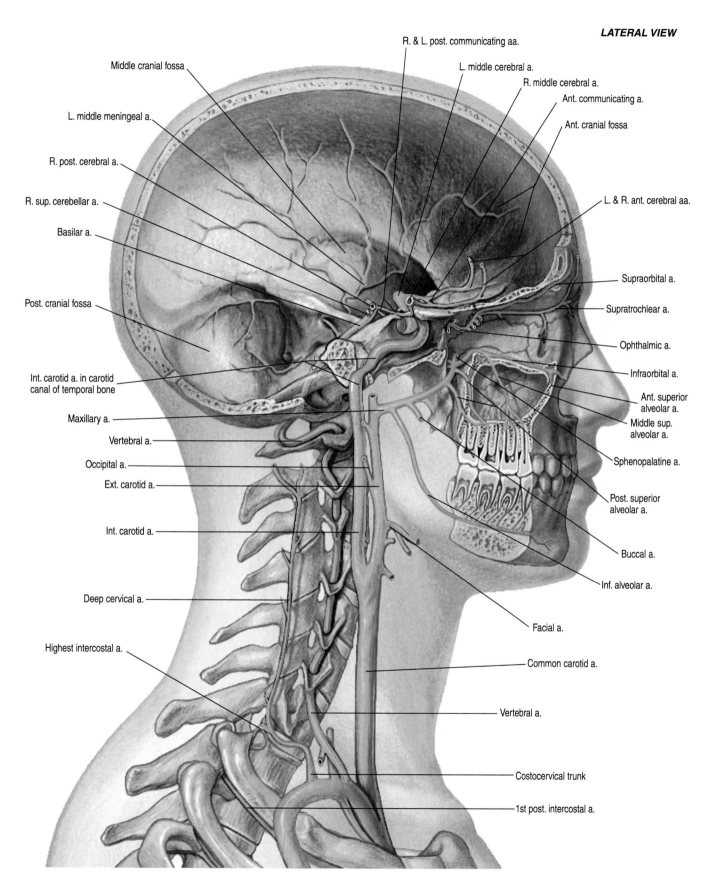

Middle cranial fossa

R. & L. post. communicating aa.

L. middle cerebral a.

R. middle cerebral a.

Ant. communicating a.

Ant. cranial fossa

L. middle meningeal a.

R. post. cerebral a.

R. sup. cerebellar a.

Basilar a.

L. & R. ant. cerebral aa.

Supraorbital a.

Supratrochlear a.

Post. cranial fossa

Ophthalmic a.

Infraorbital a.

Int. carotid a. in carotid canal of temporal bone

Ant. superior alveolar a.

Middle sup. alveolar a.

Maxillary a.

Vertebral a.

Sphenopalatine a.

Occipital a.

Ext. carotid a.

Post. superior alveolar a.

Int. carotid a.

Buccal a.

Inf. alveolar a.

Deep cervical a.

Facial a.

Highest intercostal a.

Common carotid a.

Vertebral a.

Costocervical trunk

1st post. intercostal a.

LATERAL VIEW

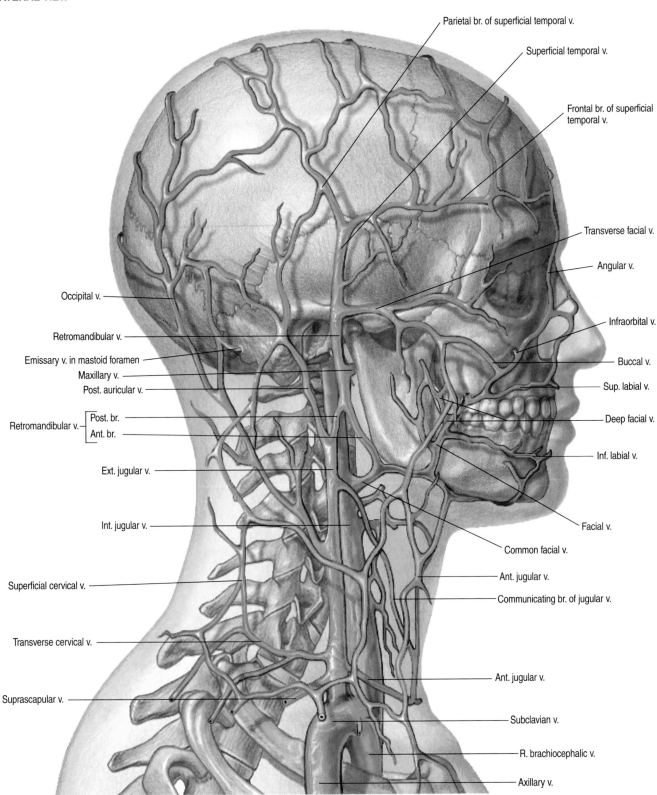

Parietal br. of superficial temporal v.

Superficial temporal v.

Frontal br. of superficial temporal v.

Transverse facial v.

Angular v.

Occipital v.

Infraorbital v.

Retromandibular v.

Emissary v. in mastoid foramen

Buccal v.

Maxillary v.

Post. auricular v.

Sup. labial v.

Retromandibular v. — Post. br.
Ant. br.

Deep facial v.

Inf. labial v.

Ext. jugular v.

Int. jugular v.

Facial v.

Common facial v.

Ant. jugular v.

Superficial cervical v.

Communicating br. of jugular v.

Transverse cervical v.

Ant. jugular v.

Suprascapular v.

Subclavian v.

R. brachiocephalic v.

Axillary v.

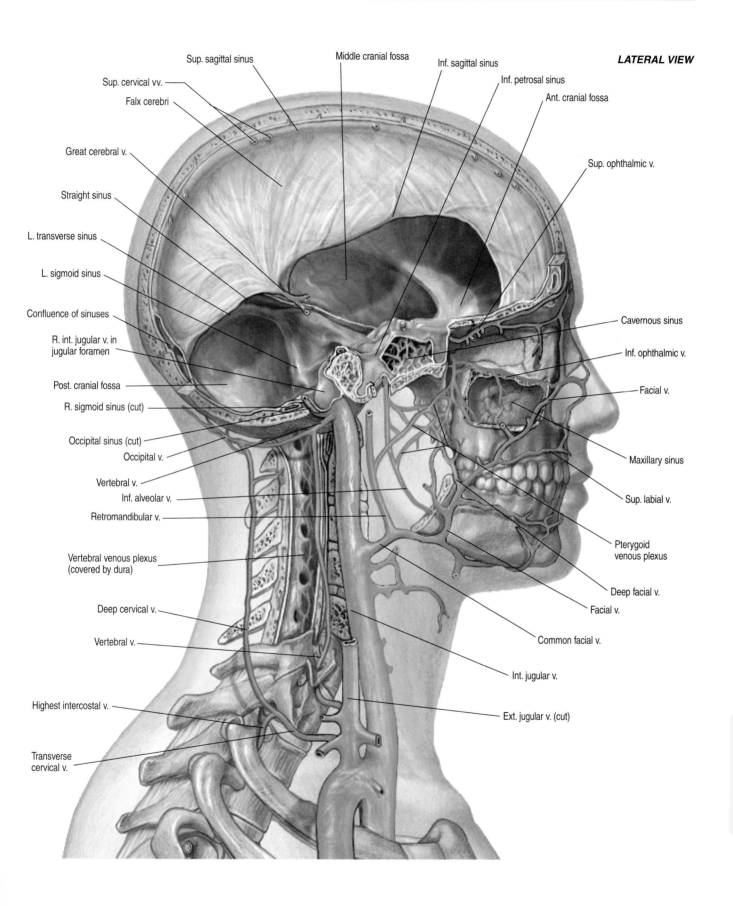

Sup. sagittal sinus

Sup. cervical vv.

Falx cerebri

Great cerebral v.

Straight sinus

L. transverse sinus

L. sigmoid sinus

Confluence of sinuses

R. int. jugular v. in jugular foramen

Post. cranial fossa

R. sigmoid sinus (cut)

Occipital sinus (cut)

Occipital v.

Vertebral v.

Inf. alveolar v.

Retromandibular v.

Vertebral venous plexus (covered by dura)

Deep cervical v.

Vertebral v.

Highest intercostal v.

Transverse cervical v.

Middle cranial fossa

Inf. sagittal sinus

Inf. petrosal sinus

Ant. cranial fossa

LATERAL VIEW

Sup. ophthalmic v.

Cavernous sinus

Inf. ophthalmic v.

Facial v.

Maxillary sinus

Sup. labial v.

Pterygoid venous plexus

Deep facial v.

Facial v.

Common facial v.

Int. jugular v.

Ext. jugular v. (cut)

Dermatomes & Cutaneous Innervation
Plate 7.34

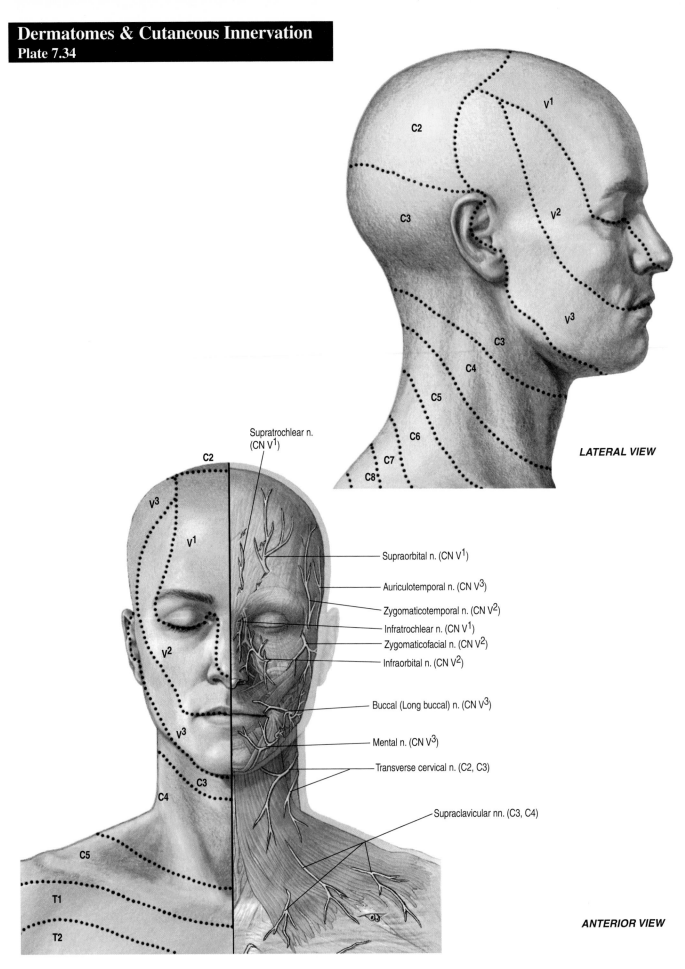

LATERAL VIEW

C2

V¹

C3

V²

V³

C3

C4

C5

C6

C7

C8

Supratrochlear n. (CN V¹)

C2

V³

V¹

V²

V³

C3

C4

C5

T1

T2

Supraorbital n. (CN V¹)

Auriculotemporal n. (CN V³)

Zygomaticotemporal n. (CN V²)

Infratrochlear n. (CN V¹)

Zygomaticofacial n. (CN V²)

Infraorbital n. (CN V²)

Buccal (Long buccal) n. (CN V³)

Mental n. (CN V³)

Transverse cervical n. (C2, C3)

Supraclavicular nn. (C3, C4)

ANTERIOR VIEW

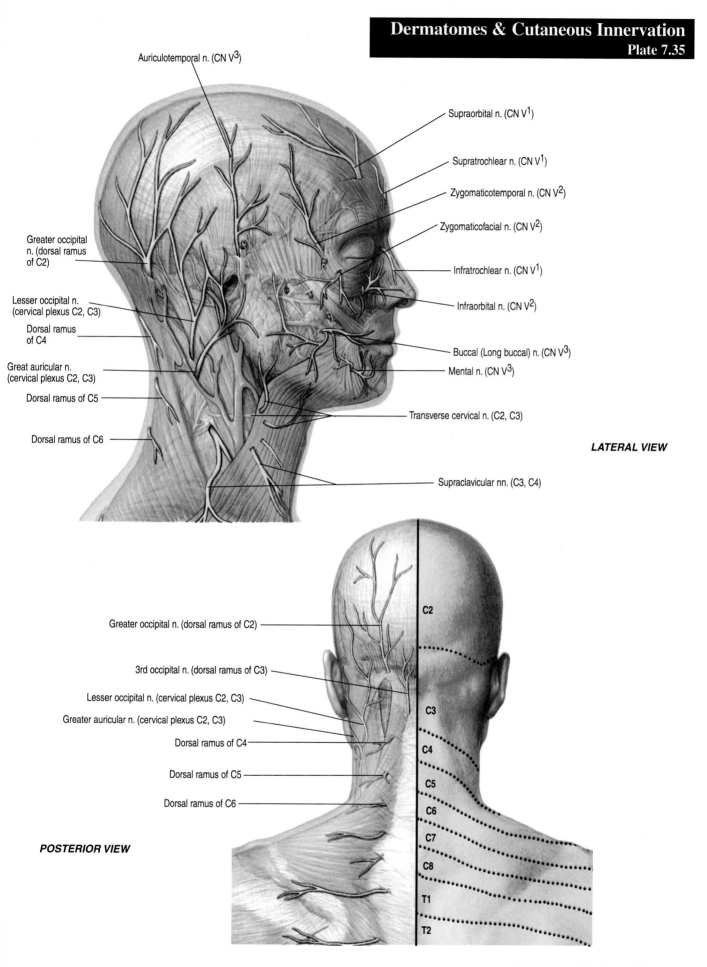

Auriculotemporal n. (CN V^3)

Supraorbital n. (CN V^1)

Supratrochlear n. (CN V^1)

Zygomaticotemporal n. (CN V^2)

Zygomaticofacial n. (CN V^2)

Greater occipital n. (dorsal ramus of C2)

Infratrochlear n. (CN V^1)

Infraorbital n. (CN V^2)

Lesser occipital n. (cervical plexus C2, C3)

Dorsal ramus of C4

Buccal (Long buccal) n. (CN V^3)

Mental n. (CN V^3)

Great auricular n. (cervical plexus C2, C3)

Dorsal ramus of C5

Transverse cervical n. (C2, C3)

Dorsal ramus of C6

LATERAL VIEW

Supraclavicular nn. (C3, C4)

Greater occipital n. (dorsal ramus of C2)

C2

3rd occipital n. (dorsal ramus of C3)

C3

Lesser occipital n. (cervical plexus C2, C3)

Greater auricular n. (cervical plexus C2, C3)

C4

Dorsal ramus of C4

C5

Dorsal ramus of C5

C6

Dorsal ramus of C6

C7

C8

POSTERIOR VIEW

T1

T2

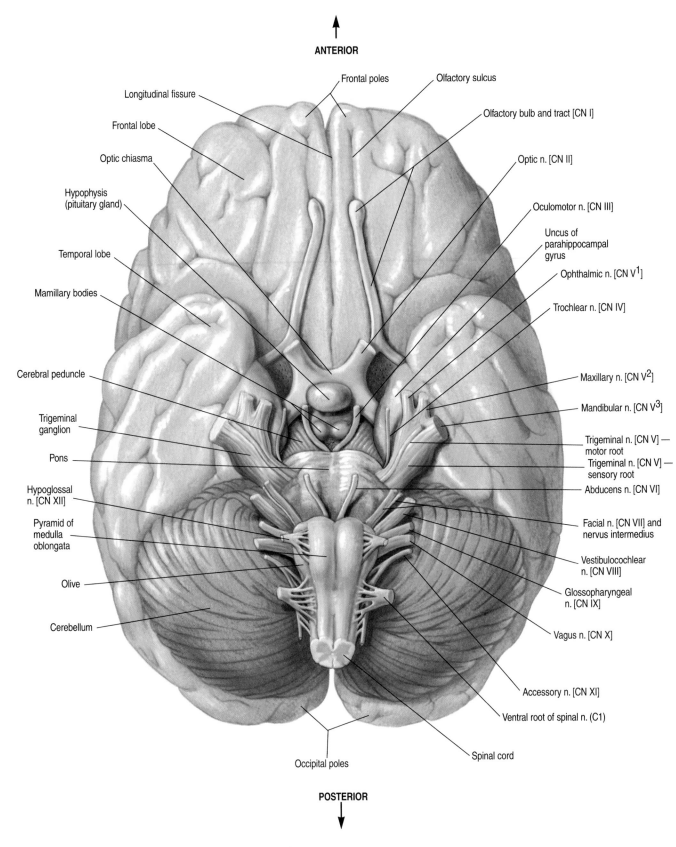

ANTERIOR

Longitudinal fissure

Frontal poles

Olfactory sulcus

Frontal lobe

Olfactory bulb and tract [CN I]

Optic chiasma

Optic n. [CN II]

Hypophysis
(pituitary gland)

Oculomotor n. [CN III]

Uncus of
parahippocampal
gyrus

Temporal lobe

Ophthalmic n. [CN V¹]

Mamillary bodies

Trochlear n. [CN IV]

Cerebral peduncle

Maxillary n. [CN V²]

Mandibular n. [CN V³]

Trigeminal
ganglion

Trigeminal n. [CN V] —
motor root

Pons

Trigeminal n. [CN V] —
sensory root

Hypoglossal
n. [CN XII]

Abducens n. [CN VI]

Facial n. [CN VII] and
nervus intermedius

Pyramid of
medulla
oblongata

Vestibulocochlear
n. [CN VIII]

Olive

Glossopharyngeal
n. [CN IX]

Cerebellum

Vagus n. [CN X]

Accessory n. [CN XI]

Ventral root of spinal n. (C1)

Occipital poles

Spinal cord

POSTERIOR

INFERIOR SURFACE OF BRAIN, BRAINSTEM & SPINAL CORD

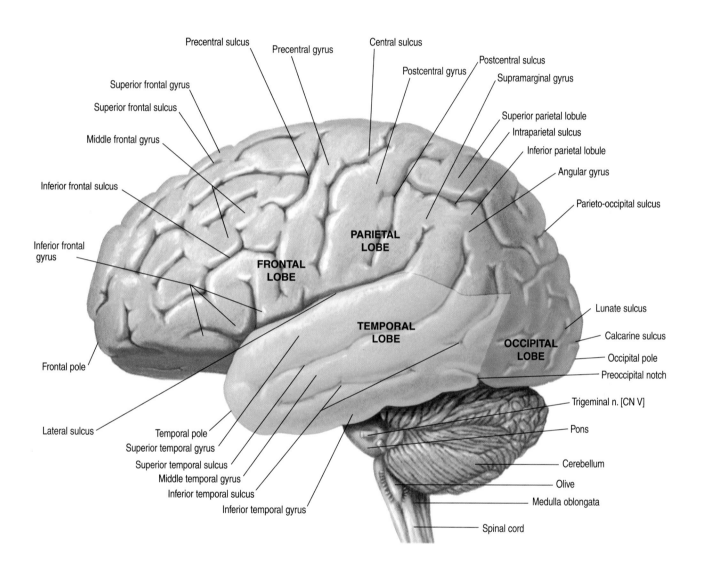

Precentral sulcus

Precentral gyrus

Central sulcus

Postcentral sulcus

Postcentral gyrus

Supramarginal gyrus

Superior frontal gyrus

Superior frontal sulcus

Superior parietal lobule

Intraparietal sulcus

Middle frontal gyrus

Inferior parietal lobule

Angular gyrus

Inferior frontal sulcus

Parieto-occipital sulcus

Inferior frontal gyrus

PARIETAL LOBE

FRONTAL LOBE

Lunate sulcus

Calcarine sulcus

TEMPORAL LOBE

OCCIPITAL LOBE

Occipital pole

Preoccipital notch

Frontal pole

Trigeminal n. [CN V]

Pons

Lateral sulcus

Cerebellum

Temporal pole

Superior temporal gyrus

Olive

Superior temporal sulcus

Medulla oblongata

Middle temporal gyrus

Inferior temporal sulcus

Spinal cord

Inferior temporal gyrus

LEFT LATERAL VIEW OF BRAIN & BRAINSTEM

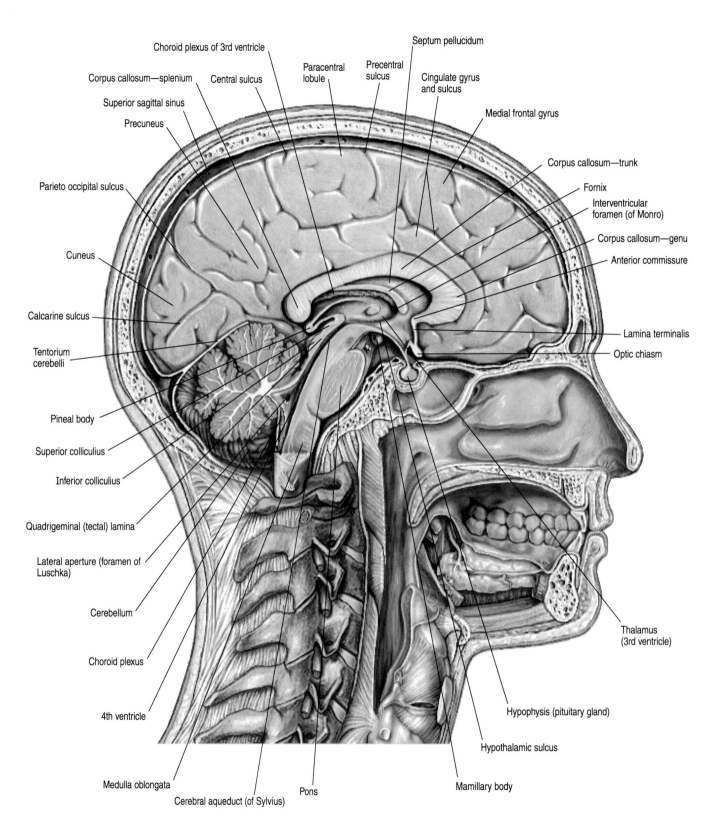

Choroid plexus of 3rd ventricle

Corpus callosum—splenium

Central sulcus

Paracentral lobule

Precentral sulcus

Septum pellucidum

Cingulate gyrus and sulcus

Superior sagittal sinus

Precuneus

Medial frontal gyrus

Corpus callosum—trunk

Fornix

Parieto occipital sulcus

Interventricular foramen (of Monro)

Corpus callosum—genu

Cuneus

Anterior commissure

Calcarine sulcus

Lamina terminalis

Tentorium cerebelli

Optic chiasm

Pineal body

Superior colliculius

Inferior colliculius

Quadrigeminal (tectal) lamina

Lateral aperture (foramen of Luschka)

Cerebellum

Choroid plexus

Thalamus (3rd ventricle)

4th ventricle

Medulla oblongata

Cerebral aqueduct (of Sylvius)

Pons

Hypophysis (pituitary gland)

Hypothalamic sulcus

Mamillary body

LATERAL VIEW WITH BRAIN & BRAINSTEM MEDIAN SECTIONED

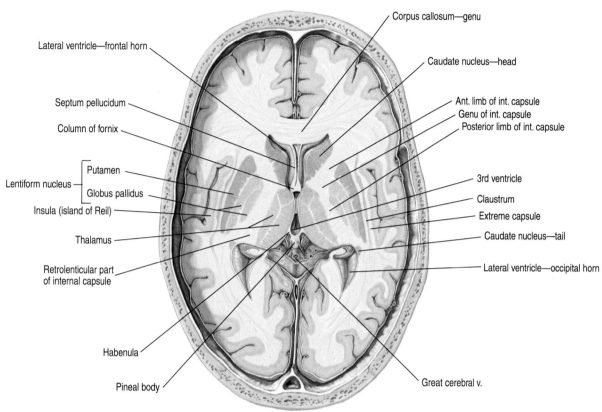

Corpus callosum—genu

Lateral ventricle—frontal horn

Caudate nucleus—head

Septum pellucidum

Ant. limb of int. capsule
Genu of int. capsule
Posterior limb of int. capsule

Column of fornix

Putamen
Lentiform nucleus
Globus pallidus

3rd ventricle

Insula (island of Reil)

Claustrum

Extreme capsule

Thalamus

Caudate nucleus—tail

Retrolenticular part
of internal capsule

Lateral ventricle—occipital horn

Habenula

Pineal body

Great cerebral v.

HORIZONTAL SECTIONS OF BRAIN

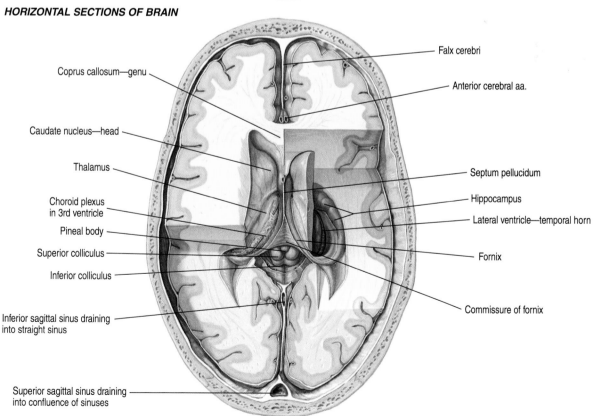

Coprus callosum—genu

Falx cerebri

Anterior cerebral aa.

Caudate nucleus—head

Thalamus

Septum pellucidum

Choroid plexus
in 3rd ventricle

Hippocampus

Lateral ventricle—temporal horn

Pineal body

Superior colliculus

Fornix

Inferior colliculus

Inferior sagittal sinus draining
into straight sinus

Commissure of fornix

Superior sagittal sinus draining
into confluence of sinuses

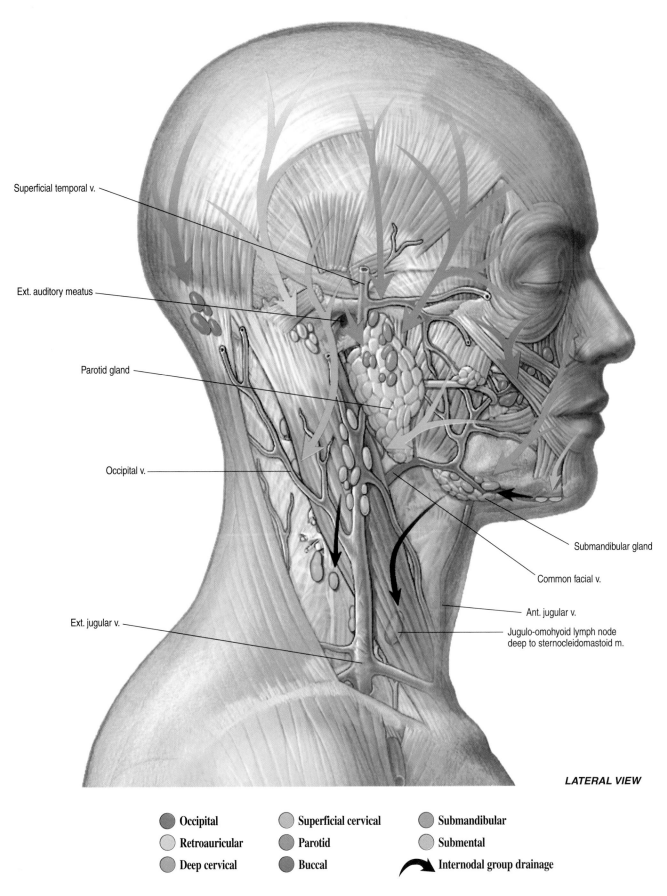

Superficial temporal v.

Ext. auditory meatus

Parotid gland

Occipital v.

Ext. jugular v.

Submandibular gland

Common facial v.

Ant. jugular v.

Jugulo-omohyoid lymph node
deep to sternocleidomastoid m.

LATERAL VIEW

- Occipital
- Retroauricular
- Deep cervical
- Superficial cervical
- Parotid
- Buccal
- Submandibular
- Submental
- Internodal group drainage

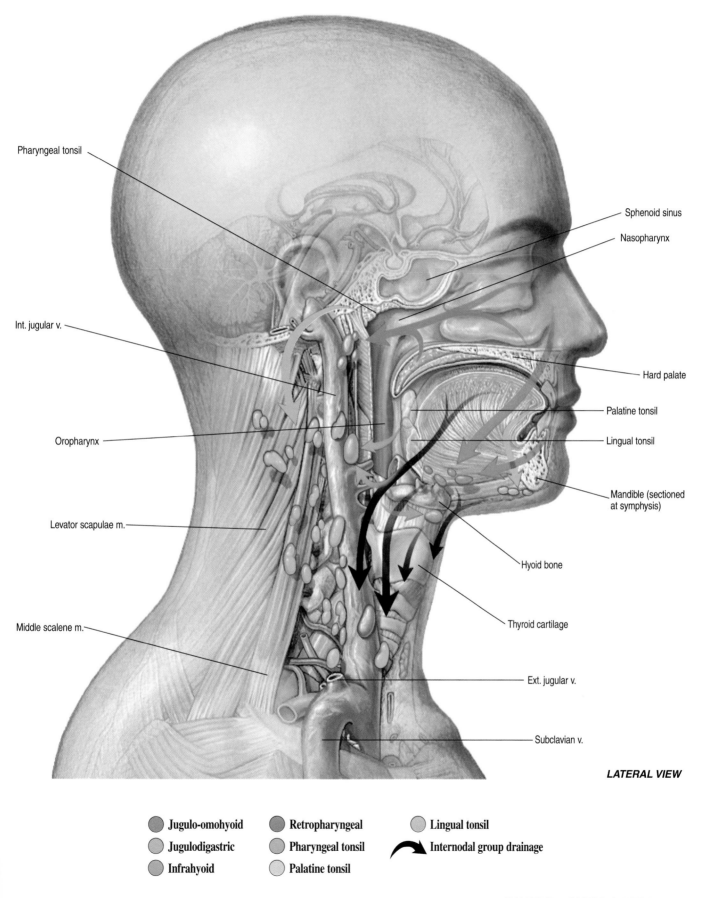

Pharyngeal tonsil

Sphenoid sinus

Nasopharynx

Int. jugular v.

Hard palate

Palatine tonsil

Oropharynx

Lingual tonsil

Mandible (sectioned at symphysis)

Levator scapulae m.

Hyoid bone

Middle scalene m.

Thyroid cartilage

Ext. jugular v.

Subclavian v.

LATERAL VIEW

Jugulo-omohyoid   Retropharyngeal   Lingual tonsil

Jugulodigastric   Pharyngeal tonsil   Internodal group drainage

Infrahyoid   Palatine tonsil

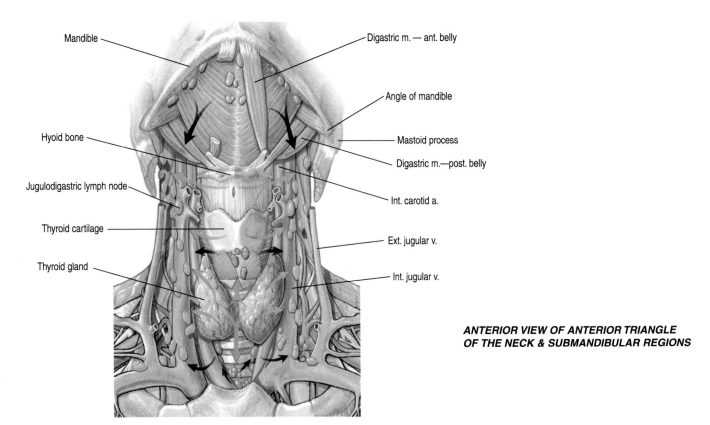

Mandible

Hyoid bone

Jugulodigastric lymph node

Thyroid cartilage

Thyroid gland

Digastric m. — ant. belly

Angle of mandible

Mastoid process

Digastric m.—post. belly

Int. carotid a.

Ext. jugular v.

Int. jugular v.

**ANTERIOR VIEW OF ANTERIOR TRIANGLE
OF THE NECK & SUBMANDIBULAR REGIONS**

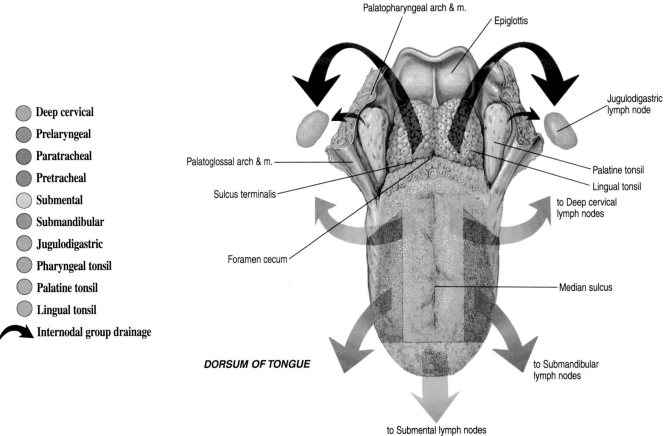

Deep cervical

Prelaryngeal

Paratracheal

Pretracheal

Submental

Submandibular

Jugulodigastric

Pharyngeal tonsil

Palatine tonsil

Lingual tonsil

Internodal group drainage

Palatopharyngeal arch & m.

Epiglottis

Jugulodigastric lymph node

Palatoglossal arch & m.

Sulcus terminalis

Foramen cecum

Palatine tonsil

Lingual tonsil

to Deep cervical lymph nodes

Median sulcus

to Submandibular lymph nodes

DORSUM OF TONGUE

to Submental lymph nodes

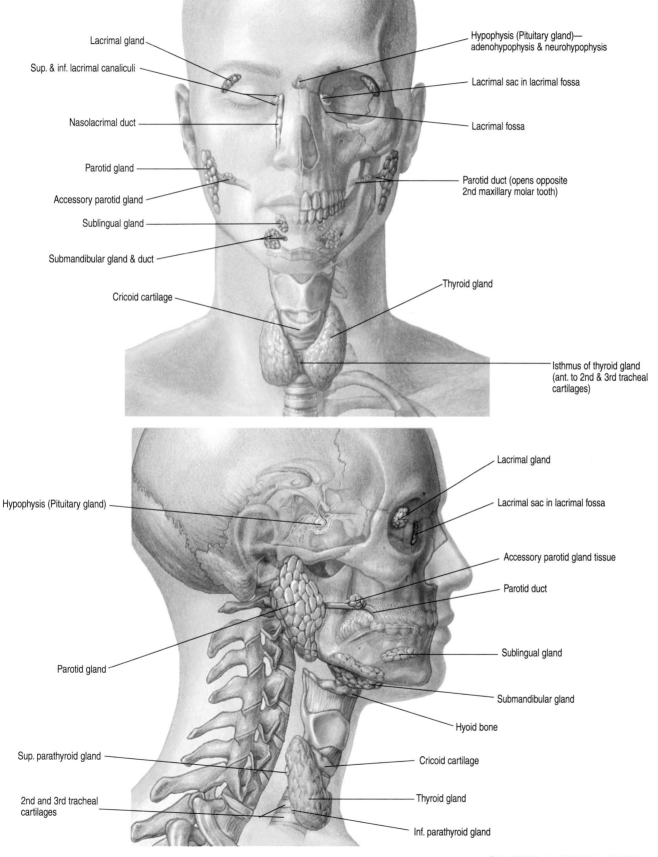

Lacrimal gland

Sup. & inf. lacrimal canaliculi

Nasolacrimal duct

Parotid gland

Accessory parotid gland

Sublingual gland

Submandibular gland & duct

Cricoid cartilage

Hypophysis (Pituitary gland)—
adenohypophysis & neurohypophysis

Lacrimal sac in lacrimal fossa

Lacrimal fossa

Parotid duct (opens opposite
2nd maxillary molar tooth)

Thyroid gland

Isthmus of thyroid gland
(ant. to 2nd & 3rd tracheal
cartilages)

Hypophysis (Pituitary gland)

Parotid gland

Sup. parathyroid gland

2nd and 3rd tracheal
cartilages

Lacrimal gland

Lacrimal sac in lacrimal fossa

Accessory parotid gland tissue

Parotid duct

Sublingual gland

Submandibular gland

Hyoid bone

Cricoid cartilage

Thyroid gland

Inf. parathyroid gland

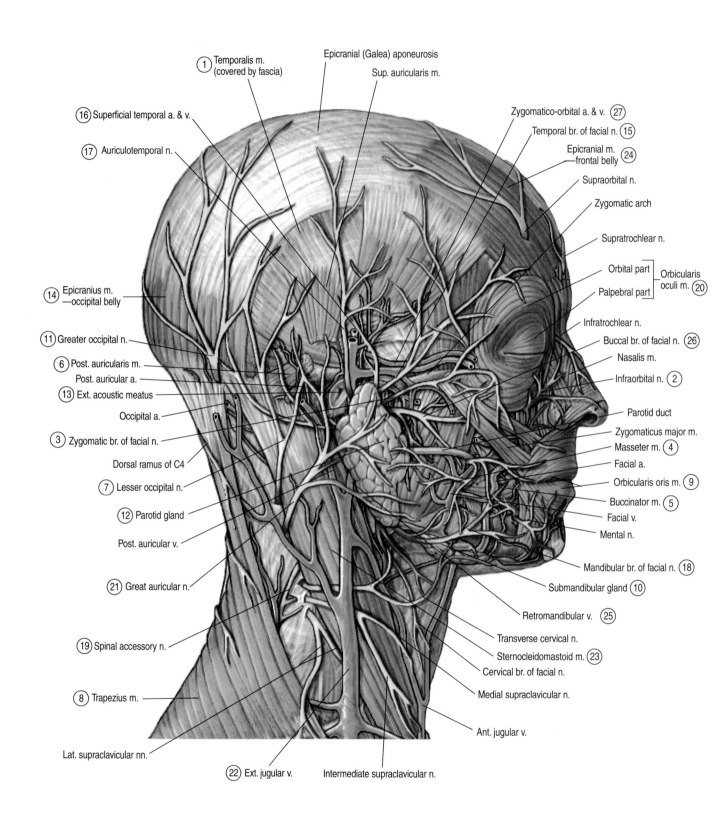

Temporalis m. (covered by fascia) ①

Epicranial (Galea) aponeurosis

Sup. auricularis m.

⑯ Superficial temporal a. & v.

⑰ Auriculotemporal n.

Zygomatico-orbital a. & v. ㉗

Temporal br. of facial n. ⑮

Epicranial m. —frontal belly ㉔

Supraorbital n.

Zygomatic arch

Supratrochlear n.

Orbital part ⎤
                ⎥ Orbicularis
Palpebral part ⎦ oculi m. ⑳

⑭ Epicranius m. —occipital belly

Infratrochlear n.

Buccal br. of facial n. ㉖

Nasalis m.

⑪ Greater occipital n.

⑥ Post. auricularis m.

Post. auricular a.

⑬ Ext. acoustic meatus

Occipital a.

Infraorbital n. ②

Parotid duct

③ Zygomatic br. of facial n.

Zygomaticus major m.

Masseter m. ④

Dorsal ramus of C4

Facial a.

⑦ Lesser occipital n.

Orbicularis oris m. ⑨

Buccinator m. ⑤

⑫ Parotid gland

Facial v.

Post. auricular v.

Mental n.

Mandibular br. of facial n. ⑱

㉑ Great auricular n.

Submandibular gland ⑩

Retromandibular v. ㉕

Transverse cervical n.

⑲ Spinal accessory n.

Sternocleidomastoid m. ㉓

Cervical br. of facial n.

Medial supraclavicular n.

⑧ Trapezius m.

Ant. jugular v.

Lat. supraclavicular nn.

㉒ Ext. jugular v.

Intermediate supraclavicular n.

LATERAL VIEW

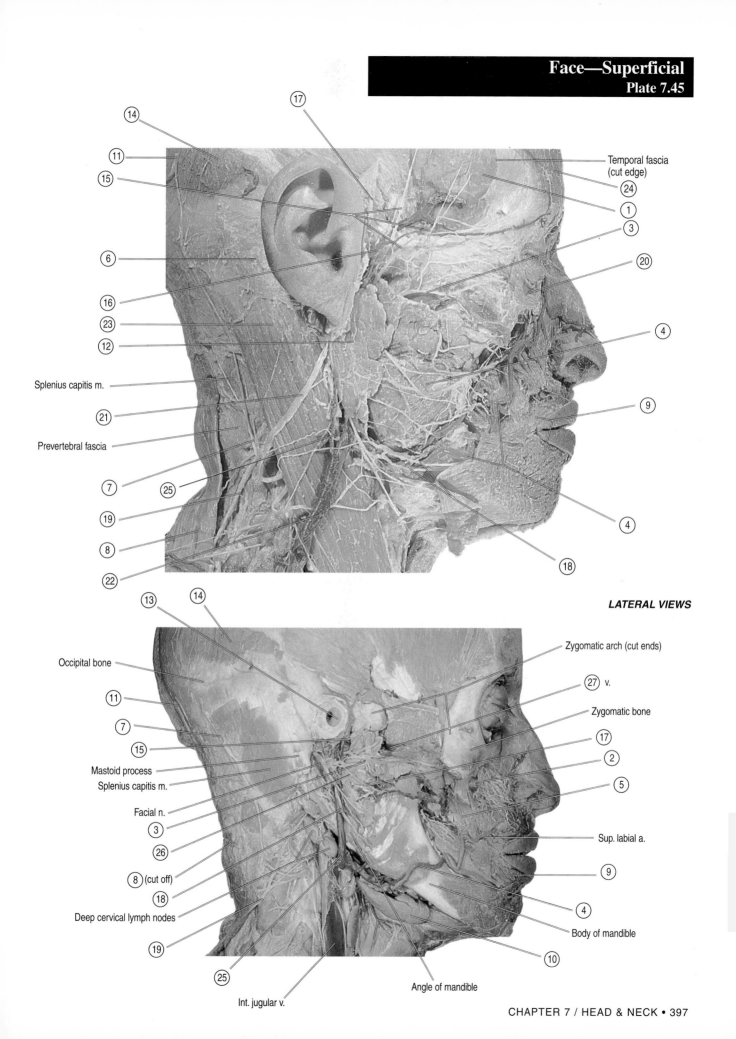

Temporal fascia
(cut edge)

Splenius capitis m.

Prevertebral fascia

LATERAL VIEWS

Occipital bone

Zygomatic arch (cut ends)

Zygomatic bone

Mastoid process

Splenius capitis m.

Facial n.

Sup. labial a.

Deep cervical lymph nodes

Body of mandible

Int. jugular v.

Angle of mandible

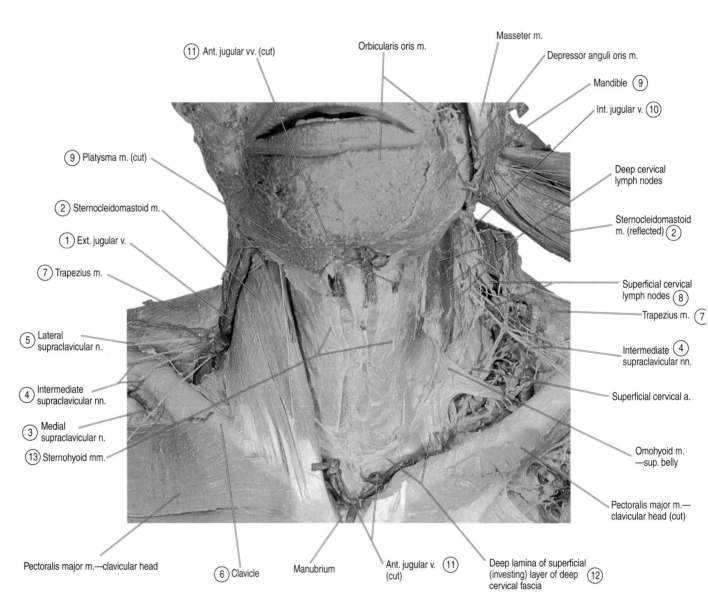

(11) Ant. jugular vv. (cut)

Orbicularis oris m.

Masseter m.

Depressor anguli oris m.

Mandible (9)

Int. jugular v. (10)

(9) Platysma m. (cut)

Deep cervical lymph nodes

(2) Sternocleidomastoid m.

Sternocleidomastoid m. (reflected) (2)

(1) Ext. jugular v.

(7) Trapezius m.

Superficial cervical lymph nodes (8)

Trapezius m. (7)

(5) Lateral supraclavicular n.

Intermediate (4) supraclavicular nn.

(4) Intermediate supraclavicular nn.

Superficial cervical a.

(3) Medial supraclavicular n.

(13) Sternohyoid mm.

Omohyoid m. —sup. belly

Pectoralis major m.— clavicular head (cut)

Pectoralis major m.—clavicular head

(6) Clavicle

Manubrium

Ant. jugular v. (11) (cut)

Deep lamina of superficial (investing) layer of deep cervical fascia (12)

**ANTERIOR VIEW OF NECK WITH DEEPER STRUCTURES
EXPOSED ON LEFT SIDE**

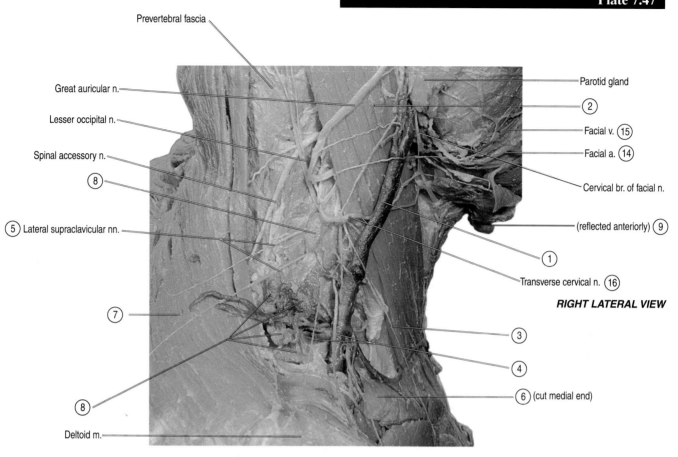

Prevertebral fascia

Great auricular n.

Lesser occipital n.

Spinal accessory n.

(8)

(5) Lateral supraclavicular nn.

(7)

(8)

Deltoid m.

Parotid gland

(2)

Facial v. (15)

Facial a. (14)

Cervical br. of facial n.

(reflected anteriorly) (9)

(1)

Transverse cervical n. (16)

RIGHT LATERAL VIEW

(3)

(4)

(6) (cut medial end)

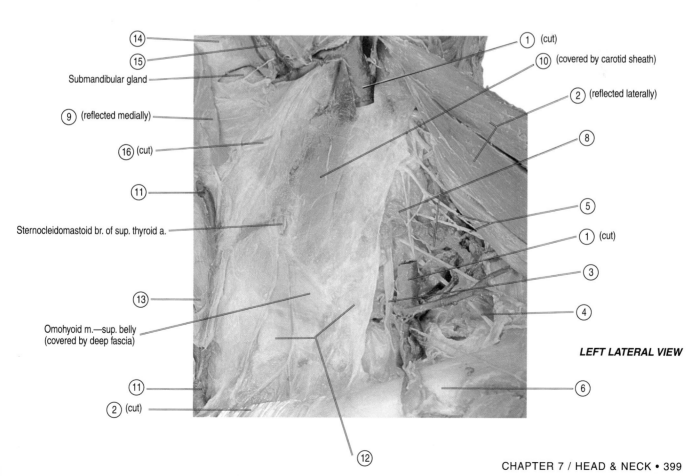

(14)

(15)

Submandibular gland

(9) (reflected medially)

(16) (cut)

(11)

Sternocleidomastoid br. of sup. thyroid a.

(13)

Omohyoid m.—sup. belly
(covered by deep fascia)

(11)

(2) (cut)

(12)

(1) (cut)

(10) (covered by carotid sheath)

(2) (reflected laterally)

(8)

(5)

(1) (cut)

(3)

(4)

LEFT LATERAL VIEW

(6)

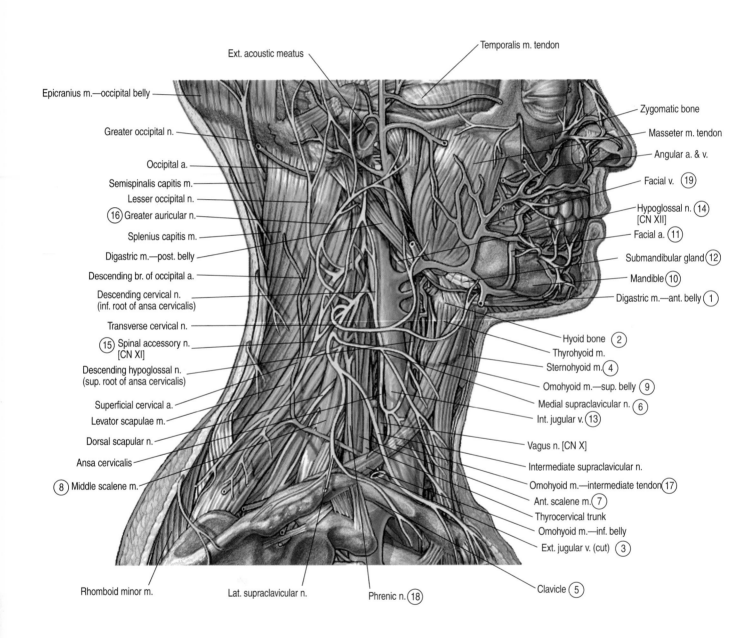

Ext. acoustic meatus

Temporalis m. tendon

Epicranius m.—occipital belly

Zygomatic bone

Greater occipital n.

Masseter m. tendon

Occipital a.

Angular a. & v.

Semispinalis capitis m.

Facial v. (19)

Lesser occipital n.

Hypoglossal n. (14)
[CN XII]

(16) Greater auricular n.

Splenius capitis m.

Facial a. (11)

Digastric m.—post. belly

Submandibular gland (12)

Descending br. of occipital a.

Mandible (10)

Descending cervical n.
(inf. root of ansa cervicalis)

Digastric m.—ant. belly (1)

Transverse cervical n.

Hyoid bone (2)

(15) Spinal accessory n.
[CN XI]

Thyrohyoid m.

Sternohyoid m. (4)

Descending hypoglossal n.
(sup. root of ansa cervicalis)

Omohyoid m.—sup. belly (9)

Superficial cervical a.

Medial supraclavicular n. (6)

Levator scapulae m.

Int. jugular v. (13)

Dorsal scapular n.

Vagus n. [CN X]

Ansa cervicalis

Intermediate supraclavicular n.

(8) Middle scalene m.

Omohyoid m.—intermediate tendon (17)

Ant. scalene m. (7)

Thyrocervical trunk

Omohyoid m.—inf. belly

Ext. jugular v. (cut) (3)

Rhomboid minor m.

Lat. supraclavicular n.

Phrenic n. (18)

Clavicle (5)

LATERAL VIEW

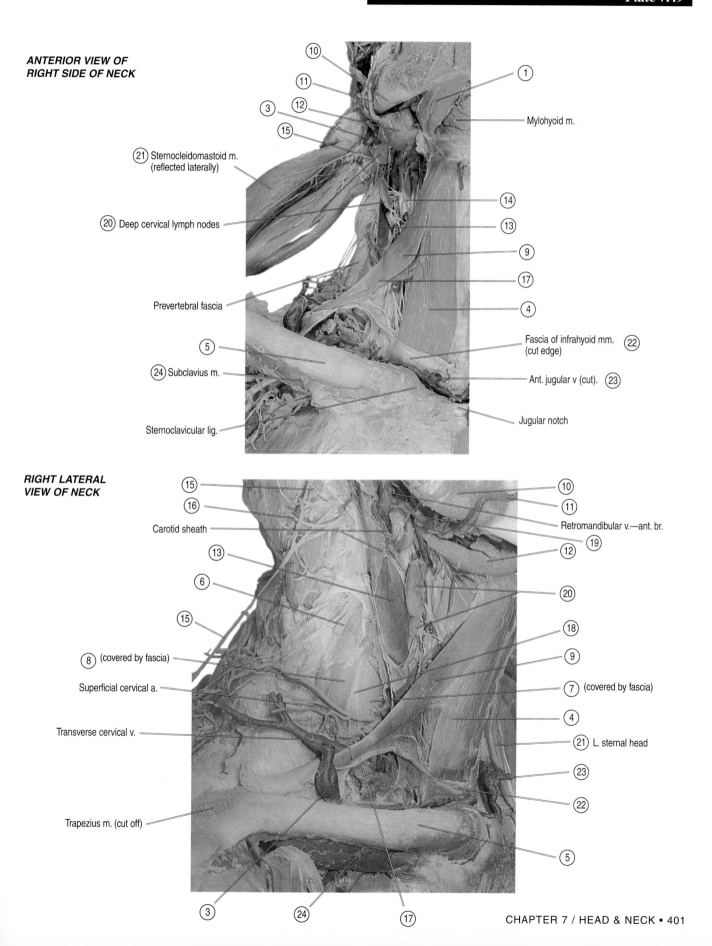

ANTERIOR VIEW OF RIGHT SIDE OF NECK

10
11
1 — Mylohyoid m.
3
12
15
21 Sternocleidomastoid m. (reflected laterally)
20 Deep cervical lymph nodes
14
13
9
17
Prevertebral fascia
4
5 — Fascia of infrahyoid mm. (cut edge) 22
24 Subclavius m. — Ant. jugular v (cut). 23
Sternoclavicular lig. — Jugular notch

RIGHT LATERAL VIEW OF NECK

15
16
Carotid sheath
13
6
15
8 (covered by fascia)
Superficial cervical a.
Transverse cervical v.
Trapezius m. (cut off)

10
11
Retromandibular v.—ant. br.
12 19
20
18
9
7 (covered by fascia)
4
21 L. sternal head
23
22
5

3   24   17

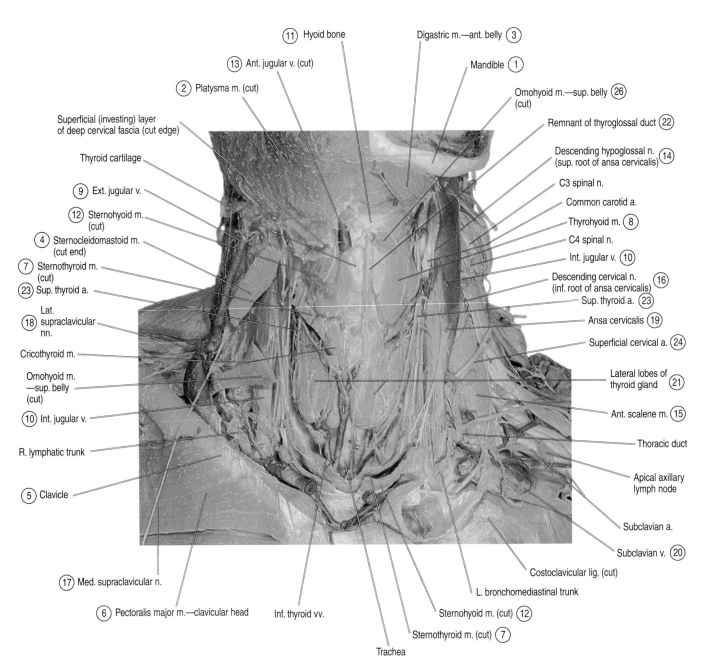

⑪ Hyoid bone

Digastric m.—ant. belly ③

⑬ Ant. jugular v. (cut)

Mandible ①

② Platysma m. (cut)

Omohyoid m.—sup. belly ㉖ (cut)

Superficial (investing) layer of deep cervical fascia (cut edge)

Remnant of thyroglossal duct ㉒

Descending hypoglossal n. ⑭ (sup. root of ansa cervicalis)

Thyroid cartilage

C3 spinal n.

⑨ Ext. jugular v.

Common carotid a.

⑫ Sternohyoid m. (cut)

Thyrohyoid m. ⑧

④ Sternocleidomastoid m. (cut end)

C4 spinal n.

Int. jugular v. ⑩

⑦ Sternothyroid m. (cut)

Descending cervical n. ⑯ (inf. root of ansa cervicalis)

㉓ Sup. thyroid a.

Sup. thyroid a. ㉓

⑱ Lat. supraclavicular nn.

Ansa cervicalis ⑲

Superficial cervical a. ㉔

Cricothyroid m.

Lateral lobes of thyroid gland ㉑

Omohyoid m. —sup. belly (cut)

Ant. scalene m. ⑮

⑩ Int. jugular v.

R. lymphatic trunk

Thoracic duct

Apical axillary lymph node

⑤ Clavicle

Subclavian a.

Subclavian v. ⑳

⑰ Med. supraclavicular n.

Costoclavicular lig. (cut)

L. bronchomediastinal trunk

⑥ Pectoralis major m.—clavicular head

Inf. thyroid vv.

Sternohyoid m. (cut) ⑫

Sternothyroid m. (cut) ⑦

Trachea

**ANTERIOR VIEW OF NECK
WITH DEEP STRUCTURES ON RIGHT SIDE**

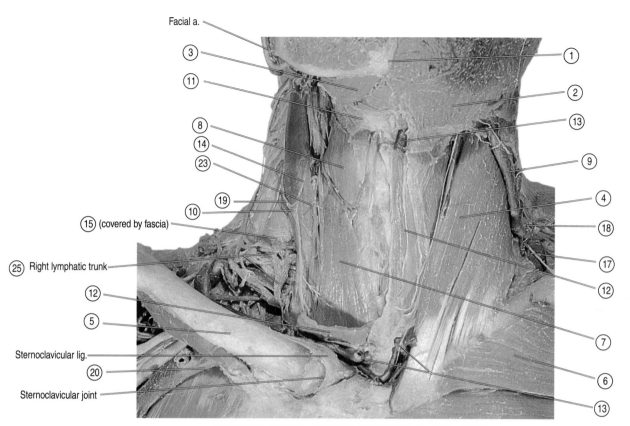

Facial a.

③

⑪

⑧

⑭

㉓

⑲

⑩

⑮ (covered by fascia)

㉕ Right lymphatic trunk

⑫

⑤

Sternoclavicular lig.

⑳

Sternoclavicular joint

①

②

⑬

⑨

④

⑱

⑰

⑫

⑦

⑥

⑬

ANTERIOR VIEW OF NECK WITH DEEPER STRUCTURES ON RIGHT SIDE

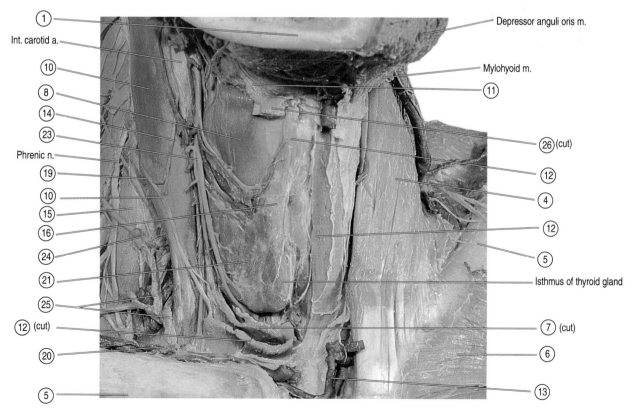

①

Int. carotid a.

⑩

⑧

⑭

㉓

Phrenic n.

⑲

⑩

⑮

⑯

㉔

㉑

㉕

⑫ (cut)

⑳

⑤

Depressor anguli oris m.

Mylohyoid m.

⑪

㉖ (cut)

⑫

④

⑫

⑤

Isthmus of thyroid gland

⑦ (cut)

⑥

⑬

ANTEROLATERAL VIEW OF RIGHT SIDE OF NECK

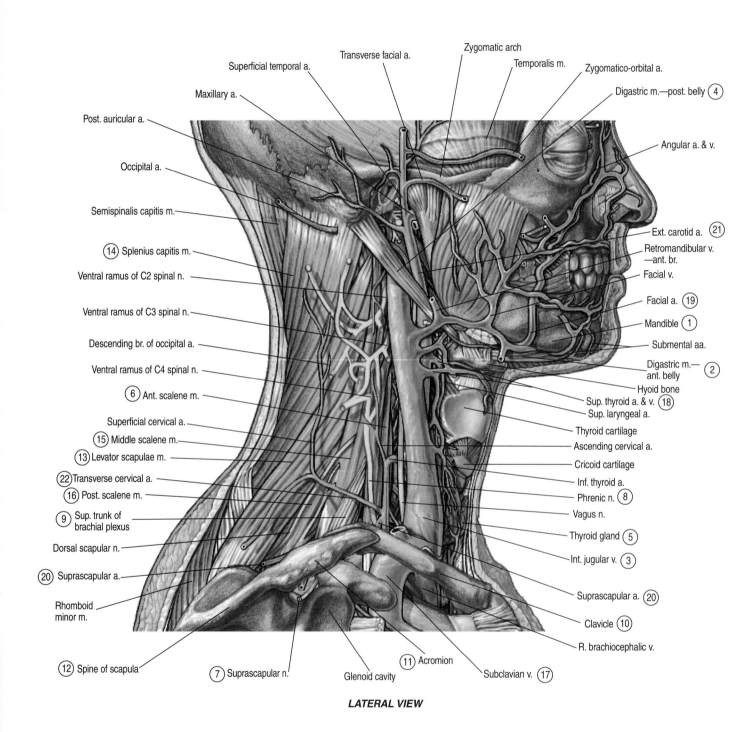

Transverse facial a.

Zygomatic arch

Superficial temporal a.

Temporalis m.

Zygomatico-orbital a.

Maxillary a.

Digastric m.—post. belly ④

Post. auricular a.

Angular a. & v.

Occipital a.

Semispinalis capitis m.

Ext. carotid a. ㉑

⑭ Splenius capitis m.

Retromandibular v. —ant. br.

Ventral ramus of C2 spinal n.

Facial v.

Ventral ramus of C3 spinal n.

Facial a. ⑲

Descending br. of occipital a.

Mandible ①

Ventral ramus of C4 spinal n.

Submental aa.

⑥ Ant. scalene m.

Digastric m.— ant. belly ②

Hyoid bone

Superficial cervical a.

Sup. thyroid a. & v. ⑱

⑮ Middle scalene m.

Sup. laryngeal a.

⑬ Levator scapulae m.

Thyroid cartilage

㉒ Transverse cervical a.

Ascending cervical a.

⑯ Post. scalene m.

Cricoid cartilage

Inf. thyroid a.

⑨ Sup. trunk of brachial plexus

Phrenic n. ⑧

Vagus n.

Dorsal scapular n.

Thyroid gland ⑤

㉑ Suprascapular a.

Int. jugular v. ③

Rhomboid minor m.

Suprascapular a. ⑳

⑫ Spine of scapula

Clavicle ⑩

R. brachiocephalic v.

⑦ Suprascapular n.

⑪ Acromion

Glenoid cavity

Subclavian v. ⑰

LATERAL VIEW

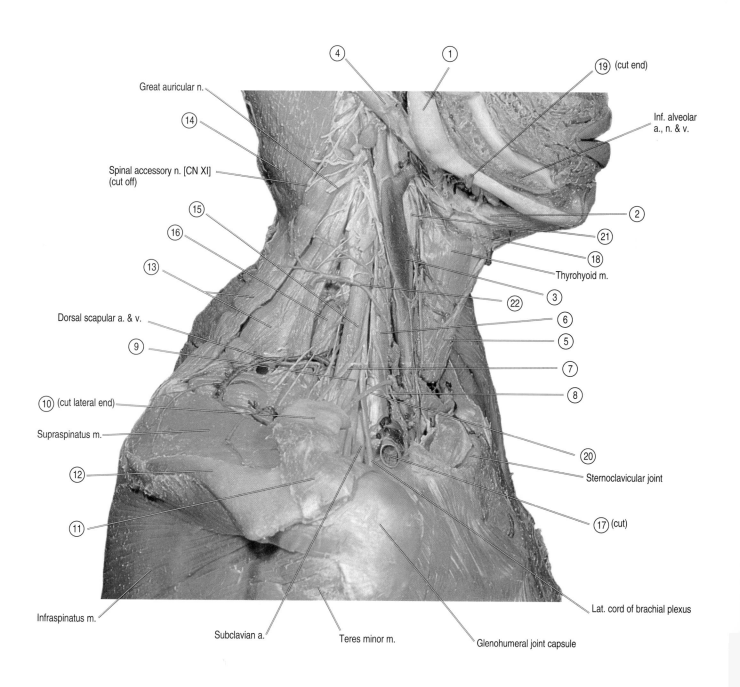

Great auricular n.

④ ① ⑲ (cut end)

Inf. alveolar
a., n. & v.

⑭

Spinal accessory n. [CN XI]
(cut off)

②

⑮ ㉑

⑯ ⑱

⑬ Thyrohyoid m.

Dorsal scapular a. & v. ㉒ ③

⑥

⑨ ⑤

⑦

⑩ (cut lateral end) ⑧

Supraspinatus m.

⑫ ⑳

Sternoclavicular joint

⑪

⑰ (cut)

Infraspinatus m. Lat. cord of brachial plexus

Subclavian a. Teres minor m. Glenohumeral joint capsule

LATERAL VIEW

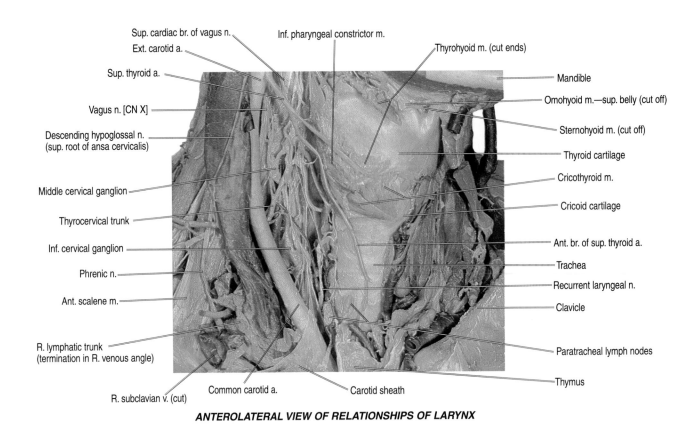

Sup. cardiac br. of vagus n.

Ext. carotid a.

Sup. thyroid a.

Vagus n. [CN X]

Descending hypoglossal n.
(sup. root of ansa cervicalis)

Middle cervical ganglion

Thyrocervical trunk

Inf. cervical ganglion

Phrenic n.

Ant. scalene m.

R. lymphatic trunk
(termination in R. venous angle)

R. subclavian v. (cut)

Common carotid a.

Inf. pharyngeal constrictor m.

Thyrohyoid m. (cut ends)

Mandible

Omohyoid m.—sup. belly (cut off)

Sternohyoid m. (cut off)

Thyroid cartilage

Cricothyroid m.

Cricoid cartilage

Ant. br. of sup. thyroid a.

Trachea

Recurrent laryngeal n.

Clavicle

Paratracheal lymph nodes

Thymus

Carotid sheath

ANTEROLATERAL VIEW OF RELATIONSHIPS OF LARYNX

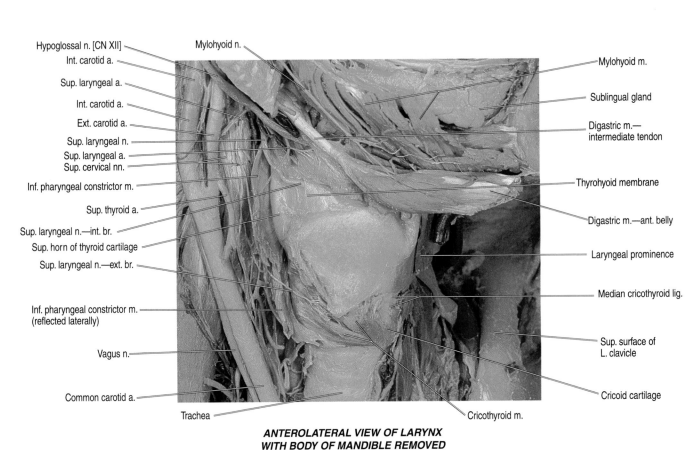

Hypoglossal n. [CN XII]

Int. carotid a.

Sup. laryngeal a.

Int. carotid a.

Ext. carotid a.

Sup. laryngeal n.

Sup. laryngeal a.

Sup. cervical nn.

Inf. pharyngeal constrictor m.

Sup. thyroid a.

Sup. laryngeal n.—int. br.

Sup. horn of thyroid cartilage

Sup. laryngeal n.—ext. br.

Inf. pharyngeal constrictor m.
(reflected laterally)

Vagus n.

Common carotid a.

Trachea

Mylohyoid n.

Mylohyoid m.

Sublingual gland

Digastric m.—
intermediate tendon

Thyrohyoid membrane

Digastric m.—ant. belly

Laryngeal prominence

Median cricothyroid lig.

Sup. surface of
L. clavicle

Cricoid cartilage

Cricothyroid m.

**ANTEROLATERAL VIEW OF LARYNX
WITH BODY OF MANDIBLE REMOVED**

**ANTEROLATERAL VIEW
OF LARYNX**

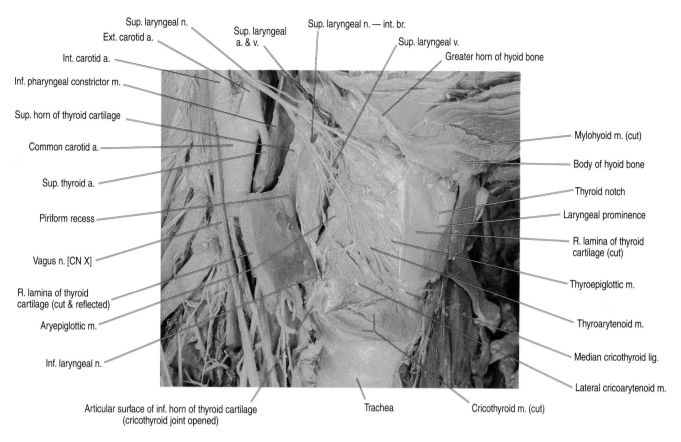

Sup. laryngeal n.

Ext. carotid a.

Int. carotid a.

Inf. pharyngeal constrictor m.

Sup. horn of thyroid cartilage

Common carotid a.

Sup. thyroid a.

Piriform recess

Vagus n. [CN X]

R. lamina of thyroid
cartilage (cut & reflected)

Aryepiglottic m.

Inf. laryngeal n.

Sup. laryngeal
a. & v.

Sup. laryngeal n. — int. br.

Sup. laryngeal v.

Greater horn of hyoid bone

Mylohyoid m. (cut)

Body of hyoid bone

Thyroid notch

Laryngeal prominence

R. lamina of thyroid
cartilage (cut)

Thyroepiglottic m.

Thyroarytenoid m.

Median cricothyroid lig.

Lateral cricoarytenoid m.

Articular surface of inf. horn of thyroid cartilage
(cricothyroid joint opened)

Trachea

Cricothyroid m. (cut)

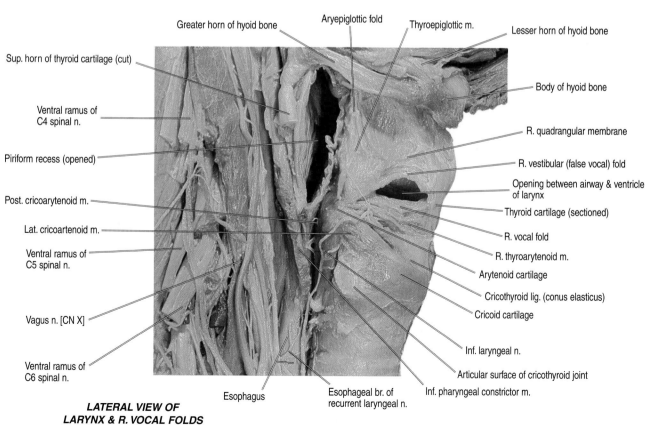

Greater horn of hyoid bone

Aryepiglottic fold

Thyroepiglottic m.

Lesser horn of hyoid bone

Sup. horn of thyroid cartilage (cut)

Ventral ramus of
C4 spinal n.

Piriform recess (opened)

Post. cricoarytenoid m.

Lat. cricoartenoid m.

Ventral ramus of
C5 spinal n.

Vagus n. [CN X]

Ventral ramus of
C6 spinal n.

Body of hyoid bone

R. quadrangular membrane

R. vestibular (false vocal) fold

Opening between airway & ventricle
of larynx

Thyroid cartilage (sectioned)

R. vocal fold

R. thyroarytenoid m.

Arytenoid cartilage

Cricothyroid lig. (conus elasticus)

Cricoid cartilage

Inf. laryngeal n.

Articular surface of cricothyroid joint

Inf. pharyngeal constrictor m.

Esophagus

Esophageal br. of
recurrent laryngeal n.

**LATERAL VIEW OF
LARYNX & R. VOCAL FOLDS**

POSTERIOR VIEW OF LARYNX

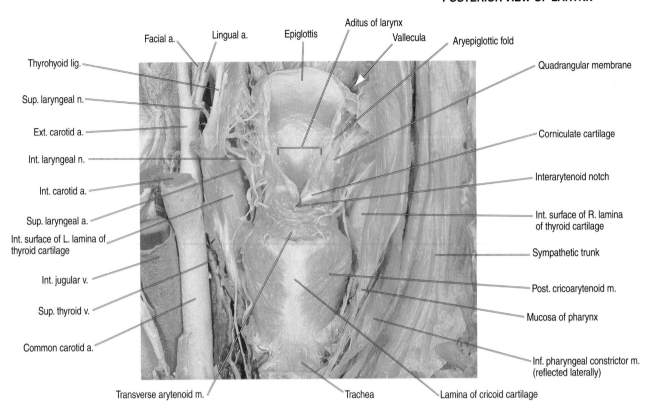

Facial a.

Lingual a.

Epiglottis

Aditus of larynx

Vallecula

Aryepiglottic fold

Thyrohyoid lig.

Sup. laryngeal n.

Ext. carotid a.

Int. laryngeal n.

Int. carotid a.

Sup. laryngeal a.

Int. surface of L. lamina of thyroid cartilage

Int. jugular v.

Sup. thyroid v.

Common carotid a.

Quadrangular membrane

Corniculate cartilage

Interarytenoid notch

Int. surface of R. lamina of thyroid cartilage

Sympathetic trunk

Post. cricoarytenoid m.

Mucosa of pharynx

Inf. pharyngeal constrictor m. (reflected laterally)

Transverse arytenoid m.

Trachea

Lamina of cricoid cartilage

ANTERIOR

Epiglottis

Sup. laryngeal v.

Tubercle of epiglottis

SUPERIOR VIEW OF LARYNX

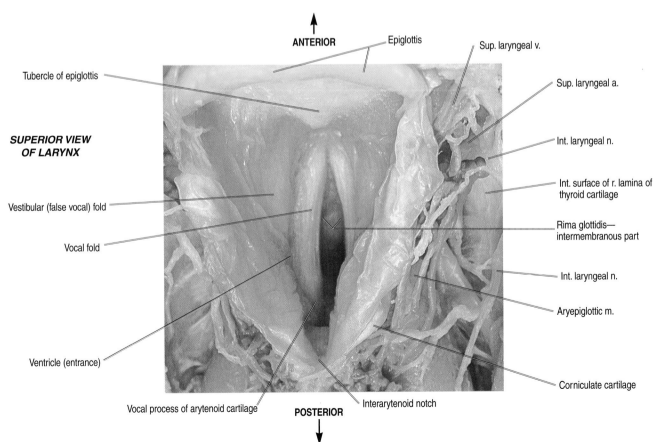

Sup. laryngeal a.

Int. laryngeal n.

Int. surface of r. lamina of thyroid cartilage

Rima glottidis— intermembranous part

Int. laryngeal n.

Aryepiglottic m.

Corniculate cartilage

Vestibular (false vocal) fold

Vocal fold

Ventricle (entrance)

Vocal process of arytenoid cartilage

Interarytenoid notch

POSTERIOR

MEDIAL VIEW OF LEFT HALF OF LARYNX

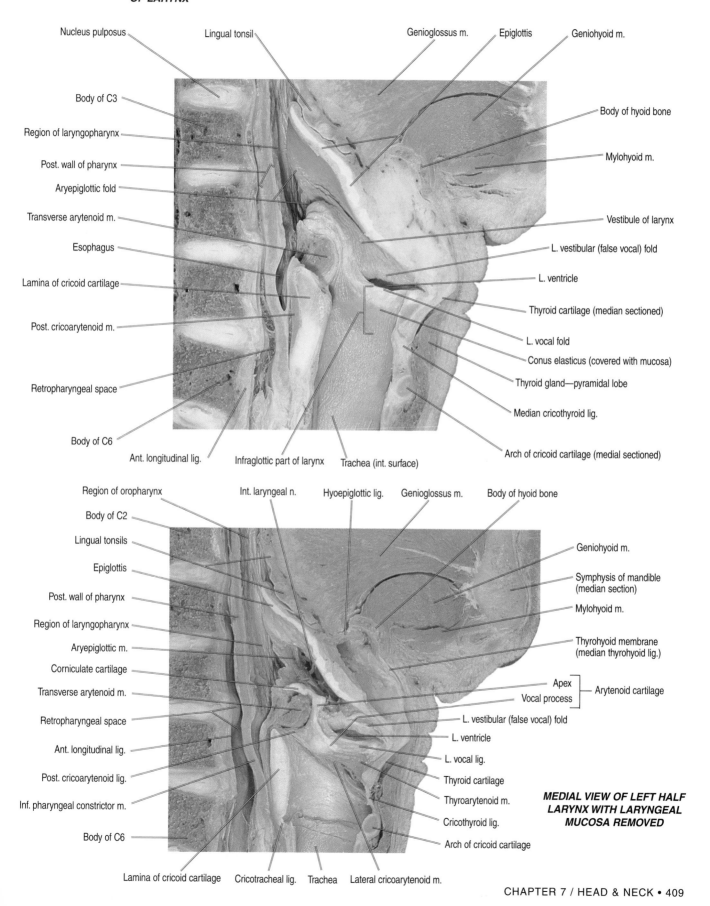

Nucleus pulposus

Lingual tonsil

Genioglossus m.

Epiglottis

Geniohyoid m.

Body of C3

Region of laryngopharynx

Post. wall of pharynx

Aryepiglottic fold

Transverse arytenoid m.

Esophagus

Lamina of cricoid cartilage

Post. cricoarytenoid m.

Retropharyngeal space

Body of C6

Ant. longitudinal lig.

Infraglottic part of larynx

Trachea (int. surface)

Body of hyoid bone

Mylohyoid m.

Vestibule of larynx

L. vestibular (false vocal) fold

L. ventricle

Thyroid cartilage (median sectioned)

L. vocal fold

Conus elasticus (covered with mucosa)

Thyroid gland—pyramidal lobe

Median cricothyroid lig.

Arch of cricoid cartilage (medial sectioned)

Region of oropharynx

Int. laryngeal n.

Hyoepiglottic lig.

Genioglossus m.

Body of hyoid bone

Body of C2

Lingual tonsils

Epiglottis

Post. wall of pharynx

Region of laryngopharynx

Aryepiglottic m.

Corniculate cartilage

Transverse arytenoid m.

Retropharyngeal space

Ant. longitudinal lig.

Post. cricoarytenoid lig.

Inf. pharyngeal constrictor m.

Body of C6

Geniohyoid m.

Symphysis of mandible (median section)

Mylohyoid m.

Thyrohyoid membrane (median thyrohyoid lig.)

Apex
Vocal process
— Arytenoid cartilage

L. vestibular (false vocal) fold

L. ventricle

L. vocal lig.

Thyroid cartilage

Thyroarytenoid m.

Cricothyroid lig.

Arch of cricoid cartilage

MEDIAL VIEW OF LEFT HALF LARYNX WITH LARYNGEAL MUCOSA REMOVED

Lamina of cricoid cartilage

Cricotracheal lig.

Trachea

Lateral cricoarytenoid m.

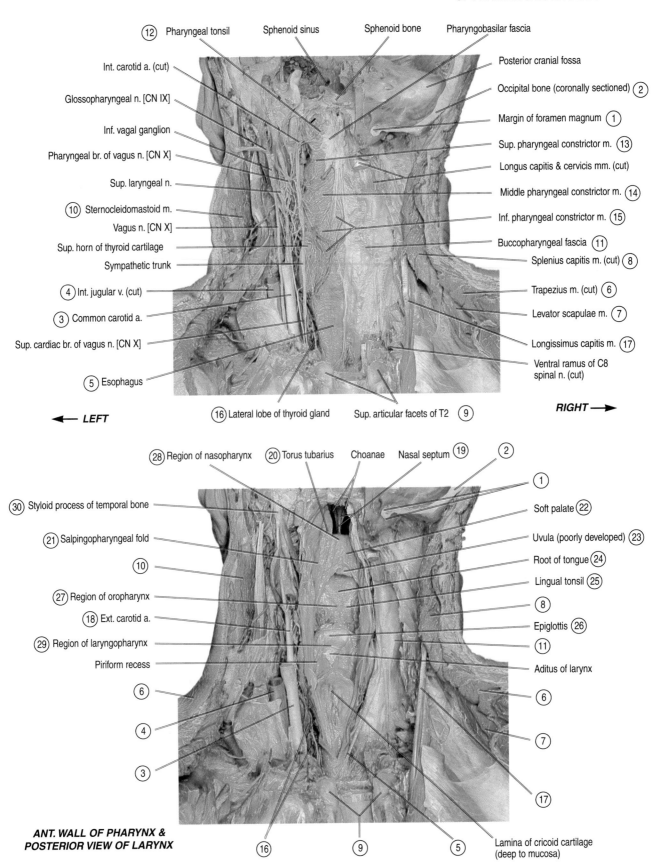

POSTERIOR VIEW OF POST. WALL OF PHARYNX & ESOPHAGUS

(12) Pharyngeal tonsil

Sphenoid sinus

Sphenoid bone

Pharyngobasilar fascia

Int. carotid a. (cut)

Glossopharyngeal n. [CN IX]

Inf. vagal ganglion

Pharyngeal br. of vagus n. [CN X]

Sup. laryngeal n.

(10) Sternocleidomastoid m.

Vagus n. [CN X]

Sup. horn of thyroid cartilage

Sympathetic trunk

(4) Int. jugular v. (cut)

(3) Common carotid a.

Sup. cardiac br. of vagus n. [CN X]

(5) Esophagus

Posterior cranial fossa

Occipital bone (coronally sectioned) (2)

Margin of foramen magnum (1)

Sup. pharyngeal constrictor m. (13)

Longus capitis & cervicis mm. (cut)

Middle pharyngeal constrictor m. (14)

Inf. pharyngeal constrictor m. (15)

Buccopharyngeal fascia (11)

Splenius capitis m. (cut) (8)

Trapezius m. (cut) (6)

Levator scapulae m. (7)

Longissimus capitis m. (17)

Ventral ramus of C8 spinal n. (cut)

← LEFT

(16) Lateral lobe of thyroid gland

Sup. articular facets of T2 (9)

RIGHT →

(28) Region of nasopharynx

(20) Torus tubarius

Choanae

Nasal septum (19)

(2)

(30) Styloid process of temporal bone

(21) Salpingopharyngeal fold

(10)

(27) Region of oropharynx

(18) Ext. carotid a.

(29) Region of laryngopharynx

Piriform recess

(6)

(4)

(3)

(1)

Soft palate (22)

Uvula (poorly developed) (23)

Root of tongue (24)

Lingual tonsil (25)

(8)

Epiglottis (26)

(11)

Aditus of larynx

(6)

(7)

(17)

ANT. WALL OF PHARYNX & POSTERIOR VIEW OF LARYNX

(16)

(9)

(5)

Lamina of cricoid cartilage (deep to mucosa)

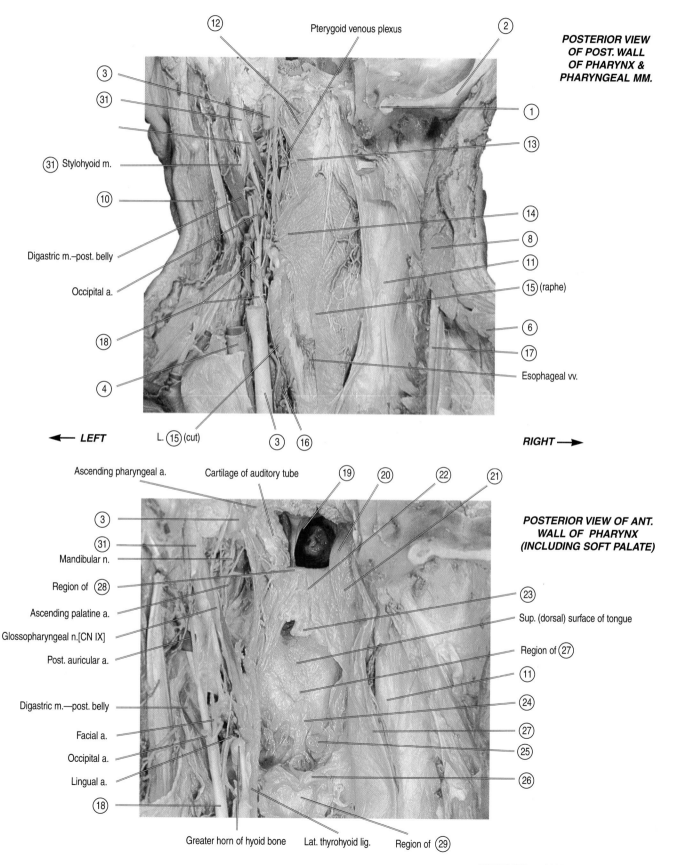

⑫ Pterygoid venous plexus ②

POSTERIOR VIEW OF POST. WALL OF PHARYNX & PHARYNGEAL MM.

③
㉛
㉛ Stylohyoid m.
⑩
Digastric m.–post. belly
Occipital a.
⑱
④

①
⑬
⑭
⑧
⑪
⑮ (raphe)
⑥
⑰
Esophageal vv.

◀— **LEFT**   L. ⑮ (cut)   ③ ⑯   **RIGHT** —▶

Ascending pharyngeal a.   Cartilage of auditory tube   ⑲ ⑳ ㉒ ㉑

POSTERIOR VIEW OF ANT. WALL OF PHARYNX (INCLUDING SOFT PALATE)

③
㉛
Mandibular n.
Region of ㉘
Ascending palatine a.
Glossopharyngeal n.[CN IX]
Post. auricular a.
Digastric m.—post. belly
Facial a.
Occipital a.
Lingual a.
⑱

㉓
Sup. (dorsal) surface of tongue
Region of ㉗
⑪
㉔
㉗
㉕
㉖

Greater horn of hyoid bone   Lat. thyrohyoid lig.   Region of ㉙

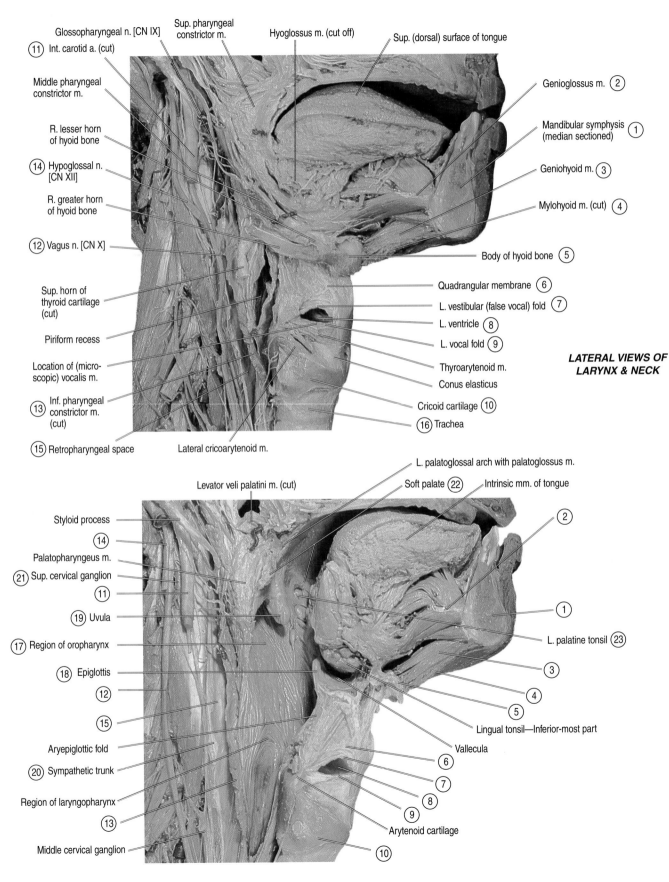

Glossopharyngeal n. [CN IX]
(11) Int. carotid a. (cut)

Middle pharyngeal constrictor m.

R. lesser horn of hyoid bone

(14) Hypoglossal n. [CN XII]

R. greater horn of hyoid bone

(12) Vagus n. [CN X]

Sup. horn of thyroid cartilage (cut)

Piriform recess

Location of (microscopic) vocalis m.

(13) Inf. pharyngeal constrictor m. (cut)

(15) Retropharyngeal space

Sup. pharyngeal constrictor m.

Hyoglossus m. (cut off)

Sup. (dorsal) surface of tongue

Genioglossus m. (2)

Mandibular symphysis (median sectioned) (1)

Geniohyoid m. (3)

Mylohyoid m. (cut) (4)

Body of hyoid bone (5)

Quadrangular membrane (6)

L. vestibular (false vocal) fold (7)

L. ventricle (8)

L. vocal fold (9)

Thyroarytenoid m.

Conus elasticus

Cricoid cartilage (10)

(16) Trachea

Lateral cricoarytenoid m.

LATERAL VIEWS OF LARYNX & NECK

Levator veli palatini m. (cut)

L. palatoglossal arch with palatoglossus m.

Soft palate (22)

Intrinsic mm. of tongue

Styloid process

(14)

Palatopharyngeus m.

(21) Sup. cervical ganglion

(11)

(19) Uvula

(17) Region of oropharynx

(18) Epiglottis

(12)

(15)

Aryepiglottic fold

(20) Sympathetic trunk

Region of laryngopharynx

(13)

Middle cervical ganglion

(2)

(1)

L. palatine tonsil (23)

(3)

(4)

(5)

Lingual tonsil—Inferior-most part

Vallecula

(6)

(7)

(8)

(9)

Arytenoid cartilage

(10)

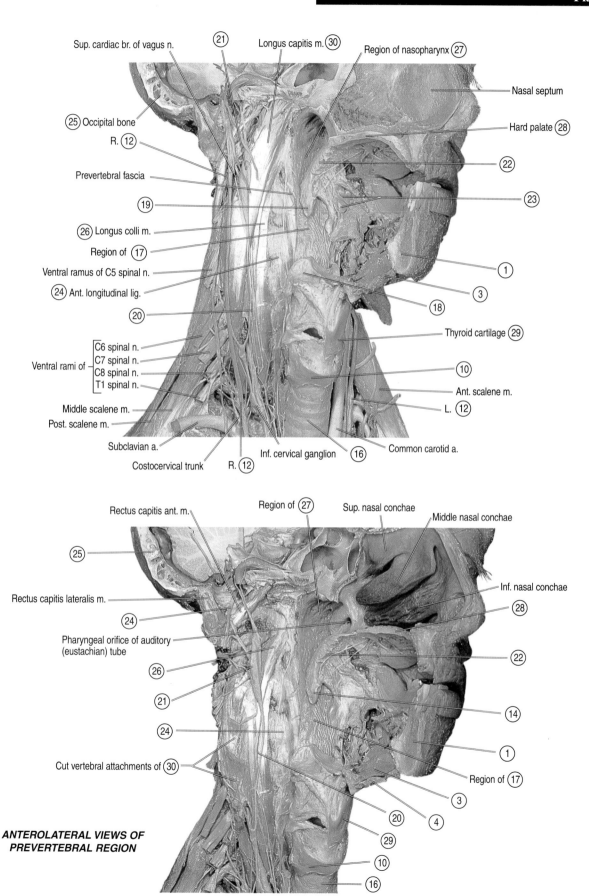

Sup. cardiac br. of vagus n.
㉑
Longus capitis m. ㉚
Region of nasopharynx ㉗
Nasal septum

㉕ Occipital bone
Hard palate ㉘

R. ⑫
㉒

Prevertebral fascia
㉓

⑲

㉖ Longus colli m.

Region of ⑰
①

Ventral ramus of C5 spinal n.
③

㉔ Ant. longitudinal lig.
⑱

⑳
Thyroid cartilage ㉙

C6 spinal n.
C7 spinal n.
Ventral rami of
C8 spinal n.
⑩
T1 spinal n.

Ant. scalene m.

Middle scalene m.
L. ⑫
Post. scalene m.

Subclavian a.
Common carotid a.
Costocervical trunk
R. ⑫
Inf. cervical ganglion
⑯

Rectus capitis ant. m.
Region of ㉗
Sup. nasal conchae
Middle nasal conchae

㉕

Rectus capitis lateralis m.
Inf. nasal conchae

㉔
㉘

Pharyngeal orifice of auditory
(eustachian) tube
㉒

㉖

㉑
⑭

㉔
①

Cut vertebral attachments of ㉚
Region of ⑰

③

⑳
④

**ANTEROLATERAL VIEWS OF
PREVERTEBRAL REGION**
㉙

⑩

⑯

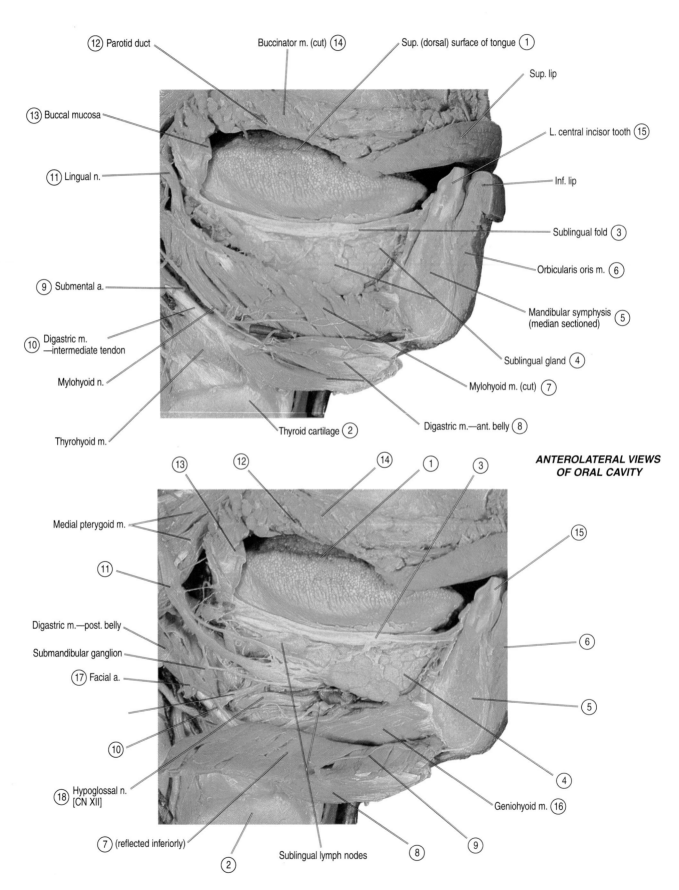

12 Parotid duct
Buccinator m. (cut) 14
Sup. (dorsal) surface of tongue 1
Sup. lip
13 Buccal mucosa
L. central incisor tooth 15
11 Lingual n.
Inf. lip
Sublingual fold 3
Orbicularis oris m. 6
9 Submental a.
Mandibular symphysis 5 (median sectioned)
10 Digastric m. —intermediate tendon
Sublingual gland 4
Mylohyoid n.
Mylohyoid m. (cut) 7
Thyrohyoid m.
Thyroid cartilage 2
Digastric m.—ant. belly 8

ANTEROLATERAL VIEWS OF ORAL CAVITY

13 12 14 1 3

Medial pterygoid m.
15
11
Digastric m.—post. belly
6
Submandibular ganglion
17 Facial a.
5
10
18 Hypoglossal n. [CN XII]
4
Geniohyoid m. 16
7 (reflected inferiorly)
Sublingual lymph nodes
8 9
2

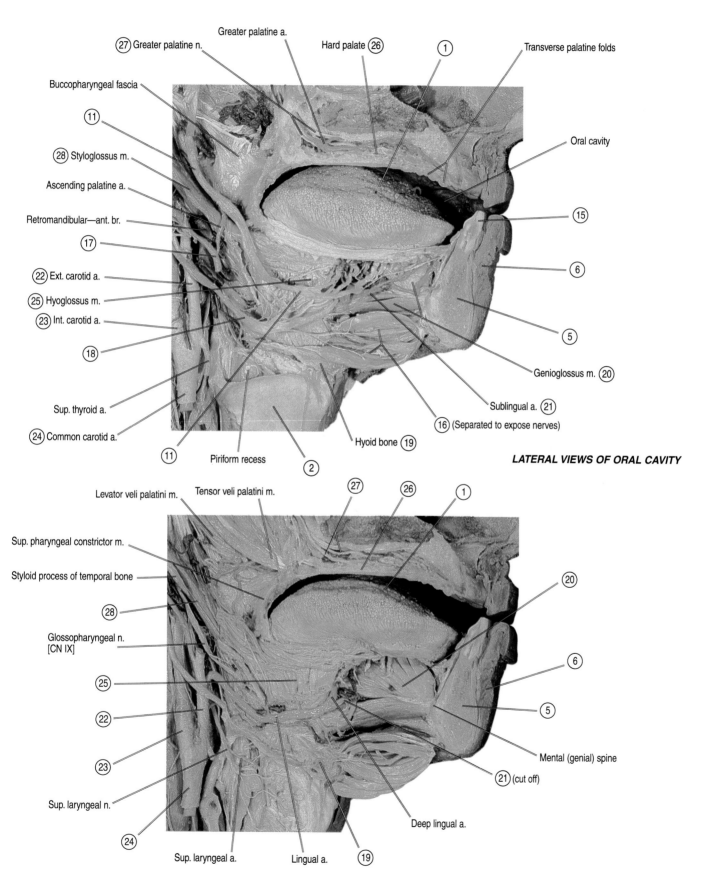

Greater palatine a.

(27) Greater palatine n. Hard palate (26) (1) Transverse palatine folds

Buccopharyngeal fascia

(11) Oral cavity

(28) Styloglossus m.

Ascending palatine a.

Retromandibular—ant. br. (15)

(17) (6)

(22) Ext. carotid a.

(25) Hyoglossus m.

(23) Int. carotid a. (5)

(18) Genioglossus m. (20)

Sup. thyroid a. Sublingual a. (21)

(24) Common carotid a. (16) (Separated to expose nerves)

(11) Hyoid bone (19)

Piriform recess (2)

LATERAL VIEWS OF ORAL CAVITY

Levator veli palatini m. Tensor veli palatini m. (27) (26) (1)

Sup. pharyngeal constrictor m.

Styloid process of temporal bone (20)

(28)

Glossopharyngeal n.
[CN IX] (6)

(25) (5)

(22)

(23) Mental (genial) spine

(21) (cut off)

Sup. laryngeal n.

(24) Deep lingual a.

Sup. laryngeal a. Lingual a. (19)

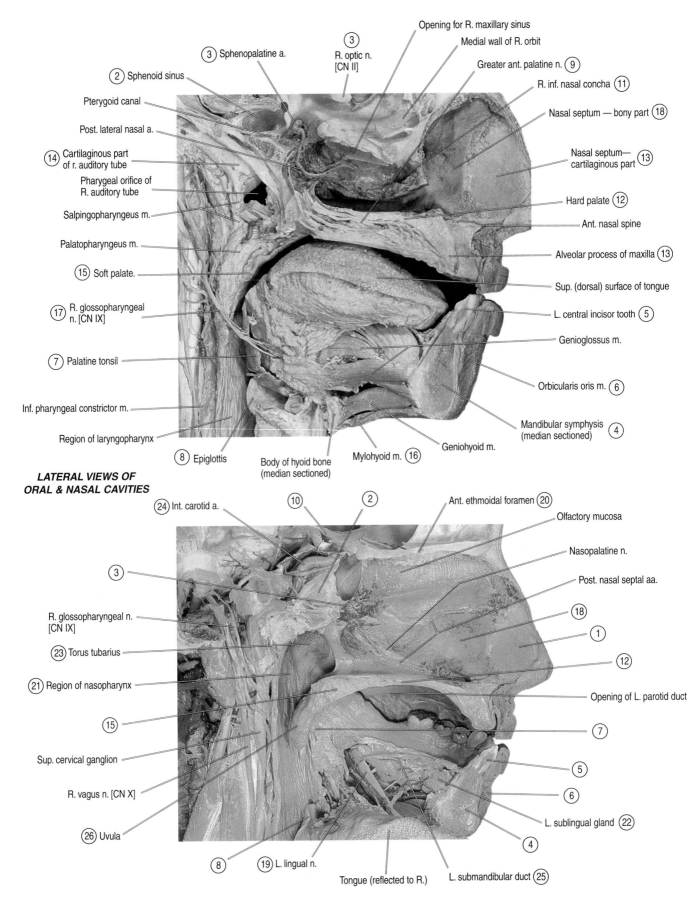

Opening for R. maxillary sinus

Medial wall of R. orbit

③ Sphenopalatine a.

③ R. optic n. [CN II]

Greater ant. palatine n. ⑨

② Sphenoid sinus

R. inf. nasal concha ⑪

Pterygoid canal

Nasal septum — bony part ⑱

Post. lateral nasal a.

Nasal septum— cartilaginous part ⑬

⑭ Cartilaginous part of r. auditory tube

Pharyngeal orifice of R. auditory tube

Hard palate ⑫

Salpingopharyngeus m.

Ant. nasal spine

Palatopharyngeus m.

Alveolar process of maxilla ⑬

⑮ Soft palate.

Sup. (dorsal) surface of tongue

⑰ R. glossopharyngeal n. [CN IX]

L. central incisor tooth ⑤

Genioglossus m.

⑦ Palatine tonsil

Orbicularis oris m. ⑥

Inf. pharyngeal constrictor m.

Mandibular symphysis (median sectioned) ④

Region of laryngopharynx

⑧ Epiglottis

Body of hyoid bone (median sectioned)

Mylohyoid m. ⑯

Geniohyoid m.

LATERAL VIEWS OF ORAL & NASAL CAVITIES

㉔ Int. carotid a.

⑩

②

Ant. ethmoidal foramen ⑳

Olfactory mucosa

③

Nasopalatine n.

Post. nasal septal aa.

R. glossopharyngeal n. [CN IX]

⑱

㉓ Torus tubarius

①

㉑ Region of nasopharynx

⑫

Opening of L. parotid duct

⑮

⑦

Sup. cervical ganglion

⑤

R. vagus n. [CN X]

⑥

㉖ Uvula

L. sublingual gland ㉒

④

⑧

⑲ L. lingual n.

Tongue (reflected to R.)

L. submandibular duct ㉕

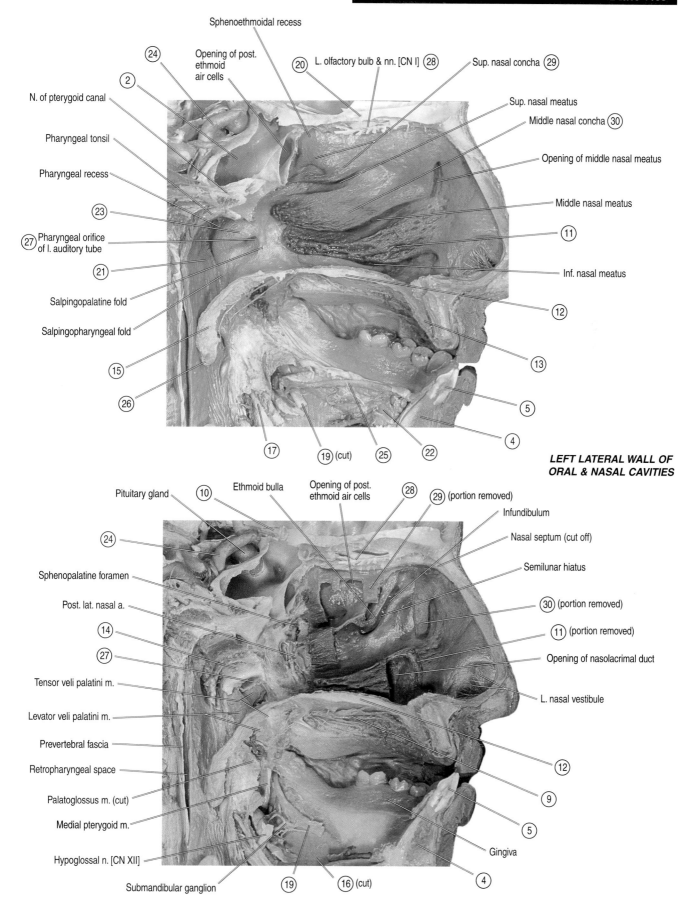

Sphenoethmoidal recess

㉔

Opening of post. ethmoid air cells

②

N. of pterygoid canal

Pharyngeal tonsil

Pharyngeal recess

㉓

㉗ Pharyngeal orifice of l. auditory tube

㉑

Salpingopalatine fold

Salpingopharyngeal fold

⑮

㉖

⑰   ⑲ (cut)   ㉕   ㉒

⑳ L. olfactory bulb & nn. [CN I] ㉘

Sup. nasal concha ㉙

Sup. nasal meatus

Middle nasal concha ㉚

Opening of middle nasal meatus

Middle nasal meatus

⑪

Inf. nasal meatus

⑫

⑬

⑤

④

LEFT LATERAL WALL OF ORAL & NASAL CAVITIES

Pituitary gland   ⑩   Ethmoid bulla

Opening of post. ethmoid air cells

㉘

㉙ (portion removed)

Infundibulum

Nasal septum (cut off)

㉔

Sphenopalatine foramen

Post. lat. nasal a.

⑭

㉗

Tensor veli palatini m.

Levator veli palatini m.

Prevertebral fascia

Retropharyngeal space

Palatoglossus m. (cut)

Medial pterygoid m.

Hypoglossal n. [CN XII]

Submandibular ganglion

⑲   ⑯ (cut)   ④

Semilunar hiatus

㉚ (portion removed)

⑪ (portion removed)

Opening of nasolacrimal duct

L. nasal vestibule

⑫

⑨

⑤

Gingiva

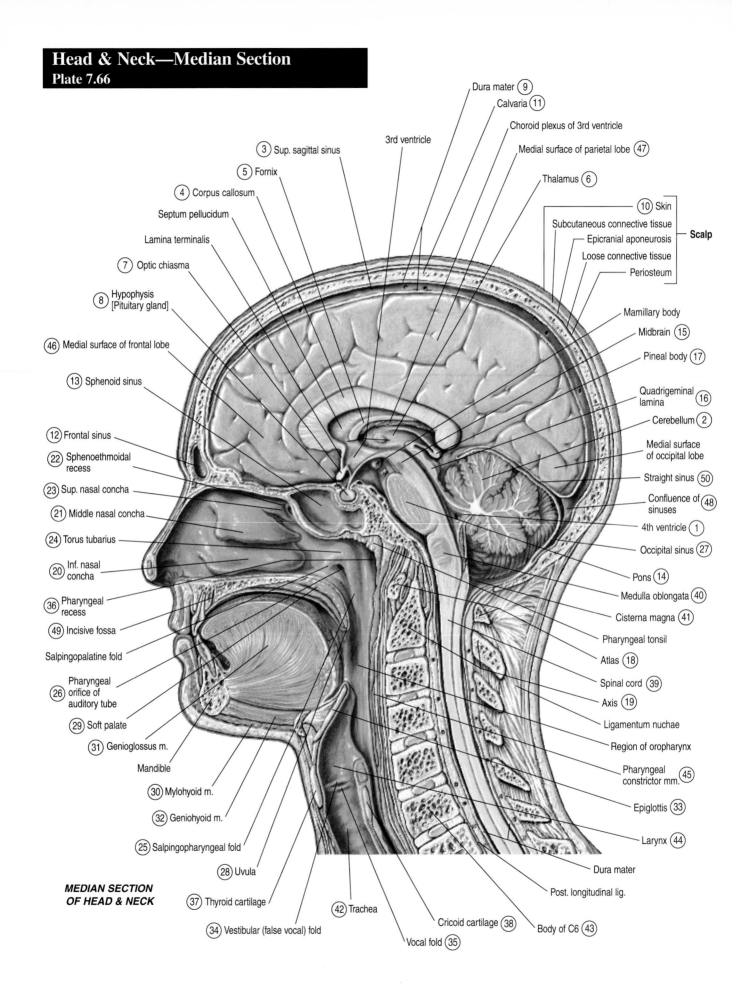

Dura mater (9)
Calvaria (11)
Choroid plexus of 3rd ventricle
Medial surface of parietal lobe (47)
3rd ventricle
(3) Sup. sagittal sinus
Thalamus (6)
(5) Fornix
(4) Corpus callosum
(10) Skin
Septum pellucidum
Subcutaneous connective tissue
Epicranial aponeurosis — **Scalp**
Lamina terminalis
Loose connective tissue
(7) Optic chiasma
Periosteum
(8) Hypophysis [Pituitary gland]
Mamillary body
Midbrain (15)
(46) Medial surface of frontal lobe
Pineal body (17)
(13) Sphenoid sinus
Quadrigeminal lamina (16)
Cerebellum (2)
(12) Frontal sinus
Medial surface of occipital lobe
(22) Sphenoethmoidal recess
Straight sinus (50)
(23) Sup. nasal concha
Confluence of sinuses (48)
(21) Middle nasal concha
4th ventricle (1)
(24) Torus tubarius
Occipital sinus (27)
(20) Inf. nasal concha
Pons (14)
(36) Pharyngeal recess
Medulla oblongata (40)
(49) Incisive fossa
Cisterna magna (41)
Salpingopalatine fold
Pharyngeal tonsil
Pharyngeal orifice of auditory tube (26)
Atlas (18)
Spinal cord (39)
(29) Soft palate
Axis (19)
(31) Genioglossus m.
Ligamentum nuchae
Mandible
Region of oropharynx
(30) Mylohyoid m.
Pharyngeal constrictor mm. (45)
(32) Geniohyoid m.
Epiglottis (33)
(25) Salpingopharyngeal fold
Larynx (44)
(28) Uvula
Dura mater

MEDIAN SECTION OF HEAD & NECK
Post. longitudinal lig.
(37) Thyroid cartilage
(42) Trachea
Cricoid cartilage (38)
Body of C6 (43)
(34) Vestibular (false vocal) fold
Vocal fold (35)

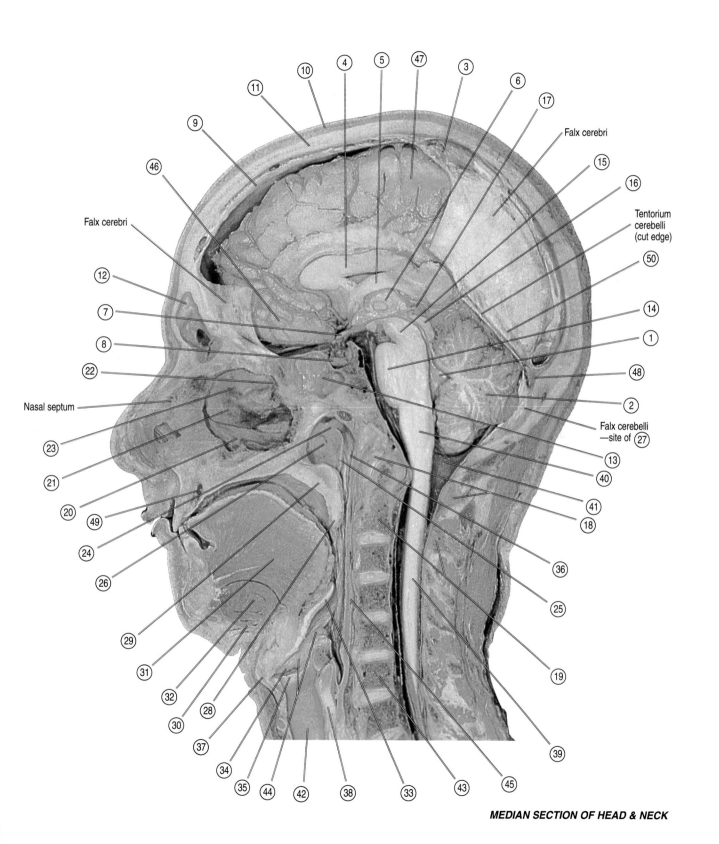

Falx cerebri

Falx cerebri

Tentorium
cerebelli
(cut edge)

Nasal septum

Falx cerebelli
—site of (27)

MEDIAN SECTION OF HEAD & NECK

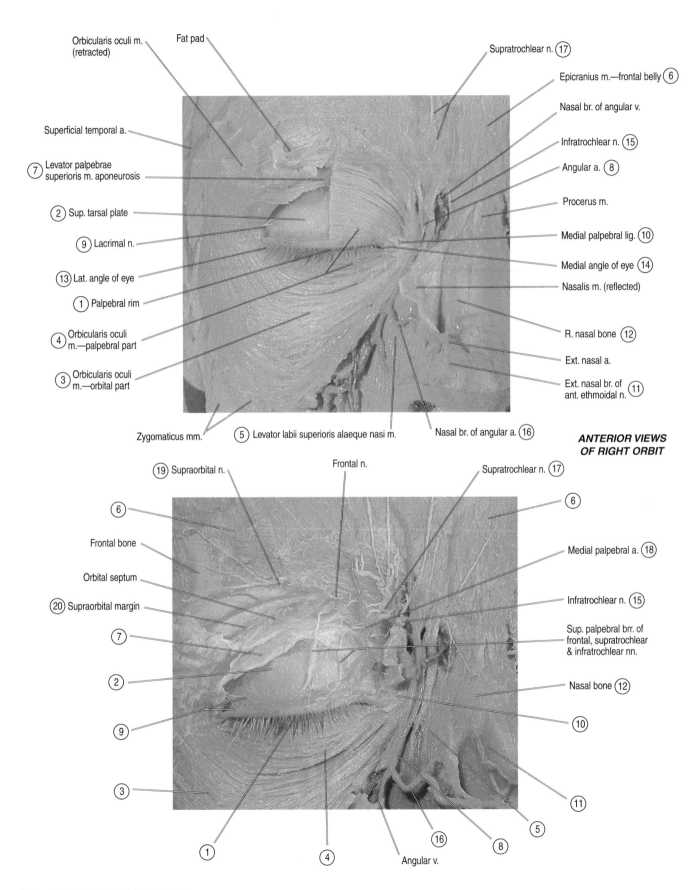

Orbicularis oculi m. (retracted)

Fat pad

Supratrochlear n. (17)

Epicranius m.—frontal belly (6)

Nasal br. of angular v.

Superficial temporal a.

Infratrochlear n. (15)

Angular a. (8)

(7) Levator palpebrae superioris m. aponeurosis

Procerus m.

(2) Sup. tarsal plate

Medial palpebral lig. (10)

(9) Lacrimal n.

Medial angle of eye (14)

(13) Lat. angle of eye

Nasalis m. (reflected)

(1) Palpebral rim

R. nasal bone (12)

(4) Orbicularis oculi m.—palpebral part

Ext. nasal a.

(3) Orbicularis oculi m.—orbital part

Ext. nasal br. of ant. ethmoidal n. (11)

Zygomaticus mm.

(5) Levator labii superioris alaeque nasi m.

Nasal br. of angular a. (16)

ANTERIOR VIEWS OF RIGHT ORBIT

(19) Supraorbital n.

Frontal n.

Supratrochlear n. (17)

(6)

(6)

Frontal bone

Medial palpebral a. (18)

Orbital septum

(20) Supraorbital margin

Infratrochlear n. (15)

(7)

Sup. palpebral brr. of frontal, supratrochlear & infratrochlear nn.

(2)

Nasal bone (12)

(9)

(10)

(3)

(11)

(1)

(4)

(16)

(8)

(5)

Angular v.

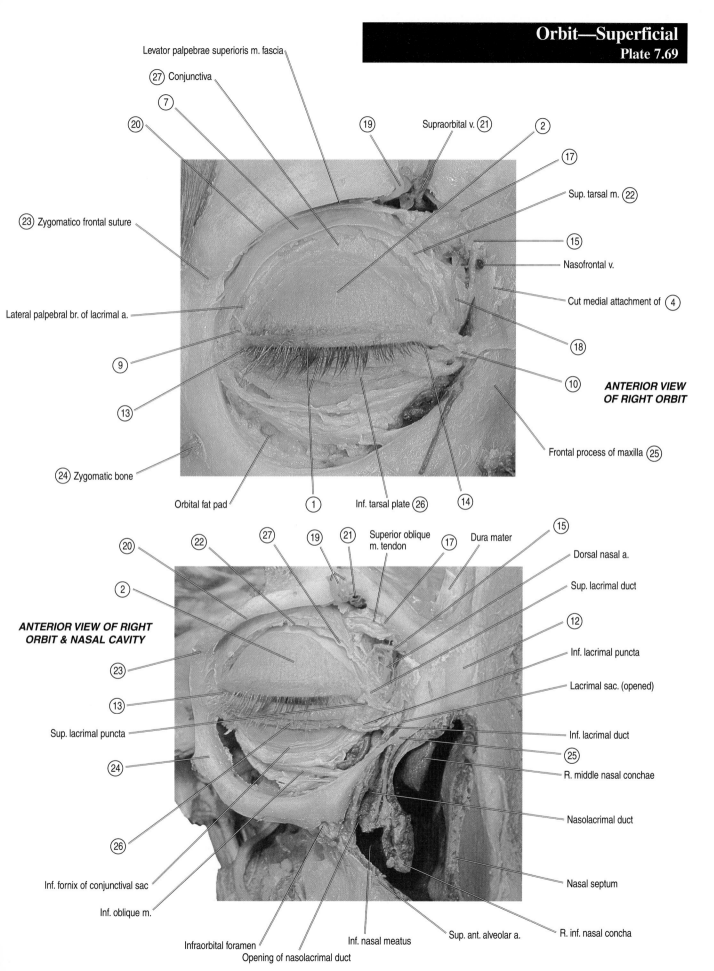

Levator palpebrae superioris m. fascia

(27) Conjunctiva

(7)

(20)

(23) Zygomatico frontal suture

Lateral palpebral br. of lacrimal a.

(9)

(13)

(24) Zygomatic bone

Orbital fat pad

(1)

Inf. tarsal plate (26)

(14)

(19)

Supraorbital v. (21)

(2)

(17)

Sup. tarsal m. (22)

(15)

Nasofrontal v.

Cut medial attachment of (4)

(18)

(10)

**ANTERIOR VIEW
OF RIGHT ORBIT**

Frontal process of maxilla (25)

**ANTERIOR VIEW OF RIGHT
ORBIT & NASAL CAVITY**

(20)

(22)

(27)

(19)

(21)

Superior oblique
m. tendon

(17)

Dura mater

(15)

Dorsal nasal a.

Sup. lacrimal duct

(12)

Inf. lacrimal puncta

Lacrimal sac. (opened)

Inf. lacrimal duct

(25)

R. middle nasal conchae

Nasolacrimal duct

Nasal septum

R. inf. nasal concha

(2)

(23)

(13)

Sup. lacrimal puncta

(24)

(26)

Inf. fornix of conjunctival sac

Inf. oblique m.

Infraorbital foramen

Opening of nasolacrimal duct

Inf. nasal meatus

Sup. ant. alveolar a.

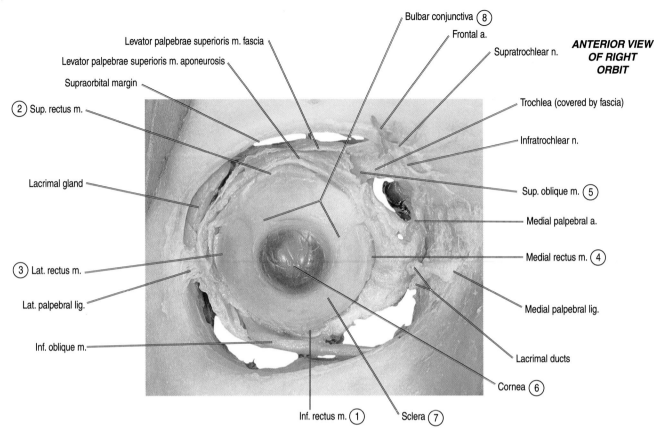

Bulbar conjunctiva ⑧
Frontal a.
Supratrochlear n.

Levator palpebrae superioris m. fascia
Levator palpebrae superioris m. aponeurosis
Supraorbital margin

**ANTERIOR VIEW
OF RIGHT
ORBIT**

Trochlea (covered by fascia)
Infratrochlear n.

② Sup. rectus m.

Lacrimal gland

Sup. oblique m. ⑤
Medial palpebral a.

③ Lat. rectus m.

Medial rectus m. ④

Lat. palpebral lig.

Medial palpebral lig.

Inf. oblique m.

Lacrimal ducts

Cornea ⑥

Inf. rectus m. ①   Sclera ⑦

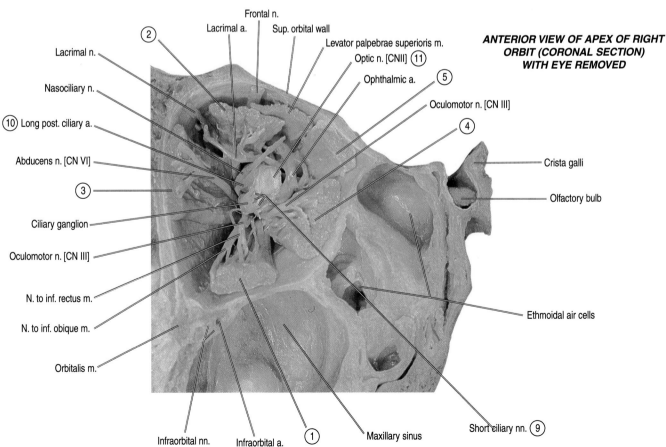

Frontal n.
Lacrimal a.   Sup. orbital wall
②
Levator palpebrae superioris m.
Optic n. [CNII] ⑪

**ANTERIOR VIEW OF APEX OF RIGHT
ORBIT (CORONAL SECTION)
WITH EYE REMOVED**

Lacrimal n.

Ophthalmic a.   ⑤

Nasociliary n.

Oculomotor n. [CN III]

⑩ Long post. ciliary a.

④

Abducens n. [CN VI]

Crista galli

③

Olfactory bulb

Ciliary ganglion

Oculomotor n. [CN III]

N. to inf. rectus m.

N. to inf. obique m.

Ethmoidal air cells

Orbitalis m.

Short ciliary nn. ⑨

Infraorbital nn.   Infraorbital a.   ①   Maxillary sinus

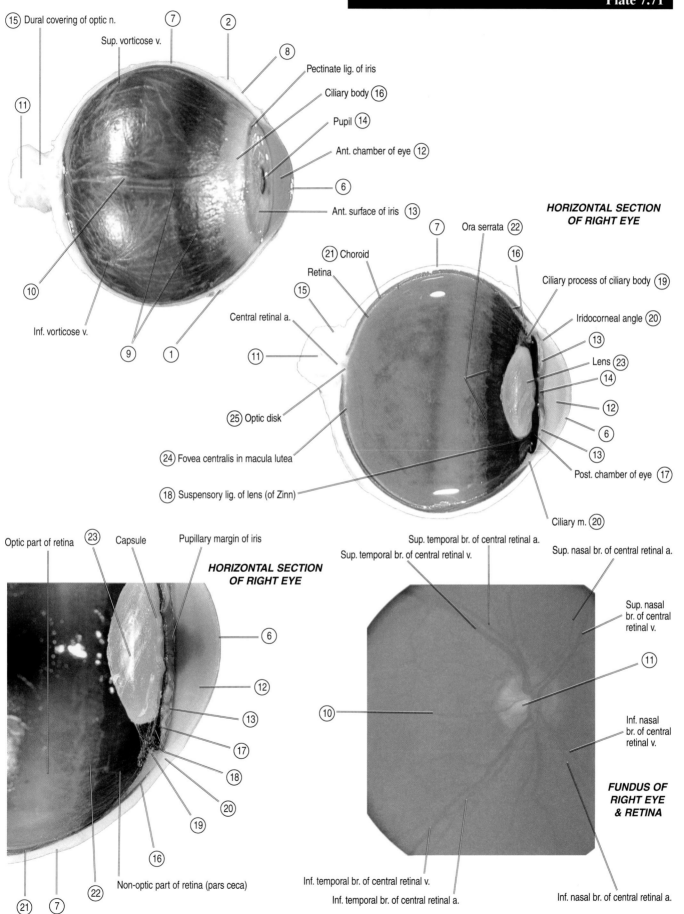

LATERAL VIEW OF VASCULAR TUNIC OF RIGHT EYE

(15) Dural covering of optic n.
(7)
(2)
Sup. vorticose v.
(8)
Pectinate lig. of iris
Ciliary body (16)
Pupil (14)
Ant. chamber of eye (12)
(11)
(6)
Ant. surface of iris (13)
(10)
Inf. vorticose v.
(9)
(1)

HORIZONTAL SECTION OF RIGHT EYE

(7)   Ora serrata (22)
(21) Choroid   (16)
Retina
Ciliary process of ciliary body (19)
(15)
Central retinal a.
Iridocorneal angle (20)
(13)
Lens (23)
(14)
(11)
(12)
(6)
(13)
(25) Optic disk
Post. chamber of eye (17)
(24) Fovea centralis in macula lutea
(18) Suspensory lig. of lens (of Zinn)
Ciliary m. (20)

Optic part of retina   (23)   Capsule   Pupillary margin of iris

HORIZONTAL SECTION OF RIGHT EYE

(6)
(12)
(13)
(17)
(18)
(20)
(19)
(16)
Non-optic part of retina (pars ceca)
(21)
(7)
(22)

Sup. temporal br. of central retinal a.
Sup. temporal br. of central retinal v.
Sup. nasal br. of central retinal a.
Sup. nasal br. of central retinal v.
(11)
(10)
Inf. nasal br. of central retinal v.

FUNDUS OF RIGHT EYE & RETINA

Inf. temporal br. of central retinal v.
Inf. temporal br. of central retinal a.
Inf. nasal br. of central retinal a.

LATERAL VIEW OF RIGHT ORBIT

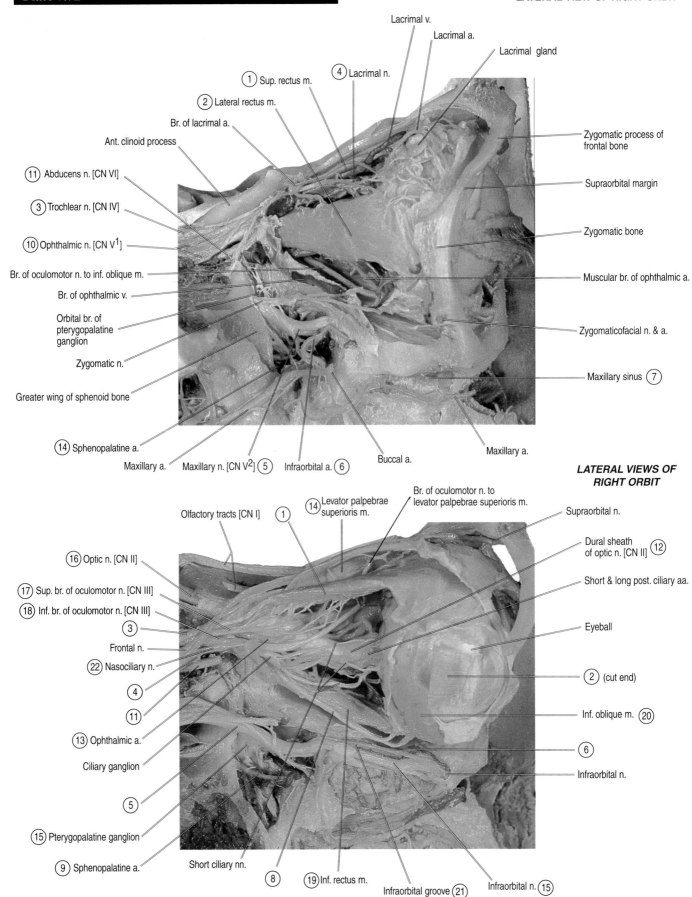

Lacrimal v.

Lacrimal a.

Lacrimal gland

(1) Sup. rectus m.

(4) Lacrimal n.

(2) Lateral rectus m.

Br. of lacrimal a.

Ant. clinoid process

Zygomatic process of frontal bone

Supraorbital margin

(11) Abducens n. [CN VI]

(3) Trochlear n. [CN IV]

Zygomatic bone

(10) Ophthalmic n. [CN V¹]

Br. of oculomotor n. to inf. oblique m.

Muscular br. of ophthalmic a.

Br. of ophthalmic v.

Orbital br. of pterygopalatine ganglion

Zygomaticofacial n. & a.

Zygomatic n.

Greater wing of sphenoid bone

Maxillary sinus (7)

(14) Sphenopalatine a.

Maxillary a.   Maxillary n. [CN V²] (5)   Infraorbital a. (6)   Buccal a.   Maxillary a.

LATERAL VIEWS OF RIGHT ORBIT

Olfactory tracts [CN I]   (1)   (14) Levator palpebrae superioris m.   Br. of oculomotor n. to levator palpebrae superioris m.   Supraorbital n.

(16) Optic n. [CN II]

Dural sheath of optic n. [CN II] (12)

(17) Sup. br. of oculomotor n. [CN III]

Short & long post. ciliary aa.

(18) Inf. br. of oculomotor n. [CN III]

(3)

Eyeball

Frontal n.

(22) Nasociliary n.

(2) (cut end)

(4)

(11)

Inf. oblique m. (20)

(13) Ophthalmic a.

(6)

Ciliary ganglion

Infraorbital n.

(5)

(15) Pterygopalatine ganglion

(9) Sphenopalatine a.   Short ciliary nn.   (8)   (19) Inf. rectus m.   Infraorbital groove (21)   Infraorbital n. (15)

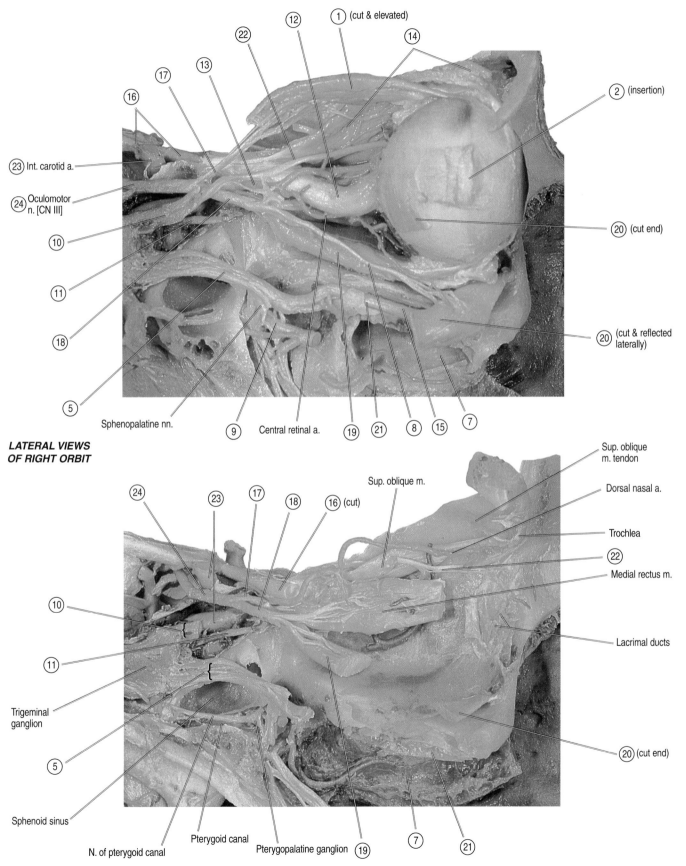

① (cut & elevated)

⑫

㉒

⑭

② (insertion)

⑰

⑬

⑯

㉓ Int. carotid a.

㉔ Oculomotor n. [CN III]

⑩

⑪

⑱

⑤

⑳ (cut end)

⑳ (cut & reflected laterally)

Sphenopalatine nn.

⑨   Central retinal a.   ⑲ ㉑ ⑧ ⑮ ⑦

LATERAL VIEWS OF RIGHT ORBIT

Sup. oblique m. tendon

Sup. oblique m.

Dorsal nasal a.

㉔   ㉓   ⑰   ⑱   ⑯ (cut)

Trochlea

㉒

Medial rectus m.

⑩

⑪

Lacrimal ducts

Trigeminal ganglion

⑤

⑳ (cut end)

Sphenoid sinus

N. of pterygoid canal   Pterygoid canal   Pterygopalatine ganglion ⑲   ⑦   ㉑

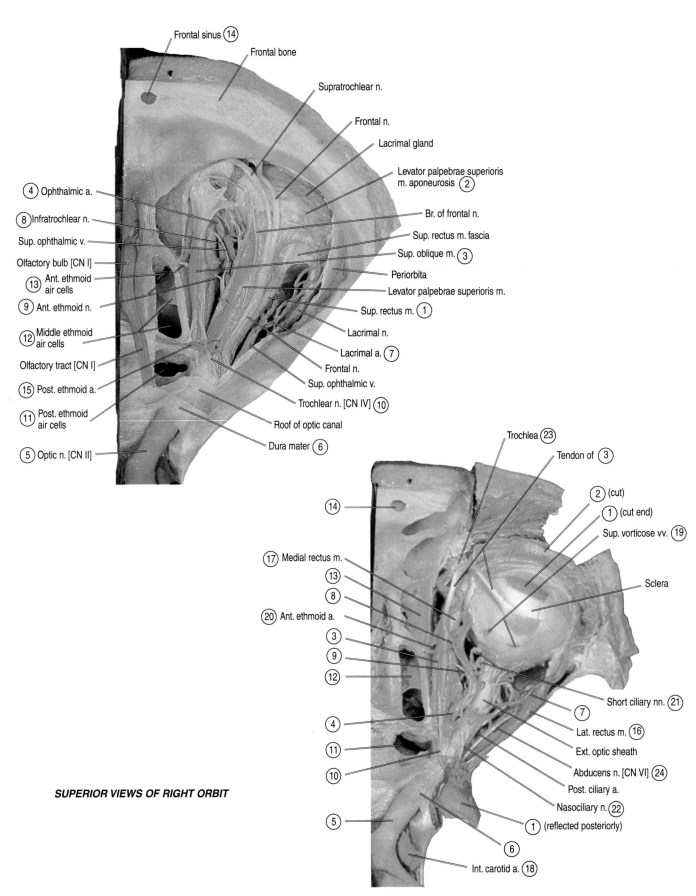

Frontal sinus (14)

Frontal bone

Supratrochlear n.

Frontal n.

Lacrimal gland

Levator palpebrae superioris
m. aponeurosis (2)

(4) Ophthalmic a.

(8) Infratrochlear n.

Sup. ophthalmic v.

Olfactory bulb [CN I]

(13) Ant. ethmoid
air cells

(9) Ant. ethmoid n.

(12) Middle ethmoid
air cells

Olfactory tract [CN I]

(15) Post. ethmoid a.

(11) Post. ethmoid
air cells

(5) Optic n. [CN II]

Br. of frontal n.

Sup. rectus m. fascia

Sup. oblique m. (3)

Periorbita

Levator palpebrae superioris m.

Sup. rectus m. (1)

Lacrimal n.

Lacrimal a. (7)

Frontal n.

Sup. ophthalmic v.

Trochlear n. [CN IV] (10)

Roof of optic canal

Dura mater (6)

Trochlea (23)

Tendon of (3)

(2) (cut)

(1) (cut end)

Sup. vorticose vv. (19)

Sclera

(14)

(17) Medial rectus m.

(13)

(8)

(20) Ant. ethmoid a.

(3)

(9)

(12)

(4)

(11)

(10)

Short ciliary nn. (21)

(7)

Lat. rectus m. (16)

Ext. optic sheath

Abducens n. [CN VI] (24)

Post. ciliary a.

Nasociliary n. (22)

(1) (reflected posteriorly)

(5)

(6)

Int. carotid a. (18)

SUPERIOR VIEWS OF RIGHT ORBIT

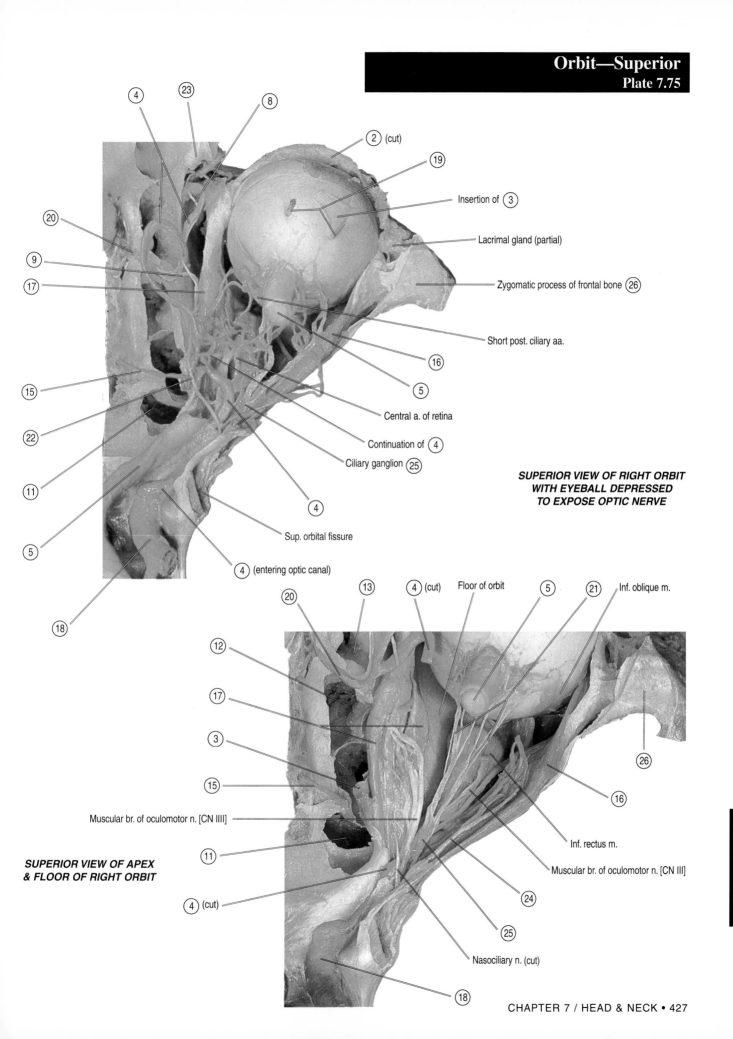

④
㉓
⑧
② (cut)
⑲
Insertion of ③
Lacrimal gland (partial)
⑳
⑨
⑰
Zygomatic process of frontal bone ㉖
Short post. ciliary aa.
⑯
⑤
Central a. of retina
⑮
Continuation of ④
㉒
Ciliary ganglion ㉕
⑪
④

*SUPERIOR VIEW OF RIGHT ORBIT
WITH EYEBALL DEPRESSED
TO EXPOSE OPTIC NERVE*

⑤
Sup. orbital fissure
④ (entering optic canal)
⑱

⑬
④ (cut)
Floor of orbit
⑤
㉑
Inf. oblique m.
⑳
⑫
⑰
㉖
③
⑯
⑮
Muscular br. of oculomotor n. [CN IIII]
Inf. rectus m.
⑪
Muscular br. of oculomotor n. [CN III]

*SUPERIOR VIEW OF APEX
& FLOOR OF RIGHT ORBIT*

④ (cut)
㉔
㉕
Nasociliary n. (cut)
⑱

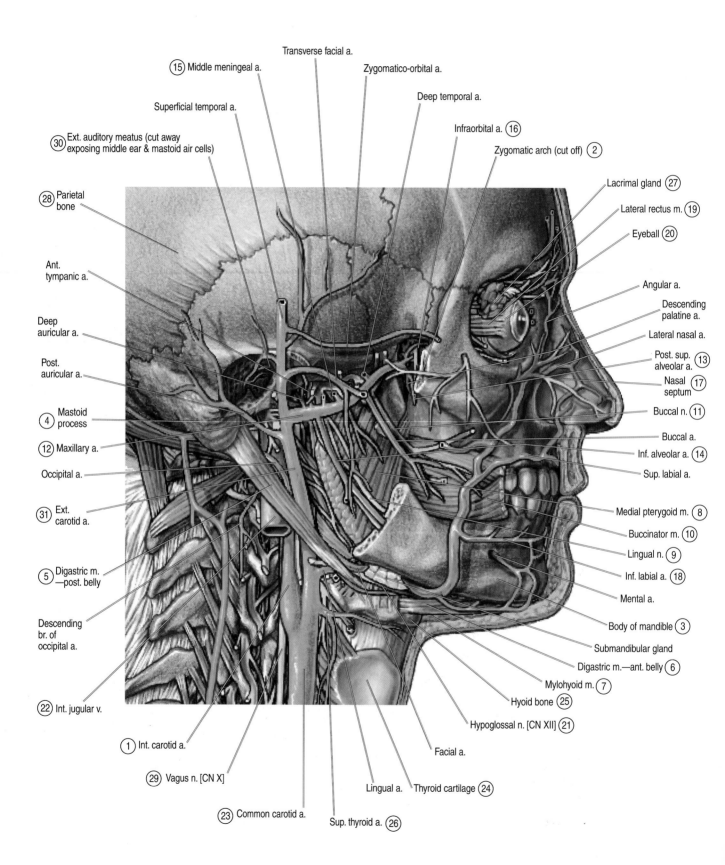

(15) Middle meningeal a.

Transverse facial a.

Zygomatico-orbital a.

Deep temporal a.

Superficial temporal a.

Infraorbital a. (16)

(30) Ext. auditory meatus (cut away exposing middle ear & mastoid air cells)

Zygomatic arch (cut off) (2)

Lacrimal gland (27)

(28) Parietal bone

Lateral rectus m. (19)

Eyeball (20)

Ant. tympanic a.

Angular a.

Descending palatine a.

Deep auricular a.

Lateral nasal a.

Post. auricular a.

Post. sup. (13) alveolar a.

Nasal (17) septum

Buccal n. (11)

(4) Mastoid process

(12) Maxillary a.

Buccal a.

Inf. alveolar a. (14)

Occipital a.

Sup. labial a.

(31) Ext. carotid a.

Medial pterygoid m. (8)

Buccinator m. (10)

Lingual n. (9)

(5) Digastric m. —post. belly

Inf. labial a. (18)

Mental a.

Descending br. of occipital a.

Body of mandible (3)

Submandibular gland

Digastric m.—ant. belly (6)

Mylohyoid m. (7)

(22) Int. jugular v.

Hyoid bone (25)

Hypoglossal n. [CN XII] (21)

(1) Int. carotid a.

(29) Vagus n. [CN X]

Facial a.

Lingual a.

Thyroid cartilage (24)

(23) Common carotid a.

Sup. thyroid a. (26)

LATERAL VIEW

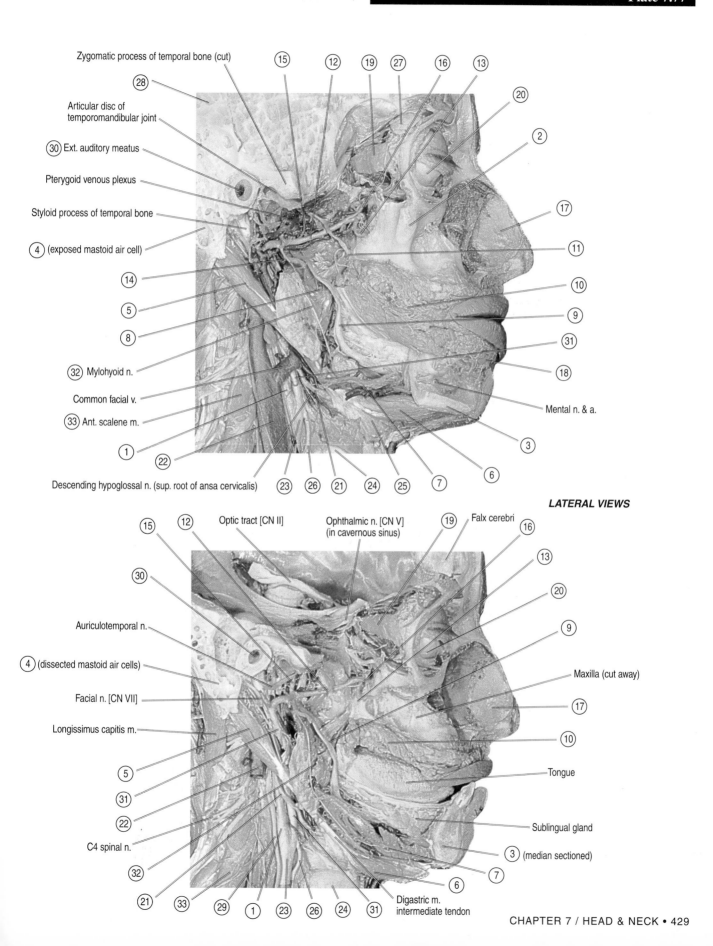

Zygomatic process of temporal bone (cut)

(28)

Articular disc of
temporomandibular joint

(30) Ext. auditory meatus

Pterygoid venous plexus

Styloid process of temporal bone

(4) (exposed mastoid air cell)

(14)

(5)

(8)

(32) Mylohyoid n.

Common facial v.

(33) Ant. scalene m.

(1)

(22)

Descending hypoglossal n. (sup. root of ansa cervicalis)

(15) (12) (19) (27) (16) (13)

(20)

(2)

(17)

(11)

(10)

(9)

(31)

(18)

Mental n. & a.

(3)

(23) (26) (21) (24) (25) (7) (6)

LATERAL VIEWS

(15) (12) Optic tract [CN II] Ophthalmic n. [CN V] (19) Falx cerebri (16)
(in cavernous sinus)

(30)

(13)

(20)

Auriculotemporal n.

(9)

(4) (dissected mastoid air cells)

Maxilla (cut away)

Facial n. [CN VII]

(17)

Longissimus capitis m.

(10)

(5)

Tongue

(31)

(22)

Sublingual gland

C4 spinal n.

(3) (median sectioned)

(32)

(7)

(21) (33) (29) (1) (23) (26) (24) (31) (6)

Digastric m.
intermediate tendon

Infratemporal Fossa
Plate 7.78

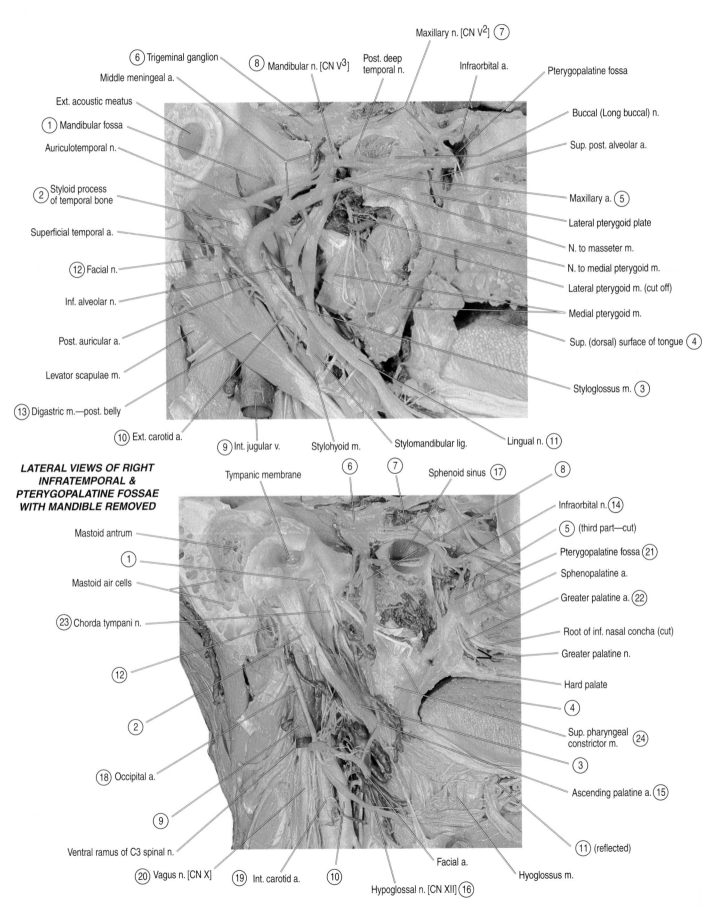

Maxillary n. [CN V²] ⑦

⑥ Trigeminal ganglion

Middle meningeal a.

⑧ Mandibular n. [CN V³]

Post. deep temporal n.

Infraorbital a.

Pterygopalatine fossa

Ext. acoustic meatus

① Mandibular fossa

Buccal (Long buccal) n.

Auriculotemporal n.

Sup. post. alveolar a.

② Styloid process of temporal bone

Maxillary a. ⑤

Superficial temporal a.

Lateral pterygoid plate

N. to masseter m.

⑫ Facial n.

N. to medial pterygoid m.

Inf. alveolar n.

Lateral pterygoid m. (cut off)

Post. auricular a.

Medial pterygoid m.

Levator scapulae m.

Sup. (dorsal) surface of tongue ④

⑬ Digastric m.—post. belly

Styloglossus m. ③

⑩ Ext. carotid a.

⑨ Int. jugular v.

Stylohyoid m.

Stylomandibular lig.

Lingual n. ⑪

LATERAL VIEWS OF RIGHT INFRATEMPORAL & PTERYGOPALATINE FOSSAE WITH MANDIBLE REMOVED

Tympanic membrane

⑥

⑦

Sphenoid sinus ⑰

⑧

Infraorbital n. ⑭

Mastoid antrum

⑤ (third part—cut)

①

Pterygopalatine fossa ㉑

Mastoid air cells

Sphenopalatine a.

㉓ Chorda tympani n.

Greater palatine a. ㉒

Root of inf. nasal concha (cut)

⑫

Greater palatine n.

②

Hard palate

④

⑱ Occipital a.

Sup. pharyngeal constrictor m. ㉔

③

⑨

Ascending palatine a. ⑮

Ventral ramus of C3 spinal n.

⑪ (reflected)

⑳ Vagus n. [CN X]

⑲ Int. carotid a.

⑩

Facial a.

Hyoglossus m.

Hypoglossal n. [CN XII] ⑯

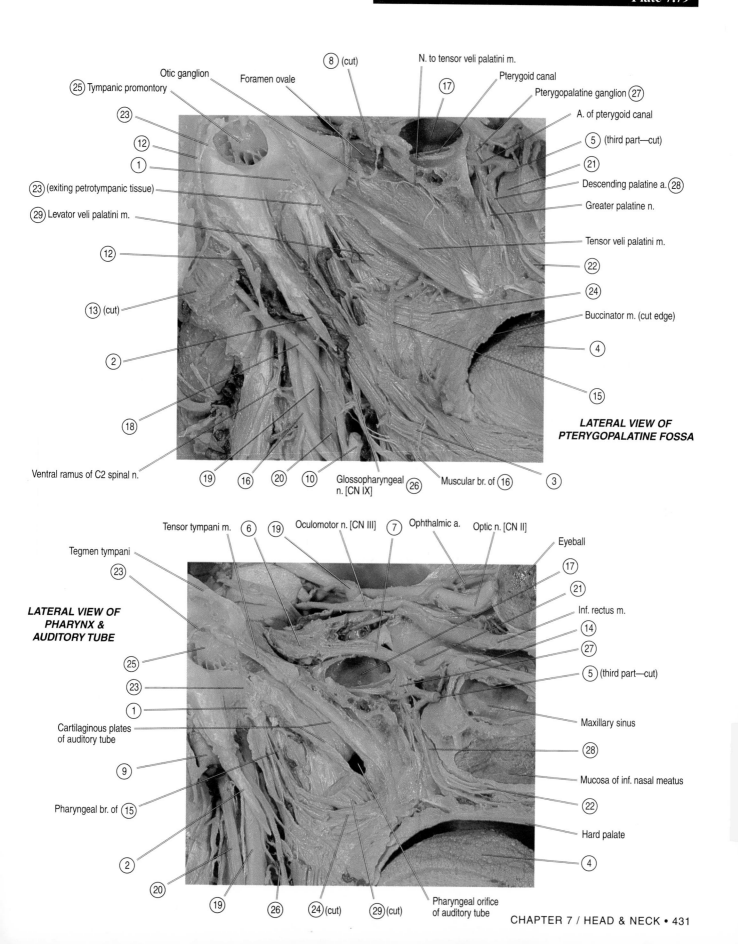

⑧ (cut)

N. to tensor veli palatini m.

Pterygoid canal

Pterygopalatine ganglion ㉗

⑰

A. of pterygoid canal

⑤ (third part—cut)

㉕ Tympanic promontory

Otic ganglion

Foramen ovale

㉓

⑫

①

㉑

㉓ (exiting petrotympanic tissue)

Descending palatine a. ㉘

Greater palatine n.

㉙ Levator veli palatini m.

⑫

Tensor veli palatini m.

㉒

㉔

⑬ (cut)

Buccinator m. (cut edge)

②

④

⑮

Ventral ramus of C2 spinal n.

**LATERAL VIEW OF
PTERYGOPALATINE FOSSA**

⑱

⑲ ⑯ ⑳ ⑩ Glossopharyngeal ㉖ Muscular br. of ⑯ ③
n. [CN IX]

Tensor tympani m. ⑥ ⑲ Oculomotor n. [CN III] ⑦ Ophthalmic a. Optic n. [CN II] Eyeball

Tegmen tympani

㉓

⑰

㉑

**LATERAL VIEW OF
PHARYNX &
AUDITORY TUBE**

Inf. rectus m.

⑭

㉕

㉗

⑤ (third part—cut)

㉓

①

Maxillary sinus

Cartilaginous plates
of auditory tube

㉘

⑨

Mucosa of inf. nasal meatus

Pharyngeal br. of ⑮

㉒

②

Hard palate

④

⑳

⑲ ㉖ ㉔ (cut) ㉙ (cut) Pharyngeal orifice
of auditory tube

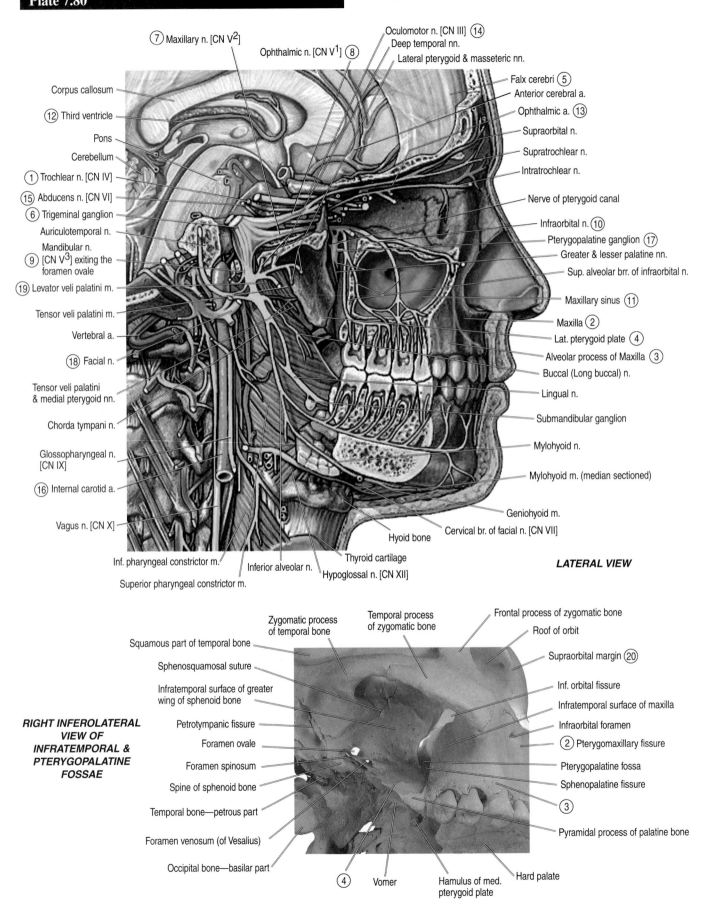

⑦ Maxillary n. [CN V²]

Ophthalmic n. [CN V¹] ⑧

Oculomotor n. [CN III] ⑭
Deep temporal nn.
Lateral pterygoid & masseteric nn.

Corpus callosum

⑫ Third ventricle

Pons

Cerebellum

① Trochlear n. [CN IV]

⑮ Abducens n. [CN VI]

⑥ Trigeminal ganglion

Auriculotemporal n.

Mandibular n.
⑨ [CN V³] exiting the
foramen ovale

⑲ Levator veli palatini m.

Tensor veli palatini m.

Vertebral a.

⑱ Facial n.

Tensor veli palatini
& medial pterygoid nn.

Chorda tympani n.

Glossopharyngeal n.
[CN IX]

⑯ Internal carotid a.

Vagus n. [CN X]

Inf. pharyngeal constrictor m.

Superior pharyngeal constrictor m.

Inferior alveolar n.

Hypoglossal n. [CN XII]

Thyroid cartilage

Hyoid bone

Falx cerebri ⑤
Anterior cerebral a.
Ophthalmic a. ⑬
Supraorbital n.
Supratrochlear n.
Intratrochlear n.

Nerve of pterygoid canal

Infraorbital n. ⑩
Pterygopalatine ganglion ⑰
Greater & lesser palatine nn.
Sup. alveolar brr. of infraorbital n.

Maxillary sinus ⑪

Maxilla ②
Lat. pterygoid plate ④
Alveolar process of Maxilla ③
Buccal (Long buccal) n.

Lingual n.

Submandibular ganglion

Mylohyoid n.

Mylohyoid m. (median sectioned)

Geniohyoid m.

Cervical br. of facial n. [CN VII]

LATERAL VIEW

**RIGHT INFEROLATERAL
VIEW OF
INFRATEMPORAL &
PTERYGOPALATINE
FOSSAE**

Zygomatic process
of temporal bone

Squamous part of temporal bone

Sphenosquamosal suture

Infratemporal surface of greater
wing of sphenoid bone

Petrotympanic fissure

Foramen ovale

Foramen spinosum

Spine of sphenoid bone

Temporal bone—petrous part

Foramen venosum (of Vesalius)

Occipital bone—basilar part

Temporal process
of zygomatic bone

Frontal process of zygomatic bone
Roof of orbit
Supraorbital margin ⑳

Inf. orbital fissure
Infratemporal surface of maxilla
Infraorbital foramen
② Pterygomaxillary fissure
Pterygopalatine fossa
Sphenopalatine fissure
③

Pyramidal process of palatine bone

④ Vomer

Hamulus of med.
pterygoid plate

Hard palate

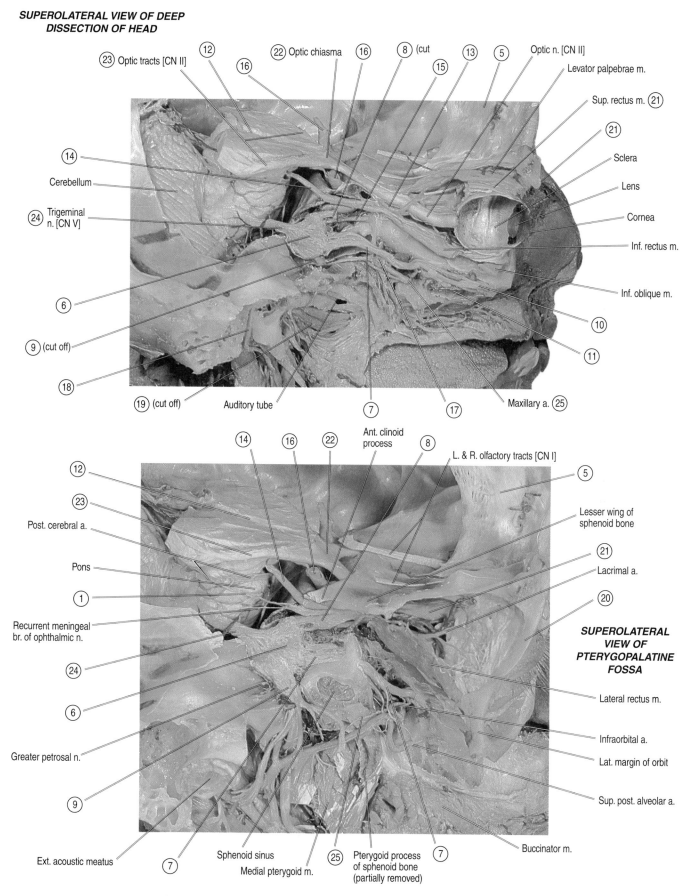

SUPEROLATERAL VIEW OF DEEP DISSECTION OF HEAD

㉓ Optic tracts [CN II]
⑫
⑯
㉒ Optic chiasma
⑯
⑧ (cut
⑮
⑬
⑤
Optic n. [CN II]
Levator palpebrae m.
Sup. rectus m. ㉑
㉑
Sclera
⑭
Lens
Cerebellum
Cornea
㉔ Trigeminal n. [CN V]
Inf. rectus m.
⑥
Inf. oblique m.
⑩
⑨ (cut off)
⑪
⑱
⑲ (cut off)   Auditory tube   ⑦   ⑰   Maxillary a. ㉕

⑭   ⑯   ㉒   Ant. clinoid process   ⑧   L. & R. olfactory tracts [CN I]
⑫
⑤
㉓
Post. cerebral a.
Lesser wing of sphenoid bone
Pons
㉑
①
Lacrimal a.
⑳
Recurrent meningeal br. of ophthalmic n.
SUPEROLATERAL VIEW OF PTERYGOPALATINE FOSSA
㉔
⑥
Lateral rectus m.
Greater petrosal n.
Infraorbital a.
Lat. margin of orbit
⑨
Sup. post. alveolar a.
Ext. acoustic meatus   Sphenoid sinus   ㉕   Pterygoid process of sphenoid bone (partially removed)   ⑦   Buccinator m.
⑦   Medial pterygoid m.

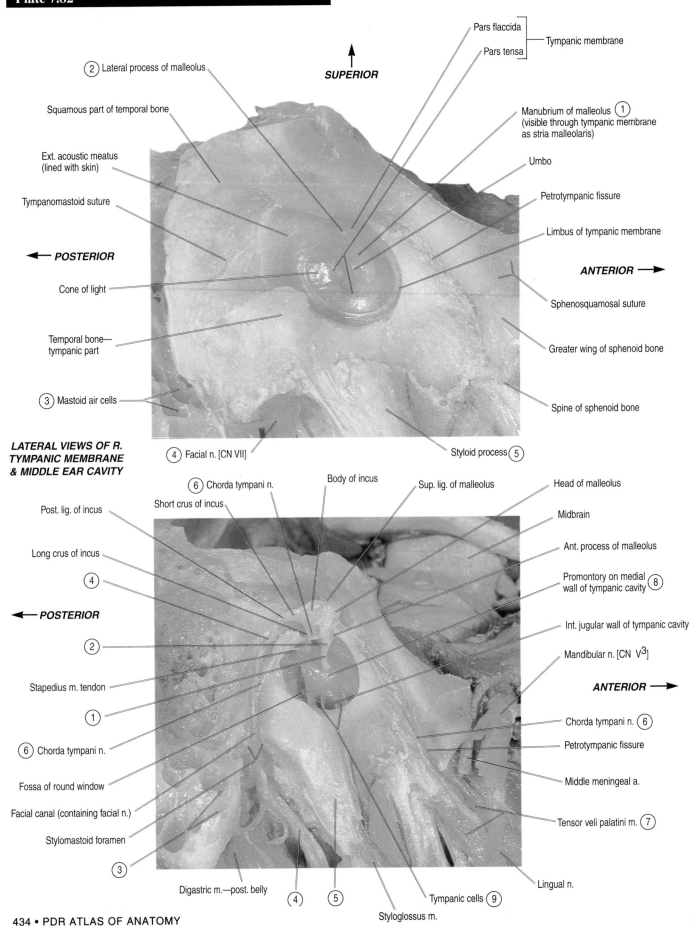

Pars flaccida ⎤
Pars tensa ⎦ Tympanic membrane

② Lateral process of malleolus

Squamous part of temporal bone

Ext. acoustic meatus (lined with skin)

Tympanomastoid suture

SUPERIOR

Manubrium of malleolus ①
(visible through tympanic membrane as stria malleolaris)

Umbo

Petrotympanic fissure

Limbus of tympanic membrane

← POSTERIOR

ANTERIOR →

Cone of light

Temporal bone— tympanic part

Sphenosquamosal suture

Greater wing of sphenoid bone

③ Mastoid air cells

Spine of sphenoid bone

LATERAL VIEWS OF R. TYMPANIC MEMBRANE & MIDDLE EAR CAVITY

④ Facial n. [CN VII]

Styloid process ⑤

⑥ Chorda tympani n.

Body of incus

Sup. lig. of malleolus

Head of malleolus

Short crus of incus

Midbrain

Post. lig. of incus

Ant. process of malleolus

Long crus of incus

Promontory on medial wall of tympanic cavity ⑧

④

← POSTERIOR

Int. jugular wall of tympanic cavity

②

Mandibular n. [CN V³]

Stapedius m. tendon

ANTERIOR →

①

⑥ Chorda tympani n.

Chorda tympani n. ⑥

Petrotympanic fissure

Fossa of round window

Middle meningeal a.

Facial canal (containing facial n.)

Stylomastoid foramen

Tensor veli palatini m. ⑦

③

Lingual n.

Digastric m.—post. belly

④ ⑤

Tympanic cells ⑨

Styloglossus m.

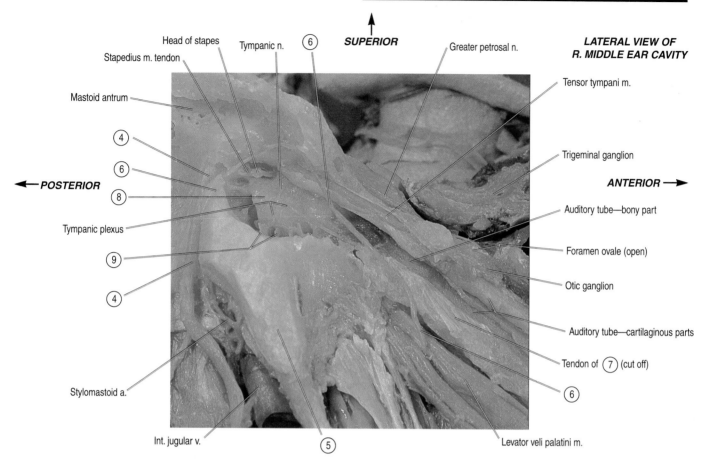

LATERAL VIEW OF
R. MIDDLE EAR CAVITY

Head of stapes

Stapedius m. tendon

Tympanic n.

⑥

SUPERIOR

Greater petrosal n.

Tensor tympani m.

Mastoid antrum

Trigeminal ganglion

④

⑥

◄ POSTERIOR

⑧

ANTERIOR ►

Tympanic plexus

Auditory tube—bony part

Foramen ovale (open)

⑨

Otic ganglion

④

Auditory tube—cartilaginous parts

Stylomastoid a.

Tendon of ⑦ (cut off)

⑥

Int. jugular v.

⑤

Levator veli palatini m.

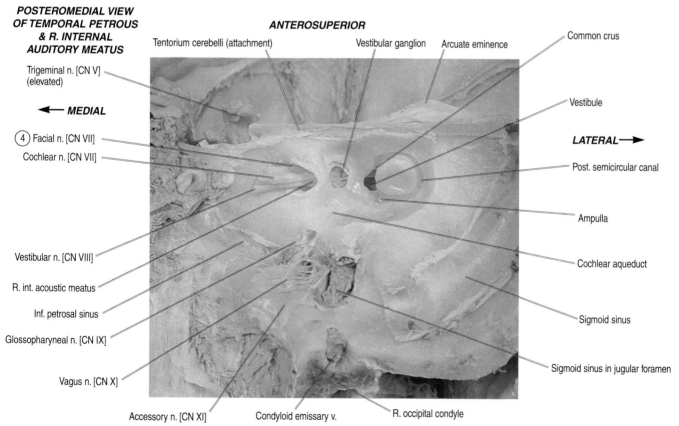

POSTEROMEDIAL VIEW
OF TEMPORAL PETROUS
& R. INTERNAL
AUDITORY MEATUS

ANTEROSUPERIOR

Common crus

Tentorium cerebelli (attachment)

Vestibular ganglion

Arcuate eminence

Trigeminal n. [CN V]
(elevated)

Vestibule

◄ MEDIAL

LATERAL ►

④ Facial n. [CN VII]

Cochlear n. [CN VII]

Post. semicircular canal

Ampulla

Vestibular n. [CN VIII]

R. int. acoustic meatus

Cochlear aqueduct

Inf. petrosal sinus

Glossopharyneal n. [CN IX]

Sigmoid sinus

Vagus n. [CN X]

Sigmoid sinus in jugular foramen

Accessory n. [CN XI]

Condyloid emissary v.

R. occipital condyle

Cranial and Autonomic Nerves

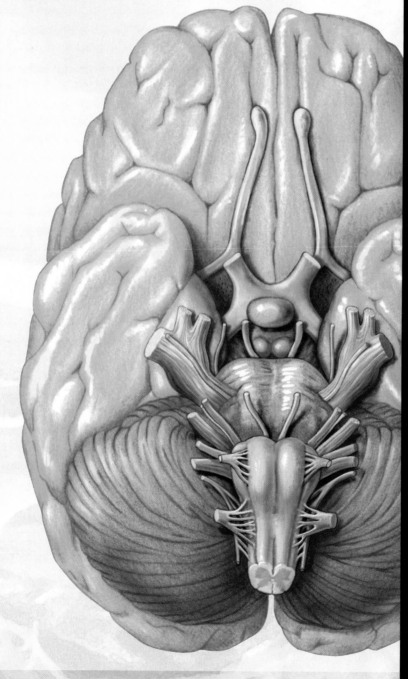

Chapter 8

Cranial Nerve Functions
Table 8.1

| Nerve | Efferent or Motor | | Afferent or Sensory | | |
	Striated Muscles	Smooth & Cardiac Muscles & Glands	Skin	Mucous Membranes & Organs	Special Senses
CN I					Olfaction or sensation of smell
CN II					Vision or sight
CN III	Supplies all muscles of eyeball except lateral rectus	Parasympathetic to ciliary m. (lens) & sphincter m. of iris of eye		Proprioceptive fibers from eye m.	
CN IV	Supplies superior oblique mm. of eyeball			Proprioceptive fibers from eye m.	
CN V	Supplies muscles of mastication & tensors of tympanic membrane & palate & mylohyoid m. ant. belly of digastric m.	Carries parasympathetic preganglionic nerve fibers of CN, III, VII & IX	Face & ant. part of scalp	Teeth, mucous membrane of mouth, nose & eye, general sensory from anterior two-thirds of tongue	Taste (fibers from chorda tympani) from ant. two-thirds of tongue
CN VI	Supplies lateral rectus m. of eyeball			Proprioceptive fibers from lateral rectus m.	
CN VII	Supplies muscles of facial expression, stapedius m., stylohyoid m., & post. belly of digastric m.	Parasympathetic nervus intermedius; glands of mouth, nose & palate; lacrimal gland; submandibular & sublingual glands	Ext. ear	Proprioceptive fibers from muscles of facial expression	Nervus intermedius, taste, ant. two-thirds of tongue
CN VIII					Hearing & equilibrium
CN IX	Supplies stylopharyngeus m.	Parasympathetic to parotid gland		Internal surface of tympanic membrane, middle ear, pharynx & general sensory from tongue (post. one-third)	Taste from post. one-third of tongue
CN X	Supplies muscles of pharynx & larynx	Parasympathetic to organs in neck, thorax & abdomen	Ext. acoustic meatus & tympanic membrane	Organs in neck, thorax & abdomen, general sensory from root of tongue	Taste, epiglottis
CN XI	Supplies muscles of soft palate, pharynx, larynx (from cranial root & distributed in vagus n.) & sternocleidomastoid & trapezius m.				
CN XII	Supplies extrinsic & intrinsic mm. of tongue except palatoglossus m. (from cranial root distributed in vagus n.)				

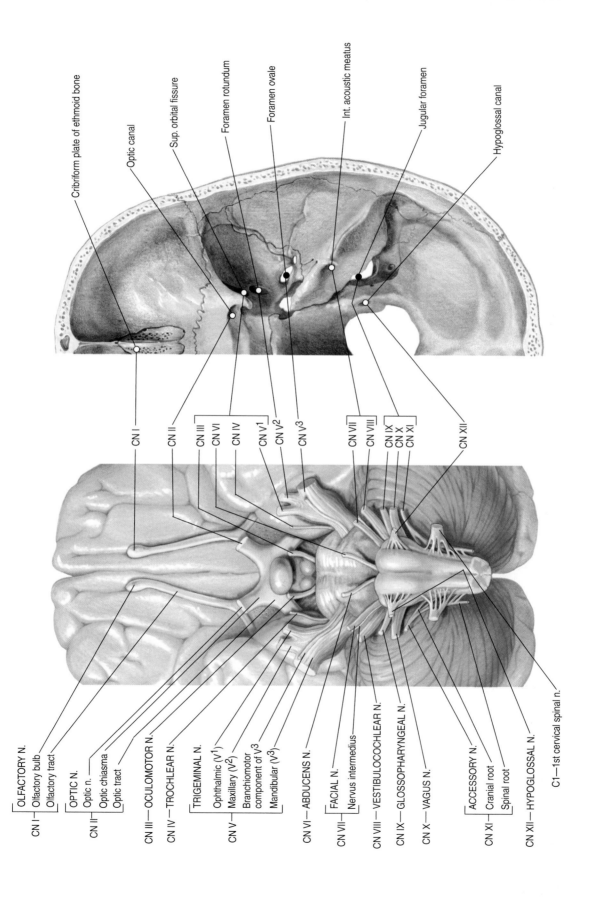

Cribriform plate of ethmoid bone

Optic canal

Sup. orbital fissure

Foramen rotundum

Foramen ovale

Int. acoustic meatus

Jugular foramen

Hypoglossal canal

CN I
CN II
CN III
CN VI
CN IV
CN V¹
CN V²
CN V³
CN VII
CN VIII
CN IX
CN X
CN XI
CN XII

CN I — OLFACTORY N. — Olfactory bulb — Olfactory tract

CN II — OPTIC N. — Optic n. — Optic chiasma — Optic tract

CN III — OCULOMOTOR N.

CN IV — TROCHLEAR N.

CN V — TRIGEMINAL N. — Ophthalmic (V¹) — Maxillary (V²) — Branchiomotor component of V³ — Mandibular (V³)

CN VI — ABDUCENS N.

CN VII — FACIAL N. — Nervus intermedius

CN VIII — VESTIBULOCOCHLEAR N.

CN IX — GLOSSOPHARYNGEAL N.

CN X — VAGUS N.

CN XI — ACCESSORY N. — Cranial root — Spinal root

CN XII — HYPOGLOSSAL N.

C1 — 1st cervical spinal n.

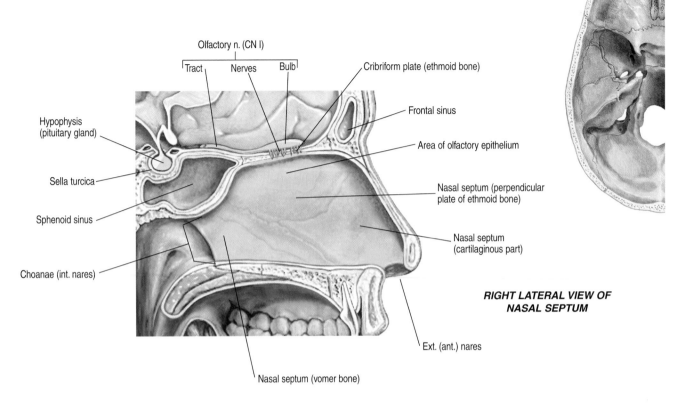

Olfactory n. (CN I)

Tract Nerves Bulb

Cribriform plate (ethmoid bone)

Frontal sinus

Hypophysis
(pituitary gland)

Area of olfactory epithelium

Sella turcica

Nasal septum (perpendicular
plate of ethmoid bone)

Sphenoid sinus

Nasal septum
(cartilaginous part)

Choanae (int. nares)

Nasal septum (vomer bone)

Ext. (ant.) nares

**RIGHT LATERAL VIEW OF
NASAL SEPTUM**

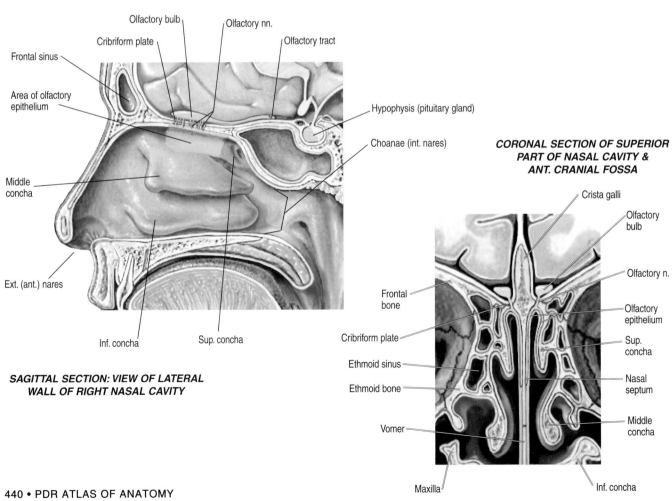

Olfactory bulb

Olfactory nn.

Cribriform plate

Olfactory tract

Frontal sinus

Area of olfactory
epithelium

Hypophysis (pituitary gland)

Choanae (int. nares)

Middle
concha

**CORONAL SECTION OF SUPERIOR
PART OF NASAL CAVITY &
ANT. CRANIAL FOSSA**

Ext. (ant.) nares

Inf. concha

Sup. concha

**SAGITTAL SECTION: VIEW OF LATERAL
WALL OF RIGHT NASAL CAVITY**

Crista galli

Olfactory
bulb

Olfactory n.

Frontal
bone

Olfactory
epithelium

Cribriform plate

Sup.
concha

Ethmoid sinus

Nasal
septum

Ethmoid bone

Middle
concha

Vomer

Maxilla

Inf. concha

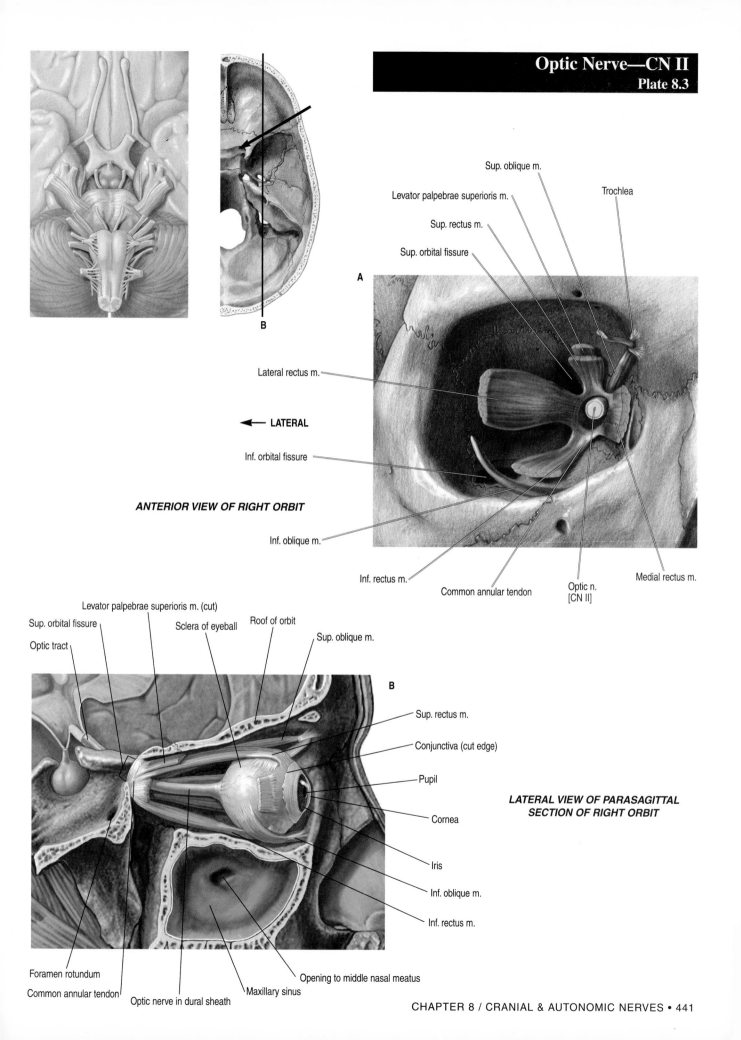

A

Sup. oblique m.

Levator palpebrae superioris m.

Trochlea

Sup. rectus m.

Sup. orbital fissure

Lateral rectus m.

◄— LATERAL

Inf. orbital fissure

ANTERIOR VIEW OF RIGHT ORBIT

Inf. oblique m.

Inf. rectus m.

Common annular tendon

Optic n.
[CN II]

Medial rectus m.

Levator palpebrae superioris m. (cut)

Sclera of eyeball

Roof of orbit

Sup. orbital fissure

Optic tract

Sup. oblique m.

B

Sup. rectus m.

Conjunctiva (cut edge)

Pupil

**LATERAL VIEW OF PARASAGITTAL
SECTION OF RIGHT ORBIT**

Cornea

Iris

Inf. oblique m.

Inf. rectus m.

Foramen rotundum

Common annular tendon

Optic nerve in dural sheath

Maxillary sinus

Opening to middle nasal meatus

Oculomotor Nerve—CN III
Plate 8.4

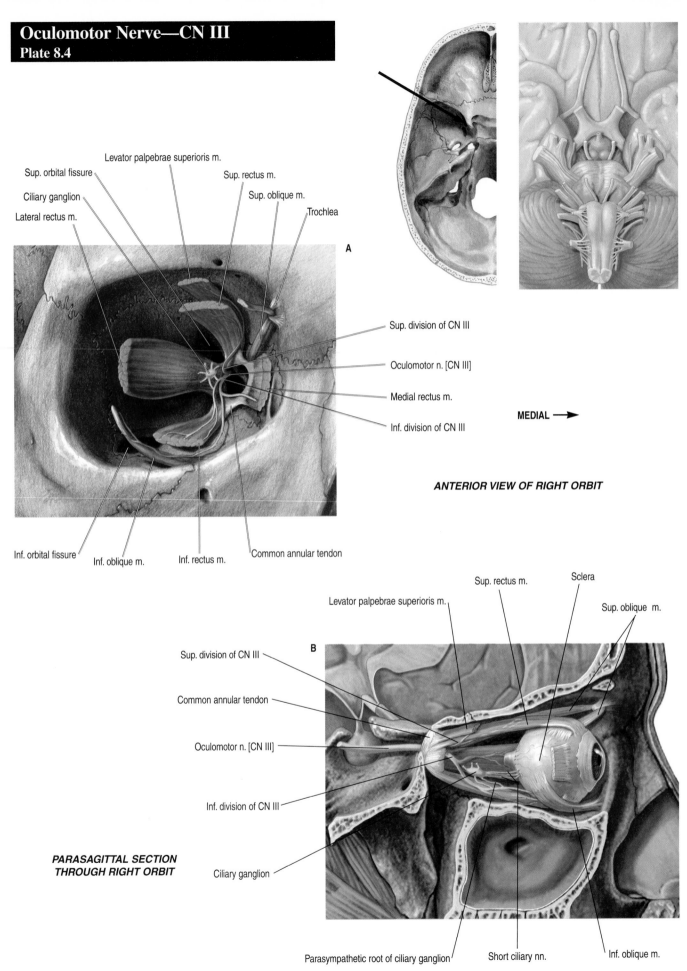

Sup. orbital fissure

Levator palpebrae superioris m.

Ciliary ganglion

Sup. rectus m.

Lateral rectus m.

Sup. oblique m.

Trochlea

A

Sup. division of CN III

Oculomotor n. [CN III]

Medial rectus m.

Inf. division of CN III

MEDIAL ⟶

ANTERIOR VIEW OF RIGHT ORBIT

Inf. orbital fissure

Inf. oblique m.

Inf. rectus m.

Common annular tendon

Sup. rectus m.

Sclera

Levator palpebrae superioris m.

Sup. oblique m.

Sup. division of CN III

B

Common annular tendon

Oculomotor n. [CN III]

Inf. division of CN III

*PARASAGITTAL SECTION
THROUGH RIGHT ORBIT*

Ciliary ganglion

Parasympathetic root of ciliary ganglion

Short ciliary nn.

Inf. oblique m.

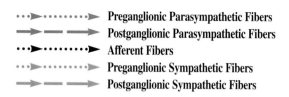

Preganglionic Parasympathetic Fibers
Postganglionic Parasympathetic Fibers
Afferent Fibers
Preganglionic Sympathetic Fibers
Postganglionic Sympathetic Fibers

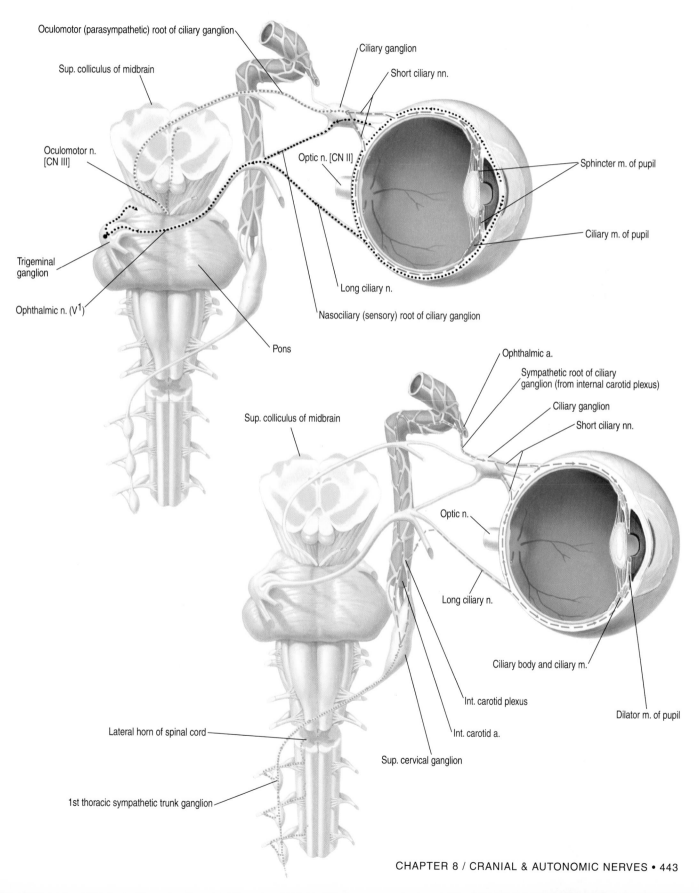

Oculomotor (parasympathetic) root of ciliary ganglion

Sup. colliculus of midbrain

Ciliary ganglion

Short ciliary nn.

Oculomotor n. [CN III]

Optic n. [CN II]

Sphincter m. of pupil

Trigeminal ganglion

Ciliary m. of pupil

Ophthalmic n. (V^1)

Long ciliary n.

Pons

Nasociliary (sensory) root of ciliary ganglion

Ophthalmic a.

Sympathetic root of ciliary ganglion (from internal carotid plexus)

Ciliary ganglion

Short ciliary nn.

Sup. colliculus of midbrain

Optic n.

Long ciliary n.

Ciliary body and ciliary m.

Int. carotid plexus

Dilator m. of pupil

Int. carotid a.

Lateral horn of spinal cord

Sup. cervical ganglion

1st thoracic sympathetic trunk ganglion

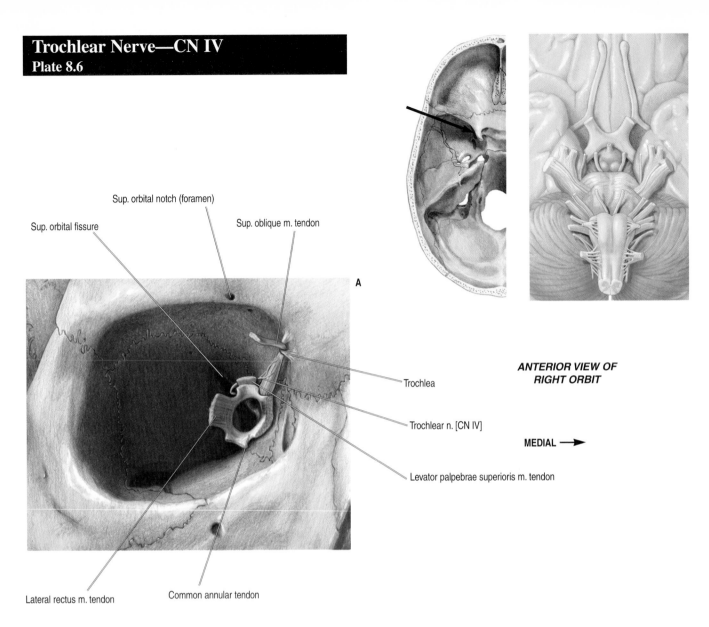

Sup. orbital notch (foramen)

Sup. orbital fissure

Sup. oblique m. tendon

A

Trochlea

Trochlear n. [CN IV]

Levator palpebrae superioris m. tendon

Lateral rectus m. tendon

Common annular tendon

ANTERIOR VIEW OF RIGHT ORBIT

MEDIAL ⟶

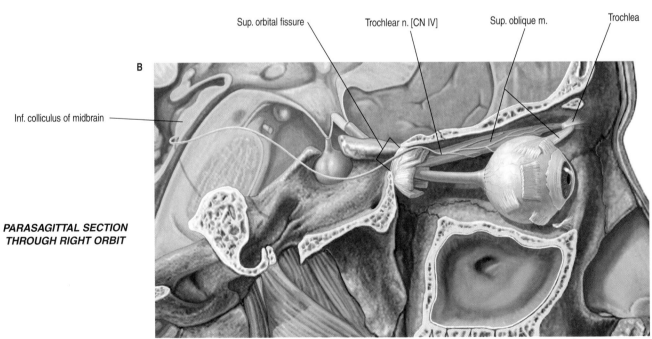

Sup. orbital fissure

Trochlear n. [CN IV]

Sup. oblique m.

Trochlea

B

Inf. colliculus of midbrain

PARASAGITTAL SECTION THROUGH RIGHT ORBIT

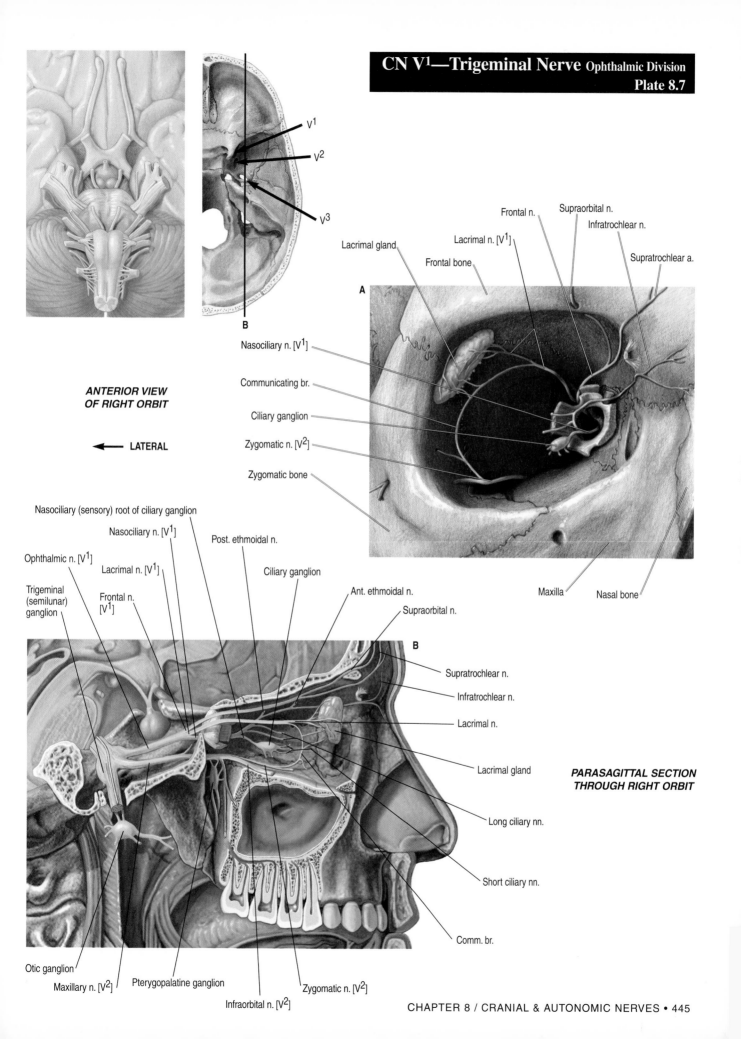

ANTERIOR VIEW OF RIGHT ORBIT

← **LATERAL**

Lacrimal gland

Frontal bone

Frontal n.

Lacrimal n. [V¹]

Supraorbital n.

Infratrochlear n.

Supratrochlear a.

A

Nasociliary n. [V¹]

Communicating br.

Ciliary ganglion

Zygomatic n. [V²]

Zygomatic bone

V¹

V²

V³

B

Maxilla

Nasal bone

Nasociliary (sensory) root of ciliary ganglion

Nasociliary n. [V¹]

Post. ethmoidal n.

Ophthalmic n. [V¹]

Lacrimal n. [V¹]

Ciliary ganglion

Ant. ethmoidal n.

Supraorbital n.

Trigeminal (semilunar) ganglion

Frontal n. [V¹]

B

Supratrochlear n.

Infratrochlear n.

Lacrimal n.

Lacrimal gland

PARASAGITTAL SECTION THROUGH RIGHT ORBIT

Long ciliary nn.

Short ciliary nn.

Otic ganglion

Maxillary n. [V²]

Pterygopalatine ganglion

Infraorbital n. [V²]

Zygomatic n. [V²]

Comm. br.

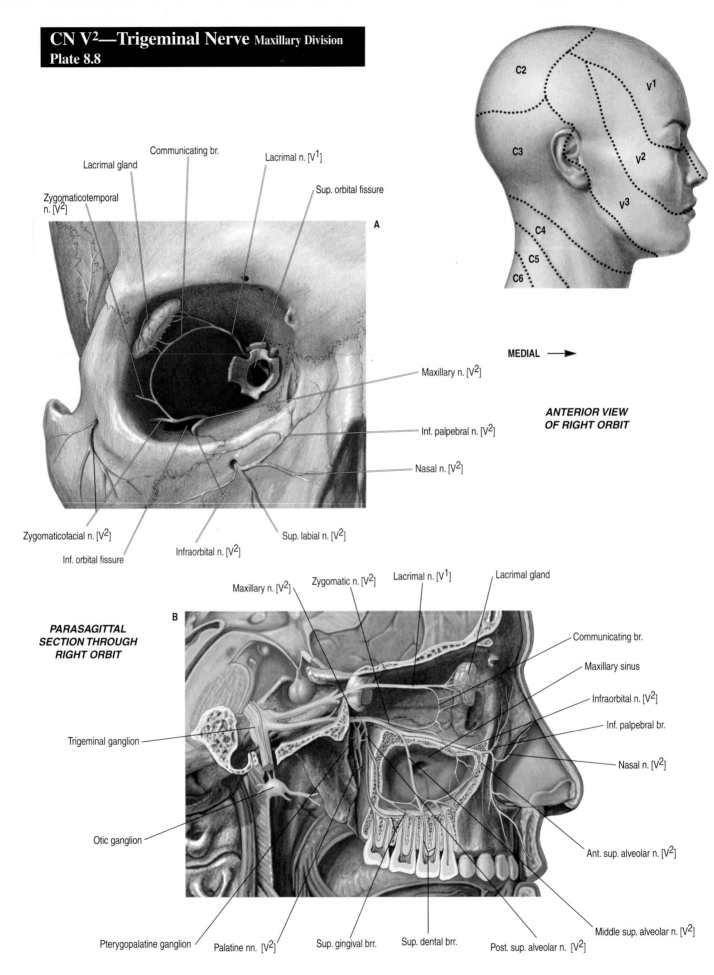

C2

C3

V¹

V²

V³

C4

C5

C6

MEDIAL ⟶

ANTERIOR VIEW OF RIGHT ORBIT

Zygomaticotemporal n. [V²]

Lacrimal gland

Communicating br.

Lacrimal n. [V¹]

Sup. orbital fissure

A

Maxillary n. [V²]

Inf. palpebral n. [V²]

Nasal n. [V²]

Zygomaticofacial n. [V²]

Inf. orbital fissure

Infraorbital n. [V²]

Sup. labial n. [V²]

PARASAGITTAL SECTION THROUGH RIGHT ORBIT

B

Maxillary n. [V²]

Zygomatic n. [V²]

Lacrimal n. [V¹]

Lacrimal gland

Communicating br.

Maxillary sinus

Infraorbital n. [V²]

Inf. palpebral br.

Nasal n. [V²]

Trigeminal ganglion

Otic ganglion

Ant. sup. alveolar n. [V²]

Pterygopalatine ganglion

Palatine nn. [V²]

Sup. gingival brr.

Sup. dental brr.

Post. sup. alveolar n. [V²]

Middle sup. alveolar n. [V²]

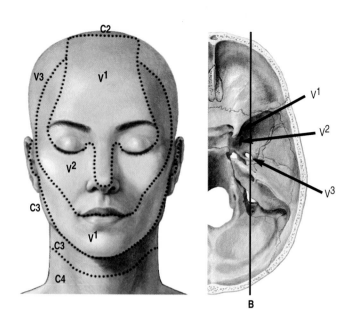

B

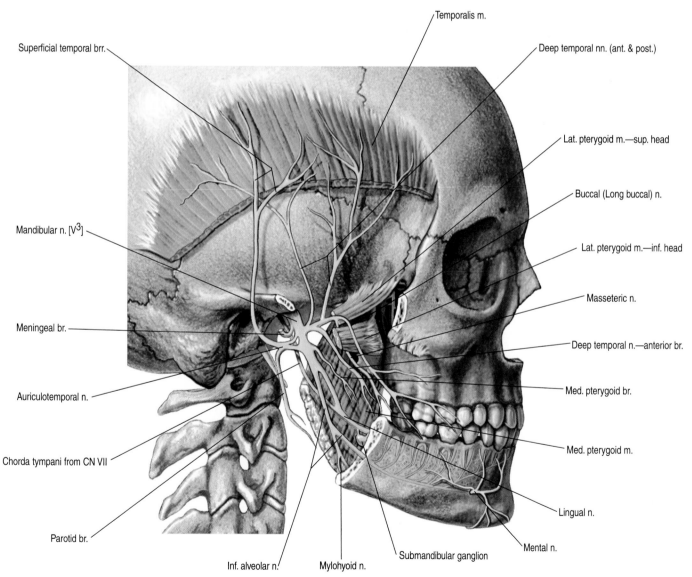

Temporalis m.

Superficial temporal brr.

Deep temporal nn. (ant. & post.)

Lat. pterygoid m.—sup. head

Buccal (Long buccal) n.

Mandibular n. [V³]

Lat. pterygoid m.—inf. head

Masseteric n.

Meningeal br.

Deep temporal n.—anterior br.

Auriculotemporal n.

Med. pterygoid br.

Med. pterygoid m.

Chorda tympani from CN VII

Lingual n.

Parotid br.

Mental n.

Inf. alveolar n.

Mylohyoid n.

Submandibular ganglion

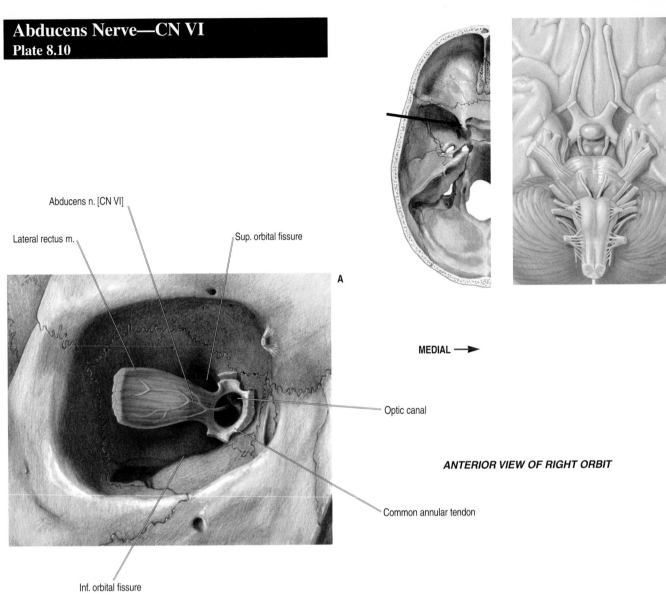

Abducens n. [CN VI]

Lateral rectus m.

Sup. orbital fissure

A

MEDIAL ⟶

Optic canal

ANTERIOR VIEW OF RIGHT ORBIT

Common annular tendon

Inf. orbital fissure

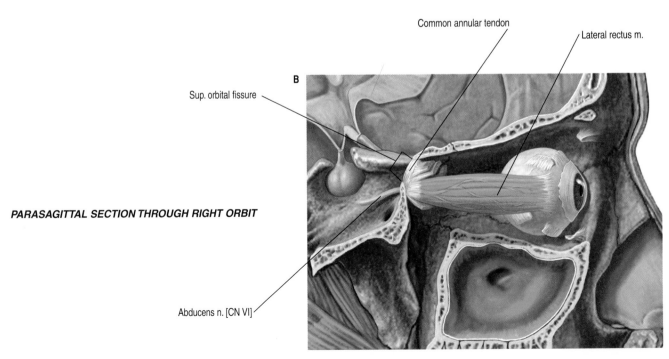

Common annular tendon

Lateral rectus m.

Sup. orbital fissure

B

PARASAGITTAL SECTION THROUGH RIGHT ORBIT

Abducens n. [CN VI]

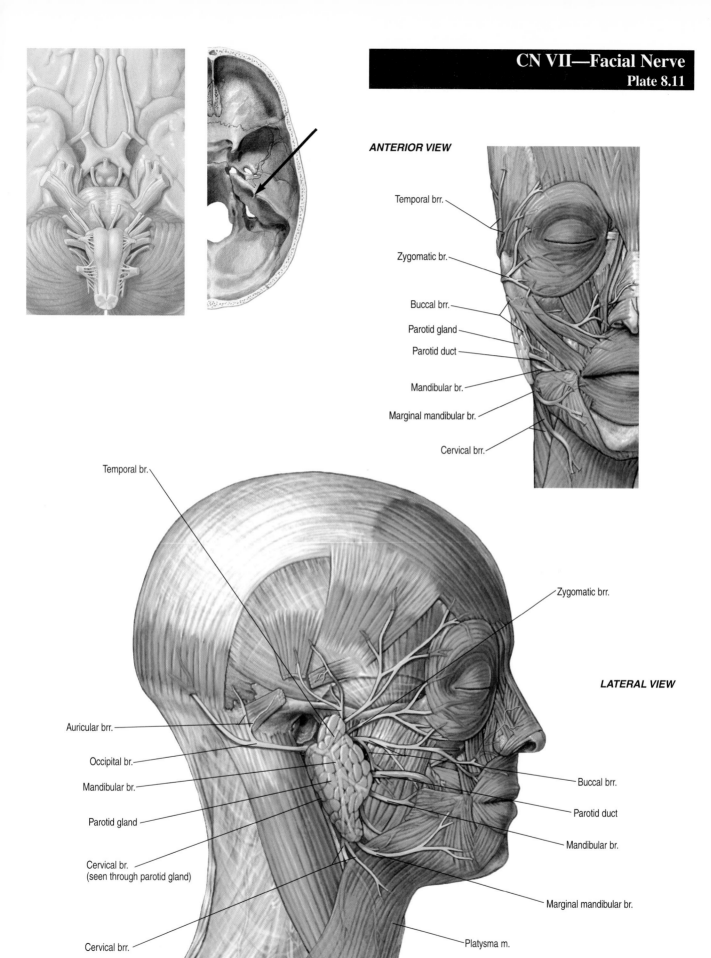

ANTERIOR VIEW

Temporal brr.

Zygomatic br.

Buccal brr.

Parotid gland

Parotid duct

Mandibular br.

Marginal mandibular br.

Cervical brr.

Temporal br.

Zygomatic brr.

LATERAL VIEW

Auricular brr.

Occipital br.

Mandibular br.

Parotid gland

Cervical br.
(seen through parotid gland)

Cervical brr.

Buccal brr.

Parotid duct

Mandibular br.

Marginal mandibular br.

Platysma m.

Pterygopalatine Ganglion
Plate 8.12

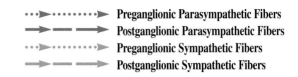
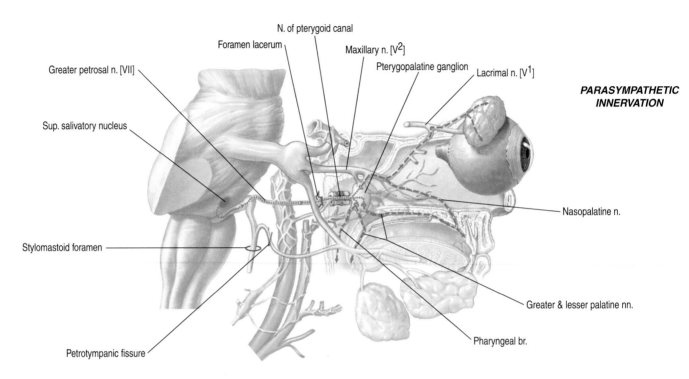

N. of pterygoid canal

Foramen lacerum

Maxillary n. [V²]

Pterygopalatine ganglion

Greater petrosal n. [VII]

Lacrimal n. [V¹]

PARASYMPATHETIC INNERVATION

Sup. salivatory nucleus

Nasopalatine n.

Stylomastoid foramen

Greater & lesser palatine nn.

Pharyngeal br.

Petrotympanic fissure

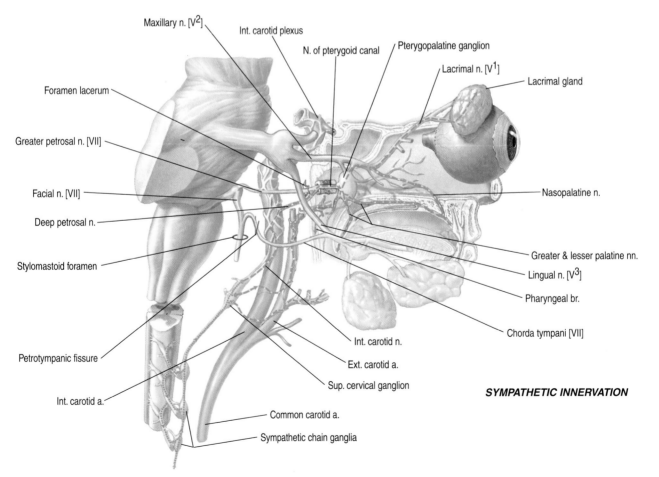

Maxillary n. [V²]

Int. carotid plexus

N. of pterygoid canal

Pterygopalatine ganglion

Foramen lacerum

Lacrimal n. [V¹]

Lacrimal gland

Greater petrosal n. [VII]

Nasopalatine n.

Facial n. [VII]

Deep petrosal n.

Greater & lesser palatine nn.

Stylomastoid foramen

Lingual n. [V³]

Pharyngeal br.

Chorda tympani [VII]

Petrotympanic fissure

Int. carotid n.

Ext. carotid a.

Sup. cervical ganglion

SYMPATHETIC INNERVATION

Int. carotid a.

Common carotid a.

Sympathetic chain ganglia

Preganglionic Parasympathetic Fibers
Postganglionic Parasympathetic Fibers
Preganglionic Sympathetic Fibers
Postganglionic Sympathetic Fibers

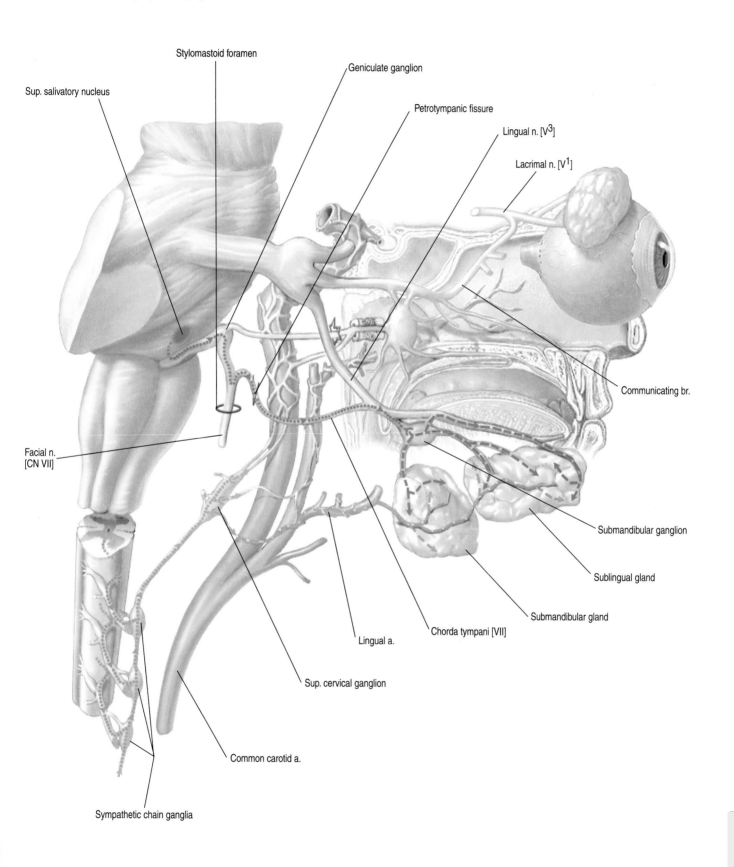

Stylomastoid foramen

Sup. salivatory nucleus

Geniculate ganglion

Petrotympanic fissure

Lingual n. [V^3]

Lacrimal n. [V^1]

Communicating br.

Facial n.
[CN VII]

Submandibular ganglion

Sublingual gland

Submandibular gland

Chorda tympani [VII]

Lingual a.

Sup. cervical ganglion

Common carotid a.

Sympathetic chain ganglia

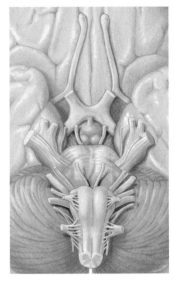

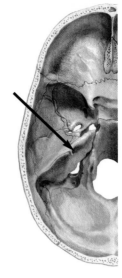

**HORIZONTAL SECTION THROUGH TEMPORAL BONE
AND CHAMBERS OF THE EAR**

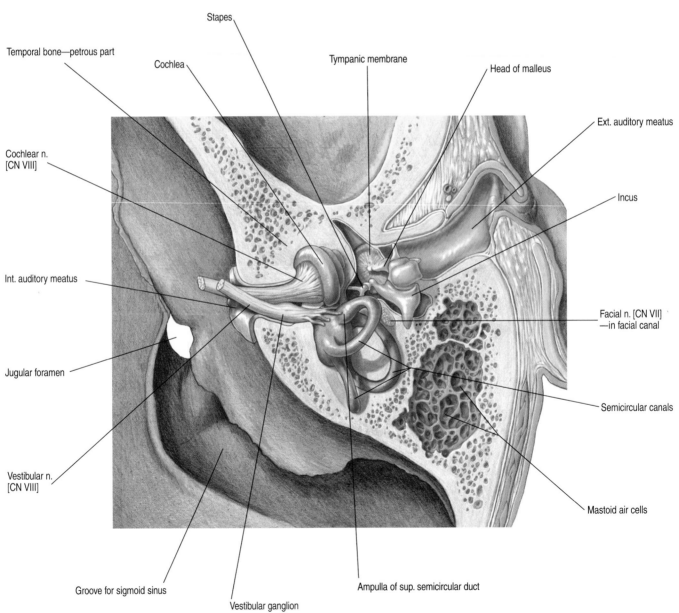

Stapes

Temporal bone—petrous part

Cochlea

Tympanic membrane

Head of malleus

Ext. auditory meatus

Cochlear n.
[CN VIII]

Incus

Int. auditory meatus

Facial n. [CN VII]
—in facial canal

Jugular foramen

Semicircular canals

Vestibular n.
[CN VIII]

Mastoid air cells

Groove for sigmoid sinus

Vestibular ganglion

Ampulla of sup. semicircular duct

Preganglionic Parasympathetic Fibers
Postganglionic Parasympathetic Fibers
Afferent Fibers
Preganglionic Sympathetic Fibers
Postganglionic Sympathetic Fibers

Mandibular n. [V³]

Geniculate ganglion of facial n. [VII]

Tympanic n. [IX]

Greater petrosal n. [VII]

Tympanic plexus

Lesser petrosal n. [IX]

Pterygopalatine ganglion

Foramen ovale

Parotid gland

Sup. ganglion of glossopharyngeal n. [IX]

Inf. (petrosal) ganglion of glossopharyngeal n. [IX]

Otic ganglion

Sup. ganglion of vagus n. [X]

Inf. (nodose) ganglion of vagus n. [X]

Chorda tympani [VII]

Vagus n. [X]

Glossopharyngeal n. [IX]

Lingual n. [V³]

Sup. cervical sympathetic ganglion

Foramen cecum of tongue

Posferior 1/3rd of tongue

Int. carotid a.

Sympathetic chain

Sulcus terminalis

Chorda tympani (br. of CN VII)

Ext. carotid a.

Anterior 2/3rds of tongue

Vallate papillae

Filiform papillae

Common carotid a.

Fungiform papillae

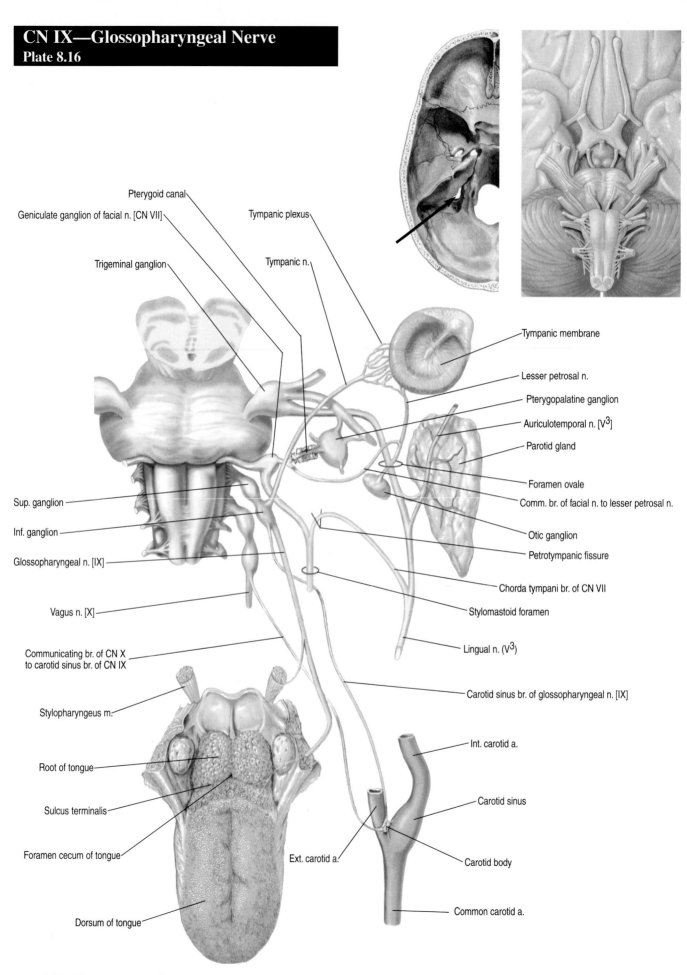

Pterygoid canal

Geniculate ganglion of facial n. [CN VII]

Tympanic plexus

Tympanic n.

Trigeminal ganglion

Tympanic membrane

Lesser petrosal n.

Pterygopalatine ganglion

Auriculotemporal n. [V³]

Parotid gland

Foramen ovale

Comm. br. of facial n. to lesser petrosal n.

Sup. ganglion

Inf. ganglion

Otic ganglion

Petrotympanic fissure

Glossopharyngeal n. [IX]

Chorda tympani br. of CN VII

Stylomastoid foramen

Vagus n. [X]

Lingual n. (V³)

Communicating br. of CN X
to carotid sinus br. of CN IX

Carotid sinus br. of glossopharyngeal n. [IX]

Stylopharyngeus m.

Int. carotid a.

Root of tongue

Sulcus terminalis

Carotid sinus

Foramen cecum of tongue

Ext. carotid a.

Carotid body

Dorsum of tongue

Common carotid a.

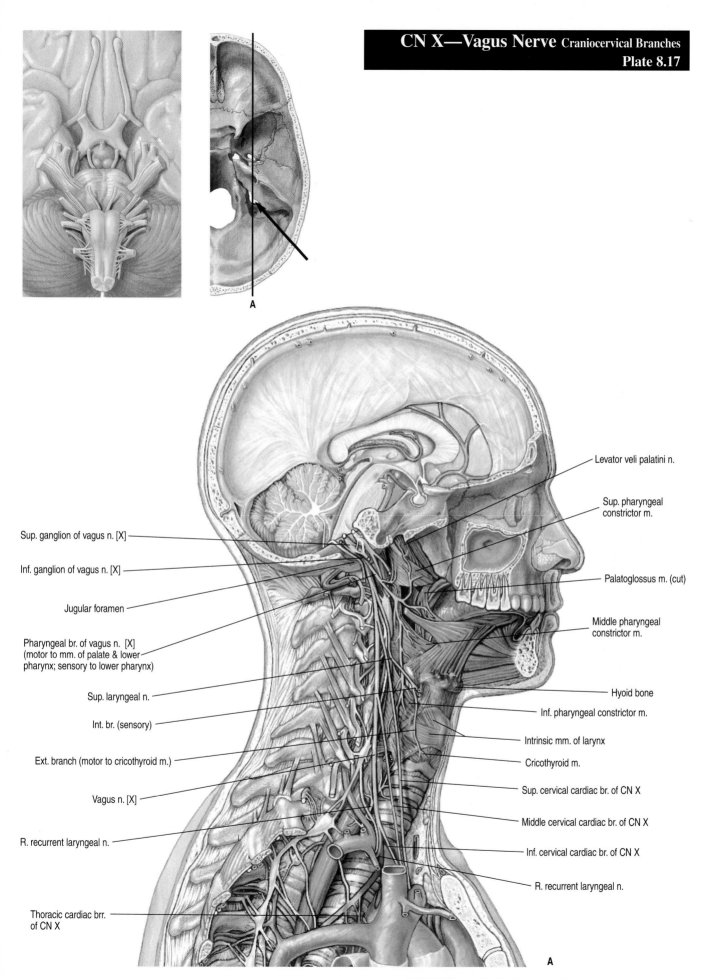

Levator veli palatini n.

Sup. pharyngeal
constrictor m.

Sup. ganglion of vagus n. [X]

Inf. ganglion of vagus n. [X]

Jugular foramen

Pharyngeal br. of vagus n. [X]
(motor to mm. of palate & lower
pharynx; sensory to lower pharynx)

Sup. laryngeal n.

Int. br. (sensory)

Ext. branch (motor to cricothyroid m.)

Vagus n. [X]

R. recurrent laryngeal n.

Thoracic cardiac brr.
of CN X

Palatoglossus m. (cut)

Middle pharyngeal
constrictor m.

Hyoid bone

Inf. pharyngeal constrictor m.

Intrinsic mm. of larynx

Cricothyroid m.

Sup. cervical cardiac br. of CN X

Middle cervical cardiac br. of CN X

Inf. cervical cardiac br. of CN X

R. recurrent laryngeal n.

A

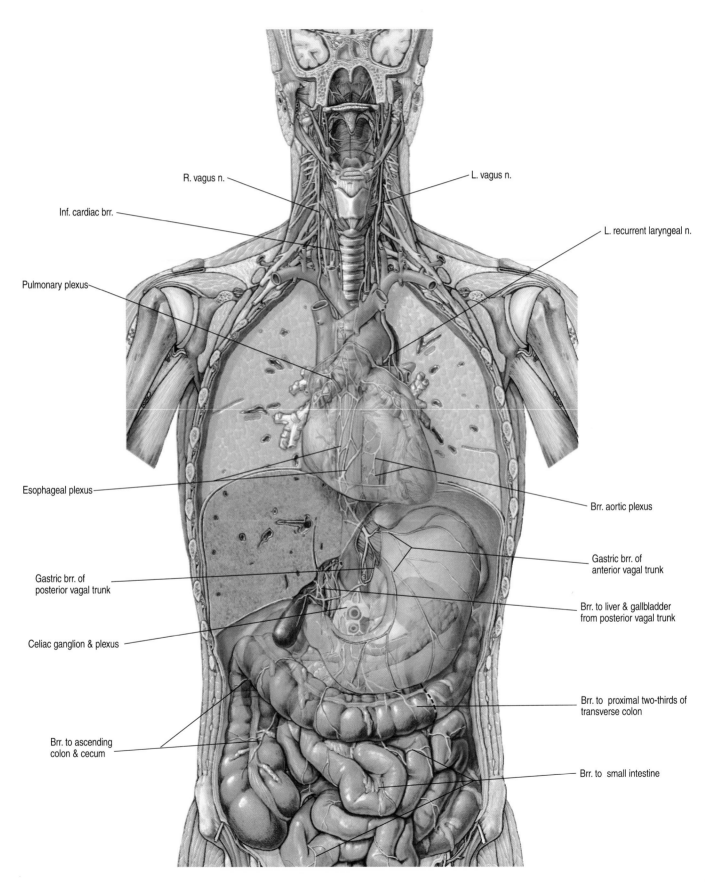

R. vagus n.

L. vagus n.

Inf. cardiac brr.

L. recurrent laryngeal n.

Pulmonary plexus

Esophageal plexus

Brr. aortic plexus

Gastric brr. of anterior vagal trunk

Gastric brr. of posterior vagal trunk

Brr. to liver & gallbladder from posterior vagal trunk

Celiac ganglion & plexus

Brr. to proximal two-thirds of transverse colon

Brr. to ascending colon & cecum

Brr. to small intestine

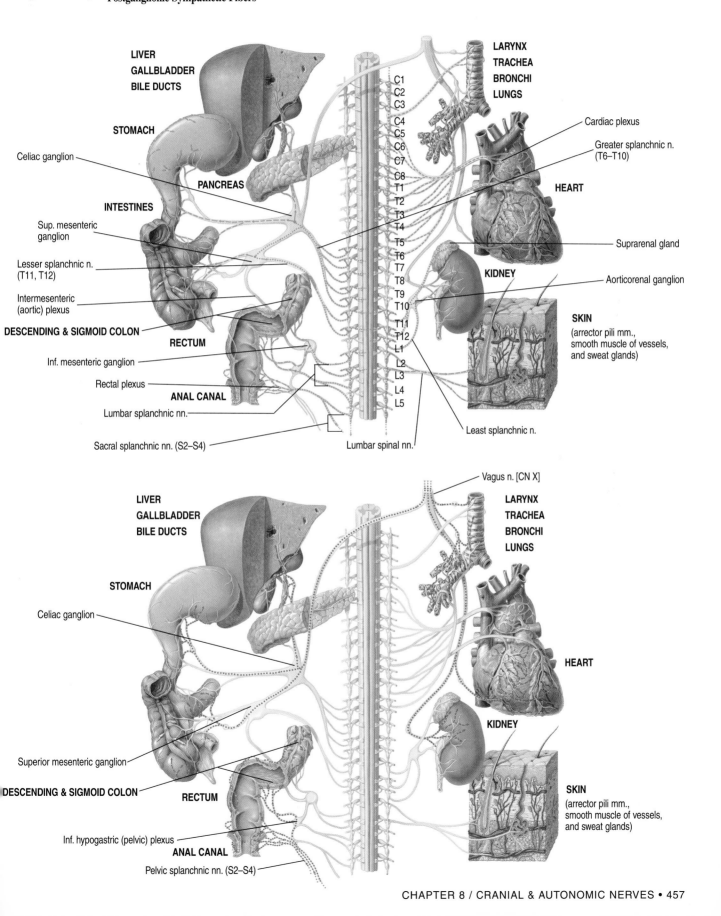

Preganglionic Parasympathetic Fibers
Postganglionic Parasympathetic Fibers
Preganglionic Sympathetic Fibers
Postganglionic Sympathetic Fibers

LIVER
GALLBLADDER
BILE DUCTS

STOMACH

Celiac ganglion

PANCREAS

INTESTINES

Sup. mesenteric ganglion

Lesser splanchnic n. (T11, T12)

Intermesenteric (aortic) plexus

DESCENDING & SIGMOID COLON

RECTUM

Inf. mesenteric ganglion

Rectal plexus

ANAL CANAL

Lumbar splanchnic nn.

Sacral splanchnic nn. (S2–S4)

Lumbar spinal nn.

LARYNX
TRACHEA
BRONCHI
LUNGS

C1 C2 C3 C4 C5 C6 C7 C8 T1 T2 T3 T4 T5 T6 T7 T8 T9 T10 T11 T12 L1 L2 L3 L4 L5

Cardiac plexus

Greater splanchnic n. (T6–T10)

HEART

Suprarenal gland

KIDNEY

Aorticorenal ganglion

Least splanchnic n.

SKIN
(arrector pili mm., smooth muscle of vessels, and sweat glands)

LIVER
GALLBLADDER
BILE DUCTS

STOMACH

Celiac ganglion

Superior mesenteric ganglion

DESCENDING & SIGMOID COLON

RECTUM

Inf. hypogastric (pelvic) plexus

ANAL CANAL

Pelvic splanchnic nn. (S2–S4)

Vagus n. [CN X]

LARYNX
TRACHEA
BRONCHI
LUNGS

HEART

KIDNEY

SKIN
(arrector pili mm., smooth muscle of vessels, and sweat glands)

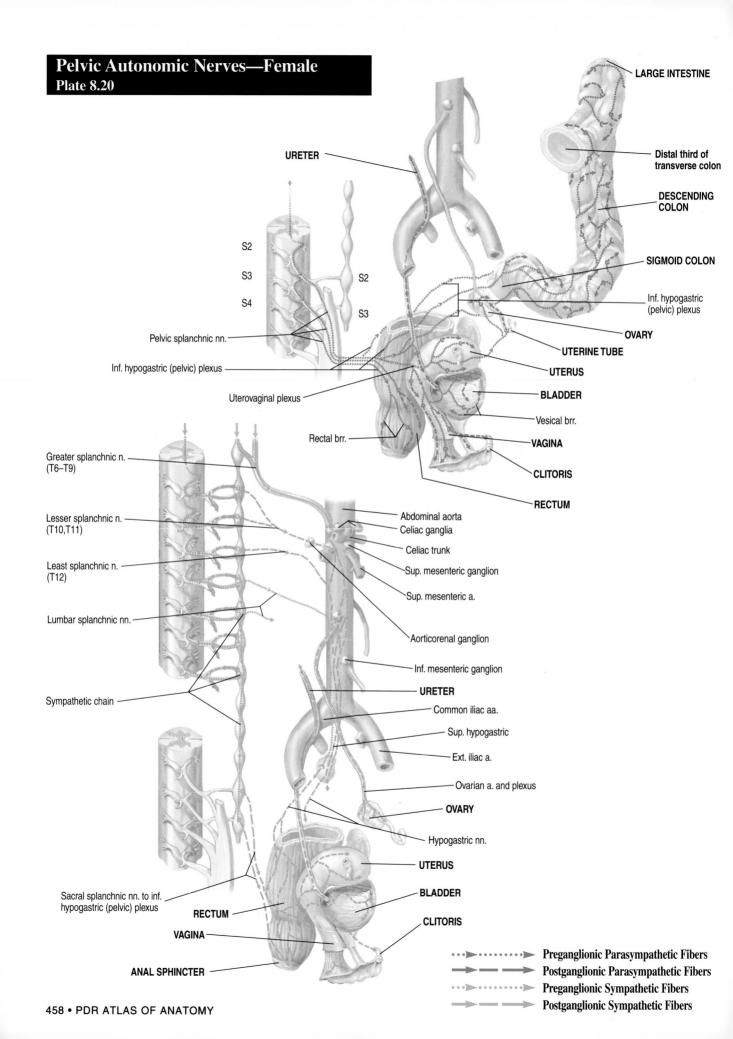

LARGE INTESTINE

Distal third of transverse colon

DESCENDING COLON

URETER

S2

S3

S4

S2

S3

SIGMOID COLON

Inf. hypogastric (pelvic) plexus

OVARY

UTERINE TUBE

UTERUS

Pelvic splanchnic nn.

Inf. hypogastric (pelvic) plexus

Uterovaginal plexus

BLADDER

Vesical brr.

Rectal brr.

VAGINA

CLITORIS

RECTUM

Greater splanchnic n. (T6–T9)

Abdominal aorta

Celiac ganglia

Celiac trunk

Lesser splanchnic n. (T10,T11)

Sup. mesenteric ganglion

Sup. mesenteric a.

Least splanchnic n. (T12)

Aorticorenal ganglion

Lumbar splanchnic nn.

Inf. mesenteric ganglion

URETER

Common iliac aa.

Sup. hypogastric

Sympathetic chain

Ext. iliac a.

Ovarian a. and plexus

OVARY

Hypogastric nn.

UTERUS

BLADDER

Sacral splanchnic nn. to inf. hypogastric (pelvic) plexus

CLITORIS

RECTUM

VAGINA

ANAL SPHINCTER

Preganglionic Parasympathetic Fibers
Postganglionic Parasympathetic Fibers
Preganglionic Sympathetic Fibers
Postganglionic Sympathetic Fibers

Preganglionic Parasympathetic Fibers
Postganglionic Parasympathetic Fibers
Preganglionic Sympathetic Fibers
Postganglionic Sympathetic Fibers

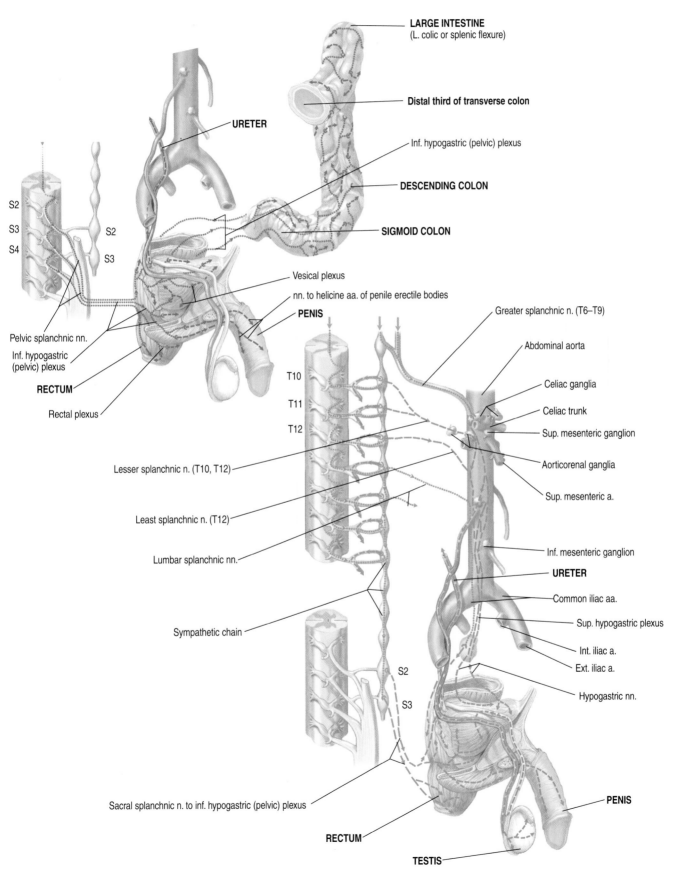

LARGE INTESTINE
(L. colic or splenic flexure)

Distal third of transverse colon

Inf. hypogastric (pelvic) plexus

DESCENDING COLON

SIGMOID COLON

URETER

S2
S3
S4

S2

S3

Vesical plexus

nn. to helicine aa. of penile erectile bodies

PENIS

Pelvic splanchnic nn.

Inf. hypogastric
(pelvic) plexus

RECTUM

Rectal plexus

Greater splanchnic n. (T6–T9)

Abdominal aorta

Celiac ganglia

Celiac trunk

Sup. mesenteric ganglion

Aorticorenal ganglia

Sup. mesenteric a.

T10

T11

T12

Lesser splanchnic n. (T10, T12)

Least splanchnic n. (T12)

Lumbar splanchnic nn.

Inf. mesenteric ganglion

URETER

Common iliac aa.

Sup. hypogastric plexus

Int. iliac a.

Ext. iliac a.

Hypogastric nn.

Sympathetic chain

S2

S3

Sacral splanchnic n. to inf. hypogastric (pelvic) plexus

PENIS

RECTUM

TESTIS

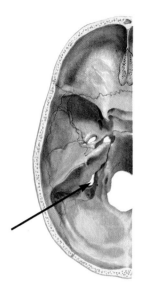
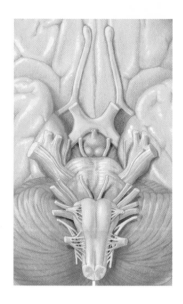

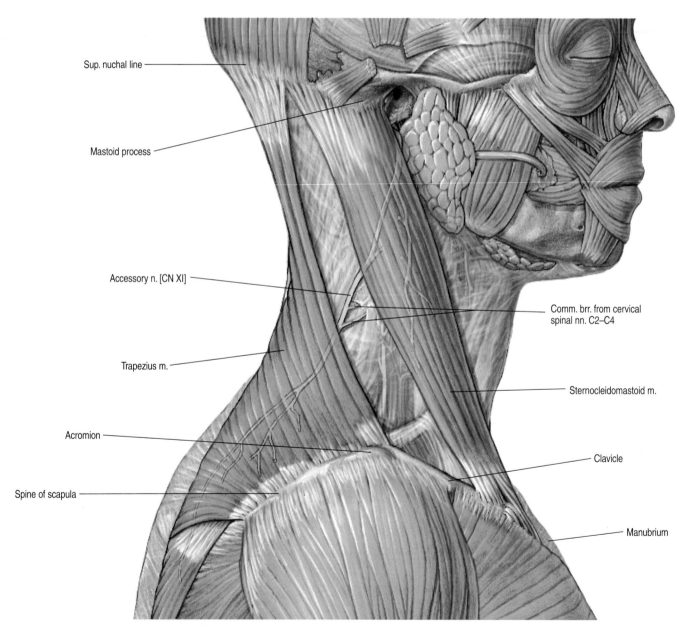

Sup. nuchal line

Mastoid process

Accessory n. [CN XI]

Comm. brr. from cervical spinal nn. C2–C4

Trapezius m.

Sternocleidomastoid m.

Acromion

Clavicle

Spine of scapula

Manubrium

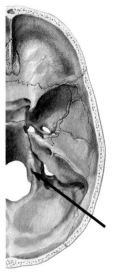

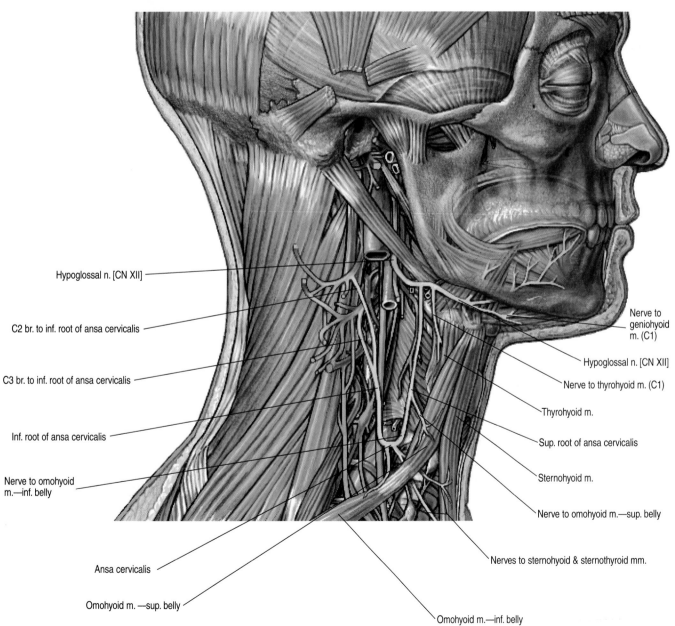

Hypoglossal n. [CN XII]

C2 br. to inf. root of ansa cervicalis

C3 br. to inf. root of ansa cervicalis

Inf. root of ansa cervicalis

Nerve to omohyoid m.—inf. belly

Ansa cervicalis

Omohyoid m.—sup. belly

Omohyoid m.—inf. belly

Nerve to geniohyoid m. (C1)

Hypoglossal n. [CN XII]

Nerve to thyrohyoid m. (C1)

Thyrohyoid m.

Sup. root of ansa cervicalis

Sternohyoid m.

Nerve to omohyoid m.—sup. belly

Nerves to sternohyoid & sternothyroid mm.

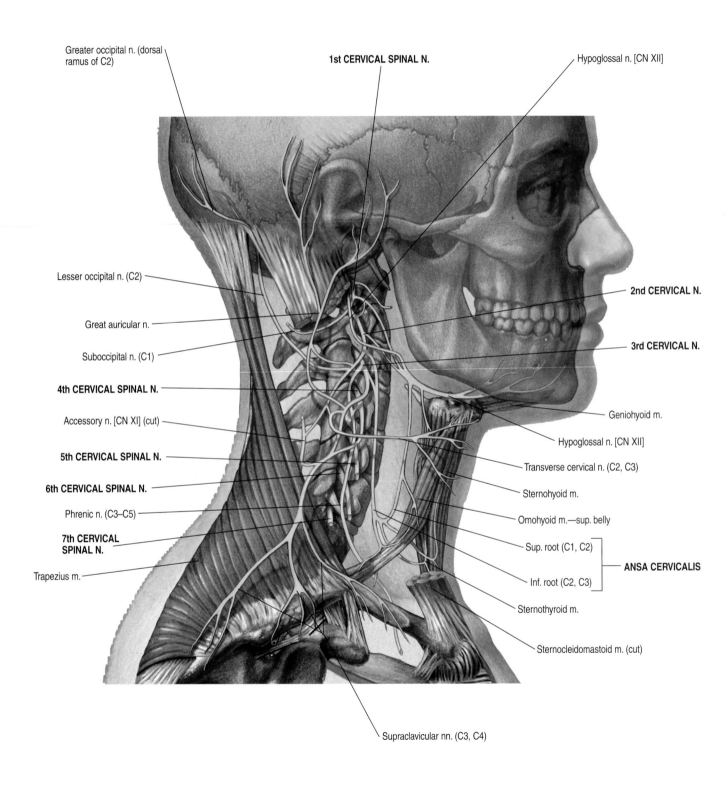

Greater occipital n. (dorsal ramus of C2)

1st CERVICAL SPINAL N.

Hypoglossal n. [CN XII]

Lesser occipital n. (C2)

2nd CERVICAL N.

Great auricular n.

3rd CERVICAL N.

Suboccipital n. (C1)

Geniohyoid m.

4th CERVICAL SPINAL N.

Accessory n. [CN XI] (cut)

Hypoglossal n. [CN XII]

Transverse cervical n. (C2, C3)

5th CERVICAL SPINAL N.

Sternohyoid m.

6th CERVICAL SPINAL N.

Omohyoid m.—sup. belly

Phrenic n. (C3–C5)

Sup. root (C1, C2)

7th CERVICAL SPINAL N.

Inf. root (C2, C3)

ANSA CERVICALIS

Trapezius m.

Sternothyroid m.

Sternocleidomastoid m. (cut)

Supraclavicular nn. (C3, C4)

Overview of Cranial Nerves

Nerve	Efferent or Motor			Afferent or Sensory	
	Striated Muscles	Smooth & Cardiac Muscles & Glands	Skin	Mucous Membranes & Organs	Special Senses
CN I					Olfaction or sensation of smell
CN II					Vision or sight
CN III	Supplies all muscles of eyeball except lateral rectus & superior oblique mm.	Parasympathetic to ciliary m. (lens) & sphincter m. of iris of eye		Proprioceptive fibers from eye m.	
CN IV	Supplies superior oblique m. of eyeball			Proprioceptive fibers from eye m.	
CN V	Supplies muscles of mastication, tensors of tympanic membrane, palate, mylohyoid m. & ant. belly of digastric m.	Carries parasympathetic preganglionic nerve fibers of CN, III, VII & IX	Face & ant. part of scalp	Teeth, mucous membrane of mouth, nose & eye, general sensory from ant. two-thirds of tongue	Taste (fibers from chorda tympani) from ant. two-thirds of tongue
CN VI	Supplies lateral rectus m. of eyeball			Proprioceptive fibers from lateral rectus m.	
CN VII	Supplies muscles of facial expression, stapedius m., stylohyoid m. & post. belly of digastric m.	Parasympathetic nervus intermedius; glands of mouth, nose & palate; lacrimal gland; submandibular & sublingual glands	Ext. ear	Proprioceptive fibers from muscles of facial expression	Nervus intermedius, taste, ant. two-thirds of tongue
CN VIII					Hearing & equilibrium
CN IX	Supplies stylopharyngeus m.	Parasympathetic to parotid gland		Internal surface of tympanic membrane, middle ear, pharynx & general sensory from tongue (post. third)	Taste, from post. third of tongue
CN X	Supplies muscles of pharynx and larynx	Parasympathetic to organs in neck, thorax & abdomen	Ext. acoustic meatus & tympanic membrane	Organs in neck, thorax & abdomen, general sensory from root of tongue	Taste, epiglottis
CN XI	Supplies muscles of soft palate, pharynx, larynx (from cranial root & distributed in vagus n.)& sternocleidomastoid & trapezius m.				
CN XII	Supplies extrinsic & intrinsic mm. of tongue except palatoglossus m.				

Index

radial, 276, 278, 324–325
grooves on
intertubercular, 276
radial nerve, 283
head of, 276–277, 314–316
necks of
anatomical, 276–277, 315
surgical, 276–277, 312, 315
supracondylar ridges of
lateral, 276–279, 287
medial, 276–279
trochlea of, 276, 278
tubercles of
greater, 4, 6, 276–277, 283, 301, 312–313,
315
crest of, 276, 312
inferior facet of, 283
middle facet of, 283
lesser, 4, 276, 282, 315
crest of, 276, 282–283
Hypophysis. *See* Gland, pituitary

Ileum, 112, 114–116, 130, 132–134, 136–137,
139, 176
gluteal surface of, 154–155, 202–203
terminal part of, 132–133
Ilium, 217
ala of, 211, 254
arcuate line of, 153
body of, 154–155, 210–211, 254–255
Impression(s)
cardiac, 74–75
colic, 126–128
costal, 127
duodenal, 126–127
esophageal, 126–127
gastric, 126
renal, 126–127
right, 128
suprarenal, 126
trigeminal, 361
Incisure, intertragic, 346
Incus, 365, 452
body of, 365, 434
crura of, 434
long, 434
short, 434
head of, 365
lenticular process of, 365
ligament of, posterior, 434
long, 365
short, 365
Infundibulum, 417
of uterine tube, 180–181
Inlet, thoracic, 93, 102–103
Innervation
cutaneous, 36–37
of head and neck, 386–387
segmental
of lower limb, 234
of upper limb, 300
Intertendinous connections, 287, 330
Interthalamic adhesions, 391
Insula (island of Reil), 391
Intestine(s), 457
arteriograph of, 134
large, 134, 136–139, 458–459
vasculature of, 134, 138–139
small, 130–133
radiology of, 131
vagus (CN X) nerve branches to, 456
vasculature of, 131
Inversion, of ankle, 234
Iris, 346, 369, 441
anterior surface of, 423
pectinate ligament of, 423

pupillary margin of, 423
Ischium, 210, 254
body of, 154–155, 211, 254–255
ramus of, 219
Isthmus, of thyroid, 380, 395, 403

Jejunum, 112–116, 118, 120–125, 129–134, 139
JOINT(S), 18–19
acromioclavicular, 315
actions of, 234, 300
of ankle
subtalar, 234
talocrural, 234
atlanto–occipital, 27, 344
capsules of, 330, 333, 338–339
carpometacarpal, 339
1st
abduction of, 300
extension of, 300
flexion of, 300
opposition of, 300
reposition of, 300
of thumb, 336, 339
cricoarytenoid, 364
cricothyroid, 364
capsules of, 365
articular, 377
fibrous, 376
of elbow, 300, 324–325
extension of, 300
flexion of, 300
glenohumeral, 300
abduction of, 300
adduction of, 300
capsule of, 312, 314, 316–317, 405
extension of, 300
flexion of, 300
rotation of
external (lateral), 300
internal (medial), 300
of hip, 210, 254–255
articular capsule of, 153
interphalangeal
distal, 300, 339
capsules of, 331
extension of, 300
flexion of, 300
proximal, 339
capsules of, 331
extension of, 300
flexion of, 300
of knee, 263–264
articular capsule of, 243
posterior surface of, 262
fibrous capsule of, 263
synovial capsule of, 250, 263
transverse ligament of, 263–264
manubriosternal, 18
metacarpophalangeal, 300, 339
abduction of, 300
capsules of, 331
extension of, 300
flexion of, 300
of thumb, 339
metatarsophalangeal, of foot, 234
radiocarpal, 300
extension of, 300
flexion of, 300
radioulnar, 300
pronation of, 300
supination of, 300
sacroiliac, 154–155, 210–211, 254–255
of shoulder, capsule of, 328–329
sternoclavicular, 403, 405
articular disc of, 18
tarsal, transverse line of, 271

tarsometatarsal, line of, 271
temporomandibular, 345–346
articular disc of, 369, 429
fibrous capsule of, 369
tibiofibular
distal, 212
proximal, 210, 262
of wrist, 324–325
xiphisternal, 18
zygapophyseal, 19
articular capsule of, 19
Jugum, sphenoidal, 358
Junction, rectosigmoid, 206

Kidneys, 144–145, 457
left, 69, 111, 113, 129, 139–141, 146–147
margin of, lateral, 111, 144
poles of
inferior, 144
superior, 144
right, 70, 111, 113, 140–141, 146–147
ureteric branch of, 144
Knee, 263–265
anterior, 261
articular capsule of, 243
posterior surface of, 262
extension of, 234
fibrous capsule of, 263
flexion of, 234
lateral, 261
medial, 261
posterior, 262
radiograph of, lateral, 265
synovial capsule of, 250, 263
transverse ligament of, 263–264

Labium, labia
majus, 151, 161, 172, 174
minus, 151, 161, 172, 190, 192, 194, 196, 198,
200
Labrum
acetabular, 153, 203
glenoid, 314–315
Lake, lacrimal, 346
Lamina(e), 19
of cricoid cartilage, 364–365, 377, 408–410
deep, of superficial (investing) layer of deep
cervical fascia, 398–399
quadrigeminal (tectal), 390, 418–419
terminalis, 390, 418
of thyroid cartilage, 364–365, 407
internal surface of, 408
of vertebral arch, 12–15
Laryngopharynx, region of, 409–410, 412, 416
Larynx, 418–419, 457
aditus of, 408, 410
anterior, superficial, 406
infraglottic part of, 409
lateral
internal, 407
wall of, 409
muscles of, intrinsic, 455
posterior, 408
superior, 408
vestibule of, 409
Leg
anterior, 256
cross section of, 259
lateral, 257
medial, 260
posterior, 258
Lens, 423, 433
suspensory ligament of (of Zinn), 423
LIGAMENT(S), 18–19. *See also* Ligamentum
acromioclavicular, 315

fissure of, 357
  groove for, 357
  superior, groove for, 357
renal, 144
sagittal
  inferior, 385, 391
  superior, 385, 390–391, 418–419
sigmoid, 435
  groove for, 357, 361, 452
  in jugular foramen, 435
  left, 385
  right, 385
sphenoidal, 350–351, 360, 393, 410, 416–418,
  425, 430–431, 433, 440
  opening into, 359
straight, 385, 391, 418–419
tarsal, 270–271
transverse, left, 385
transverse venous, groove for, 357
Skeleton, 276–279
  laryngeal, 364–365
  of lower limb, 210–213
  muscle attachments, 4–7
  of pelvis, 152–153
  of spine, 8–9
Skin, 457
  of scalp, 418–419
Snuffbox, anatomical, 274
Space(s)
  epidural, 41
    fat in, 35
  intercostal
    2nd, 18
    4th, 21
    5th, 21
  intersphincteric, 163
  intervertebral, between T4 and T5, 93
  peritoneal
    female, 188
    male, 189
  quadrangular, 312
    transmitting axillary nerve, 328–329
    transmitting posterior circumflex humeral
      artery, 328–329
  retromammary, 47
  retropharyngeal, 380–381, 409, 412, 417
  retropubic, 178–179, 188–189
  subarachnoid, 35, 41
  subdural, 35
  suprasternal, 380
  triangular, 312
Sphincter
  anal, 163, 458
    external, 156, 159, 159t, 163, 180, 184, 190,
      192–201, 204, 206
      deep part, 162–163
      subcutaneous part, 162–163
      superficial part, 162–163
    internal, 162–163
    muscles of, 163, 163t
  pupillae, 443
  pyloric, 122, 124, 129–131, 136, 138
  urethrae, 157, 159, 159t, 160–161, 190–191,
    194, 197, 199
    portion of urogenital diaphragm, 196, 198
Spine. *See also* Column(s), vertebral
  iliac, 211
    anterior
      inferior, 8, 152–155, 210, 215, 254–255
      superior, 2, 4–5, 8, 23, 42–44, 50–57, 111,
        150–155, 203, 208, 210, 215, 242–244,
        254–255
    posterior
      inferior, 5–7, 18, 152–155, 162, 211,
        248–249
      superior, 3, 5–7, 18, 22, 26, 60–61,
        152–155, 162, 202, 211, 254

ischial, 18, 153–155, 157–158, 162, 186, 216,
  254–255
mental (genial), 363, 415
nasal
  anterior, 344–345, 348, 352, 360, 416
  posterior, 362
of scapula, 3, 5–6, 277, 281, 283, 306, 313,
  315, 328–329, 404–405, 460
skeleton of, 8–9
of sphenoid bone, 358–359, 432, 434
Spleen, 69, 111, 113–115, 117–125, 130, 132,
  134, 139, 141
  hilum of, 122
Splenium, of corpus callosum, 390–391
Stapes, 365, 452
  base of, 365
  crus of, 365
    anterior, 365
    posterior, 365
  head of, 365, 435
  neck of, 365
Sternum, 2, 33, 66, 80, 100, 104, 281, 308–309
  body of, 4–5, 8, 18, 21, 23, 40, 42–43, 51, 68,
    93, 274, 276, 312
  4th costal notch of, 18
Stomach, 68, 112–113, 118–121, 132, 457
  body of, 114–115, 117–120, 130–131
  cardiac part of, 118, 130
  fluid level in, 101
  fundus of, 114–115, 117–120, 130–131
  greater curvature of, 117–118
  lesser curvature of, 118–119
  pyloric part of, 118–120, 130–131
Stria, malleolaris, 434
Sulcus
  for abducens nerve, 358
  calcarine, 390
  carotid, 358–359
  cingulate, 390
  coronary, 83, 89
  deltopectoral, 274
  frontal
    inferior, 389
    superior, 389
  gluteal, 208–209
  hypothalamic, 390
  intertubercular, 4
  interventricular, posterior, 83
  intraparietal, 389
  lateral, 389
  lunate, 389
  median, 347, 394
  mentolabial, 346
  nasolabial, 346
  occipital
    lateral, 389
    transverse, 389
  olfactory, 388
  parieto–occipital, 389–390
  postcentral, 389–390
  precentral, 389–390
  pterygopalatine, 359
  tali, 270
  temporal
    inferior, 389
    superior, 389
  terminalis, 347, 394, 454
  for vena cava, inferior, 127–128
Supination, of radioulnar joint, 300
Surface(s)
  of acetabulum, lunate, 153–155
  of anterior body wall, internal, 48–49
  articular, 264
  of articular capsule of knee joint, posterior, 262
  of body of pubis, lateral, 197, 199
  cranial, lateral, 354
  of diaphragm, thoracic, 105

of femur
  inferior articular, 256
  popliteal, 222, 262
  shaft of, posterior, 219
of foot
  dorsal, 208–209
  plantar, 208–209
of frontal lobe of brain, medial, 418–419
of glenoid fossa, articular, 315
of greater wings of sphenoid bone
  cerebral, 358–359
  infratemporal, 359, 362, 432
  orbital, 348–349, 359–360
  temporal, 358–359
of hand
  dorsal, 274–275
  palmar, 274–275
of ileum, gluteal, 154–155, 202–203
of inferior horn of thyroid cartilage, articular,
  407
of iris, anterior, 423
of lamina of thyroid cartilage, internal, 408
of lateral condyle of femur, articular, 264
of levator ani muscle, inferior, 203
of liver, diaphragmatic, 126–127
of lung
  costal, 75
  diaphragmatic, 74–75, 78
  vertebral, 74–75
of maxilla, infratemporal, 432
of medial condyle of femur, articular, 264
  mediastinal, 74
of occipital lobe of brain, medial, 418
  popliteal, 211
of sacrum, auricular, 16
of talus, articular, 268–269
of tibia
  medial, 260–261
  superior articular, 263
of tongue, superior, 411–412, 414–416,
  430–431
of trachea, internal, 409
of zygomatic bone, orbital, 348–349
Surface anatomy
  of lower limb, 208–209
  of thorax, 66–67
  of trunk, 2–3
  of upper limb, 274–275
Sustentaculum tali, 213, 267, 269–271
Suture(s)
  coronal, 344–345, 352
  intermaxillary, 362
  lambdoid, 344, 350–352
  palatine, median, 355
  palatomaxillary, 362
  sagittal, 344, 349, 355
  sphenosquamosal, 362, 432, 434
  squamous, 352
  tympanomastoid, 434
  zygomatic frontal, 421
Symphysis
  mandibular, 380, 409, 412–417
    medial section, 350–351
  pubic, 4–5, 9, 112, 150–153, 156–158,
    174–175, 178–187, 201, 210, 250, 254–255

Tail
  of breast, axillary, 42, 46
  of caudate nucleus, 391
  of epididymis, 175
  of pancreas, 122–123
Talus, 212, 270
  articular surface of, 268–269
  head of, 213, 225, 267, 270–271
  neck of, 270
  trochlea of, 212, 270–271